46.7

264

FRENCH LIBERAL
THOUGHT
IN THE
EIGHTEENTH
CENTURY

hARPER ✦ τORChBOOKS

*A reference-list of Harper Torchbooks, classified
by subjects, is printed at the end of this volume.*

37016

FRENCH LIBERAL THOUGHT

IN THE EIGHTEENTH CENTURY

*A Study of Political Ideas from
Bayle to Condorcet*

KINGSLEY MARTIN

edited by J. P. MAYER

HARPER TORCHBOOKS / THE ACADEMY LIBRARY
HARPER AND ROW, PUBLISHERS
New York

TO
GOLDSWORTHY LOWES DICKINSON

FRENCH LIBERAL THOUGHT IN THE EIGHTEENTH CENTURY

© Kingsley Martin, 1962

Printed in the United States of America.

This book was originally published in 1929 by Ernest Benn Ltd., London; a second edition, revised, in 1954 by New York University Press, New York, and The Turnstile Press Ltd., London; and a third edition, revised, by Phoenix House Ltd., London, in 1962. It is here reprinted by arrangement.

First HARPER TORCHBOOK edition published 1963 by Harper & Row, Publishers, Incorporated 49 East 33rd Street, New York 16, New York

EDITOR'S FOREWORD

The present work, long, established as a text-book in British and American universities, has been out of print for years. Even on the second-hand book market it was difficult to obtain, and the library copies showed signs of strain through over-use. No other book in the English language has superseded it, which is, perhaps, the greatest compliment one can pay to its author. Paul Hazard in France, Ernst Cassirer in Germany, Carl Becker in the United States, Basil Willey in this country, have all in recent years contributed to our deeper understanding of the spirit of the eighteenth century, but none of these writers, eminent as they are, has made Kingsley Martin's volume superfluous.

One reason for the persistent vitality of this book lies in its method. Mr. Martin illustrates it when he writes: " In this inquiry there are three influences to consider: firstly, the inheritance with which the ideas came into the eighteenth century; secondly, the social conditions and political events in which they developed, and thirdly, the individual peculiarities of men whose own experience necessarily affected the shape and the phraseology of the creed they formulated." Thus Mr. Martin uses a combination of three methods: the " great thinker " method, the philosophic and chronological methods (page 19). I believe that it is this methodological insight which has made the author avoid the pitfalls into which so many histories of political ideas have fallen. They neglect, to use Mr. Martin's own words, " the selective power of events, the actual importance of minor writers in forming doctrines which other and more famous men completed."

Another reason why the present book has kept its freshness must undoubtedly be seen in the fact that its author built its foundation on the original sources. His analysis, for instance, of the influence of the *salons* is remarkable. So is his treatment of Bayle, Voltaire, Diderot and Rousseau. His interpretation of Montesquieu is, perhaps, less congenial, though he maps out with accuracy and pertinence the influence of the *Esprit des Lois.* I could mention another point where I differ from him. I feel he underrates the influence of the aristocracy and the *notables* during the preparatory period of the French Revolution, though of course recent research has added much to our knowledge since Mr. Martin wrote his book. His picture of the economic and constitutional framework of pre-revolutionary France is perhaps too much influenced by Taine, whereas I see it more through the eyes of Tocqueville. Yet this or other points cannot change the author's general appreciation.

He admirably elucidates the formative influence of eighteenth century political thought upon the ideas of 1789. He knows that new historical principles grow slowly. Consequently he deals at length with the seventeenth century: it laid the ground for the new ideas of civil and political liberty, scientific humanism and economic liberalism which the eighteenth century perfected and transmitted for good or for worse to the following generations.

Mr. Martin is by no means blind to the limitations of the eighteenth century philosophers: "The mistakes of the *philosophes*" he writes, "were due to their failure to realize that natural law has a changing and developing content. When Montesquieu compared the customs of one country with those of another he distinguished permanent underlying principles from superficial differences due to local circumstances; but he spoke as if the principles themselves were always constant, and as if geography and climate modified their application without any help from the development of social life itself. Voltaire, whose historical perspective was truer, though narrower, could write: ' The empire of custom is vaster than that of nature: it extends over manners, over all usages: it covers the scene of the universe with variety: nature spreads unity there, establishing everywhere a small number of invariable principles: the foundations, therefore, are everywhere the same, and culture produces varying fruits.' Even here the invariable principles seem static, and the idea that the needs of men in primitive society might not prove an adequate guide to those of modern civilization, totally absent.

EDITOR'S FOREWORD

The Aristotelean conception of the natural as the full development of the potentialities rather than as the original constitution of the organism seldom makes its appearance in the
eighteenth century." (*page* 134) These sentences are full of
meaning. The eighteenth century opened man's mind to the
historical nature of our world but it remained the task of the
following century to discover the philosophic implications that
individuum est ineffabile.

I accepted with great pleasure Mr. Martin's invitation to
see his book through the press. As editor of Tocqueville's
Ancien Régime I have had to cover within recent years much
of its ground. Moreover, it is easier to edit the book of a living
friend than the works of the illustrious dead. Needless to say,
I have taken advantage of the fact that the author of the
present book is very much alive. He has seen all my altera-
tions, and he has generously—in the tolerant, humanist
tradition of the eighteenth century—given his approval to
them. Our agreement was not always so readily forthcoming
when we discussed contemporary problems during the long
years of our friendship. . . . Apart from correcting very few
minor errors or misprints, I have added a bibliography which
may help the student to follow up some of the problems
where the author has left off, or where more recent research
will implement Mr. Martin's findings.

I am confident that this volume will keep its place as an
outstanding text-book for a long time to come.

J. P. Mayer

Stoke Poges, Bucks.
August, 1953.

PREFACE TO THE 1962 EDITION

THIS book traces the formation during the eighteenth century of western man's creed of progress and democracy. Progress followed the march of science; democracy assumed man's 'perfectability', or at least his indefinite improvement, through education, liberty, equality and international brotherhood. The West has today become sceptical of the assumptions on which its imposing industrial edifice has been built. We boasted that we were 'master of things'; today our science seems likely to destroy us, or to lead, if destruction is avoided, rather to Huxley's brave new world than to the Utopias of Condorcet or H. G. Wells. But at the very moment when the western world flounders in uncertainty, the emergent nations of Asia, Africa and Latin America are seizing upon the creed of progress and democracy with an enthusiasm as great as that of eighteenth-century French revolutionaries.

The cause of this is not far to seek. The needs and aspirations of African nationalists in Kenya, the Congo or the Transvaal, of Asians in Malaya or Nepal, of peons in Brazil or Indians in Peru, are essentially the same as those of the serf, the petty tradesman or the frustrated intellectual of eighteenth-century Europe. Equality still means the abolition of privilege by birth or wealth; liberty is still the call for the rights of man and a share in government; the brotherhood of man is still an aspiration springing from the idealists' pursuit of international peace. Progress in the undeveloped areas of the twentieth century means, just as it did to the French *philosophes* two centuries ago, the application of science to human welfare. For hungry and deprived people it means a limitless prospect of health and prosperity; it means today, as it did to the more far-sighted eighteenth-century thinkers, a socialist rather than a laissez-faire economy. So, while we in the West fear the future, the less fortunate majority of mankind grows confident that our shop-soiled creed will not only bring them the riches it has brought to us, but also the happiness that we once erroneously thought we should gain by the accumulation of wealth.

The subject-matter of this book is thus more alive than ever.

PREFACE

As we study the revolutionary hopes of the eighteenth century, we are compelled to ask whether the truths, that then seemed so certain, are eternal or whether they were only hopes that men naturally cherish as they emerge from feudalism, are inspired by nationalism, and endowed with the new techniques of industrial development.

The answer is surely that these aspirations are firmly grounded in men's social needs, but that the creed of progress and democracy was shaped and limited by the circumstances of Europe two hundred years ago, and often defended by arguments that we now know to be erroneous. Today no one will assume that the Goddess of Reason can be as easily installed in place of the older gods as eighteenth-century rationalists imagined. We know that magic and superstition have survived and are active in the unconscious lives of western people who believe that they have repudiated them, while they are still a dominating and retarding influence in the less developed countries of Africa and Latin America. Again the concept of equality—a permanent aspiration which is basic to all the great religions of the world—need not be discarded because we no longer suffer from the delusion that the mind of the child at birth is a blank sheet and that human behaviour is adequately explained by the search for pleasure and the avoidance of pain. No one will gainsay the African in demanding liberty, but all of us smile unhappily when he talks as if 'one man, one vote' is a talisman to happiness. Eighteenth-century thinkers assumed that if the press were free and education universal, then the greatest happiness of the greatest number would be assured. Two centuries later we have yet to evolve a system of education and mass information that guarantees that public opinion will be enlightened and honestly informed. Again, the West has had its fill of national glory and misery, but we find it impossible to warn emergent countries that nationalist sentiment may be the enemy of that human brotherhood of which it is in part the fulfilment. As to the right of property the landless and dispossessed in colonial countries demand, as did the followers of John Locke, the right to possess the fruits of their own labour; we watch with anxiety their struggle to build societies in which the right of property is not degraded into a claim to own the fruits of other people's labour.

So it comes about that this creed which was revolutionary in its conception in Europe is again revolutionary in its rebirth today. If its background and evolution is understood, we may ourselves be more careful not to throw out the baby with the bath-water and more helpful to those who need not repeat our errors.

KINGSLEY MARTIN.

London,
April 1962.

PREFACE TO THE FIRST EDITION

In this book I have tried to discover what that social creed which we have since learned to call Liberalism meant to the eighteenth-century thinkers who formulated and popularized it. If this creed is much blown upon to-day, that may be due in part to its intrinsic defects as a system of thought; in part to the inadequacy of a fighting creed made in a comparatively simple agricultural society to meet the needs of a more highly organized industrial one; in part to the acquisition of new scientific and especially psychological knowledge; and in part to our own failure to differentiate between the essential principles and the accidental accretions of a philosophy which for historical rather than logical reasons was passed on to succeeding centuries as a single body of thought. With this in mind I have set out to inquire what words like Liberty, Equality and Fraternity meant to men who believed that the principles they embodied were in themselves solutions for the problems of society, and to discover why the idea of progress came to be related to that of democracy and why both seemed to their exponents to involve a particular political and economic programme.

The clue to the political thought of any period lies in the conflict between various views of human nature. Theories continually change, but the main division between authoritarian and libertarian remains the same at all periods. In the eighteenth century, Church and State were founded on the belief that human nature was essentially bad and capable of regeneration only through the gift of Grace and the exercise of absolute sovereignty. From the Renaissance onwards that view had been challenged by free-thinkers, who held that life was made to be enjoyed, and that men needed not Grace but freedom to develop their faculties, to cultivate the arts and to profit by the pleasures of society. The peculiar interest of the eighteenth century, however, lies in the growth and apparent triumph of a third view, which repudiated clerical discipline and transformed Renaissance hedonism. It substituted knowledge for Grace as the means of salvation, and held that the prospect of improving men and society could serve as an ideal, sufficient to co-ordinate men's purposes and provide them with a criterion of right and wrong. This effort to give men a secular religion —a religion which is the real basis of Liberalism and the Socialism which is its lineal heir—is the theme of this book. The task of tracing the conflict between these three attitudes to life is rendered harder, but not impossible, by the fact that each of them is liable to degeneration : that Christianity may become mere dogmatism and ritualism, that Epicureanism may become mere pleasure-seeking, and that the " religion of humanity " may become mere humanitarianism. And the conflict between the three remains as real and as interesting to-day as it was before the French Revolution. While there are many who, like the *libertins*, deny the need for any religious faith as a foundation for society, and some who find solace in cathedrals or search for new interpretations of ancient creeds, there are others who still maintain the religion of progress and humanity. Thus, for instance, Mr H. G. Wells, who is the modern representative of the *philosophes* (he is, that is to say, a philosophic journalist who believes that science, organization and the popularization of knowledge are the keys to human happiness), has recently declared his unaltered adherence to their faith. In his *Open Conspiracy* he again sketches in outline the course which mankind must follow if it is to " escape from the insecurity of an animal which has been evolved and which may presently be degraded or extinguished in the play of material things," and confesses that this outline, which is in all essentials the same as that of Condorcet's *Tableau historique*, is " the truth and the way of salvation." He challenges his contemporaries to say whether service in the cause of human progress is not sufficient as an ideal and as a religion for each of us. That is not a question to which an historical book can offer an answer. But a better appreciation of the historical genesis of this creed and a fuller examination of the intellectual assumptions on which it was built up may make it easier, amid all the modern criticism of democracy and progress, to decide whether we are still able to accept this ideal which has inspired so many who cannot profess the religion of the Churches.

PREFACE

The book was begun some years ago, when a bye-Fellowship at Magdalene College, Cambridge, gave me the opportunity of research. It was continued while I held a research studentship and Assistant-Lectureship at the London School of Economics. It has been completed in a less academic but no less stimulating atmosphere. The air of Manchester is humid but not sleepy.

Professor Laski is the most generous of friends, and I have made use of his time, his amazing knowledge and fertility, and his scarcely less remarkable library. I should also like to thank Mr R. H. Soltau, Dr Morris Ginsberg, Mr van der Sprenkel, Mr R. T. Clark and Mr Herbert Agar, who have all helped me with criticism and suggestions. My wife has collaborated with me both in writing and revising the book.

K. M.

MANCHESTER, *January* 1929.

CONTENTS

CHAPTER I

Introductory. The Revolution the climax of a century in which a new set of answers to fundamental questions had been gaining increasing acceptance. Economic Liberalism, Newtonian science and representative government triumph over feudalism, clericalism and divine monarchy. Reasons for eighteenth-century acceptance and twentieth-century rejection of the Revolutionary creed. Difficulty of quantitative revision.

Analysis of the creed of 1789. The Declaration of Rights. The temporary harmony between natural rights and utility.

The complex inheritance of these ideas. No single line of development. Liberty and Equality not always connected. Particular meaning of such words in their own age : the universal expression of particular grievances. New application of these ideas in the sixteenth century : their fusion with seventeenth-century science. Basic importance of Locke and Newton.

Result of new psychology and new physics to provide the sceptic with a faith. Progress takes the place of Christianity.

PART ONE

THE EMERGENCE OF THE REVOLUTIONARY CREED

CHAPTER II

The struggle for sovereignty in the seventeenth century which in England resulted in the victory of Parliament ended in France in the absolutism of Louis XIV. Louis' theory of internal and external sovereignty : his disregard of the French Constitution and use of *raison d'état.*

The " excesses " of Louis' policy lead to party divisions in France and to the beginning of social criticism. Firstly the revocation of the Edict of Nantes leads to a revival of the theory of popular rights. Bossuet and Jurieu.

CONTENTS

CHAPTER II—*continued*

PART TWO
THE CREED AND ITS ENVIRONMENT

CHAPTER III

CONTENTS

CHAPTER IV

Laughter is released by the death of Louis XIV. The libertinism and veiled criticism of the *Lettres Persanes* characteristic of philosophic movement. *Philosophes* are journalists and humanists with a common object of propaganda. A conscious party 1751 onwards. Two limitations of the *philosophes* : censorship to evade and *salons* to please.

Effect of the censorship. Damage to intellectual honesty. Devices of the *philosophes* for evasion : their successful struggle for freedom of publication.

Effect of the *salons* on *philosophes,* who depend on them for every form of patronage. The demand for wit. Best work done away from *salons.* Influence of the *philosophes* upon the *salons* : the literary drawing-rooms of the seventeenth century develop into the philosophic and finally into the political *salons* of the Revolution. The impact of Rousseau. The release of emotion and the end of a great tradition.

PART THREE

THE CREED DEVELOPS

CHAPTER V

The concrete significance of the abstract terms in vogue in the eighteenth century. Meaning of reason, nature and humanity. The philosophy they implied involved the acceptance of a scientific metaphysic and a rational psychology. Locke's account of human nature supported by travellers' accounts of the rational savage.

Deism and natural religion. Voltaire popularizes English thought. Newton and the deistic controversy. Voltaire's common-sense theology: his fear of materialism.

The rights of man. Civil liberty justified by natural law and utility. Common-sense politics of Voltaire and the *Encyclopædia* : demand for equality before the law, not economic equality, civil liberty, not democracy. Aim : to persuade enlightened despots to introduce British liberty.

CONTENTS

CHAPTER V—*continued*

Ecrasez l'infame. Voltaire contradicts the sceptical conclusion of *Candide* by his work for toleration. The attack on the Church breeds doubt, which is the historical basis for tolerance. The work of Voltaire. Popularization of scientific outlook.

CHAPTER VI

Montesquieu differs from the other Encyclopædists in thinking that natural law is difficult to apply and that a science of society must rest on deductions from collected facts. A radical who founded the "comparative school," championed the feudal constitution of France and laid the foundation of Burke's conservatism.

The argument of *L'Esprit des Lois*. Relationship between law and environment. Example from the "Decadence of the Romans." Criticism of *L'Esprit des Lois*.

Relationship of government to climate and geography. Comparison of types of government. Liberty results from the "separation of powers." The astonishing effects in U.S.A. and other countries of Montesquieu's mistaken idea of British government. The mechanical theory of the Constitution—checks and balances. Montesquieu's influence on one school of revolutionaries ; he is not in the main stream of liberal thought.

CHAPTER VII

The philosophy of the *Encyclopædia*. Holbach and Helvétius push Voltaire's common-sense philosophy to its logical conclusions—materialism, utilitarianism and democracy.

Discussion at Holbach's dinners. Theories of La Mettrie, Diderot and Holbach. Terrifying thesis of the *Système de la Nature*. Holbach's atheism ends with the deification of Nature.

Helvétius' explicit utilitarianism. His idea of a science of society contrasted with Montesquieu's. Pleasure-pain psychology and the origin of the passions. The problem of government is to make virtue and self-interest coincide. The possibility of perfecting society by education and legislation.

CONTENTS

CHAPTER VII—*continued*

CHAPTER VIII

CONTENTS

CHAPTER IX

CONTENTS

CHAPTER X

The problem of international peace in the eighteenth century. The theory of international law—sovereign states voluntarily obeying the law of nature. Machiavelli, Grotius and his successors.

The seventeenth- and eighteenth-century State disregards even the moral obligation laid down by Grotius. The "Balance of Power." The anarchy of Europe in the eighteenth century. Montesquieu and armaments. War administration as seen from inside by Bernis. Voltaire's account of the origin and conduct of war.

The idea of peace. Physiocrats think peace must follow free trade. Their reliance on the despot to conform to natural harmony. Rousseau's edition of Saint-Pierre's *Perpetual Peace* and his insistence that democratic revolution must precede any kind of international government. Kant agrees peace more likely when democracies take place of despotisms. First result of democracy in Revolution to stimulate patriotism, increasing the number of those who have a stake in the country and are ready to fight for it. Kant right, though, in thinking idea of international federation an "idea of reason" which would grow, not through the operation of natural harmony, but through deliberate effort.

PART FOUR

THE COMPLETION OF THE REVOLUTIONARY CREED

CHAPTER XI

The new religion of progress—one which blends the utilitarians' emphasis on the value of terrestrial happiness with the idea of duty towards the race. A new attitude towards time involved in the "religion of humanity." Way cleared for it by scientific advance : the idea of a past Golden Age and the Christian belief in a life hereafter both discredited. Doctrine only complete when historical laws are worked out showing the past advance of humanity.

The growth of the historical idea of progress. Bacon, Pascal, Fontenelle, Bossuet, Voltaire, Montesquieu, Turgot, Chastellux. Progress the result of

CONTENTS

CHAPTER XI—*continued*

applying scientific knowledge. The beginning of scientific Utopias—Mercier, Volney and Restif de la Bretonne. Condorcet's *Tableau historique* summarizes the whole religion of democracy and progress. Reasons why the two ideas are obviously one to him. The nine epochs of advancing knowledge, freedom and equality.

The future certainly glorious, because natural laws were now mastered and evolution therefore conscious. No limits to the possible improvement of human nature and of society by deliberate change of environment.

Summary. The reasons for loss of faith in the religion of the French Revolution. Its value.

CHAPTER I

INTRODUCTORY—THE RELIGION OF THE FRENCH REVOLUTION

1. LIBERTY, EQUALITY AND FRATERNITY

In 1685, by an extravagant act of piety and sovereignty, Louis XIV. outlawed his Protestant subjects. There was scarcely a whisper of protest, except from the exiles themselves. The Revocation of the Edict of Nantes marked the summit of the power of the French monarchy. The *ancien régime* had reached its perfect form, a unified nation, under an absolute and conquering monarch, supported by a strong bureaucracy, a courtly aristocracy and an obedient populace. After 1685 the decline of the *ancien régime* visibly began. During the century which elapsed before the French Revolution, ideas which were incompatible with the existing social, religious and political system were gaining steadily in force and coherence. It was no longer possible to prevent the thoughtful and the discontented from discussing those social, political and religious questions which authority always prefers to regard as finally settled. In the reign of Louis XV. an inquiring child had his choice between the old answers, supported by authority, and the new answers, first implicit in the murmurs of malcontents and the curses of heretics, and then increasingly explicit in the writings of the *philosophes*. Many of these ideas were at least as old as Aristotle, St Thomas Aquinas or Rabelais, but they were new in their eighteenth-century application and new in their fusion with seventeenth-century science. By the time of the Revolution they had ceased to be tentative answers to doubtful questions and had become a series of dogmas, articles in a new religion. The Revolution was, therefore, the climax of a long process: a dramatic moment when feudalism, clericalism and divine monarchy collapsed, making way for the era of economic Liberalism, modern science and representative government.

It would, of course, be untrue to suggest that every

Frenchman was a sincere Catholic[1] and an unhesitating believer in the divine monarchy in 1685, or that the theses of popular sovereignty, natural right and secular progress were universally accepted in 1789. Nevertheless, the common and unthinking assumptions of most ordinary men and women in the seventeenth century were that all the doctrines of the miraculous Church were indisputable; that men were born wicked and could be saved only through the Church and her priests; that the King, reigning over France by divine right, was endowed with absolute power; that legal and social inequality, feudal privilege and arbitrary government were part of the permanent order of things and unalterable. By 1789 these instinctive assumptions had been replaced by another system of ideas in the minds of almost all the urban population of France, and its social, though not its religious, aspects were accepted with equal enthusiasm by the peasantry. The old creed, which had been dominant under Louis XIV., was a lost cause at the fall of the Bastille; and the new creed, which had been shaping itself piecemeal in the minds of scientists and men of letters in the seventeenth century, had become a religion to the deputies who met in the States-General. For these revolutionary doctrines in their final form served all the purposes of a religion. Liberty, Equality and Fraternity were the new watchwords which embodied an ancient and continuous social ideal—a community of equal and free citizens, conscious of a common heritage and a common goal. At the Revolution this vision seemed closer to realization than it has at any other moment of history; men believed that they were in fact equal, and needed only to cast off their chains and to proclaim their common brotherhood. Their faith was upheld by a new metaphysic, an ethic, a series of dogmas and a means of grace. Science had substituted a natural for a supernatural explanation of the universe: knowledge, not obedience, was the gate of salvation; the key was held by men of science, the true priesthood, less exclusive intermediaries between man and the hidden

---

[1] Moralists were already deploring the rapid growth of scepticism in Paris even in the mid-seventeenth century. Indifference and heresy, however, have never ceased to be dangerous since they were denounced by St Paul.

mysteries of nature. Finally the doctrine of progress transformed the whole from a philosophy into a working faith: men could believe in the ultimate success of the causes for which they worked, since there were natural and historical forces greater than themselves working with them.

The new religion won its way in the nineteenth century as a fighting creed, intellectually and spiritually victorious, flaunting the prestige and the terrors of its revolutionary triumphs. It was generally accepted in Europe in spite of the continued resistance of the traditional Church, the ancient monarchies and the surviving aristocracy. Both democracy and progress— ideas closely connected in history but not necessarily in logic —were attacked by numerous critics, and the spokesmen of the industrial workers in every country objected to the application of democratic principles in the interests of men of property. It was not until the twentieth century, however, that the revolutionary creed was widely discredited, that its fundamental assumptions were shaken, or that any but isolated thinkers doubted that truth and the future were substantially on its side.

In the twentieth century, new knowledge and bewildering experience have once more brought disillusion, scepticism and a paralysing sense of impotence. Nowhere except in the United States, where prosperity strangles criticism, do ideas of democracy and progress still command religious respect. The same causes which undermined the *ancien régime* are again at work in Europe: a shifting of the balance of economic power, new answers given by science to physical, biological and psychological questions, the failure of institutions to satisfy not only the aspirations of idealists but also the plain needs of ordinary men and women, and, finally, the example of countries where liberty and democracy are openly scouted—all these have united to weaken the authority of the nineteenth-century creed. Indeed it would be strange if a creed, forged in the battle against the eighteenth-century institutions, a weapon used to secure individual liberty in a comparatively simple agricultural society, proved adequate as a basis for the organization of a complex industrial society. Yet, because that creed came into the

3

nineteenth century as a single system of ideas, to be accepted or rejected as a whole, any failure in practice, or doubt thrown upon its underlying philosophy, seems to threaten the whole. Men are not quick to admit that one article of a creed may be true and another false, that its philosophic basis may not be entirely absurd because dogmatically held or loosely stated. Theory seldom proceeds by quantitative methods, and equilibrium is not easily found in the shock of reaction. The discovery that inheritance plays a larger part than our fore-fathers have believed, and reason a smaller part than politicians and philosophers have imagined, is supposed to render futile all deliberate effort to improve social behaviour by environmental change. Strangely enough it is not argued that the cause of failure has been our inadequate use of the reason we do possess, but that, since it is weaker than we believed, reason may be neglected in future as a helpless servant of instinct. A misunderstood Freudianism superimposed upon a misapplied Darwinism is a potent weapon of destruction. It becomes easy to dismiss the hope of a free and equal community as an illusion of childhood.

It may nevertheless be worth while to examine the conditions under which the ideas of the Revolution won their way, to discover what were the claims made for them by their eighteenth-century champions, and what philosophic arguments seemed to justify democratic government, equal rights and social progress. Such an investigation may throw light on the nature of this faith and do something not only to explain the cause of failure and disappointment, but also to turn impatience and disgust into critical appraisement. A fuller understanding of the historical perspective might temper the joyful ardour with which men continually throw out the babies with the bath water. The creed of the Revolution is worthy of a closer examination than its champions or its enemies are usually willing to accord it.

Equality, Liberty and Fraternity are ideals for which men still strive, even though their attainment now seems a more difficult matter than it did a century and a half ago. We no longer expect to build a science of government on first principles, and we are not able to believe that men, whatever their race, class or colour, are naturally equal in capacity. It no longer seems obvious that liberty consists in the exercise of certain fixed and definable rights and that universal brotherhood will be the inevitable result of destroying national and class barriers. It may nevertheless be worth while to diminish, as far as may be, the social inequalities which destroy the hope of communal life, and natural rights may still have significance even though they demand a new interpretation in an age which analyses human nature more thoroughly and less confidently. Even the idea of a peaceful world-federation is not necessarily futile because we can no longer assume its automatic arrival through the operation of free trade and natural harmony.

The positive doctrines which sprang from these ideals are naturally inadequate to twentieth-century discontents. It is well to admit their inadequacy but not to forget their value. Personal liberty still needs champions in an age which has learned that release from stone walls does not make freedom. Equality of rights, even in the limited and legal sense, is a cause for which men must fight no less strenuously when they have discovered that the right of property needs drastic modification if they are to enjoy the substance, and not only prate of the shadow, of liberty and equality. Indeed the rights which the eighteenth-century *philosophes* demanded were not on a par : unlike thought and free speech, property is limited in amount, and one man's right of ownership restricts the rights of another. This was not so obviously true in an agricultural society in which landed property was widely distributed, and in which the outcry against inequality was directed against legal privilege rather than against the irresponsible power of money. The principle of legal equality remains valuable, however, in spite of the fact that the poor can never be really equal with the rich before the law, or in any other way. Similarly the political interpretation of democracy has disappointed the hopes of enthusiasts, but the conception of responsible and even of representative government may survive the failure of some of the usual methods of enforcing responsibility and organizing representation.

2. ARTICLES OF FAITH

In 1789 the National Assembly of France summarized the principles of the Revolution. In the Declaration of the Rights of Man, "the representatives of the people of France, considering ignorance, neglect or contempt of the rights of man to be the sole cause of public misfortunes and the corruption of government," set forth, as they believed, for all time, "these natural, sacred and inalienable rights." [1] These were the rights of "Liberty, Property, Security and Resistance to Oppression." The Declaration proceeded to define liberty as the right to act without any restraint except that imposed by law, and to assume that, in a country where the law was "an expression of the will of the community," all actions would be legally permitted to the citizen except those which injured the equal exercise of rights by other persons. The right of property, it further explained, meant that the State would not interfere with the free enjoyment of ownership or confiscate property "except in cases of evident public necessity, and then after payment of a just indemnity." "Security" would result from the existence of a single legal system, equally applicable to all, administered by courts which presumed innocence until guilt was proved. The right to resist oppression implied that any government could be legitimately overthrown which trampled upon individual liberty. In order that these rights might be for ever guaranteed, they were to be embodied in

---

[1] Thirteen years earlier the American colonies had anticipated this Declaration, explaining their reasons for assuming "among the powers of the earth the separate and equal station to which the laws of nature and nature's God entitled them. . . . We hold these things to be self-evident, that all men are created equal, that they are endowed by their Creator with certain inalienable Rights, that these are Life, Liberty, and the pursuit of Happiness." The authority of governments was justified only if it secured these rights for every individual, and it was justly forfeited where the rights of men were violated. In the year of the French Revolution the thirteen American States formed a federal Constitution, resting on a basis of popular consent and guaranteeing individual rights by the mechanism of the separation of powers. Some years later they added a Bill of Rights, which was intended to summarize the gains of the past and to secure individual liberty from infringement by the wills of peoples or governments.

a written Constitution, which could not be changed by any ordinary legislative procedure.

In England, where no sudden revolution took place, Jeremy Bentham analysed the French Declaration of Rights and declared it to be mere "bawling on paper." He had himself found a more stable if less absolute philosophy of liberty in contemporary French literature; it was in Helvétius that he had first found the greatest-happiness principle explicitly stated. Why could not the French deputies base their demands on sound utilitarian arguments instead of indulging in vague declamations about eternal and inalienable rights? Why could they not say that, in their opinion, the greatest happiness of the greatest number would be promoted if certain rights were, under present circumstances, legally bestowed upon every individual? Starting from this basis, he proceeded to justify on grounds of utility the very rights which the French were claiming on grounds of nature. Men should be treated equally, because they were all susceptible to pain and pleasure, and had equal needs; they should be given civil and political liberty, because a man's happiness depends on his opportunity to follow his own interest without interference; they should be allowed property, because without it there is no incentive to produce nor harmony between private interests and public welfare. Security is essential if men are to know how to promote their own good, and as for the right to resist oppression, men are always justified in overthrowing corrupt and arbitrary governments if they can. Thus the substance of the Utilitarian creed, for the time at least, coincided with the Revolutionary doctrine: utility and natural law agreed because they were weapons against the same evils, and in every European country middle-class persons, who were neither theoretical exponents of natural law nor systematic Utilitarians, but who resented bad government and thought they could govern better themselves, were found to be making similar demands and advocating the same changes. They strove to abolish all monopolies and privileges; they looked forward to a new age of equality, when they should have liberty to trade, to speak, and to worship or not, as they chose.

The French Revolution was so great a release of the human

spirit, and its grandiose phrases cloaked needs so urgently felt everywhere, that their satisfaction seemed to offer men permanent happiness. The same optimism was to be found wherever the principles of the Revolution prevailed. Bentham himself was not less confident than Jefferson; and if it was a French deputy who asked for a constitution equally valid for all times and all places, and Sièyes who declared that he had completed the science of government, it was Bentham's most intimate disciple, James Mill, who remarked, when explaining the virtues of democracy, that if his arguments were not valid, the task of finding a good government must be for ever abandoned. For the time being, then, the two great trends of Liberal thought were in practical agreement: the Utilitarian and the exponent of natural rights both wanted the same things, made the same fundamental assumptions about the nature of man and society, and were equally confident that the recognition of their principles would render men happy and virtuous.

The substance of their common creed may be expressed in a series of propositions. The only justification for the State is the promotion of the happiness of its citizens. Men are rational: they are, that is, able to perceive the good, to discover means of attaining it, and to direct their lives by their knowledge and experience. This ability to seek rational ends by rational means is shared by all normal men, who are, generally speaking, equal not only in their elementary needs but also in their natural capacities. To attain happiness, therefore, men need and are equally entitled to liberty: the function of the State is to preserve men's rights, not supervise their use of them. Since rational beings best know their own interests, no conqueror, autocrat or aristocracy can have the right or capacity to govern: the laws, therefore, should accord with popular wishes, and must be administered by an executive which is responsible to the people or their representatives. Finally, since men learn by experience, it follows that with the destruction of ancient forms of government, the inauguration of an era of equality, and the advance of scientific knowledge, men can constantly improve their society, achieve greater happiness and ultimately perfection.

8

INTRODUCTORY

3. THE DEVELOPMENT OF THE REVOLUTIONARY CREED

These propositions were stated with new significance in eighteenth-century France. They were, of course, not new in themselves. It would be convenient if ideas were born like Athene, fully armed from the head of Zeus, or arrived less aggressively like Aphrodite, perfectly shaped from the foam of the sea. In fact, it is otherwise. They are born, like other children of this earth, trailing clouds of glory and of shame, heirs and victims of an historic past, bearing the stamp of their progenitors, misshapen by the accidental circumstances of birth, compelled to fight for existence, developing as best they may in the stress of conflict. Their development is surprising and their maturity unlike that expected by those who first nourished them, not only because every idea is a compound of past associations, and charged with hidden explosives, but also because the social *milieu* exercises a rigorous selective and transmuting influence. Established institutions—the Church, the State and the Law—have everything to lose and nothing to gain by change, while at most times the inertia of ordinary citizens increases the astonishing capacity which any society has for absorbing, digesting or rejecting the most unassimilative of matter and remaining apparently unaffected by the process. New facts and new ideas are imperceptibly incorporated, not deliberately substituted; somehow or other they are reconciled with the most incompatible views until suddenly, it seems, the work is done and everyone unites in declaring that a new age has arrived.

To describe the origin and growth of the individual tenets of the new creed would therefore be a complex and unlikely story, which would begin at least as early as fifth-century Greece. It would not be an account of a tidy or logical evolution. In the history of ideas logical relations may be unrelated in fact and actual relations may leap centuries. The new doctrines had appeared in earlier generations, and had served in their time a variety of causes; they had been frequently in opposition to each other and been advanced by groups which seemed, in general, their enemies. Some of the ideas of the

9

Revolution could be traced to ancient Sparta, others to Athens ; in one form or another they were all discussed by Plato and Aristotle. They appeared in the Roman Republic and in the Empire ; in Mediæval Christendom they fought for and against the Papacy. They gained new vitality in the Renaissance, and in the Reformation the national king was often their champion. For the time, at least, the prince, not the common man, profited by their success, and, although the cause of mental freedom was advanced by the humiliation of the priesthood, political liberty seemed farther off under national monarchs than it had been in the Middle Ages.

The conception of natural law which served the cause of liberty in the seventeenth and eighteenth centuries was of Stoic origin ; it had been transformed by its combination with the *jus gentium* of Roman Law ; it had flowed on, an undercurrent beneath the main stream of mediæval thought ; it had emerged at the Renaissance, and was used to support tyranny as well as to overthrow it. The claim to toleration, which was commonly based upon an appeal to natural law before it was supported by Utilitarian arguments, was at length accepted, not because men recognized its social value or respected one another's opinions, but because, after many attempts to found states upon a single religion had failed, the religious wearily accepted the view of the sceptics that the extermination of neighbours who differed from you was too troublesome, uneconomic and dangerous a business. The scientist and freethinker indeed had often found most toleration under despots, who were not so slow as their subjects to realize that political unity and national peace were preferable to religious conformity and civil war.

There has been no single line of development with liberty, equality and fraternity on one side, and tyranny and oppression on the other. The idea of equality has sometimes meant that all the children of God must be assumed to be of equal spiritual value ; has sometimes been a plea for freedom by natural inheritance ; and sometimes an argument for the opposite idea, that all goods should be equally shared amongst weak and strong alike. Similarly the demand for liberty, though at times expressed in universal language, has commonly been made by a particular group desiring a specific reform. Indeed until the French Revolution itself liberty meant, as a rule, religious and civil liberty, which was more likely to be secured under an enlightened monarch than under a popular government where, as in some of the American colonies, a fanatical group might be as intolerant as the Papacy itself. As for the theory of popular sovereignty, its principal champions had been lawyers, who derived the Mediæval Empire from the free vote of the Roman Assembly, and sixteenth-century Jesuits, who eloquently explained that it was the duty of the faithful to overthrow kings who failed in zeal for the Pope or the Society of Jesus.

Such words as Liberty, Equality and Fraternity are catch-words which deceive the historians as well as the populace. Analysis shows that they have commonly been the battle-cry of groups suffering from oppression, ready to become oppressors in their turn; anxious to overthrow privilege in order themselves to exercise a more rigorous monopoly, and proclaiming the brotherhood of man within their own ranks in order more effectively to tyrannize over their neighbours. Those who have made revolutions have usually known what they meant by liberty and equality with a fair degree of accuracy: they have invoked the goddess of freedom in their struggle against specific forms of oppression. They have not been worshippers of vague abstractions. It is the philosophers and historians in search of systems and universal explanations who have supposed the concrete demands of the moment to be conscious aspirations after the eternal good. But it is also easy to make the opposite mistake. The realist who analyses social discontent, and finds that philosophic ideas are merely rationalizations for subjective desires, misses the mark even more widely than his idealistic colleagues. It is true that the idea of a liberty, an equality and a brotherhood which would include every class, colour and nation has been only the rare dream of isolated individuals, yet the universal element has persisted and grown in spite of partial interpretations and frequent betrayals.

The Christian slave in ancient Rome or modern America was comforted by the thought that earthly inequalities would be remedied in heaven, where the last would be first and the first would be last. The peasantry who rose to demand the rights of Adam in the fourteenth century, and the Anabaptists who demanded the restoration of Christ's Church on earth in the sixteenth, the Diggers and Levellers who thought that the land was equally the property of every man in the seventeenth, the Parisian shopkeeper who, inspired by Rousseau and Mably, claimed the rights of man in the eighteenth, and the Trade Unionist who asked that each should be rewarded according to his needs in the nineteenth century—each of these and many other groups were moved directly by the pricking of particular grievances. But the historian is right in seeing their struggles as all part of a single movement. In each period there have been men who related their own wants to those of their neighbours, who were not satisfied with the filling of their own stomachs, and were in search of a society where the hunger neither of the body nor of the mind should go unsatisfied. The vision of such a society has haunted the ages; in the eighteenth century it became conscious, and seemed closer to realization than at any other period in history.

The Liberal application of the historic phrases of democracy first appears in modern history when the sovereignty of the Renaissance monarch ceased to appear an advantage and grew to be an oppression to the middle class. At the end of the Middle Ages the supreme need was for order and protection against lawless feudalism, but the class of men who had been prepared to support tyranny for the sake of security began to fret against the tyrant's interference with their trade, their thought and their religion. In the case of Holland this revolt took a national form. The Dutch asserted their national and religious independence, while Althusius, profiting by Jesuit example, revived the doctrine of popular sovereignity to justify revolt against a legitimate king. A little later the English, accounted by all contemporaries the least stable and most disorderly of peoples, executed one king, deposed another, and, in the course of the struggle, united the ancient theories of natural law and individual rights with the conception of responsible government and popular sovereignty. The British settlement of 1689 became, therefore, the pattern of free government for European Liberals.

The chief theorist of 1689 was John Locke, in whose writings democratic ideas first became associated with the scientific movement which had been growing since the Renaissance. For Locke was not only an exponent of natural law, toleration and government by consent, but was also a doctor, a scientist and a rationalistic philosopher. Above all, he was the originator of a psychology which provided democratic government with a scientific basis. After Locke, it was possible to give reasons for holding that men were rational beings, with equal needs and capacities, almost all able under free government to develop, to learn, and to build on the basis of experience. Pascal had been wrong: men were not born in sin and destined for destruction, but born in ignorance and destined through reason to work out their own salvation.

Locke's scientific and political conclusions were the logical outcome of tendencies already far advanced in contemporary science and philosophy. The attack on the Ptolemaic cosmogony usually connected with the names of Copernicus and Galileo, the determination of Descartes to begin metaphysics with the known and to accept only deductions made from axiomatic premises, the insistence of Bacon upon the experimental and inductive method—all these shook the metaphysical basis upon which political and also religious authority were founded. The ground was cleared for a new scientific treatment of the universe, in which the human race abandonod its claims to preferential treatment. At the same time the individual's responsibility was increased by the substitution of human inquiry and human will for supernatural revelation and providential guidance. Protestantism had overthrown the priesthood and —in its ideal, if not in its organized forms—claimed for every individual direct access to the Almighty, or, at least, the Almighty's own account of Himself in the Bible. The scientists were also individualists, and were also sure that their approach to truth was the only reliable one. Leaving ultimate philosophic problems unexplored, they set out to build solely upon the basis of external and measurable experience. Their assumptions, which only gradually became conscious and acknowledged, were that all problems were ultimately soluble by the methods they had found useful, and that the concepts of matter and energy which led to such surprising immediate results in the early days of modern science provided a satisfactory and even a final explanation of the physical universe.

The success of seventeenth-century scientists, culminating in the unequalled achievements of Newton, silenced remaining doubts, and seemed, to the eighteenth century, to establish for ever the validity of what Newton had regarded only as a hypothesis. Even the unanswered and perhaps unanswerable criticisms of David Hume were neglected by his contemporaries, who naturally preferred to work at the open task before them rather than speculate upon its possible limitations. Eighteenth-century writers neglected at least half of their Cartesian inheritance. The great philosophers and scientists of the seventeenth century were not under the delusion that they had escaped from dualism, nor did they lay down a materialistic dogma about the ultimate nature of reality. They were as much " vitalists " as materialists, and in different circumstances—if, for instance, the Catholic Church in the eighteenth century had been true to its spiritualist philosophy—much of the clerical rigidity and intolerance associated with the scientific spirit might have been avoided.

In the eighteenth century, however, the mechanical assumptions which Newton and his predecessors laid down as a basis for research invaded other spheres of thought to which they were inapplicable.[1]

The study of individual psychology, which was the great feature of the age of La Rochefoucauld and La Bruyère, was

---

[1] Professor Whitehead says that the seventeenth and the two succeeding centuries were dominated by physical concepts very unsuited to biology ; they "set for it an insoluble problem of matter and life and organism with which biologists are now wrestling" (*Science and the Modern World*, p. 51). This is just to the eighteenth century but not to the seventeenth. The unmechanical aspects of the work of Descartes, Spinoza and Leibniz seemed to the eighteenth merely to prove that they had feared the Church or failed in logic. There was enough truth in this view to make it easy for the Encyclopædists to neglect the difficulties which the Cartesians had failed to overcome.

continued in the succeeding century by only a few comparatively obscure writers.[1] Moreover the same mechanical assumptions, based in this case upon the sensationalist empiricism of Locke, affected political and economic as well as purely scientific thought, and the social speculations of the eighteenth and nineteenth centuries also suffered from a tendency to apply these mechanical assumptions to problems of social organization to which they were altogether unsuitable. Even analogies drawn from mechanics were misleading in political thought. The form in which democratic ideas were passed on from the seventeenth to the eighteenth century was already influenced by the study of physics. For Locke, whose political ideas dominated the eighteenth century, approached politics from the point of view of a seventeenth-century physicist, and made it possible for his followers to treat problems of individual and social psychology exactly as if they were set to dam rivers or to build bridges. A mechanical psychology is at the root of all eighteenth-century thought : empiricism and democracy developed side by side, not only because they were two aspects of the revolt against the spiritual and political authority of the *ancien régime*, but because they were logically connected, and based upon similar concepts. The religion of the Revolution was thus founded on the belief that all men and all societies were capable of improvement by deliberate and scientific adjustment of their environment.

From the beginning of the eighteenth century, therefore, there were two strands of thought, both subversive of orthodoxy. In the first place there were the sceptics, who did not accept the philosophic assumptions upon which society was founded and who remained without delusions about the past or hope for the future. It is to this eighteenth century that the twentieth returns with such empty satisfaction. In the second place there were

---

[1] Perhaps Vauvenargues is the most interesting of them. Although Voltaire expressed a boundless admiration for him, his intuitive psychology and literary manner were so exceptional in the eightcenth century that his contemporaries completely failed to understand him. For an excellent account of Vauvenargues and an appreciation of his effort to find a more satisfactory psychological theory see *Luc de Clapiers, Marquis de Vauvenargues*, by Miss May Wallas.

the apostles of progress, who were not content with repudiating existing creeds and who found in science and history grounds for believing in the indefinite improvement of the human race. Religious scepticism was a stage on the route to a new faith in human perfectibility.

By the reign of Louis XV. most educated French people had ceased to accept the philosophic assumptions upon which society was founded, and had lost confidence in the economic and political institutions of the *ancien régime*. Almost all of them were sceptics in matters of religion. Even such officials of the Church as defended Catholicism were inspired not by faith but by fear; institutionalists, they naturally assumed that moral laxity would result from the decay of religious authority. They gave, as Condorcet said, a " half-submission," remaining " free to believe what they liked, provided that they believed something incomprehensible." In the same way, existing political and economic systems were seldom championed on the ground that they were good, but were supported because social disruption seemed their only alternative. Where there is no coherent faith, no commonly accepted scale of values, no ideals at which the intellect does not scoff, no confident sense that anything in particular is worth while, there is not likely to be great art or literature on the one hand, or striking material achievement on the other. The cultured aristocracy of the eighteenth century was acutely conscious that a great epoch had passed, and it remained under the spell of Louis XIV. and of Racine, outwardly satisfied with its own sterility. It had no confidence in the future and no understanding of current intellectual movements, which appeared to be merely uncouth, Gothic and in the worst of taste. God, immortality and the Divine Monarch were natural subjects for witticisms, while democracy, until the period of the American revolution, was a somewhat remote topic which arose in discussions of ancient history. If they had considered the matter seriously at all, Madame du Deffand and her friends would certainly have agreed with the Abbé Coignard in repudiating the Declaration of the Rights of Man " because of the excessive and unfair separation it establishes between man and the gorilla." The sceptical eighteenth century is, therefore, not wholly a twentieth-century invention. Yet it was only a restricted social circle which was as sceptical of the goodness of man as it was of the goodness of God.

The main trend of eighteenth-century thought was all in the opposite direction. Beyond the circle of those who clung to the dead forms, and could conceive of no freer society, a new philosophy, confident and assertive, was in process of formation. Scepticism was an aristocratic attitude. The middle class was sceptical of Catholicism and Divine Right, but altogether free from that paralysing scepticism which leads men to doubt whether they are capable of any conscious control over their social life or future. The new philosophy, which was to be completed at the Revolution, was a blend of many elements which had one thing in common. They were all assertions in different forms of what the *ancien régime* denied, that ordinary men and women were able by the exercise of their own will and reason to form a society in which they would be happy and in which they could develop and realize all their natural faculties. This conception of equality, the basic notion of democracy, had been undermining feudalism and steadily transforming conceptions of art, literature and politics since the later Middle Ages. The eighteenth-century thinkers who advanced this democratic movement were few of them democrats in the political sense, but in their long battle with an authoritarian church, a feudal aristocracy and an arbitrary government they made a new synthesis and passed their diverse and loosely connected doctrines of revolt on to the nineteenth century as the simple, final and indubitable truth. At the Revolution itself the conclusions of science seemed to justify the most fervent declarations of popular orators. It was a moment of extra-ordinary agreement, in which politicians, scientists, poets and business men all held the same view. It was only gradually that the superficial unity disappeared and underlying disagreements became apparent. For the moment, it seemed scientifically sensible, as well as politically sound, to trust the intelligence and good will of the people, even though in practice one drew the line somewhere. It was certainly easier not to ask whom

" the people " were and with what they were to be trusted. In any case, the lowly were exalted and the mighty cast down. The people themselves, as Heine said, could "wield their own sceptre and crown with which the monkeys had played."

The literature dealing with the philosophic doctrines of the eighteenth century is immense. A large part of it is concerned with a single controversy—the degree of influence exercised by the *philosophes* upon the French Revolution. That fundamental problem is unavoidable, and is briefly discussed in the third chapter of this book. My main object, which has already been indicated and may now be conveniently summarized, is a different one. I have traced the gradual formation of the creed of the Revolution from the critical point of view of the twentieth century and attempted to show to what extent the democratic and progressive principles which dominated nineteenth-century politics were conditioned by the temporary and local circumstances of the French *ancien régime*. The *philosophes* of the eighteenth century popularized not only a faith in humanity and an ideal of a free and equal society, but also specific economic and political doctrines and a psychological and biological theory. Their followers accepted the ideal, the programme and the scientific basis with equal enthusiasm. If we would understand how that creed stands to-day the first necessity is to discover the relationship between these entirely separable but commonly connected aspects of the Revolutionary principles and so build an historical foundation upon which modern criticism may proceed with less danger of confusing essential elements with the accidental products of particular conditions and personalities.

In this inquiry there are three influences to consider : firstly, the inheritance with which the ideas came into the eighteenth century ; secondly, the social conditions and political events in which they developed, and thirdly, the individual peculiarities of men whose own experience necessarily affected the shape and the phraseology of the creed they formulated. If personality

18

INTRODUCTORY

alone were important it would be possible to adopt the convenient method, commonly favoured by historians of political thought, of devoting a chapter to each great writer or school of writers. This method would have the advantage of explaining how certain arguments and phrases which have survived their time originated in the genius of men like Montesquieu and Rousseau. And writers so influential and dominant as these can be (and are in this book) treated separately. The exclusive use of this method, however, has disastrous consequences : it neglects the selective power of events, the actual importance of minor writers in forming doctrines which other and more famous men completed, and it leads to the writing of almost valueless histories, in which each famous writer continues the work of his predecessor with a pleasing but quite unhistorical continuity. Whatever history is, it does not consist in the biographies of great men, and whatever the influences which affect the evolution of thought they cannot be explained by cataloguing the theories of famous writers. An exclusively logical treatment of ideas, apart from their social environment, is scarcely more likely to succeed than a purely personal one, while a method which deals with ideas in the chronological order of their appearance would be useful to no one except a compiler of bibliographies.

Each of these methods—the " great thinker " method, the philosophic method and the chronological method—has grave defects. Yet simplification is unavoidable. The plan adopted in this book is that combination of all three which seems most suited to its particular object. Since that object is to show how far the evolution of a particular set of ideas was influenced by the conditions of the eighteenth century, I have dealt with the lives and personalities of writers only when their individual peculiarities—the most obvious example is Rousseau—have given their doctrines a permanent stamp which would otherwise be unexplained. Writers whose importance was predominantly literary and whose works do not enter into the main current of revolutionary philosophy are omitted, or referred to only by way of illustration. Emphasis throughout the book is upon the relation of the ideas to eighteenth-century conditions, and to the selective as well as the formative influence of that environment upon the dominant ideas of 1789.

In pursuance of these principles, Part One deals with the emergence of all the Revolutionary doctrines during the reign of Louis XIV., and thus explains the form in which ideas of civil and political liberty, scientific humanism and economic liberalism came into the eighteenth century.

Part Two describes the conditions and events which enabled them to spread and conquer during the reigns of Louis' successors. It shows how the economic structure of society created a Revolutionary class ready for subversive doctrines, how the constitutional struggle between the monarchy, the religious parties and the *Parlements* increasingly discredited, from the middle of the century onwards, both the Crown and the Church, and gave rise to the revival of the legal theory of natural law. Chapter III. then deals with the economic and political environment. Chapter IV is concerned with the conditions of intellectual co-operation in the century—with the effects of persecution and censorship upon the doctrines of the *philosophes* and with the subtler but no less powerful influence of *salon* patronage, upon which depended academic and literary success as well as the hope of effective propaganda.

Having sketched in this background it becomes possible in Part Three to examine the development of the ideas themselves, and to explain in more detail how far they were the product of that environment. Chapter V. explains the importance of Lockean psychology and Newtonian physics to the Revolutionary outlook, and shows how an initial position was reached by Voltaire which was potent as a weapon against clerical absolutism and irresponsible government but inadequate as a basis for a new régime. Voltaire's politics were no more satisfactory than his metaphysics. He fought for liberty but did not analyse its meaning. We see in Chapter VI. how Montesquieu evolved a new method of political philosophy, and how an extremely influential theory of free government was built on his interpretation of the British Constitution. Chapter VII. traces the way in which the less compromising Encyclopædists pushed Voltaire's premises to more logical conclusions, reaching, in some cases, a complete materialism and a rigid utilitarianism. The search for liberty, moreover, seemed to them to necessitate representative government as well as the safeguarding of civil rights. With the advent of Rousseau, to whose philosophy Chapter VIII. is devoted, a sentimental belief in the sovereignty of the people takes the place of this utilitarian argument, and political democracy finds its most powerful advocate. The theory of liberty in the eighteenth century has thus completed its evolution and is left with two rival defences, which are only with difficulty reconciled at the Revolution.

So far the philosophic basis of the Revolutionary creed has been examined, and the particular meaning of liberty in the eighteenth century analysed. Chapter IX. deals with the idea of equality and explains how it came about that the nineteenth century inherited a doctrine which made the free ownership of private property seem equivalent to social equality, and neglected, until the industrial worker became strong enough to champion it, the alternative conception, also widely stated in the eighteenth century, that social equality was possible only where communism, or at least a large measure of socialism, was in operation.

There remains the Revolutionary conception of fraternity, and Chapter X. explains how the theory of universal harmony, the growing conception of international law and the revolt from the dynastic wars of the eighteenth century led to a belief that international brotherhood was possible. The problem of establishing perpetual peace was fully discussed by economic theorists and by Rousseau and Kant.

The eighteenth-century conceptions of liberty, equality and fraternity have thus been analysed, and their relation to the conditions of their growth defined. In the final chapter we see how all the ideas of the century are summarized and given life and religious power by their alliance with the doctrine of progress, stated in comprehensive form by Condorcet. Here we have a theory which rests on the psychology of Locke and the physics of Newton, which utilizes the view which had long been growing that history is a story not of the degradation but of the continuous improvement of man, which has reasons

for believing that with the advance of science, and the establishment of liberty, equality and fraternity, there are no limits to
the possible improvement of society and of human nature
itself. The problem to which this book offers no answer, but
perhaps supplies some material for an answer, is the extent to
which this theory is really discredited in a disappointed age.

CHAPTER II

THE LEVIATHAN STATE

I. SILENCE—THE THEORY OF ABSOLUTISM

"Le peuple entra dans le sanctuaire : il leva le voile qui doit toujours couvrir tout ce que l'on peut dire, tout ce que l'on peut croire du droit des peuples et de celui des rois, qui ne s'accordent jamais si bien ensemble que dans la silence" (*Mémoires du Cardinal de Retz*).

In the seventeenth century the English and the French monarchies were both engaged in a struggle to secure their sovereignty. In both countries the absolute power of Pope and Emperor had passed to the national King ; in France sixteenth-century lawyers had made Henry IV. the residuary legatee of the Roman Empire and, in England, Hobbes, with even greater assurance, had justified the irresponsible sovereignty of the Stuarts on a Utilitarian basis. In England Divine Right was effectively countered by the doctrine of fundamental law ; behind all human laws, Coke held, there existed a law of nature, a moral law, which no Government was entitled to violate. Its practical expression was to be found not only in Biblical precepts but also in the Common Law of England ; English kings had recognized its final authority, embodied in the Coronation Oath and the provisions of Magna Charta. The Puritan House of Commons willingly utilized Coke's theory in its struggle with Charles I., but the revolutionary settlement of 1689 resulted not in the recognition of a fundamental Constitution but in the doctrine of government by consent and the assumption by Parliament of the sovereignty wrested from the Stuarts. "The divine right of the Whig landowner " took the place of the divine right of the monarchy.[1]

In France the seventeenth-century contest ended in the complete triumph of the monarchy. The Bourbons were stronger than the Stuarts for many reasons. The power of the French monarchy, like that of the English, was founded on national

---

[1] It was left to the United States of America to revert to Coke's theory and to attempt to embody the political certainties of mankind in a fundamental Constitution, superior to any regular legislative body, and capable of interpretation only by an independent judiciary.

opposition to the Papacy and the desire of the trading middle class and populace for the destruction of the lawless power of the feudal aristocracy. But the humiliation of the aristocracy had been of a different kind in the two countries : in France, as de Tocqueville said, the aristocracy had lost their powers and kept their privileges, while in England they had lost their privileges and kept their power. The new English aristocracy, created by the Tudors and employed by them in local and central government, itself led the rebellion against the monarchy which had called it into existence. Religious and economic grievances also united a large section of the middle class against the Stuarts.

In France the monarchy made no attempt to extract money from the aristocracy, seldom even called upon it for military service, and entrusted the administration of the country to *intendants*, directly responsible to the central Government. Moreover the middle class was far less formidable ; the reformed Church had won only a precarious foothold, and was loyal to a king who tolerated its existence. The States-General, having no control over taxation, was easily dispensed with, and was not called again after its presentation of grievances in 1614. The only constitutional check upon the royal power was the right of the legal *Parlements* to register the King's edicts, but their resistance or criticism could always be overruled by a ceremonial *lit de justice*.

The *Fronde*, therefore, could never reach the dimensions of the English rebellion. Without disinterested leadership, religious enthusiasm or constitutional machinery through which to work, the movement quickly degenerated into a series of Court intrigues, and was crushed. Yet it was not insignificant. Its theory closely resembled that of the early stages of the contemporary rebellion in England. The spokesmen of the *Fronde* relied on the same principles as the English Puritans, admitting the legitimacy of royal authority as long as it was exercised in accordance with a fundamental law embodied in French custom and tradition. The King's edicts, they insisted, could be constitutionally enforced only after free registration by the *Parlements*. Pamphleteers, like Claude Joly, went further, and talked of popular sovereignty and natural rights.[1]

Some observers expected the *Fronde* to lead to other rebellions, and finally to a limitation of the King's authority. Cardinal de Retz, who played so prominent a part himself in the revolt, believed that it marked the awakening of public opinion, the beginning of an era of criticism in which men would demand constitutional safeguards against arbitrary government. "The people entered the sanctuary and raised the veil which ought always to hide all that can be said or believed about the rights of peoples and kings, who never agree so well as in a relationship of silence. *La Salle du Palais* violated these mysteries." [2]

The *Fronde*, however, did not mark the beginning of an age of criticism, but paved the way for the despotism of Louis XIV. For the time, at least, the people were the more firmly excluded from the shrine. Between 1651 and 1680 the relationship of silence, which de Retz judged the only safe one between absolute monarch and subject, was more completely established than at any other time in modern history. Louis never forgot the *Fronde*, and after Mazarin's death in 1661 never appointed another Prime Minister. He left little room for the critic. The right of printing was reduced to a minimum; the censorship was increased and the periodic Press disappeared. The Paris *Parlement* became merely a court of justice, and between 1673 and the death of Louis in 1715 its right of remonstrance was only once exercised.[3] The rule of the *intendants* and the

---

[1] A good summary of the political theory of the *Fronde* is contained in Sée, *Les Idées politiques en France au XVIIᵉ Siècle.*

[2] " L'on chercha en s'éveillant, comme à tâtons, les lois : l'on ne les trouva plus ; l'on s'effara, l'on cria, l'on se les demanda ; et, dans cette agitation, les questions que leurs explications firent naître, d'obscures qu'elles étaient et vénérables par leur obscurité, devinrent problématiques, et dès là, a l'égard de la moitié du monde, odieuses. La peuple entra dans le sanctuaire ; il leva le voile qui doit toujours couvrir tout ce que l'on peut dire, tout ce que l'on peut croire du droit des peuples et de celui des rois, qui ne s'accordent jamais si bien ensemble que dans le silence. La Salle du Palais profana ces mystères " (*Mémoires du Cardinal de Retz*, ed. Feillet, t. i., p. 294).

[3] The *Parlement* protested on the occasion of the registration of the Bull *Unigenitus* in 1713.

use of royal councils were extended, and the old provincial assemblies were deprived of their functions. "It was God's will," said Louis, "that the subject should obey without discrimination."

In the *Mémoires* of Louis XIV. the three great arguments for sovereign kingship were for the first time completely blended. Louis inherited the *suprema potestas* of the Roman Emperor, rediscovered by sixteenth-century lawyers for the benefit of Renaissance kings; his, too, was the *dominium* of the feudal overlord, with the ultimate right to dispose at will of all land usually considered private property, but actually only held in usufruct; finally, as Christian Prince, elect of God and deputy of Christ, his authority over the minds, bodies and consciences of his subjects was proven both by Old Testament example and New Testament precept.

In Louis the Renaissance State and the Sovereign Monarchy had reached their apogee. The Crown, the State and the Nation were but three words for the same thing. The interests and the will of the Monarch were those of the State, and assumed to be also those of the Nation. In all things they were final and admitted neither limit nor responsibility. In external relations the State was its own justification; it recognized no obligations except those it cared to impose on itself and no responsibility except its own expansion. The maxims of Rome were at Louis' disposal. "What the King wills is law" and "*salus reipublicæ suprema lex*" are one and the same thing in a state where the people's will is presumed to be included in that of the King. Royal caprice and *raison d'état* are indistinguishable. In his *Politique* Bossuet painted an ideal portrait of his King; he was indeed the Leviathan; "a great people united in a single person, *une raison secrète* shut within a single head and governing all the body of the State." Louis always regarded himself as free from any international obligations, and informed the Dauphin that expressions of permanent friendship and alliance in treaties were useful only as diplomatic courtesies.[1] Throughout his

---

[1] Cp. *Louis XIV. Œuvres* (ed. Grouvelle), i. 64. It is interesting to compare this passage with the precept of Machiavelli : "Quelques clauses specieuses qu'on y mette d'union, d'amitié, de se procurer respectivement toutes sortes d'avantages."

reign he treated the conception of international law, which found its first expression in European politics in the Treaty of Westphalia in 1648, as the Renaissance " Prince " was bidden to do, apologizing from time to time when it seemed convenient but never being deterred from following his own interests. Machiavelli was always denounced and always obeyed. God, no doubt, remained the final judge, but, except for questions of religious dogma, the State, not the Church, was His interpreter. The King, supreme head of the State, was himself divine, declared Bossuet on behalf of Louis, and of his interpretation of " *raison d'état* " God was the only arbiter. And even God's judgment did not seem always very sound : at least it is reported that Louis, in the midst of the defeats of the War of the Spanish Succession, cried : " The Lord might have remembered what I have done for Him ! " [1] Apparently Louis and his God differed as to the true " *raison d'état.*"

In the second place, as feudal overlord of France, he was, he declared, the ultimate owner and disposer of all the property held by his subjects. In an edict of 1692 he claimed that there was " no right better established nor more inseparably attached to our crown " than that of universal control and disposal " over all the lands of the Kingdom." [2] Finally as God's chosen ruler and father of his people, the King's actions were altogether above criticism. No one had the right to offer him advice or

---

[1] Quoted by Delaisi, *Political Myths and Economic Realities*, p. 60. Louis had been trained to believe himself divine from boyhood—and his later flatterers were no less gross. There were priests who called him "immortal" and declared that in Louis "one could see the lineaments of the Holy Trinity itself," "that he was a prodigy of God's grace whose wisdom is an argument which by itself suffices to convince atheists." A society preacher on the occasion of the birth of the Dauphin compared the King with God Himself and his son with Jesus Christ—*vide* Puaux, *L'Évolution des Théories politiques du Protestantisme français*, 67, and Ogg, *Europe in the Seventeenth Century*, 283.

[2] The doctrine of state socialism implicit in this remark led to no immediate results, though believers in "natural right," like Jurieu, considered Louis' autocracy as menacing to property as to religious freedom. The later struggles between the lower and the privileged orders upon the question of taxation are foreshadowed in Louis' doctrine that in comparison with the Crown all subjects are equal.

to demand explanation. To make a king responsible to his subjects was, in Louis' view, to pervert the order God gave to the world. " *Raison d'état* " he defined in words which embody the perennial defence of irresponsible government. State policy is necessarily "unknown and obscure to all those who do not govern." In his secret and lonely wisdom the sovereign is compelled to conduct a foreign and domestic policy which may perhaps result in apparent disaster : if it appears so, it is because the ways of the sovereign, like those of Providence, are past finding out. If, like God, we could view our sufferings from the point of view of eternity, the death and devastation resulting from a monarch's wars might be as justifiable as the destruction caused by a providential earthquake. The Jesuit Bonhours expressed Louis' view emphatically : " As the Prince is the most living image of God on earth, he ought to be like God, who governs the world by methods unknown to men and who makes us always feel the effects of his kindness and justice without showing us the designs of his wisdom." [1] And Louis himself told the Dauphin that, "holding, as it were, the place of God, we seem to participate in His wisdom, as in His authority ; for instance, in what concerns discernment of human character, allocation of employments and distribution of rewards." [2]

Irresponsible to men, Louis acknowledged himself responsible to God. As a father, the King must not be criticized, but he must protect his children, seek their welfare, lead the docile and punish the disobedient. His domestic policy was accordingly one of paternal protection. Kingship was an exacting profession, and Louis' days were spent in the exact routine of official detail. If his nights were spent with Mademoiselle de la Vallière and her successors, that, he explained, was permitted by his conscience on the condition that the affairs of his heart were never permitted to interfere with the affairs of state.

Colbert's economic policy was an attempt to increase the political and military power of France by extending its Colonial Empire, adding to its treasure and encouraging its industries. He was not a complete mercantilist, but he hoped that taxing

---

[1] Bonhours, S.J., *Entretiens d'Ariste et d'Eugène*, 181.
[2] *Œuvres*, ii. 283.

the foreigner and restricting the export of grain would add to the strength and independence of France. This theory involved constant State supervision. Louis' cultural policy was similar in theory, and practically more successful. Versailles became the centre of European culture and the graveyard of the French aristocracy. A great school of classical authors wrote for an aristocracy now finally reduced to a glittering and expensive impotence.

Such a complete arrogation of irresponsible sovereignty was novel. Hitherto it had been generally assumed that the monarch, though supreme, was bound by the fundamental laws of France. Bodin, the first French thinker to construct the theory of royal sovereignty, assumed that the King would obey the Salic Law of succession and adhere to the ancient Constitution and customs of France. To conform to these was in the nature of the French monarchy, even though, Bodin held, nothing but harm could come of any popular machinery to enforce royal responsibility. Even Bossuet, Louis' most thorough apologist, drew a careful distinction between absolute and arbitrary power. The royal authority, he declared, was " divine, paternal and absolute," but this did not mean that it would be exercised "unreasonably." Absolute and arbitrary government, he said, were different things. The King's power is absolute " in the sense that it is independent of all human authority. But it does not follow that it may be arbitrary." The King would not destroy his kingdom or violate the rights of property : the persons of loyal subjects would not be wilfully interfered with, and custom, divine in origin, would act as a useful guide for the monarch. Louis, however, paid no more heed to these limitations in practice than he had in theory. He even argued that he could alienate French soil for his private advantage ; he disregarded the Salic Law and totally ignored the ancient French Constitution. As Madame de Staël explained later : " In France it is liberty which is old and despotism which is new." Arbitrary government began with Louis XIV.

2. THE RIGHTS OF ORDINARY MEN—THE PROTESTANTS AND THE EDICT OF NANTES

During the first thirty years of Louis' reign the gods showed no sign of envying his success. According to their wont they waited till his own infatuation brought him disaster; and Nemesis, with her usual wilfulness, reserved her final visitation for his great-grandson. There are, however, practical limits to all power, however extravagantly justified. The rule of the Bourbons rested primarily on the instinctive obedience called forth by the royal divinity. But it rested also upon the services which they rendered to France. Henry IV. and Richelieu had given the French people order and unity instead of civil war, had enforced toleration at the expense of fanaticism. Their foreign policy had been moderate; it had given France more power and some " glory " in Europe; their home government had been strong, centralized and not generally oppressive. This was the policy which Louis inherited and finally discarded.

There was a contradiction in Louis' policy. As a true Renaissance Prince he should have preserved at least the semblance of constitutional government, his foreign wars should have stopped short of extravagance and, above all, his religious policy should have been always politic and national, and never sincere or Roman. As it was, he undermined the power of the monarchy in all three ways: firstly, by the revocation of the Edict of Nantes he drove out his most industrious subjects and united Protestant Europe against him; secondly, by ceaseless war he involved himself in bankruptcy and the mass of his peasant subjects in penury; thirdly, by adopting a Jesuit instead of a national religious policy he divided his country into warring camps.

The silence was broken and criticism, though whispered till his death, grew daily more bitter and more penetrating. It was Louis XIV., not the *frondeurs*, who brought the people into the shrine of government. The story of France from the revocation of the Edict of Nantes in 1685 until the meeting of the States-General, more than a century later, is the story of the gradual breakdown of the religious and political absolutism of the *ancien régime* and the gradual construction of a religion based on secular and libertarian assumptions. The foundation of the new creed was laid under Louis XIV.

Louis' religious policy was mainly responsible for the interruption of the mystic silence. Since the accession of Henry IV. the Pope's authority in France had been restricted to questions of doctrine, the French Church had become predominantly Gallican, and royal policy was dictated by secular considerations. The Pope had little more direct influence than in a Protestant country. In 1682, when Louis was involved in a dispute with the Pope concerning his right to make ecclesiastical appointments without Papal sanction, the bishops, inspired by Bossuet, proclaimed themselves uncompromisingly Gallican. Their resolutions rested on the theory that even on matters of doctrine the Pope was ultimately subject to a united Council of the Church, and that he had no right to any part in the internal government of the French Church.[1] Religious controversy might rage in France : Molinist and Thomist might abuse each other. Pascal might expose Escobar and the casuistry of Jesuit practice, and the stricter Catholics might recommend the forcible conversion of Protestants, but as long as the King put the unity and security of France first he had nothing to fear from any section of the Church.

The revocation of the Edict of Nantes showed that the King had finally turned his back upon a secular and national policy. The Protestants had been consistently loyal ; they had taken no hand in the *Fronde*, and in 1652 had reminded the King that they were "Frenchmen as well as members of the Reformed Church." "We only ask," they declared, " to be able to live and die in the service of your Majesty in the just liberties which have been granted us, above all in those of our consciences and in the exercise of our religion ; without which life is not only indifferent to us but bitter, and death desirable." Louis, however, hated dissent of any description, political or religious. He readily paid heed when he was told that the

---

[1] *Vide* Loyson, *L'Assemblée de Clergé de France de 1682*, for a documented and honest account of a curious and commonly misrepresented chapter in ecclesiastical history.

Protestants could be " converted " if the interpretation of the Edict was " strict " and if the missionaries were not too gentle and were adequately aided by dragoons.[1] In 1685 he decided that the process of " conversion," the full horrors of which he may not have understood, was complete. The Edict of Nantes, therefore, which alone gave Protestantism a legal footing in France, was revoked as " unnecessary." Claude protested in vain that it was a " jest which suited ill the dignity of so great a King to say that he revoked the Edict only because it had become useless. It was much as if a father who had cut his children's throats with his own hands boasted of being thereby quit of the duty of nourishing and protecting them." [2] Perhaps one day the King would realize what he was doing. His mask would be torn away and everyone would see that the King's great qualities were reducible to " sovereign self-love, to a pride without equal, to an extreme love for great reputation, to a conscience which was intimidated by the magnitude of his sins, fornications, adulteries and acts of violence, and which was therefore attempting to appease God by external observance of religion and a deceptive display of zeal."

The results of the revocation were far-reaching. Du Bosc's [3] solemn warning, uttered as early as 1668, that " it would depopulate his kingdom by more than a million persons, whose flight would inflict a striking injury to business, to manufacturers, to labour, to art and crafts, and indeed in every way to the well-being of the State," was exactly justified in the event. Its effects were not only disastrous in themselves but they also contributed directly to the national bankruptcy. Blenheim and Ramillies were the practical reply to the revocation. Moreover, Louis had opened the way for criticism. Exiled Protestants refurbished the weapons of their sixteenth-century predecessors, laid aside since the time of Henry IV. In addition they borrowed from the well-stocked armoury of

---

[1] Strict interpretation, which meant, in fact, constant persecution, began as early as 1655, and "conversion bureaux" were instituted in 1676.

[2] Quoted by Puaux, *op. cit.*, 38.

[3] *Vide* Puaux, *op. cit.*, 42 ff.

English Parliamentarians whom they met in Holland. Through their medium France and all educated Europe learned the philosophy of the Revolution of 1688.

In the year after James' flight from England an anonymous writer published *Les Soupirs de la France esclave.*[1] "I look with compassion," began the author, "upon the cruel tempest with which my country is threatened. I weep for the desolation of its towns and the ruin of what the tyranny of its government has allowed to remain." He proceeded to recount the ancient liberties destroyed by Louis, the venality of the law under his régime, the destruction of the *noblesse*, once "the most illustrious in the world," and now turned into a "parcel of beggars," a system of taxation which reduced the peasants to the condition of "African slaves." "To-day a thousand channels are open through which the blood of the people is drawn to run into the abyss of the insatiable greed and immeasurable ambition of the Prince." Louis, finding the Louvre, Saint-Germains and Fontainebleau insufficient, must needs expend the taxation wrung from the poor upon a new palace at Versailles. Was it a Christian or a Turkish prince who drove millions into battle for his own ends, who made himself all and the people nothing, who recognized no law, and committed the final crime of driving out loyal and industrious subjects because of their fidelity to their consciences? "Who would not shed tears to see so many millions of men reduced to such a profound misery to satisfy the whims of a single man?"

Jurieu, the Protestant pastor, was not content with denunciations. His spirit was that of the Scottish Covenanters; like them, he argued that a king whose life was ungodly, who persecuted the saints and destroyed their spiritual liberty, immediately ceased to be legitimate. He pushed the argument further, anticipating Locke's vindication of the recent English revolutions. The King is a magistrate appointed to safeguard the liberty of his subjects, whose duty it is to depose him if he violates their rights. Every relationship, even that of husband and wife or father and child, involves mutual obligations; whenever

---

[1] A pamphlet attributed to Michel Lavassor.

power is arbitrarily exercised an implicit contract is revoked. Above all comes the duty of worshipping in accordance with conscience. Even if the people were now as foolish as Hobbes thought them once to have been, and attempted to surrender all their rights to the King, it would be impossible for them to do so. For a man's religion was the sole affair of himself and God, and the attempt to coerce conscience was not only wicked but necessarily futile. Thus there were obvious limits to royal power: "Every citizen governed by a king has the right to depose him as soon as he exceeds the limits of his authority."[1] The people were ultimately sovereign: they "alone have no need to be right in order that their acts may be valid." The responsibility was ultimately theirs, and God was their only judge.

Jurieu's attack was not left unanswered. Bossuet undertook the task of refutation.[2] He upheld Louis' claim to Divine Right, using both the patriarchal arguments of Filmer and the Utilitarian ones of Hobbes. Kings, as the Old Testament proved, were directly instituted by God, but they were to be obeyed by subjects not only because it was the duty of children to obey their father but also because division of authority meant misery. To talk of men possessing rights of any kind before the foundation of government seemed as absurd to Bossuet as it had to Hobbes. There were no natural rights: rights were the result, not the cause, of government; against the sovereign there could be no rights, and without his authority the life of man was necessarily intolerable.

Jurieu had asked what reason subjects could possibly have for promising obedience to a single irresponsible individual who could tyrannize over them at will. Bossuet answered by comparing society to an army. Why do soldiers obey without question or contract? Because each one knows that destruction

---

[1] Quoted by Dedieu, *Le Rôle politique des Protestants français*, 66.
[2] Bossuet published his *Variations des Protestants* in 1688. For the controversy it provoked *vide* Rébelliau, *Bossuet*. Jurieu's *Histoire critique des Dogmes et des Cultes* (1704) emphasized changes of Catholic doctrine, pointing out that even the Fathers of the Church were heretics judged by existing orthodoxy. Bossuet denounced the suggestion as blasphemy, but scarcely refuted his opponent.

necessarily follows disobedience. Discipline is maintained not only by the sanction of punishment but also because the rank and file recognize its necessity. To allow discussion or admit any rights of conscience is to make way for anarchy, to encourage every individual to set up his own puny judgment against constituted authority and to make way for disunion, heresy and damnation.

Bossuet did not see the danger of this argument. By appealing to utility he weakened the claim to divine right, and to call the atheist Hobbes to his support was to offer his opponents the most valuable of hostages.[1] The appeal to an unalterable contract in Hobbes is, in fact, negligible—his strength lies in the argument, borrowed by Bossuet, that sovereignty alone brings union, greatness and prosperity. But at the root of this argument is the idea of consent, and the suggestion of possible rebellion. If the strongest reason for obedience is the danger of anarchy, men who find tyranny intolerable will some time prefer to run the risk of disobedience. Bossuet talked of kings " like gods," and Hobbes described them as " mortal gods," but both had undermined divine right. A mortal god is, after all, a contradiction in terms ; the time will come when the bold will be tempted to throw him from his pedestal and put his mortality to the test.

3. SCEPTICISM AND SCIENCE—BAYLE AND HIS CONTEMPORARIES

Though Louis' persecution of the Protestants was economically disastrous, it did not divide France internally. Some writers did indeed contrast the pious lives of the heretics with the loose morals of their persecutors, but Gallicans and Jesuits alike supported the royal policy, and the theories of Jurieu and his fellows found no immediate response, except within

---

[1] Other writers of the same period were ready to use Hobbes to justify Louis' absolutism. *Cp.* Francis Bonneau, 1660, *Eléments de la politique de M. Hobbes*. More striking is the *Traité du pouvoir absolu du Souverain*, by Elie Merlat, written in the year of the revocation, denouncing the notion of popular sovereignty and basing his vindication of royal absolutism on the arguments of Hobbes.

the Protestant community. Louis' decision to side with the Jesuits against the Jansenists, however, had immediate effects within the kingdom itself; it divided France into hostile camps and contributed to the growth of scepticism. The *Parlements* were roused to make their single protest against Louis' policy; they constituted themselves champions of Gallicanism against both Jesuits and monarch, and so began a long battle with absolutism, which lasted till the eve of the Revolution itself. Moreover, France was immediately involved in a general religious controversy in which *libertinisme* steadily gained ground. Nothing could have served the free-thinking disciples of Descartes better than a division in the Church. They held that reason, not revelation, was the key to truth, and the orthodox furthered their thesis by an effective demonstration that, whatever truth was, the Church was not agreed upon it. Once again Louis had released forces which led to Revolution.

The doctrinal differences between Jansenists and Jesuits had long troubled France. What was the true interpretation of the doctrine of grace in Paul and Augustine? Was the Calvinist view, which denied the possibility of salvation except to the elect, orthodox, as the priests of Port Royal held, or had the Jesuit Molina been right in stating that the efficacy of grace can be affected by the exercise of the individual will? The Pope long seemed doubtful, and at one time had been on the brink of censuring the Molinist view. And now that it was decided that the doctrine of grace which the Jesuits found in Jansen's *Augustinus* was heretical, were not the Jansenists still entitled to argue that the heretical doctrines were not, in fact, to be found in Jansen? Might they not discuss the question of " *fact* " while they submitted in the question of " *right* "? In any case, were Jesuit priests justified in refusing the sacraments to Jansenists who maintained a " respectful silence " on the question of fact? A more important question was really involved. What was the position of the Jesuits and of Rome in France? The strength of the Jansenists lay in the popular dislike of the Society of Jesus and of Papal influence. The asceticism of Saint-Cyran and Arnauld was a constant reproach to the comforts of Jesuit wisdom. The Jansenists emphasized the steepness of the narrow way to heaven: the Jesuits, as a free-thinking Abbé put it, "lengthened the creed and shortened the Decalogue," that the broad and worldly path might be the smoother.

Arnauld's *Frequent Confession* was an attack upon the Jesuit fathers, who, as the same critic said, changed the name of the sacrament from Penitence to Confession because they thought it sufficient to avow their sins without correcting them. Frequent confession was a pleasant way of combining a worldly life of gaiety with the certainty of eternal bliss. Balzac's "Prince" remarked: "We have now a more easy and agreeable theology; one that can be better adjusted to suit the humours of the great, which can accommodate its precepts with their interests and is not so rustic and harsh as the old theology. . . . To-day we have invented expedients which enable the thief to salve his conscience." [1]

Everyone knew the nature of these expedients, since Pascal's *Lettres provinciales*. Escobar's casuistry suggested to common men that every Jesuit was a hypocrite, who undermined the integrity of morals, and since every Jesuit was an Ultramontane, and presumably an intriguer, it seemed probable that he was also undermining the integrity of the State and ready, when the occasion arose, once again to shout for the League and Ravaillac.[2] The controversy, therefore, was concerned with power rather than with doctrine. In 1705 a Papal Bull finally condemned " respectful silence " and closed the last loophole of the Jansenists. In 1709-1710 Port Royal was razed. In 1713 the Bull *Unigenitus* denounced Quesnel's *Moral Reflections*, which contained, it seemed, one hundred and one heretical propositions, hitherto unsuspected, and all the more dangerous since they were so difficult to perceive. Each of these steps was opposed by the Paris *Parlement*, by many

---

[1] Quoted by Ogg, *op. cit.*, 344.
[2] The unpopularity of the Jesuits among the French middle class is one of the most important factors in the development of seventeenth and eighteenth century thought. A century later, in 1761, when a public trial went against the Jesuits, it was said that "the joy of the public was as if everyone had had a private fortune left him."

of the clergy, and by the mass of middle-class persons. The populace supported the Jansenists because they hated Rome, not because they had strong views about the efficacy of grace.[1]

The " Constitution," as the Bull was called, roused an immediate storm. The ninety-first of the condemned propositions seemed to imply that the Pope was infallible.[2] Cardinal de Noailles, and fourteen bishops with him, refused to accept the Bull. All the forces of Gallicanism rallied to their side ; the Sorbonne rejected the Bull, and the *Parlement* of Paris was forced to accept it only by a special exercise of royal authority. *Moral Reflections* and all books in its defence were officially suppressed, and its more resolute supporters suffered exile or imprisonment. But Louis could not calm the storm he had aroused. For the first time in his long reign he met with real opposition, and he died with the knowledge that he had destroyed the unity of the Church and undermined the authority of the monarchy. Louis had forgotten that unquestioning allegiance

---

[1] The facts in brief were these. The new edition of Quesnel's *Moral Reflections upon the New Testament* was published with a dedication to Cardinal de Noailles, the Archbishop of Paris. No book, it might have been thought, could have begun its career with more unexceptionable testimonials. It had been specially commended by Clement XI., and Father La Chaise, confessor to Louis, had constantly sought spiritual refreshment in the work, which, he said, was always edifying at whatsoever page it was opened. La Chaise's successor, Le Tellier, however, had different views ; the Society of Jesus was in bad odour at the moment in France and he felt that a Bull denouncing Quesnel's book as full of Jansenist heresies would restore the Society's prestige, re-establish the orthodoxy of Molinist at the expense of Thomist, increase the power of Jesuitism in France, and, not least, discredit somewhat Cardinal de Noailles, his Gallican rival for the King's favour. Louis, whose piety grew as old age decreased the will and power to sin, was prevailed upon by Le Tellier to request the Pope to ban *Moral Reflections*. Clement seems to have hesitated before condemning a book he had previously praised so highly, and it was only after a scene in which Cardinal Fabroni, Le Tellier's friend at the Vatican, had called the Holy Father "childish," to his face, that he gave way. A courier was dispatched the same day to Le Tellier, who personally obtained Louis' consent and immediately published the Bull. The agency of Le Tellier and the atmosphere of Jesuit intrigue surrounding the Bull accounted for much of the Gallican opposition.

[2] This proposition stated that "an unjust excommunication ought never to prevent our doing our duty." To condemn this as heretical was thought to imply that an unjust excommunication was impossible.

would in France be offered only to a king whose policy was wholly French.

The battle between *acceptants* and *recusants* did not provide an edifying spectacle.[1] The French Church divided into factions, engaged in a bitter struggle nominally over minutiæ of dogma, while the real cause, which excited universal interest, was a rivalry for political ascendancy. The most famous French ecclesiastics called each other names and gave one another the lie for motives which did not seem free from a political and personal taint.[2]

The opportunity was a good one for sceptics and there seems little doubt that their influence increased in the latter part of Louis' reign. Fénelon and Bossuet were united in deploring the danger to the Church : Fénelon complained that " instruction increases and faith diminishes," while Bossuet threw the whole of his energy into combating the spirit of unbelief. The Church seemed beset with enemies. The *libertins* were stronger than ever. Saint-Evrémond, their wittiest representative, had employed his congenial exile at the Court of Charles II. to popularize a philosophy which had troubled bishops since the later Middle Ages. He argued that the understanding could not submit to authority, that religion, after all, was a matter of temperament and that the one really odious vice was hypocrisy. He disliked violence and was no propagandist, but a sceptic and a true follower of Montaigne, holding that it was setting a high value on your own opinions to roast neighbours who did not agree with you. Life, he felt, was hard enough in any case : why not let people enjoy themselves in this world, if they chose to run the risk of damnation in the next? Like Molière, he thought Nature the finest guide, and the Epicureans her most faithful interpreters. Moderation was the key to happiness, and happiness

---

[1] The *recusants* were those who refused to accept the " Constitution" " purely and simply." On their side were ranged Jansenists, Gallicans, the *Parlements*, and the mass of citizens. On the other was the King, the Jesuits, and a number of Ultramontane bishops.

[2] The persecution of the Quietists, though far less important, gave the same impression. For the effect of the controversy between Bossuet and Fénelon and the growth of scepticism during Louis' reign *vide* Brunetière, 5e series, *La Formation de l'Idée Progrès*.

was, after all, the important thing. Austerity and excess were both bad: a good life could be found in freedom of mind and manners. "Let us not flee from the world, nor hide ourselves in the desert," he wrote. Why not be tolerant, accept each other quietly, and realize that we are, after all, very small, very fallible and with but one life we can be sure about? Wasn't it just as well to make the best of it?

The Renaissance hedonism of Saint-Evrémond, however, was no longer the Church's most serious enemy. The scientific conception of an order of nature, of a world governed by inevitable law, was gaining ground and, as it grew, the position of the Christian God seemed increasingly precarious. The scientific heresy was a more menacing restatement of the heresy of Jansenism and Calvinism: its doctrine of predestination seemed to restrict the liberty of God Himself and make Him as helpless before His own decrees as the gods of Greece had been in the hands of inexorable Fate.

Descartes had greatly increased the difficulty. He had himself remained in the Church and his disciples had striven to show that the rule of law in the physical world did not limit the free will of God or man. "Occasionalism" had been accepted by the orthodox and Father Malebranche was a good Catholic. Pascal, however, had seen the danger of scientific inquiry. "Cartesianism," he had said, "made one well-directed flick from God send the world spinning on its axis for all time."

All the thinkers of the next generation encountered the same difficulty. Fénelon's mind wrestled with the problem and found refuge in Pantheism—a cure for all difficulties, since, if, as he said, "God is all that is," the problems of finding out what He does or does not do and whether we have free will or not seem scarcely to arise. In a less mystical mood he wrote: "Two conceptions of Godhead lie before you—the one of a Ruler, good and vigilant and wise, who will be loved and feared by men, the other a First Cause, so high that he cares nothing for souls he made, for their virtue or their vices, their disobedience or their love. Examine well these two conceptions. I defy you to prefer the second to the first."

The danger had been fully exemplified in Spinoza. "If a

phenomenon were produced in the universe," he wrote, "which was contrary to the general laws of nature, it would be equally contrary to the decree of God, and if God Himself acted against the laws of nature He would be acting in a manner contrary to His own essence, which is the height of absurdity. I conclude then that nothing happens in nature which is contrary to its universal laws, nothing which is not therefore in accord with these laws and which does not result from them."

The mediævalists had believed God's attributes to be discoverable by reason : God was a father whose powers were limitless, but whose ways were reasonable even if they appeared sometimes arbitrary to the small view of individual men. The mediæval theologian had confidence in " the intelligible rationality of a personal being." No doubt, as Professor Whitehead has argued, faith in the possibility of science, in the scrutable and ordered nature of the universe, was " generated antecedently to the development of modern scientific theory." But perhaps it is too much to say that it was " an unconscious derivative from mediæval theology." [1]

For the ways of the personal God of Christianity always remained uncertain to the ordinary man, even if they were presumed to be ultimately rational. The same, it may be argued, could be said of the ways of nature, since the individual who is overtaken by an avalanche or an earthquake receives no help from the knowledge that his death is due, not to a miracle, but to natural causes. Nevertheless the change from a personal Providence to an impersonal law did involve a reaction as well as a transference from a religious to a secular state of mind. Philosophers might argue that God ruled the universe in a rational manner and that He was fulfilling a rational process when He lost His temper with the creatures He had created and drowned them in the Flood, when He permitted the sun to stand still in the heavens at the request of His servant or converted His unfaithful subjects by an occasional miracle. The Second Coming might prove rational enough, when it came, but, since it might occur at any time, its expectation left the

---

[1] *Science and the Modern World*, p. 16.

mediævalist in a precarious and awestruck state of mind. It is impossible to dissociate the notion of arbitrary and irrational behaviour from the idea of personality. A universal and an impersonal law may seem a less friendly conception; it may, at first, appear even more inscrutable and equally unaccountable in its effects upon individuals. But it leaves the way clear for thought, for experiment, for discovery and, above all, it permits men's minds to travel freely in a limitless future which they may learn in time to control. This scientific conception, there-fore, was at least as much a reaction against the arbitrary and restricted element in mediæval theology as it was a derivative from its rationality. It was in this development that Bossuet saw the greatest danger to the Church. He saw that the personal and direct intervention of God in human affairs was altogether essential to Catholicism. A Creator of eternal laws with which He never interfered was no God, and could never have founded an apostolic Church. What became of miracles, of original sin, of grace, what was the place of Christ Himself in a universe governed by inexorable and unchanging laws to which even God always adhered?[1] Science might be permitted in its own sphere, but it must be fought to the end if it interfered with revelation, if it encouraged sinful men to behave as if God were not ever-present, ever-vigilant, noting every sin and graciously permitting the fall of each one of His sparrows. "The *libertins*," he declared, "hoped to shake off the yoke

---

[1] *Cp.* Dante, *Purgatorio*, iii. 34-39 :

> " Matto è chi spera che nostra ragione
>   Possa trascorrer la infinita via,
>   Che tiene una sustanzia in tre persone.
>   State contenti, umana gente, al *quia* ;
>   Chè, se potuto aveste veder tutto,
>   Mestier non era partorir Maria."

> " Mad is he who hopes that our reason may
>   compass that infinitude which one substance
>   in three persons fills.
>   Be ye content, O human race, with the *quia* !
>   For if ye had been able to see the whole, no
>   need was there for Mary to give birth."

Translation, Temple Classics.

of this Providence which watches over us, so that they may independently maintain an unruly liberty which lets them live according to their fancy, without fear, without restraint, without discipline." He accepted the challenge boldly. It was his task to re-create the mediæval God in the minds of men. God, he declared, has made abiding laws, and has therefore the power to make or unmake them as He pleases: " He gives nature laws ; He overturns them when He wills." God's Providence is an ever-present, an immediate thing ; His inscrutable purpose is furthered not only by the common working of His laws but also by the intervention of miracles and special revelations. The whole works, if we could but see it, to a divine climax, but in the drama the individual has free choice : he may behave well or ill and God will make use both of his righteousness and his wickedness. God's purpose, however, is not altogether in-scrutable : revelation and history offer a sufficient guidance to the whole, even if the detailed process cannot always be observed in operation. Bossuet felt himself at least able to illustrate this thesis of a providential guidance in history : " There is nothing more absurd than to say that He does not mingle with the government of peoples, with the establishment or ruin of States, with the manner in which they are governed, by what princes and by what laws ; if all of these, while being carried out by men's liberty, are not guided by the hand of God so that He has sure means of directing them as He pleases, it follows that God has no part in these events and that this part of the world is entirely independent." [1] Actually the eye of faith can trace the hand of God through history : choosing the Jewish people as His instrument, He prepared the way for the greatest event, the coming of Christ, and since then has guided His Church towards its ultimate triumph.

In this historical perspective the individual can find the solution of the mystery of his temporal sufferings. He can transcend the personal outlook ; see that his own good or evil fortune is a tiny and unimportant part of a great eternal purpose. Without this understanding, the free-thinker's blasphemy is

---

[1] For all this see Brunetière, 5ᵉ series, *La Philosophie de Bossuet*.

plausible. "The *libertins* declare war on divine Providence and they find nothing stronger against it than the distribution of goods and evils which appears unjust, irregular, without any distinction between good and evil. This is where the impious entrench themselves as if in an impregnable fortress." [1] To the impious, however, the *Universal History* was surely a final answer. If we could only see clearly we should know there was, in fact, no such thing as chance. There is a point, a moment which is beyond men's sight, where God acts, where He brings all things together for good ; the eye of faith can detect the purposes of Providence where the scoffer sees the blind accidents of clashing forces.

Bossuet struggled vainly to stop the current. The idea of inevitable law, once stated, gradually undermined the conception of a personal Providence. Rationalism steadily gained ground. Among the thinkers who hastened its progress, de Maistre was right in linking Bayle and Fontenelle together as the most influential, " the fathers of modern incredulity."

Bayle, of Protestant family, exiled in Holland, fought consciously and openly to destroy faith. He invented the technique which his eighteenth-century successors adopted, and passed on to them an inexhaustible stock of arguments, pointed, erudite and unanswerable. Fontenelle, on the other hand, who was perpetual secretary to the Academy of Science, lived peacefully and long in the best society. His attack was necessarily more cautious. Throughout his work, however, alike in his *belles lettres*, his *éloges* and his specifically scientific books, there is the idea that nature is a single unity, working by fixed and ascertainable laws, and that all apparent exceptions are due to ignorance or misunderstanding. The implications of these doctrines—the certainty of natural laws and the solidarity of the sciences—were disastrous to the Catholicism of the seventeenth century. In his early work, Fontenelle, a master of " good form " and the social graces, passed over the dangerous points with a touch that was too gay to be shocking. Even in his later and more outspoken work, when his reputation and age

---

[1] Quoted by Brunetière, *op. cit.*, 61.

permitted him greater freedom, he disguised his meaning and professed orthodoxy. He was a timid but useful apostle of science and rationalism.

His first and most signal service was to begin the popularization of science. With him science ceased to be the monopoly of experts and became part of the subject-matter of literature. And it was not merely the conception of law that he popularized. He hastened the transition from Descartes to Newton. When he renounced prejudices, and sought to build only upon " evident " or axiomatic propositions, Descartes was laying down a mathematical rather than a scientific foundation. The " evidence " upon which Newton had built was not the result of immediate perception but of long labour and exact observation. Science needed both induction and deduction. By these means, Fontenelle declared in his *éloge* upon Newton, " he had at length reached conclusions which destroyed the vortices of Descartes and overturned that immense celestial edifice which we might have thought immovable." [1]

Fontenelle's second achievement was to raise the literary controversy between the " ancients " and " moderns " from the level of pedantry to that of philosophy. He saw that its tedious disputes really involved the great question whether men were progressing towards some higher form or were inferior to the heroes of antiquity. "Were the ancient trees larger than the modern ones? " Was the stuff of nature being gradually used up and mankind approaching an "old age" of feebleness? There was no reason to hold so pessimistic a doctrine. " Nature," he wrote, unconscious that he was contributing to a philosophy both of progress and of materialism, " has between its hands a certain paste which is always the same, which it unceasingly shapes and reshapes in a thousand ways, and of which it makes animals, plants and men."

---

[1] Fontenelle anticipated Voltaire in appreciating English science and in directly connecting its achievements with English liberty. Toleration was the necessary condition of intellectual life and scientific advance. Newton, he pointed out, had been knighted in England. " His name had reached the throne, where the most celebrated names do not always arrive." There was no need to draw the contrast with France more directly.

Fontenelle also stated the doctrine of the unity of knowledge. All the sciences, he declared in the preface to his *History of the Academy of the Sciences*, had so far taken nature in " little bits " (*parcelles*). But the time would come when the connection between the results of different sciences would be seen, when "we shall join together in a regular body these scattered members." "Various separate truths, of which there are so many, show their relations and mutual dependence so forcibly to the mind that it seems that, after having been detached from one another by a kind of violence, they naturally seek to re-unite." It was this unity which the Encyclopædists set out to prove. Science was the key not only to particular truths but to truth itself.

Men were slow to grasp the significance of this doctrine. They were always retarded by their credulity; they tended, Fontenelle remarked, to believe first and collect their evidence afterwards. Yet his indirect attack had its effect. His readers were inevitably driven to contrast the evidence for the Christian cosmogony with the evidence for Newtonian physics. Nor could a student of Fontenelle fail to see that there might be less reputable explanations of miracles than the orthodox ones : in his *History of Oracles* he described the trickery by which pagan priests established the reputation of their oracles with simple and uncritical folk, and left the reader to wonder if the liquefaction of St Januarius' blood might be similarly explained.

Fontenelle led men gently from faith in Christianity to religious scepticism and from religious scepticism to a new faith in science. Pierre Bayle was a still more potent influence. To give a full account of his achievements would be to recount the history of eighteenth-century thought. Referring to him, Diderot remarked that the Encyclopædists had " their contemporaries under Louis XIV." If he had said their master he would not have exaggerated. The form, the method and the inspiration, as well as much of the contents of the *Encyclopædia*, originated in Bayle. Voltaire's shafts flew more directly to their mark than Bayle's, but they were borrowed from him. The critical examination of historical sources, which made Voltaire the most workmanlike of eighteenth-century French historians, came from Bayle. The habit of treating the Bible as an inaccurate source-book, placing its contradicting accounts side by side, and submitting Jehovah or the Mother of God to the same kind of criticism as Jupiter or Venus, came from Bayle.[1] Too much has been claimed for the English deists as an influence upon eighteenth-century France ; for Bayle was a deist before Tindal or Toland ; he provided the arguments for natural religion before Bolingbroke or Shaftesbury, and Voltaire learned more from the *Dictionnaire* than from Clarke. As a champion of toleration Bayle preceded Locke, and nothing substantial was added to his argument until John Stuart Mill's *Liberty*, a century and three-quarters later.[2]

Bayle, the son of a Protestant minister, had been converted to Catholicism, reconverted to Protestantism, and finally become equally doubtful of all religions. Finding the condition of a relapsed heretic a dangerous one in most countries, he settled in Rotterdam, where he became Professor of Philosophy in 1681. In 1684 he began his *Nouvelles de la République de Lettres*, one of the earliest critical periodicals. The revocation of the Edict of Nantes directly affected him : in 1685 his brother died a victim to the persecution of Louis. His constant advocacy of free-thought in the *République de Lettres* was supplemented by his *Ce que c'est la France toute Catholique*, his *Commentaire philosophique* and his *Dictionnaire historique et critique*. His arguments, however, were scarcely more pleasing to the Huguenots than to their Catholic persecutors. For toleration with Bayle meant the right to err and the duty to doubt, not the permission to believe in the Reformed Church and the duty to reciprocate persecution if the opportunity arose. From the beginning his works were attacked by Protestants as well as burned by Catholics, and in 1693 he lost the Chair of

---

[1] Biblical criticism, beginning in England about the same time, was greatly aided by Bayle's contemporary, Richard Simon ; like Malebranche, he argued that miracles should be tested by the ordinary rules of evidence and thought it unlikely that God would break His own eternal laws.

[2] Locke's *Essay on Toleration* appeared in 1689 and Bayle's *Commentaire philosophique* in 1686.

Philosophy through Protestant animosity. But he continued to write, and his *Dictionnaire*, a unique compilation of improper information, appeared four years later.

Bayle's work was the application of Cartesian principles to every branch of thought; he began, like Descartes, by ridding himself of current prejudices, but, unlike Descartes, he pressed on to the most dangerous conclusions. There were, he said,[1] three main rules to observe. The first was not to attack your opponents until you had made sure of your facts. He had frequent opportunity of illustrating the dangers of forgetting this principle at the expense of his opponents. The second was to realize that "proofs of feeling conclude nothing": if your object is to discover what is true, passion should be banished from discussion. The reason why Bayle's influence was so lasting, and also so unobtrusive, was because he obeyed this maxim and left the enjoyable task of turning his facts and arguments into diatribes to his successors. The third rule was that nothing should be accepted without evidence which amounted to proof. Nothing should be taken for granted, nothing considered too sacred or too obvious to be examined. Thus Bayle's own task was, above all, to submit the whole scheme of ideas, assumptions and dogmas to an equal and un-ceremonious examination : all the certainties of society became doubts when he handled them, all the authorities seemed foolish dogmatists, and the fundamental truths resolved themselves into myths and fairy stories, invented to amuse or terrify children and save their parents the trouble of more rational discipline.

If Bayle is not always a sound critic it is not for lack of digging to the roots and discovering flaws that others missed. His weakness was that in the natural enjoyment of scandalizing the orthodox and putting the solemn to ridicule he lost his sense of proportion. He has rightly been considered diffuse, and criticized for writing page after page about obscure and trivial thinkers to the neglect of the more significant and profound. His eighteenth-century followers certainly inherited these characteristics as well as his habit of assuming that the

---

[1] In his *Dictionnaire*, article *Bellarmin*.

value of an argument or doctrine is altogether destroyed by
the discovery that its logical foundation is weak. But in fact
his method was admirable for its purpose. Men must laugh
before they can think, discover their ignorance before they can
doubt, doubt before they can know what is true. Nothing
could be more effective for the production of laughter, thought
and doubt than Bayle's method of carefully stating an orthodox
view in such a way that the least critical could not miss its
absurdity. His irreverent comment upon everything—sacred,
profane, remote and familiar alike—had a similar effect. His
readers, led to smile at the follies of their ancestors in one
sentence, discovered in the next similar peculiarities in their
own generation ; they were astonished to find that the doctrines
of Christianity were often similar to those of pagan religions,
and that Nero's reasons for persecuting the Saints were those
advanced by Louis the Great. Bayle, as Madame de Lambert
suggested in 1715, did more than any other to " shake the
yoke of authority and opinion." Voltaire's judgment was
similar. "He sets forth things with such an odious fidelity,
and places the argument on both sides before our eyes with
so mean an impartiality and is so intolerably intelligible that
he puts even those of the most meagre understanding in a
position to judge and even to doubt what is told them."

The idea of toleration has found support from various
sources. Humanitarian feeling, political common sense, a belief
in the ultimate rights of the individual conscience, a trust in
reason and a scepticism about its possibilities—all these have
been its ingredients. In Bayle we find them united. No doubt
it is logically possible to hold with John Stuart Mill that the
truth is always the gainer by the statement of falsehood. But
those who have believed their own doctrine eternally true
have seldom been willing to risk the perdition of their friends
by permitting the advocacy of heresy. Historically speaking,
scepticism has been the forerunner of a genuinely tolerant
spirit. The Protestant's respect for conscience, the horror of
cruelty, the sensible statesmanship of the *Politiques*, confidence
in the methods of reason, whether in the mediæval theologian
or the scientist who took his place—all these have failed on

occasion to guard the freedom of thought which they have generally promoted. Unless there is an element of scepticism, unless, like Montaigne and Benjamin Franklin, men " doubt a little of their own infallibility " they may always become persecutors ; the exceptional moment comes when they can be persuaded that it is sometimes cruel to be kind, that it is expedient that one man should die for the people or that conscience is wrong-headed. Even the apostles of reason have occasionally been intolerant in moments of enthusiastic certainty.

Bayle's argument is singularly complete. Few have more eloquently condemned the political folly of sacrificing the reality of national harmony for the dream of religious unity, or more forcibly pointed to the cruelty of persecution and the contradiction it involved between the teaching of Christ and the actions of those who called themselves Christians. What could be more ridiculous or unworthy than to take a single phrase, " Compel them to come in," which occurs in one of Christ's parables as a pressing invitation to dinner, as an excuse for compelling men to enter a Church whose doctrines they did not share? To compel conscience was in itself a crime and an absurdity. Persecution might compel people to be hypocrites, but conscience remained its own master by its very nature. " *To compel them to come in* means to ravage, hang, kill, devastate till the individual dare not refuse to join so kindly and true a religion." What indeed could be less likely to convince either Protestants or pagans of the truth of Christianity than the cruelty, the quarrels, the unfaithfulness to their own Master, displayed by the Catholics? Hell, he remarked, must certainly contain many Catholics or its tortures would be incomplete. But Protestants were almost as bad. Nero persecuting Christians, Calvin burning Servetus and Louis murdering his subjects were all guilty of the same folly and the same crime. In his " Dialogue between a Burgomaster of Rotterdam and Jurieu," the latter is made to suggest that such unbelievers as Bayle should be silenced. "Do you consider the consequences of what you demand? " asks the Burgomaster. "You are asking for an Inquisition." "I abhor the Inquisition," says

Jurieu. "Yes, the Popish one. But do you disclaim an Inquisition of your own or an Inquisition on behalf of your own religion? We are not lukewarm. We act upon the principle of Christianity by tolerating all religions and by not suffering any Christian to hurt any other." After all, Bayle asks, "is it not true that to fight errors with blows is the same absurdity as to fight against fortresses with speeches and syllogisms?"

Three basic propositions support Bayle's plea for toleration. First, that all religious and philosophic conclusions are at best doubtful. Second, since morality is not dependent upon any brand of religion, we should take cognizance of men's behaviour, not of their nominal creed. Thirdly, Bayle held that spiritual coercion was always unwise and unjust, since God has given men an intuitive knowledge of His moral law and left it to their individual interpretation: men do not apprehend it perfectly, but it appears in some form or other in all societies, and it is frequently in active conflict with the orthodox and accepted codes which religious systems attempt to enforce.

In the first place, every religion is doubtful since there is insufficient evidence of any doctrines of sin, grace or immortality. Any doctrines not founded on verified evidence can have but a tinsel authority, "fragile as glass." In view of this uncertainty, any coercion of opinion was an unmitigated evil. The truth, if it could be found, could be discovered only by the free play of reason and science. In any case, it was none of the State's business. Bayle anticipated Locke in his purely secular view of the State. The Reformation had given birth to kings who put the material interests of their country before its religious orthodoxy. Henry IV. had consummated the political unity of France at the expense of a measure of toleration: Richelieu and Mazarin had conducted a foreign and domestic policy dictated solely by secular considerations. But Louis had returned to mediævalism and placed religious uniformity above national interest. The result was a definite enunciation of the doctrine that State policy has nothing to do with religion. The State should take no notice of opinion as such: its duty is to safeguard individual rights, and to consider religious questions only if they threaten public safety.

In the second place, Bayle pointed out that a man's sect or creed was not an index to his behaviour. Christianity was a religion of meekness, and to fight was incompatible with the teaching of the Gospel: yet Christians made good soldiers, persecuted heretics and even fought crusades in the name of the Prince of Peace. Mohammedans, on the other hand, were taught the duty of persecution, but were often tolerant. The Church had strict views about sexual morality, but Christians were not specially continent, and many courtesans were amongst the most orthodox Catholics. Atheists, who believed in no supernatural sanctions, often lived the most correct lives. Moralists like Bossuet and Father Rapin had declared that a decline in morals must accompany a decline in faith. The evidence, Bayle thought, pointed in the opposite direction. The manners of society had little or nothing to do with religion, and the chances were that a society of atheists would be as moral as a society of Catholics or other idolaters.

Finally, Bayle's Protestant faith in his own conscience and his study of various religions made him oppose every kind of spiritual coercion. In all religions there were certain universal elements, the teaching of " natural reason ": in all men there was a capacity for distinguishing between good and evil, " a certain persuasion in the soul." And the natural reason and conscience of men, the supreme tribunal, were frequently in opposition to the doctrines and commands of states and churches. Reason suggests that there is a God who created the world and it everywhere approves of the morality taught in the New Testament and in the sayings of Buddha and Confucius. But it also establishes certain axioms: it is impossible to believe such contradictions as that a part is greater than the whole or that a good God establishes a natural order and then interferes to reward some individuals with temporal happiness and to punish others with an eternity of torment. Bossuet had noticed that the free-thinkers had found their strongest argument in the apparently arbitrary distribution of earthly pains and pleasures. In Bayle's view this inequality was neither arbitrary nor Providential. There was no relationship between sin and suffering, unless sin were interpreted as neglect of the teaching of nature. Why, asked Bayle, should a man's misconduct be paid for in ill-health unless he acted in such a way as to damage his body? A stone breaks a piece of glass when it strikes it: the glass remains whole if the stone misses it. We must accept the natural order as it is and not expect God to interfere. The conception of Providence is absurd. The world is in many respects obviously bad: it follows either that God does not interfere with it or that He is not good. How can we reconcile the conception of a good God with our human experience? "Would a perfect Being amuse Himself with raising a creature to the highest point of glory in order to cast him down again to the lowest degree of ignominy? Would this not be the action of a child who has scarcely built a card-house before it knocks it over?" Is God really to be conceived of as a Father who showers favours upon men and then, when they enjoy them in their own way, punishes them for insolence as an example and a lesson to others? If so, God's method of instruction is a singularly inefficient one: for "the utility of these examples is not noticeable: every generation up to this one has needed this lesson, and there is no sign that the generations to come will be more free from such vicissitudes than earlier ones."[1]

While Bayle was advancing the arguments for natural religion in Holland, English churchmen were approaching the same position with more cautious steps.[2] Bayle's criticisms of the Church, his plea for free-thought and his individualist philosophy passed on into the main stream of eighteenth-century thought. His politics, however, were less advanced than his religious views. He believed in the "natural reason" of the average man but not much in his natural intelligence. He combined a tremendous faith in men's right to their own opinions with a consistent scepticism about their ability to improve their social and political organization. He declared that the evil of absolutism was its tendency to inflict wars upon mankind, but even so he thought a strong government better than a weak one. For the most part he concerned himself with religion and free-thought: he left

---

[1] *Dictionnaire*, article *Lucrèce*.
[2] *Vide infra*, pp. 123 ff.

the solution of economic and political problems to others who were less sceptical of the possibility of social improvement.

4. REFORM—FÉNELON, SAINT-PIERRE, VAUBAN AND THE ECONOMISTS

During Louis' reign the stringency of official censorship and the mystical prestige of the monarchy made open political criticism rare and dangerous. But as his wars became more predatory and less successful, as the burden of debt increased and taxation became correspondingly oppressive, as the stagnation of trade and the misery of the peasants grew less easy to ignore, grumbling began in all articulate classes of society. The military policy of Louvois excited anger everywhere, and though Louis was seldom directly attacked he was warned that a king has moral responsibility towards his people. The great preachers thundered against the iniquity of the Court, and dared to tell the exalted that God imposed obligations upon those to whom He gave power and opportunity. Massillon, Bourdaloue and Bossuet were not afraid to remind aristocratic audiences that Christ had thought it difficult for the rich to enter the kingdom of heaven, where the last would be first and the first last. Did not Christ cry, "Woe to the rich!" and offer eternal blessedness to Lazarus? "Oh, ye poor," Bossuet cried, in his sermon upon the dignity of poverty, "how rich you are! But oh, ye rich, how poor you are! . . . If you do not carry the burdens of the poor, yours will crush you, the weight of your ill-spent wealth will carry you into the pit; but if you share with the poor the burden of their poverty, taking part in their misery, you will deserve altogether to share in their privileges." It is not enough, he declared, "to open the eyes of the flesh upon the poor, it is necessary to consider them with the eyes of the intellect. Blessed is he who understands. The man who truly understands the mystery of charity is the one who considers the poor as the first children of the Church: who, honouring their position, thinks himself obliged to serve them: who only hopes to share in the blessings of the Church by means of charity and brotherly intercourse." He calls upon Louis to taste the joys of a " truly royal pleasure " by assuaging the sufferings of the poor. But the world is not regenerated in court chapels. The beggars who daily waited outside the chapel at Versailles, or on the steps at St Sulpice, may have fed better because of Bossuet's eloquence, but the peasant still paid away eighty per cent. of his livelihood to his king and his lord.[1]

In the later part of Louis' reign there were individual thinkers and political groups inside the kingdom bold enough to criticize the policy of the government and to suggest projects of reform. Their criticism and their suggestions followed two main lines : first, they deplored the degradation of the ancient Constitution of France and demanded that " the Orders " once again should share in government; second, they began to question the necessity of France's economic misery, to call attention to the evils of Louis' aggressive wars and to demand the reform of the whole system of excessive and arbitrary taxation.

The most influential of the reformers was Fénelon. His controversy with Bossuet, his plain speaking to the King, his championship of the shrill Quietism of Madame Guyon, brought him into disgrace, and his later years were spent as Archbishop of Cambrai and not, as he and his supporters had expected, as Archbishop of Paris. Before his exile, as tutor to the young Duke of Burgundy and later as adviser to the Opposition group whose hopes for France were centred in the Duke, Fénelon made numerous suggestions for the better government of France. His *Fables*, his *Dialogues des Morts*, his *Examen de Conscience pour un Roi* and *Télémaque* were written primarily for the Duke's instruction. All of them contained indirect political criticism, while *Télémaque* began the fashion of combining travellers' stories with Utopia-building.[2] The young Prince Télémaque, under the guidance of Mentor, visits one kingdom after another, discovers the principles of good government and finally establishes them in perfect form at Salente. Télémaque sees countries where all land is held in common, where the simple life has never been banished by tyranny, where war is unknown

---

[1] Bourdaloue's warnings to the rich were equally emphatic, *vide* his sermons, " Sur la restitution " and " Sur la richesse."

[2] For the influence of *Télémaque*, *vide* Cherel, *Fénelon au XVIIIe Siècle*.

and men's instinctive happiness finds natural opportunity without conventional restraint. In Salente itself the Platonic State is to be realized : each class does its appropriate work in harmony with the others, the children are educated and trained by the State for their special occupations, and all property is utilized for the public good, allotted in accordance with the needs of each class, and never engrossed or alienated in the interests of individuals.

Fénelon's criticism became more direct. Though he doubted the sacred character of the monarchy no more than Bossuet himself, he was far bolder in reminding the King of his duty to God and his subjects. The fundamental laws anciently observed in France could never lose their authority.[1] In a letter possibly meant for the King's eyes [2] Fénelon complained that during the last thirty years the principal Ministers of State had "overturned all the ancient maxims of State" : "On n'a plus parlé de l'Etat ni des règles ; on n'a parlé que du Roi et de son bon plaisir. On a poussé vos revenus et vos dépenses à l'infini. On vous a élevé jusqu'au ciel, pour avoir effacé, disait-on, la grandeur de tous vos prédécesseurs ensemble, c'est-à-dire pour avoir approuvé la France entière, afin d'introduire à la cour un luxe monstrueux et incurable. Ils ont voulu vous élever sur les ruines de toutes les conditions de l'Etat, comme si vous pouviez être grand en ruinant tous vos sujets, sur qui votre grandeur est fondée." In 1710 Fénelon even declared that, if he could judge by observation of his own diocese, the first shock would break down the worn-out machine : the soldiers were unpaid and uncared for ; it was surprising that they did not mutiny ; the *intendants* and their tax-collectors were everywhere swindling and ravaging the people ; bankruptcy would result if peace were not made. Taxation, he suggested, should be certain, not arbitrary : it was wrong to collect money in order to "uphold claims which did not interest the King's subjects, who would not be any the happier for an

[1] *Vide* more especially his *Examen de Conscience pour un Roi* (1734), his *Plans de Gouvernement* (1711), and *Mémoires sur la Guerre de Succession d'Espagne* (1710).
[2] *Remontrances à Louis XIV.* (about 1694).

added province." Finally he wrote to the King : "You love only your own glory and convenience. You bring everything back to yourself, as if you were the God of the Earth and all the rest were only created to be sacrificed for you. It is on the contrary you whom God has put into the world for your people."[1]

These were the evils of despotism. What was the remedy? To revive the ancient Constitution of France, to persuade the King to respect the fundamental laws and listen to the advice of the Estates. Formerly the King had not collected taxes on his sole authority. The representatives of the nation granted him funds for his extraordinary needs. In each diocese a local assembly should once again assess the taxes and in each province deputies from all three Orders should proportion the levies in accordance with the wealth of the district and supervise their collection. *Intendants* would then be superfluous and, with just administration by the deputies, taxation would become so much more profitable that the *gabelle* and other extraordinary taxes would become unnecessary. Above all, every three years the States-General, representing the Church, the *Noblesse* and the Third Estate, would be called for a session of indefinite length, would advise in matters of taxation, peace and war, and remedy and prevent abuses by keeping watch over *seigneurs* who oppressed the people or allowed their territory to go out of cultivation.

In all this Fénelon had in mind the ruined peasantry of France. But when he goes on to consider his administrative proposals in detail it is clear that his main concern was to restore the influence of the aristocracy. The old nobility and the Opposition group which gathered round the Duke of Burgundy during the later part of Louis' reign no doubt objected to the system of government because it was bad, but they objected still more because, as the Comte de Boulain-villiers put it, under Louis all Orders were " equally crushed, destroyed and annihilated."[2] Nobles like Saint-Simon resented the power of bourgeois administrators, and welcomed Fénelon's

---

[1] *Remontrances à Louis XIV. sur divers points de son Administration,* 1694.
[2] Quoted. Sée, *op. cit.,* p. 272.

proposal to reduce the King's secretaries from two hundred and eighty to forty and to establish aristocratic councils to share in the task of government.

To weaken the bureaucracy and to strengthen the power of the ancient *noblesse* were reforms which the outraged aristocracy could grasp. Nor were they averse from the historical doctrine of Boulainvilliers,[1] who declared despotism an evil innovation, individual rights sacred and *raison d'état* a screen for the individual ambition of the King. But his economic proposals were less pleasing to the aristocracy. He criticized the whole system of taxation, denounced the *gabelle* especially, proposed to redeem the national debt—mainly at the expense of the upper classes—and to establish a system of taxation in which the national expenditure should be met, at least in part, by the rich as well as by the poor.

Two contemporaries of Boulainvilliers were also remarkable as economists : Vauban, the military engineer, was a statistician and a practical critic ; Boisguillebert was more original, and may indeed be considered the earliest of the Physiocrats. Vauban's approach to economics arose from his direct experience of the provinces, whose resources it was his business to know and utilize. A tenth of the population, he calculated, was reduced to beggary, half of it was on the border-line of starvation and only a tenth could be accounted comfortable. The existing system of taxation was the central evil. In spite of Colbert's reforms in the methods of collection, at least a quarter of the *taille* collected never reached the Treasury, while the customs duties and extraordinary *aides* crushed the peasantry and fed only an idle aristocracy. The general " capitation " levy of 1694 offered the example of a more equitable system. Vauban suggested that at the end of the war

---

[1] *Vide* Boulainvilliers' *Lettres sur les anciens Parlements de France que l'on nomine Etats Généraux, Etat de la France, Histoire de l'ancien Gouvernement de la France,* and *Essais sur la Noblesse de France,* which are careful historical studies in which he maintains the thesis that the conquering Franks were the ancestors of the existing *noblesse,* and that the King, being really elected by the aristocracy, had no right to legislate by edict or to govern without the support of the Estates.

a single tax should be made on all property. For this purpose there should be a complete census of the population and of wealth. Having himself made a survey of the agricultural produce, real estate, industrial profits and luxury trades in the districts of Rouen and Vézelay, Vauban was able to explain his plan in detail. He argued that the adoption of his system without fear or favour would make the King solvent and restore national prosperity. Great fortunes would be less conspicuous, but so would poverty. Financiers, tax-farmers, lawyers, clergy and aristocracy would of course resist, but the vast mass of the poor, whose "only possessions were their limbs," whose labour enriched the community which made them so little return, would joyfully support the monarch against the forces of privilege.

Vauban's imagination did not go further. He remained in general an orthodox follower of Colbert, accepting the mercantilist view that the prosperity of France could best be attained at the expense of other nations. Inside France there should be free trade; famines would then cease and free interchange of produce at home would create national strength.[1]

As a theorist Boisguillebert was far in advance of Vauban.[2] A forerunner of the Physiocrats and of Adam Smith, it seemed to him that just as there are laws in the physical world so there must be laws in the social world. If we want our water pure we arrange for it to circulate: in the same way, if we want to keep our economic system from stagnation we must arrange for a natural flow of goods. In his dissertation on the nature of riches he goes to the heart of the matter. " Nature establishes an equal need of buying and selling in all kinds of traffic, so that the single desire of profit may be the soul of all sales, as much in the seller as in the buyer, and it is in aid

---

[1] Vauban regarded imports of luxuries as " useless and very harmful " ; all importation of manufactured goods caused money to flow from the country, and should be prohibited.

[2] He also differed from Vauban on financial reform. Equal collection of the *taille* was his remedy. " The only way," he wrote, " to avoid ruin is to suppress privilege, and make powerful persons contribute to the taxes, as they do in England."

of this equilibrium, or this balance, that both are equally compelled to understand reason and to submit to it." According
to this law, Boisguillebert believed that there is a fundamental
agreement of interests in society: " If the rich understood
their interests, they would entirely exempt the poor from taxation. Moreover, it is not only inside any particular nation that
there is this harmony of interests. States do not grow rich by
making their neighbours poor. Riches consist in the supply of
wants. Money is only a means of exchange and is intrinsic-
ally worthless. A country may be rich without much money
and the country which has only money very wretched, if it
finds it difficult to exchange it for goods." Wealth, therefore,
depends on exchange, and money is useful only in so far as it
facilitates exchange. If we are to be rich, money must circulate
quickly, and not only among a few but among the whole
population. If there were no hindrances to the process of
exchange there would be no poverty.

Freedom of exchange should be international. If corn were
allowed to circulate freely, not only in France but also between
nations, French agriculture would gain, not lose. The result
would not be famine, as some feared, but plenty. Agriculturists
would produce more than enough for French needs, and if on
some occasion there was scarcity in France, as a result of excessive exportation or failure of harvest, foreign corn would be
imported in response to the new demand.

Boisguillebert was not always consistent in his belief in
freedom, but his philosophy opens a new era in economics.
The Liberal theory of the harmony of natural interests, with
its logical deduction of *laissez-faire*, is implicit in his writing.
Nature, as the Physiocrats were later to explain in detail, was
man's Providence, not his enemy. To adjust our ways to hers
is to be reasonable. Boisguillebert was the first economist to
hold the optimistic view that the interests of man and Nature
are identical. It followed that nations should co-operate, not
contest: they should work with natural tendencies, not against
them. The only beneficial legislation is that which enables men
more freely to enjoy the wealth that Nature offers them. To
do this they must study her ways, and realize that " neither

authority nor favour releases anyone from the duty of obeying the laws of justice and reason."

Boisguillebert died in 1714 without any heed from the Government or the public. Louis defeated his critics by outliving them. Only one, the Abbé de Saint-Pierre, survived to continue his self-imposed task of finding remedies for every evil in the State. The Abbé, indeed, was the most industrious, the most honest and fearless, as well as the most prolix, writer of his age. Yet the French Academy regarded his critical spirit with smiling tolerance for twenty-four years, and it was not until 1718 that it decided upon his exclusion. Indeed Saint-Pierre's countless projects seemed to be of the kind which may easily be neglected. There was no tinge of democracy in his proposals. Even the " Polysynodies " were only Councils of the kind suggested by Fénelon, composed of the *noblesse* and the magistrates. But his *Projet pour perfectionner le Gouvernement des Etats* contained at least one significant idea. He thought that there might be a " science of government." Boulainvilliers, who had also used the phrase,[1] was almost exclusively concerned with a science of wealth, and Vauban, who had understood the value of statistics, had imagined a government which would regulate its financial system scientifically. Saint-Pierre, however, applied the idea to government as a whole, and suggested the foundation of a Political Academy, consisting of forty experts, to advise and co-operate with the monarchy.

Saint-Pierre was not content to assume that even an enlightened and scientific administration would govern well unless it had clear principles to guide it. He was perhaps the first systematic Utilitarian.[2] He stated the principle of utility with a precision equal to Bentham's. "The value," he wrote, "of a book, of a regulation, of an institution, or of any public work is proportioned to the number and grandeur of the actual pleasures which it procures and of the future pleasures which it is calculated to procure for the greatest number of men." If he anticipated the principle of which Helvétius and Bentham are usually

---

[1] Boulainvilliers, *Etats de la France* (Preface).
[2] *Vide* G. Lowes Dickinson's introduction to Miss Nuttall's translation of Saint-Pierre's *Perpetual Peace*.

believed to be the inventors, he was even more advanced in the application he made of "the greatest-happiness principle." Writing before the industrial revolution had predisposed men to *laissez-faire*, he tended to over-estimate rather than to minimize the part which the State could play in promoting happiness. His aim was to transform the irresponsible bureaucracy of Louis XIV. into an efficient and benevolent system of State socialism. He proposed that the poor should be supported by the rich and that public money should be used to promote social welfare : taxation of wealth should provide for free education, highways and canals, a central postal service and public works of all kinds.

In his belief that men were perfectible, and that good laws based upon a scientific understanding of natural principles would be sufficient to remedy all social evils, Saint-Pierre stood alone in his generation, and anticipated both the utilitarianism and the optimistic radicalism of Condorcet and the later Encyclopædists. His contemporarie sthought him a harmless oddity. But the succeeding generation admitted their debt to Saint-Pierre. His deliberate and conscious utilitarianism, his complete Erastianism, and his near approach to an historical and philosophical doctrine of progress all directly influenced the *philosophes*. Of his writings, his *Project for Perpetual Peace*, edited and indeed rewritten by Rousseau, has alone survived to be read and discussed two centuries later.[1]

In 1712 Europe was preparing for the Treaty of Utrecht, and the Abbé de Saint-Pierre, who was present at the Congress, hoped that the long war might end in something more than the usual armed peace. The famous proposal attributed by Sully to Henry IV. provided a basis for Saint-Pierre's project. It finally appeared in two immense volumes, which few were likely to read and which no statesman would have dreamed of taking seriously. To outlaw war by a League of Nations, each pledged to support the others in the event of any member-state proving aggressive, certainly seemed chimerical.

There were others, more eloquent but less ceaselessly con-

---

[1] *Vide infra,* Chapter X.

structive than the Abbé, who expressed the common hatred of war and the revolt against the futile waste of Louis' policy. Fénelon wrote: "There never was a war, even a successful war, which did not cause more harm than good to the State: we have only to consider how many families it ruins, how many men it kills, how it lays waste and depopulates all countries and how it authorizes licence." Twenty years earlier he had told Louis that his "subjects were dying of hunger; the cultivation of the soil is practically abandoned, all business is at a standstill, commerce is entirely ruined. France has become a huge hospital. The magistrates are discredited and harassed. . . . You alone have brought all this trouble upon yourself; for, the whole kingdom having been ruined, you now hold everything in your own hands, and no one can so much as live save by your bounty." [1]

The death of the King in 1715 was the signal for an outbreak of rejoicing, in which, as Saint-Simon remarked, most of his subjects except the valets of his household shared. The great barrier was down, and, though the letter of the law might remain as repressive as ever, the superstitious awe which made its strict administration possible was immediately diminished. Under Louis there had been groups of malcontents: each group was destined to expand and play its part in the spectacular overthrow of the Leviathan. First there was the remnant of the *frondeurs*, nobles who had set their hopes upon the Duke of Burgundy and looked forward to reasserting the political rights of their order. The bourgeoisie, too, hated both the Jesuits and arbitrary government, and took the part of the Jansenists and the Gallican

---

[1] *Vide* also Massillon's sermons against war, upon which Voltaire commented in the *Dic. Phil.*, art. *Guerre*. Amongst thousands of sermons upon theological absurdities and trivial religious observances "there are three or four at most, by a Frenchman named Massillon, which an honest man can read without disgust . . . you will at least find two where the orator dares say some words against this plague and crime of war which includes all plagues and crimes. The wretched spouters unceasingly talk against love, which is the only consolation of humanity and the only way of improving it: they say nothing of the abominable efforts we make to destroy it."

Parlements. The *libertins* had grown bolder during the reign and had even begun to turn their ironical attention to government as well as to religion. The ruined peasantry could not speak for themselves, but the degradation of French agriculture and the helpless misery of the bulk of Louis' subjects had already made a few intelligent men aware of new aspects of the economic problem, and aroused humanitarians to bitter criticism and imaginative speculation.

From these social divisions, first clearly marked under Louis XIV., arose the three main conceptions of government which were to struggle for acceptance in the eighteenth century. An absolute monarchy in alliance with an absolute Church, claiming divine origin and divine sanction, admitted no corporate or individual rights except those which it had itself bestowed, and repudiated every practical as well as theoretical limitation of its authority. To check this new and irresponsible sovereignty, dating only from the Renaissance, conservatism sought to restore the ancient French Constitution. Louis was reminded of his obligations to his people, of the rights of the Estates, the contractual nature of his kingship and the fundamental law of France, itself an expression of an underlying law of nature. A third philosophy was taking shape, opposed both to the revival of feudalism, and to the arbitrary development of the Renaissance monarchy.

The new philosophy, most conveniently called Liberalism, was concerned above all with the preservation of individual rights. It set men on a legal equality in opposition to feudalism, which grouped them in social strata. It challenged the right of the monarch to govern except in the interests of his subjects; it defended their rights both by an appeal to natural law and upon grounds of utility. It could ally itself for the time with the monarchy against feudalism, and with feudalism against the monarchy. On the one hand, it made use of the conception of contract, which was implicit in feudalism and as old as Stoic philosophy, to attack despotism; on the other, it looked to the monarchy as the one power strong enough to oppose the Church and to abolish the system of privilege which was all that remained of the corporate life of the Middle Ages. In the light of historical analysis it is now clear that of the three conceptions the feudal was, in any case, doomed; it was opposed to the whole trend of economic and psychological development. An absolute Church and an absolute monarch could not long maintain their position when the bourgeoisie became educated and rich, and the peasantry conscious of its degradation. The triumph of the Liberal conception of society may seem to have been unavoidable. But the form which that philosophy took was the result of actual events and the work of particular individuals in the eighteenth century.

CHAPTER III

THE FAILURE OF THE *ANCIEN RÉGIME*

I. THE INFLUENCE OF THE *PHILOSOPHES*

"La maladresse du son gouvernement a précipité cette révolution, la philosophie en a dirigé les principes, la force populaire a détruit les obstacles qui pouvaient arrêter les mouvements" (Condorcet, 9th epoch).

"Under Louis XIV. one dared not say anything; under Louis XV. one spoke low; under your Majesty one speaks aloud" (Marshal Richelieu to Louis XVI.).

THE controversy about the part played by philosophy in producing the French Revolution began with the Revolution itself, still continues, and is not likely to end so long as there are historians and philosophers to discuss it. For the Revolution is the chosen battle-ground of the idealists and materialists in history. Is the French Revolution—and by implication any similar historical event—to be explained by economic changes over which individuals have little control or by the influence of ideas which moved men to dissatisfaction with their institutions? Put thus baldly, both extreme views are a little absurd. It is impossible to deny that ideas have influence. Karl Marx himself admitted their importance and his followers assume that their own ideas at least have effects. On the other hand, it seems scarcely worth while to refute those idealists who speak as if ideas were controlling factors in history apart from the economic and social circumstances in which they work. But we do not escape the problem by pointing out that both factors are always present and that the same forces are of varying importance in different periods of history. This is the beginning, not the end of an inquiry. The problem is to find the relationship between numerous factors, roughly and unsatisfactorily classified as economic and psychological. During the Revolution itself the two points of view were explicitly stated by Mallet du Pan and Mounier. The writers of the Catholic reaction, de Maistre and Bonald, naturally felt, like Professor Babbitt[1] in America to-day, that when the world goes wrong someone must be to blame. They therefore decided that Rousseau, Voltaire and

---

[1] *Vide* Irving Babbitt, *Rousseau and Romanticism.*

the Encyclopædists were responsible for the destruction of the *ancien régime*. Later the same thesis was majestically and paradoxically expounded by Taine. He described France as a healthy individual who fell upon the ground foaming at the mouth after drinking a cup of poison. The poison, in his view, was the philosophic doctrine. Having thus attributed the Revolution to the *philosophes*, he proceeded with incomparable skill and with great erudition to show that no part of the French Constitution was in fact healthy. The real difficulty was to explain how such outworn institutions contrived to last so long.[1]

Taine's researches have always provided ammunition for his adversaries. The most forcible exponent of the opposite doctrine was Rocquain, who argued that the Revolution arose out of the struggle between King and *Parlements* rather than out of any abstract ideas.[2] Aubertin sustained a thesis similar to Rocquain's in an elaborate study of the memoir-writers of the century.[3] M. Champion supported the view that the Philosophic doctrine was unimportant by demonstrating that the *cahiers* of 1789 were almost wholly confined to a statement of economic grievances and were for the most part unconcerned with any abstract ideas.[4] M. Faguet greeted M. Champion's researches with enthusiasm, showed that the so-called revolutionary philosophy was at least as old as Bayle and, for the most part, much older; that the *philosophes* themselves did not want and would not have liked revolution, being in general enthusiastic and loyal monarchists, and that the Revolution was therefore the outcome, not of ideas, but of a breakdown in government.[5]

Under M. Lanson's guidance, however, a more just appreciation of the *philosophes* came into fashion, and M. Roustan's *Philosophes et la Société française* marked another turn of

---

[1] Taine, *Les Origines de la France contemporaine*, i. (1876-1894); *cp.* also Morley's review of Taine in *Miscellanies*.

[2] Rocquain, *L'Esprit révolutionnaire avant la Révolution*, 1878.

[3] Aubertin, *L'Esprit publie au XVIIIᵉ Siècle*, 1872.

[4] Champion, *Esprit de la Révolution française* (1887), *La France d'après les Cahiers de 1789*.

[5] Faguet, *Questions politiques*.

the tide.[1] M. Roustan made two instructive mistakes in his brilliant analysis. In the first place, when championing the *philosophes* he sometimes overstated his own thesis and went so far as to say that " the Revolution remains the work of the *philosophes* whatever M. Rocquain and M. Faguet may have thought about it." His book in fact supports a more interesting and subtle thesis than this. In the second place, M. Roustan would have clarified the issue if he had been more careful to divide it into two distinct problems. For throughout the controversy there has been a confusion, natural enough in a country so sharply divided into Liberals and Clericals. The problems of discovering what the *philosophes* taught, whether it was new or old, whether (to mention M. Faguet's patriotic preoccupation) it was " French " or not in character, and whether its intention was good or evil—these are problems of one type, and their solution does not answer for us the second problem of estimating their actual influence. M. Roustan has not altogether dissociated himself from this confusion. In studying the influence of thinkers it is far more important to know what people thought they said, what people quoted from them and attributed to them, than to know what, in fact, they did teach. M. Roustan, however, has for the most part concentrated on the second and relevant question, and has found the balance more accurately than any of his predecessors. His view is that the economic collapse of France and the actual breakdown of government had occurred long before the Revolution, and that the part of the *philosophes* was to bring the situation to a head by expressing the grievances of the dispossessed and even converting a large part of the *noblesse* itself. In 1753 d'Argenson thought a revolution imminent. There was no revolution. Why not? Because, insists M. Roustan, the *philosophes* had scarcely begun their propaganda. 1789 is in fact different from 1753, not because the peasants were more miserable or the town proletariat nearer starvation, but because during the intervening generation the doctrine of the *philosophes* had made known the grievances of all the unprivileged, encouraged the bourgeoisie in its hatred of the Church and in its

---

[1] M. Roustan's book has been translated by Frederic Whyte as *Pioneers of the French Revolution*, with an introduction by Harold J. Laski.

hopes of freedom of trade and of thought, had won the favour of great financiers and impregnated the whole *noblesse*, and even found a fluctuating support at the Court itself.

This controversy establishes three facts about the development of Liberal opinion in the eighteenth century. The first is that the economic and social conflict predisposed all the unprivileged to listen to revolutionary ideas; the second, that the constitutional and religious struggle, involving King, *Parlements*, Jansenists and Jesuits, was itself sufficient to stimulate "a revolutionary spirit"; the third that the particular form of revolutionary teaching was the work of the *philosophes*. Though "that conglomeration of disturbance and sedition" out of which the Revolution was to take shape was not the work of the *philosophes*, and though the economic forces in France and the actual breakdown in government must, in any case, have produced some such upheaval, the propaganda of the *philosophes* was necessary to destroy the aristocracy's faith in itself and to imbue the Third, and at times even the Fourth, Estate with ideas of liberty, equality and fraternity.

If this summary is any approximation to the truth, the task of the *philosophes* was at once to state in general form the grievances of the unprivileged and to place before the disillusioned a conception of a freer and happier society. In doing so they enlarged and improved ideas which had already appeared in the seventeenth century. For the most part they wrote for the discontented bourgeoisie; where their doctrines were agreeable to the mental habits of their readers and seemed to promise a fulfilment of popular social and economic aspirations, they were readily accepted and became the basis of Revolutionary change. The further implications of the new philosophy were neglected until later schools of thinkers and groups of the dispossessed realized their utility for their own purposes.

Economically, the *ancien régime* was rapidly disintegrating, and the conflict between an old and a new system of production gave rise to a social struggle between the beneficiaries of the two systems. "The world is changing," remarks the eighteenth-century Jew; "once a man's worth was determined by rank and birth, now it is determined by money." This

struggle between the privileged and the unprivileged under-
lay all other conflicts. Politically the country, governed by
unusually incompetent persons, was convulsed by a long constitutional battle, which lowered the prestige of the established
Church and State. This conflict itself undermined religious
and political authority, revived the legal doctrine of natural
law, and led to an attack upon royal sovereignty. Finally, an
able group of thinkers attacked the intellectual and moral
assumptions upon which society was based, and offered a
complete set of alternative doctrines.

2. THE CONFLICT OF CLASSES—THE REVOLT OF THE BOURGEOISIE

Socially and legally eighteenth-century France was still
feudal in structure. Feudalism had once rested upon a series
of contracts in which property and privilege were a return for
some form of service. The property and privileges commonly
remained, while the services had been either commuted or
forgotten, to be performed, if at all, by others who were outside
the feudal structure. The *noblesse*, exempt not only from the
military service which had once been demanded of it, but also
from regular taxation, still owned about a third of France,
while the clergy, who were also great landowners, drew their
principal revenue from tithes.[1] Most of the peasantry had long

---

[1] Many of the poorer *noblesse* were unable to leave their estates, and lived a
life not very different from that of the peasantry. The upper *noblesse*, however,
flocked to the capital, and, in spite of a passing fashion which popularized
agriculture as a hobby in the second half of the century, the great landowners
seldom visited the land from which they drew their wealth. They had none
of the incentives to end feudal conditions and to adopt the new methods of
agriculture which were changing eighteenth-century England from a country
of small proprietors into one of great estates and landless labourers. Pasturage
did not offer wealth to the French *noblesse*. In any case, caste stood in the way:
to make money by any other method than that of extortion was beneath the
dignity of a gentleman. It is the peculiar curse of such an aristocracy that they
draw upon an unknown reservoir of peasant labour and are always tempted to
regard it as illimitable. Their main occupation was discovering and displaying
expensive and novel luxuries, for which they were frequently unable to pay.
The Marquis de Mirabeau declared that " by the life which they led in their
châteaux the *grand seigneurs* ruined the peasants and themselves."
The higher clergy had also become a privileged class, spending a vast pro-

before succeeded in commuting personal services for money payments, and the courts were busy throughout the century with litigation between peasants and nobles about property rights. But seigniorial dues and clerical tithes[1] remained, even when the land was the property of the peasant. On the whole the French peasantry was in a far superior position to that of the serfs in most European countries, but the fact of legal freedom only made the surviving badges of servitude more intolerable.[2]

The hardships of the peasantry were increased by royal taxation, which grew always more onerous and more arbitrary. It was estimated that the most common type of peasant, the *métayer*, who owed half the produce of his land to his lord, paid a further thirty or forty per cent. to the Government, and could perhaps rely on retaining from ten to twenty per cent. for his own use. This system produced famine rather than crops. Yet rebellion was rare. In the early part of the reign

---

portion of the tithes and produce from church lands in the capital. Several eighteenth-century bishops are known to have lived in their dioceses and to have concerned themselves with religious and charitable offices, but it was said that there were always twenty bishops living in Paris, and often forty. The poorer clergy, like the poorer nobles, shared the poverty of the country.

[1] The resentment against tithes as well as against the gaming rights of the *seigneurs* is well illustrated by the famous story of a peasant who was asked, in 1789, what he hoped from the States-General. "The suppression of pigeons, rabbits and monks," he answered. "Surely this is a strange way of classifying them?" "Nay, sir, it is clear; the first devour us in the seed, the second in the blade, the third in the sheaf."

[2] The weight of feudal obligations was frequently crushing in extent as well as vexatious and arbitrary, while constant parcelling-out had so much reduced the peasants' holdings that in order to live at all most of them were forced to work as labourers for their lords and cultivate their own land when they could. Justice in many districts and in matters arising from their status was still feudal justice; the peasant could look for redress only in the lord's court when, to take a concrete instance, the lord had himself decided arbitrarily to increase the size of the measure by which his feudal dues were calculated. The lord's right to *corvée*, or forced labour, his hunting and game rights, and his right to demand that the peasants should grind their corn at his mill, amounted in some parts of the country to intolerable grievances. Ancient and humiliating rights like that of *jus primæ noctis*, made famous by Beaumarchais, had never been formally abolished. There were, of course, some prosperous peasants—a fact which Arthur Young did not fail to notice.

of Louis XIV., when war taxes added a new burden, there had been peasant risings which recalled the horrors of the "Jacqueries." But the last six years of the reign of Louis XIV., perhaps the worst ever experienced by the peasantry, passed over the ruined countryside with the calmness of death. In the reign of Louis XV. their condition improved. Later in the century, however, the bankruptcy of the Crown led to increasing royal taxation. Money was extorted even from the *noblesse*, who often attempted to recoup themselves by a stricter levy of their feudal dues and even by the revival of dues that had long been neglected. Here at last were the conditions which breed revolutionary feeling : an economic improvement followed by the fear of a relapse and the belief that new impositions were to be made. In the years immediately preceding the Revolution it needed no propaganda to incite the peasantry to demand that all feudal dues should be abolished, all classes equally taxed, and that the clerical tithes, once consecrated to the purposes of education and the relief of the poor, should be "given back to their original purpose." Upon these points all the rural *cahiers*, which were for the most part practical statements of grievances, not philosophical demands based on natural rights, were unanimous.

By 1789, therefore, the peasantry had become a great revolutionary force which only waited for a signal to abolish at a stroke all that remained of the feudal system of land tenure. In the towns there had also gathered an element which played a part in overthrowing the established order. The mediæval organization of industry had been rapidly breaking down : the ancient corporations of masters, rarely recruited from the ranks of workmen, whose own corporations were scarcely less exclusive, had long been bankrupt and were finally suppressed during Turgot's administration. With the collapse of the corporations, numbers of workmen belonging to no organization swelled the crowd of town paupers. After the treaty with England in 1776 the upward movement of prices was sharply accentuated, and the value of wages decreased. The town workers, however, were actuated by hunger, not by any realization of their interests as a class. Their rôle in the Revolution, therefore, was not in any way comparable to that of the peasantry, who knew what they wanted. They were important to the course of the Revolution only in so far as they strengthened the city mob. Their point of view seldom appears in the *cahiers*, and was neglected by the National Assembly. It was not until modern industry had created a working-class population conscious of collective interests and grievances that the town workman could become effectively revolutionary.[1]

The land revolution then was the work of the peasantry: the political revolution was at times influenced by the populace of Paris. But it was led and directed by members of the urban middle class. They had economic power as well as grievances; they were educated, and they were inspired by an idea. Their economic position had constantly improved throughout the century, and they increasingly resented the legal and social barriers which hampered their advance and reminded them of their social inferiority to a functionless and often less wealthy privileged class. The educated middle class supplied the Crown with administrators and with money; it patronized art and science; it read and appreciated the new philosophy, which was for the most part written by men who had come from its own ranks.

Not all the numerous elements which composed the middle class were equally revolutionary, though all shared in varying degree a constant grudge against the privileged aristocracy. The official class of course profited handsomely by the economic chaos. Only a comparatively small proportion of the money which came into the hands of the King's tax-collectors, estate agents, and controllers of water or forests, actually reached the Treasury. The Farmers-General, who headed this bureaucratic hierarchy and whose opportunity of enriching themselves

---

[1] Industrialism had of course begun in France long before the Revolution : there were silk mills in Lyons early in the century, and after 1775 English inventions began to transform the cotton industry. Strikes of workmen were not uncommon, but the spasmodic efforts of the *compagnons* were easily defeated. The State took the part of the masters, and in 1749 letters-patent forbade workers, under penalty of one hundred livres fine, to leave their masters without written permission, or to assemble, strike or conspire in any way to restrict the employers' freedom in the choice of workmen.

and their friends was unlimited, were perhaps the most un-popular class in France. When Louis XV. remarked that they were the support of the State, a courtier is said to have replied : " Yes, Sire ; they support it just as a rope supports a corpse hanging from the gallows." [1]

The financiers too, who lived on the deficiencies of the Royal Exchequer and made profitable contracts with the King in time of war, had little reason to complain. The Crown had borrowed so heavily from them that they were the virtual owners of the State. Living in similar style were retired men of fortune who had contrived to buy land and who tried to the best of their ability to ape the life of the old *noblesse*. They were able to buy titles of nobility and even noble husbands for their daughters, but they could not buy freedom from the contemptuous toleration of the aristocracy, nor could they fail to repay it with the hatred that accompanies a fawn-ing assumption of equality. Their interests, however, were naturally identified with those of the *noblesse*, and it is not surprising that the middle-class electors in 1789 wished to exclude the *anoblis* from representing them in the National Assembly.

There is abundant evidence that even these, the most for-tunate elements in the middle class, were tainted with revolu-tionary doctrines before the Revolution.[2] Men like Poupelinière, the financier, were the greatest patrons of the *philosophes*, and it was in their salons that Voltaire and Marmontel, and even Rousseau, felt most at home.[3] They all hated the aristocracy and the Church, and resented the failure and inefficiency of the Government. These sentiments were shared with far greater vehemence by the mass of the middle class, who did not profit by an antiquated and chaotic economic system, but existed as best they could in spite of it, and who were untroubled by any

---

[1] It is related that once at Voltaire's table, after several stories of robbers and highwaymen had been related, Voltaire was thought to have capped them all by merely saying : "There was once a Farmer-General . . ."

[2] *Cp*. Roustan, *op. cit.*, esp. chap. v.

[3] *Vide* Marmontel's *Mémoires* for the best contemporary account of the financiers' patronage of the new philosophy.

complicated connections with the aristocracy.[1] It was the business class, therefore, which most urgently demanded legal and social equality and formed the stubborn bulk of the Third Estate which refused to submit to the King and the *noblesse* when at length their opportunity arrived in 1789.

The social aspect of the Revolution becomes clear. The *cahiers* revealed the unanimous opposition of the peasantry and unprivileged middle class to the privileged *noblesse* and clergy. All the *cahiers* of the Third Estate demanded equality of rights, equal justice, free speech, the abolition of feudal dues and of the old trading corporations; they agreed in asking for a responsible executive and an elected Assembly, with full legislative power. When the *cahiers* spoke of equality they meant the abolition of privilege; when they spoke of liberty they were demanding civil rights and finally political power; when they spoke of fraternity they meant the national unity of citizens as opposed to the feudal division of classes. They spoke for the mass of the people. A powerful and wealthy trading class was everywhere growing restive of arbitrary taxation, hampering feudal and State restrictions, tariffs which benefited none but those who collected them, and private monopolies which prevented trade from further expansion. It had economic power, education, intelligence and a vision of a free State in which equality before the law would allow its virtues and activities a fitting reward. Everywhere it was hampered by those who had none of these things and whose power depended upon the accident of birth. Figaro's complaint was on behalf of the whole Third Estate: "Nobility, fortune, rank, office, how proud we are of them: what have you done to procure such blessings? You have taken the trouble to be born, no more! Otherwise an ordinary man! Whereas I, an insignificant unit in the crowd, have had to employ more science and calculation merely to gain my living than has been devoted in the last hundred years to the government of all the Spains."

Common grievances united the Third Estate. Yet its final

---

[1] France was of course still almost wholly an agricultural country, but industrialism was beginning and French commerce increasing throughout the century. Arnould calculates that it was quadrupled between 1716 and 1788.

victory over privilege was postponed until the bankruptcy of the monarchy delivered the State into its hands. The King could tax without consulting his subjects : he could not borrow from them and remain absolute. Fleury had struggled to pay off the load of debt accumulated by Louis XIV., but after his retirement no further effort was made to balance the national budget. The three great wars which Louis XV. undertook necessitated more severe taxation, and his attempts to raise money by unusual means brought him into conflict with every section of the nation.[1] The monarchy lived on loans, and administrators like d'Argenson and Bernis complained that they had almost daily to wait on the doorsteps of great financiers to beg on the Government's behalf. It was not until the administration of Turgot that any attempt was made to restore the national credit. But the efforts of Turgot and subsequent controllers failed because the principle that the very rich should live upon taxes collected from the very poor was inherent in the social structure of France. There is a limit to this process, and the State, by long borrowing, had in fact become the property of the middle class : the States-General, it has been well said, was not so much a revolutionary assembly as a meeting of the Government's creditors, called to liquidate the estate of a client whom they regarded as a fraudulent bankrupt.

3. THE CROWN AND THE *PARLEMENTS*—SOVEREIGNTY AND NATURAL LAW

The social conflict within the *ancien régime* was the underlying cause of its collapse, and the bankruptcy of the Government was its immediate occasion. Many other factors had contributed to diminish authority and to predispose the

---

[1] Attempts to tax the privileged naturally led to protests. *Parlements* even spoke of instituting a " civil list " after the English model, and demanded that Ministers should submit their accounts to public audit. The Church Assembly resisted the King's demand for a free gift, declaring that it would never " permit what had hitherto been the gift of our love to become the tribute of our obedience."

unprivileged to listen to Liberal doctrines. Indeed there were several occasions earlier in the century when Revolution seemed imminent : the degradation and failure of the monarchy and the long constitutional struggle had threatened to destroy the régime many years before the final catastrophe.

Louis XIV. had remained great even in his failure. He lost battles, but not dignity : he ruined France, but the lustre of earlier glory still hung about his head. After his death the dignity as well as the competence of the monarchy decayed. France, it is true, remained obstinately monarchical even in 1790,[1] and the cry of reformers had always been " if only the King knew." Attacks were directed, as usually happens in the prelude to a revolution, not against the monarchy, or even against the King, but against his Ministers. Nevertheless a knowledge of the "Well-beloved " led inevitably to contempt. It was not only that he lost France an Empire—and French monarchs have been forgiven everything before military defeat —but that he did so meanly and ingloriously. The revenge taken upon England in America came too late to save his credit and served only to spread subversive doctrines. The memoirs and journals·of the period agree that Louis, at his accession a handsome boy, enthusiastically acclaimed amid the rejoicings at his grandfather's funeral, gradually sank in popular esteem, until during his last illness few people minded whether he lived or died.[2]

To speak of the divine nature of the monarchy when Louis XV. was king was to strain credulity. What could be said for a monarch who officially " did nothing to-day," while his armies were defeated, his administration became increasingly corrupt and incompetent and his Treasury drifted into bankruptcy? His government became " a despotism tempered by epigrams "—epigrams which displayed him as a libertine who

---

[1] *Vide* Aulard, *History of the French Revolution,* vol. i., chap. i.

[2] Compare the oft-quoted story of a canon of Nôtre-Dame that in 1744 six thousand masses were voluntarily subscribed for Louis' recovery on the occasion of his first serious illness ; that in 1757, when Damiens attempted to assassinate him, the number was six hundred, and during his final illness only three.

did not enjoy his sensuality and a weakling who persecuted from inertia rather than from faith. Louis XIV. could afford to be the master of a series of mistresses, Louis XV., moving from one low-born woman to another, was despised as the slave of an even larger number.[1]

His funeral was a national *fête*, and placards, ribald songs and insulting epithets followed his body to the grave. The unintentional jest of the Abbé who remarked that "Louis XV. was loved by his people as tenderly as he loved them" was repeated with shouts of laughter, while common opinion seems to have been summarized in the bitter gibe thrown at his passing coffin, "vas-t'en salir l'histoire."

Louis XIV. had disregarded the ancient French Constitution and angered lawyers and churchmen by his refusal to recognize their immemorial right to offer him advice. Louis XV. was no less arrogant, but he was neither able enough nor powerful enough to prevent their protests from troubling his throne. He fought a long war with the *Parlements*, and finally took the drastic step of totally abolishing them. He never departed from the most absolute pretensions. " In my person alone," he declared in 1760, " resides the sovereign power. To me alone belongs the legislative power, independently and indivisibly. All public order emanates from me."

To state one's own supremacy, however, is not necessarily to enforce silence on others ; and during the constitutional struggle the King's royal sovereignty was widely challenged. The conflict with the *Parlements* and with powerful sections of the Church prepared the way for revolution in three ways. Firstly, it brought the populace into politics and accustomed Paris to the spectacle of rebellion ; secondly, it led to the revival of the ancient doctrine of fundamental law, which has always

---

[1] Louis' amours have been the subject of many dull books. He was doing nothing shocking in taking mistresses, the position of royal mistresses being a recognized one. On the contrary, complaints were made at his slowness of choice as a young man and his lengthy fidelity to the Queen. But he angered the aristocracy by choosing a *bourgeoise* like Madame de Pompadour. Madame du Barry's origin was still less reputable. The aristocracy complained that with their daughters at the King's disposal it was surely an insult for him to choose from the lower orders.

threatened absolutist pretensions ; thirdly, since its climax was the complete destruction of the French Constitution, reform without the calling of the States-General was rendered almost impossible.

Louis' support of the Jesuits, fluctuating though it was, brought him into violent conflict, not only with the Jansenists and the *Parlements*, but also with the whole mass of Gallican feeling. The attempt to enforce the Bull *Unigenitus* led to a struggle in which the whole country took part. "The *acceptants*," said Voltaire, "were the hundred bishops who had adhered under Louis XIV., and with them the Jesuits and the Capuchins : the *recusants* were fifteen bishops and the entire nation."

The struggle undermined Church and State authority as well as religious belief. The notary Barbier gleefully records in his journal that the battle over the Constitution was discrediting the Ultramontanes, and he remarks in 1731 that the "good town of Paris is Jansenist from top to bottom." D'Argenson adds that it was dangerous to appear in the street in a cassock. Many memoirs refer to the mockery bred by the affair of the Abbé Pâris.[1] When the Jesuits were dethroned the rejoicing seemed to Bachaumont positively indecent. Gallicanism was old enough, but the political criticism which now accompanied it was new. Hatred of the priesthood led to hatred of the Government which supported the Jesuits. "With reform in religion," remarks d'Argenson, "will come reform in government ; profane tyranny is married to ecclesiastical tyranny." The security of the monarchy itself was threatened by its subservience to the Jesuits.

As early as 1720 the Regent had been doubtful of the loyalty

---

[1] The Abbé Pâris died in 1727. His tomb became a sacred shrine, where the sick were miraculously healed and where women had convulsions, "rolling on the ground half naked, foaming at the mouth like sibyls." When the Government forcibly closed the gates of the cemetery, Voltaire made a characteristic comment :

"De par le roi, défense à Dieu
De faire miracles en ce lieu."

The Jesuits claimed God as their exclusive possession, and turned Him out like any other defaulting party leader when he deserted to the Opposition.

of his troops in the likely event of a Parisian rising on behalf of the *recusants*. In 1752 the order denying extreme unction to dying Jansenists had raised opinion to such a pitch of fury that d'Argenson, at least, feared a "national revolution," and the President of the *Parlement* of Paris warned Louis that "schism dethrones Kings more easily than whole armies can uphold them." In 1754 d'Argenson's prophecy seemed about to be fulfilled and a "Grand Remonstrance," reminiscent of that which preceded the rebellion against Charles I., was drawn up by the Paris *Parlement*. Troops armed with muskets and *lettres de cachet* were sent to overawe the *Parlement*, and both upper and lower houses of magistrates were exiled from Paris. The Remonstrance, however, was published. It protested against the action of the King in upholding the refusal of the sacrament to Jansenists, and while, as always, reiterating that nothing but zeal for the monarchy dictated the protest of the *Parlements*, it went so far as to say that "if subjects owe obedience to Kings, Kings on their side owe obedience to the laws," and added that, by disregarding the ancient liberties and traditional Constitution of France, Louis was preparing the way for a revolution. The King made concessions which averted danger and the *Parlements* returned in triumph.

Encouraging though their victory in 1754 was, the most optimistic Gallican could scarcely have hoped for the success which awaited his party. The Jesuits never seemed stronger: they dominated Catholic Europe, they ruled the Vatican and the courts of Kings. In France the Jesuit confessors of the King, the Queen and the Dauphin seemed all-powerful, while the education of the nation was still largely in their hands. But in 1761 a series of blows fell upon the Society. Their dismissal from Portugal encouraged their enemies: their trade with Martinique suffered in the war between England and France, and the litigation which arose from a consequent debt of 3,000,000 livres finally reached the upper chamber of the Paris *Parlement*. The *Parlement* did not waste its chance. It insisted on examining Jesuit doctrines, and declared them "murderous and abominable, not only in respect to the lives of citizens, but also in regard to the sacred persons of

Sovereigns." The Jesuits were prohibited from teaching in French schools.

No help came from the Crown. Choiseul and Madame de Pompadour—the reigning influences at the moment—had personal reasons for disliking the Jesuits, and Louis had been induced to believe that they were implicated in the recent attempt on his life. In 1764 the Society of Jesus was suppressed in France and during the next decade suffered indignities in almost every European country. An extraordinary outburst of rejoicing followed its fall, and the philosophic party regarded this as a sign that the Crown had left bigotry and embraced enlightenment. " I seem," said Diderot, " to see Voltaire raising his hands and eyes to heaven, as he repeats the *Nunc Dimittis*."

The destruction of the Jesuits increased the power of the *Parlements*; so too did the military disasters, which compelled Louis frequently to introduce new edicts of taxation. The *Parlements*, though forced to sanction them, had recourse to decrees setting forth that such compulsory registration of edicts " tended to the subversion of the fundamental laws of the kingdom "; that " to sustain a government by force was to teach the people that force would overthrow it." In his diary Barbier made a discerning note : " If the Government," he wrote, " succeeds in diminishing the authority and accepted rights of the *Parlements*, there will no longer be any obstacle in the way of assured despotism. If, on the contrary, the *Parlements* unite to oppose this move with strong measures, nothing can follow but a general revolution."

In 1770 the struggle came to a head. The Duc d'Aiguillon, Governor of Brittany, had come into violent conflict with the *Parlement* of his province, and was accused of participation in a Jesuit plot. He was arraigned before the Paris *Parlement*. The inquiry had already lasted two months when the King intervened and gave d'Aiguillon a complete discharge. Encouraged by Chancellor Maupeou, the King refused to listen to any protests against this arbitrary procedure, and the *Parlement* resigned. In 1771 Maupeou carried out a *coup d'état*. One hundred and sixty-eight magistrates who refused to submit were exiled from Paris, their seats confiscated and the Grand Council induced to take over the title and powers of the exiled *Parlement*. Maupeou then set up new courts of justice, entitled "Superior Councils," suppressed the *Cours des Aides*, which refused to recognize the appointed Councils, and exiled its President, Malesherbes, who had suggested the calling of the States-General. The *Châtelet* itself protested and was suppressed. Thus the whole of the ancient Constitution of France had been wiped out. It seemed that the first of Barbier's alternatives was to take place : that revolution was to be averted by the complete victory of absolutism.

This bureaucratic revolution, however, was achieved only at a price. The *Parlements* had been growing in popularity during the struggle. The lawyers found themselves in the odd position of a body of privileged aristocrats, totally hostile to all Liberal reform, upholding the Constitution of France against the Monarch amid the enthusiastic applause of a populace who looked upon them as the champions of liberty and described them as "true Romans and Fathers of their country." Their exile was the signal for another burst of popular agitation. Maupeou, now ruling almost unchecked in France, was subjected to a prolonged attack in papers and pamphlets which censured his policy and mingled prophecies of revolution with personal abuse and abstract discussions of popular sovereignty.

At every stage of this protracted conflict with the monarchy the lawyers had been compelled to base their opposition to the Crown on some basis of theory : as time went on their theory had grown less selfish and more universal. At first their anxiety had been to regain the ancient privileges upon which Louis XIV. had so often trampled. In 1715 they had asserted their traditional right to act on behalf of the nation in default of an heir to the throne and had co-operated with the Duke of Orleans in setting aside the will of Louis XIV. Thus strengthened they were able to exercise their second constitutional right of discussing royal edicts before registering them. In protesting against attempts to enforce the Bull *Unigenitus* they described themselves as guardians of the fundamental laws of France and of the monarchy itself against papal pretensions.[1]

As the struggle developed the constitutional issues became clearer. The quarrel with the monarchy involved the very topics which in England had led to revolution—the political domination of Rome and the right of the King to tax without consent. The French *Parlements*, like the English Parliament, supported their case by an appeal to fundamental and natural law. They were able to find justification in their own most famous legal writers ; they had no need to borrow from Coke. Even d'Aguesseau,[2] supporter of divine right as he was, had emphasized Bodin's view that, though there could be no right of rebellion against the King, his sovereignty was checked both by his duty to God and by his obligation to recognize the ancient usages of the French monarchy. Among these usages d'Aguesseau had expressly mentioned. the constitutional right of *Parlements* to register his edicts. Domat, the great Jansenist lawyer, provided the *Parlements* with even more palatable doctrine.[3] In his *Loi Civile*, written more than half-a-century before Montesquieu's *L'Esprit des Lois*,[4] Domat had urged that laws are not arbitrary but the result of " eternal principles," and that good laws may be deduced by " geometrical reasoning," when the underlying principles have been grasped.

[1] *Vide* Flammermont, t. i., 335, 348 : *Remontrance du 7 Avril 1735.* In France, they reminded the Regent, all laws proceeded from the monarchy. France had never been a province of Rome. Ultramontane doctrines tended "to authorize all the undertakings of the Roman Court, to render the ecclesiastic power sovereign in your kingdom, to give it a temporal authority independent of yours, maxims which, allowing it to set up its decrees as laws in the State, give it, so to speak, your Crown, and make it the absolute judge of the liberty, goods, honour and life of your subjects." " Would not this be to allow a powerful foreigner to rule your State and your subjects ? "

[2] D'Aguesseau was Chancellor till the Marquis d'Argenson succeeded him in 1718.

[3] Domat (1625-1696), in his youth a fellow-student of physics in Paris with Pascal, was King's Advocate at Clermont for thirty years. His *Loi Civil* appeared in 1694.

[4] For the influence of Montesquieu in reviving the belief in historical liberty and in encouraging the resistance of the *Parlements* by the theory of intermediate ranks and orders in society *vide* Carcassonne, *Montesquieu et le problème de la Constitution française.*

This doctrine of fundamental law was capable of indefinite expansion. Given a weak King, the right to register meant a right to remonstrate, and even to control. Moreover it opened the way to a dangerous analysis of sovereignty. Renaissance lawyers had adapted the *imperium* of the Roman Emperor for the use of the national Sovereign, but they could not totally discard the conception, always present in the Roman theory of sovereignty, that it was ultimately based upon the consent of the populace. A *lex*, from the earliest days of Rome, was valid only when accepted by the popular assembly, and Roman Emperors had been at pains to preserve at least the fiction that they ruled and legislated by popular consent. The French *Parlements* made the same claim against the national Monarch when he adopted the *imperium* of Rome: the King had the right to pass edicts, but these gained the force of law only when registered by a body representing the French people. The *Parlements* naturally fulfilled this function in the absence of a more popular body. In 1718 they therefore declared themselves to be the " true depositary of the fundamental laws of the State," the only body in the State which met without royal permission, " continually assembled to give justice to your subjects in the name and at the instruction of Your Majesty; the only channel through which the voice of the people has been able to reach you, since there has been no Assembly of the States-General." [1] It was their business, they added, to criticize royal edicts, to distinguish between passing necessities and changes in the Constitution of which they were the natural custodians: it was their function to interpret and explain new laws and provide for their execution.[2] " It is through Your *Parlement* that your laws are known and transmitted to Your people; its fidelity, its vigilance in maintaining their execution easily accustoms the people to respect them, and they think themselves fortunate in so far as determination of their welfare rests within its hands." [3] In 1730 forty lawyers went so far as to say that " according to the Constitution of the Kingdom

[1] Flammermont, t. i. 88, *Remontrance du July 1718*.
[2] Sée, *L'Evolution de la Pensée politique*, 319.
[3] Flammermont, t. i. 234, *Remontrance du 9 January 1731*.

the *Parlements* are the senate of the nation, while the King is merely the chief of the nation," and described the royal edicts as dependent upon the will of the assembled Estates, and even added that "laws are real conventions between those who govern and those who are governed." The Council of State naturally declared that this maxim was "absolutely intolerable in a monarchy, since, in depriving the Sovereign of his most august office, that of legislation, he is reduced to treat with his subjects on terms of equality by form of contract, and is consequently subject to receive the law from those to whom he ought to give it." The *Parlement* of Paris itself seemed to be approaching this point of view before it was exiled in 1763. We may trace the influence of Montesquieu's *L'Esprit des Lois*[1] in their declaration that "Your authority, Sire, is the strongest support of the legitimate liberty of Your subjects, a liberty which subjects them to You more certainly than compulsion, which binds them by ties more powerful than those of force, a liberty which, equally opposed to licence and to slavery, characterizes monarchical government. The King, the State and the Law form an inseparable whole, united in a sacred knot"; by observation of the laws the King strengthens his throne, preserves the subordination of his subjects, ensures their rights and their liberty.[2]

In 1759 the *Parlement* of Besançon added that all the King's subjects were "under the immediate protection of the laws; it is the right of a nation which your *Parlement* claims and has never ceased to claim," while the *Parlement* of Rouen spoke of "the respective rights of Sovereign and peoples," and protested against novel forms of taxation as arbitrary infringements of the "immutable" laws which form the only bond between King and people. Thus the *Parlements*, which had begun as a purely feudal body, defending their privileges, had gone on to claim that the King must obey the fundamental laws of France and of nature, and that they themselves were the guardians of these rights. Finally they spoke of a contract between King and people and hinted that the people had a right to revolt if the King violated their rights.

---

[1] Published 1748. [2] Flammermont, t. i. 407.

When Louis XVI. came to the throne, therefore, the situation was novel. The theory which held that the King's power was legitimately exercised only within the limits of fundamental law, and that the people had the right to overthrow an arbitrary government, had found wide popular acceptance. At the same time the only corporations with any right to criticize or question the Crown had been abolished. The old Constitution of France, disregarded by Louis XIV., had been formally destroyed by his successor. A return to the old type of monarchical government supported by aristocratic corporations was in any case out of the question. Turgot, therefore, hoped to save France and the monarchy by establishing new local federations instead of the ancient feudal ones. Having refused this suggestion, Louis XVI. had only two possibilities before him: either to make unlimited despotism succeed or to admit the thesis of democracy. Revolution had been instituted from above, not below: it was the work of the monarchy, not the *philosophes*.

The *philosophes*, indeed, had supported the King against the *Parlements*. They favoured "enlightened despotism" and criticized Louis, not for his despotism but for his lack of enlightenment. The accession of Louis XVI., the enlightened Monarch in person, and the appointment of Turgot as Controller-General, marked the culminating point of Voltairean influence. The abolition of the *Parlements*, resented by the mass of the middle class, had been applauded by almost all the Philosophic group, who believed in an absolute Monarch enlightened by themselves, not in a restoration of an ancient Constitution. Louis XV. had destroyed the last obstacles to the completion of an enlightened despotism. Enlightenment was forced upon Louis XVI.; he could not avoid financial reform and he could not suppress propaganda. But a resolute policy might have prevented the Revolution, or at least mitigated its violence. "Events," as Sorel puts it, "had reached the point at which there had to be either a great King or a great revolution."

Louis had then a choice of two policies. In the absence of all constitutional resistance, he could have appointed a few able administrators and attempted by his own authority to institute necessary reforms in the teeth of the aristocracy. On the other hand, he could have made a bid for popularity by dismissing Maupeou and appealing to the *Parlements*, and then to the States-General, for support in the economic crisis. The monarchy was still the centre of men's hopes, the Queen had not yet become identified with privilege and reaction, and either policy might have gained popular support. But a combination of the two was fatal. Louis attempted the policy of enlightened despotism but had not the strength of purpose necessary to defy the party of privilege or sufficient intelligence to avoid ruining any hope of success by combining it with the second incompatible policy. When at length he called the States-General, opinion had gone too far for a constitutional revolution to succeed, and the King, who was not even then faithful to the democratic principle he had invoked, was swept away to make room for less amiable despots.

Louis' counsels were divided from the beginning. The appointment of Turgot and Malesherbes in place of Maupeou and the Abbé Terray was his most certain step. But he yielded to opposite advice when he recalled the banished *Parlements* and restored the *Châtelet* and the *Cour des Aides*. Turgot warned him that the magistrates would oppose every genuine reform, and Voltaire expressed amazement that the King should sacrifice the new *Parlements* which "had always known how to obey to the old ones which had done nothing but defy him." The *Parlements* immediately justified Turgot's fears. Their triumph made them proportionately bold. For eighteen months the King supported Turgot in his battle with privilege. His policy of free trade in France, the suppression of the *maîtrises*, the abolition of the *corvée*, and the gradual transference of the burden of taxation to the shoulders of the wealthy, brought him at once into conflict with the clergy, the Court, the newly recalled *Parlements* and the financiers. Finally the Paris mob, which attributed the scarcity of bread to his reforms, demanded his dismissal. Turgot's outspoken letters warned Louis of his danger : "Remember, Sire," he wrote, " that it was weakness that brought Charles I. to the block." By yielding to a Court intrigue and dismissing Turgot, Louis threw away his greatest opportunity : Necker, more plausible, had even less chance of success.

The ministries of Turgot and Necker in fact hastened the Revolution. The education of the public was proceeding apace. For the first time the Monarchy argued with the nation. The preambles to Turgot's edicts, setting forth the reasons for reform, were worth many philosophic pamphlets, and Necker's *comptes rendus*, disingenuous though they were, let the public still further into the secrets of the Government's failure. In this final period before the Revolution the idea of " enlightened despotism " was superseded by the conception of democracy. Even in 1778, when Voltaire, paying his last visit to Paris, was greeted, as one observer declared, with " an inconceivable idolatry," the generation which worshipped him as a patriarch had already found a new prophet. Rousseau's influence had taken the place of that of the Encyclopædists and the example of the American Revolution had stimulated democratic sentiment.[1] Two hopes were everywhere discussed—the recall of the Protestants and the summoning of the States-General. Even the Paris *Parlement* had become infected with the democratic idea. Younger lawyers, trained in a generation whose inspiration was Montesquieu rather than d'Aguesseau, began to admit that the *Parlements* did not adequately represent the nation. As early as 1782 they suggested that the States - General should be summoned ; five years later they laid down the principle of " no taxes without representation " ; by 1788 they had altogether forgotten " privilege " and were ready to

---

[1] *Cp.* Condorcet, *Tableau Historique*, 9ᵉ époque : " Mais dans la guerre qui s'élevait entre deux peuples éclairés, dont l'un défendait les droits naturels de l'humanité, dont l'autre leur opposait la doctrine impie qui soumet ces droits à la prescription, aux intérêts politiques, aux conventions écrites ; cette grande cause fut plaidée au tribunal de l'opinion, en présence de l'Europe entière ; les droits des hommes furent hautement soutenus et développés sans restriction, sans réserve, dans des écrits qui circulaient avec liberté des bords de la Néva à ceux du Guadalquivir. Ces discussions pénétrèrent dans les contrées les plus asservies, dans les bourgades les plus reculées, et les hommes qui les habitaient furent étonnés d'entendre qu'ils avaient des droits ; ils apprirent à les connaître ; ils surent que d'autres hommes osaient les reconquérir ou les défendre."

ridicule all monarchs who attempted to rule without the help of their subjects.[1]

The relief to the Protestants in 1782, the free-trade treaty with England in 1786, and the final summoning of the States-General were all admissions that the policy initiated by Louis XIV. had failed. Toleration, the rights of man and the sovereignty of the people had taken the place of clerical absolutism, feudal privilege and royal despotism. In the ten years before the Revolution there was no intellectual resistance to the new religion. Balloons, mesmerism, scientific discovery, a vague humanitarianism and the "simple life" had become the vogue among the aristocracy. "They were ingenuously discussing amongst themselves the virtues of the populace, its gentleness, devotion, its innocent pleasures, when already '93 was upon them."

If the aristocracy were blind, there were many who were not. Few historical errors have been so often repeated as that the French Revolution came without warning. Social critics had frequently prophesied it throughout the preceding century, and their prophecies were the common gossip under Louis XVI.[2] The *ancien régime* had lost confidence in itself. It lasted until Calonne could no longer borrow money. Calonne himself pronounced its obsequies when he met the Notables with a statement that the ancient formula, "What the King wills, the law wills," would henceforth be abandoned for the novel preamble, "What the happiness of the people demands, the King wills." The calling of the States-General was more than a confession that the Government needed popular support; it was also an acknowledgment of the people's right to give or withhold it.

---

[1] *Vide* Sée, *op. cit.* 326.

[2] Lord Chesterfield's prophecy is well known. Other anticipations of the Revolution are referred to later, in Chapter IX.

In 1774 Rousseau wrote : "I see all the States of Europe rushing headlong to ruin ; monarchies, republics, all those nations whose origins are so glorious and whose governments were built up with so much wisdom, are falling into decay and are threatened by an imminent death. All the great nations are moaning, crushed by their own weight."

CHAPTER IV

PHILOSOPHY AND PROPAGANDA

LOUIS XIV. was a grand and tyrannous figure, an overpowering myth who subdued criticism even when he did not convince reason. At his death it was as though a spring were released and the first effect of that release was laughter. And laughter, at first a trivial gaiety in the social life of the Regency, made way for thought. The hushed circulation of sceptical comment was followed by open raillery, raillery by considered criticism, and out of criticism came visions of a better social order. In 1721 Montesquieu published the *Persian Letters*. Almost for the first time since Rabelais a book had appeared in which nothing was sacred. The attack upon French society contained in the letters of Usbec and Rica is barely disguised, though, to be sure, Persian travellers, commenting on the morals and manners prevalent in Europe, can make remarks which would be unseemly from a Frenchman, but which may nevertheless be true. The reader is imperceptibly led to the conclusion that the institutions he has revered, and the authorities he has obeyed, are perhaps unworthy of his reverence and obedience. The King, these observant Persians notice, is " a magician," who persuades men to kill one another though they have no quarrel. What else but magic could make them so irrational? Again self-constituted legislators pretend " their own wills are the laws of nature." Judges condemn "by the light within, without concerning themselves with useless knowledge." The highest aristocrat they visited was a little man who lost no " opportunity of making all who came near him sensible of his superiority, who took snuff with so much dignity, blew his nose so unmercifully, spat with so much phlegm, and caressed his dog in a manner so offensive to the company that I could not but wonder at him. Ah! I said to myself, if when I was at the Court of Persia I had behaved so I should have been considered a great fool." The religious authorities were not treated with more respect. If the King was a magician, hypnotizing men into obedience, what was the Pope himself but " an old idol "? As for the Spanish Inquisitors, they were a " cheery species of dervishes " who burnt those who differed from them about obscure trivialities. And what reason was there for believing that Christianity embodied the final truth, when there were so many religions, each claiming universal validity? It was grievous for a kindly Persian to have to entertain the idea that all these Christians who had never worshipped in a mosque would end miserably in hell. Surely, he thinks, we can all agree about certain moral principles, and leave doubtful questions of dogma to the varying judgments of the sects? It is man who has made God in his own image, and if triangles had to construct a God, the new deity would certainly consist of three sides rather than three persons. In these circumstances, was not Louis XIV. unwise in thinking to " increase the number of the faithful by diminishing the number of his subjects "? Questions, hints and criticisms of this kind are everywhere spread among the one hundred and sixty *Persian Letters*. But the correspondence of Usbec and Rica is not solely concerned with philosophy or politics, for Usbec, in seeking wisdom abroad, has abandoned the joys of a well-stocked harem from which he receives a constant stream of letters dealing with love, hatred, strife and death. Even this side of the correspondence has a certain philosophical bearing. It provides an example of the revenge of outraged nature which can be denied no more in the seraglio than in the convent. The chief object of these passages however was to please the ladies who frequented Madame de Tencin's *salon*, where Montesquieu was a constant visitor. His friends there were only likely to listen to appeals for toleration or social reform when spiced with more appetizing ingredients ; social criticism is, therefore, intermingled with descriptions of the sufferings of beautiful women and the pathos of thwarted desire in the eunuchs who assisted at their more intimate adornment.

These two characteristics, the trivial libertinism and the thin disguise of an indirect satire, were used throughout eighteenth-century literature to cover the most savage and subversive attacks. They reflect the two main conditions under which the *philosophes* wrote. It was essential to please a *salon* audience, which could enjoy an artistic and ironical attack upon social evils, but had no notion of practical and inconvenient remedies. It was also necessary to circumvent a censorship which would not permit any direct criticism of the political or religious authorities. Eighteenth-century *philosophes* made no pretence of being detached seekers after truth, and had the greatest contempt for most of what is usually called philosophy. The *philosophes* were humanists and journalists with a common object of propaganda. They wanted publicity and, unlike their Renaissance predecessors, they sought not for immortality in the praise of posterity, but for tangible and immediate influence. "Our philosopher," wrote Diderot, "does not count himself an exile in the world; he does not suppose himself in the enemy's country, he would fain find pleasure with others, and to find it he must give it; he is a worthy man who wishes to please and to make himself useful. The ordinary philosophers, who meditate too much, or rather who meditate to wrong purpose, are as surly and arrogant to all the world as great people are to those whom they do not think their equals; they flee men, and men avoid them. But our philosopher who knows how to divide himself between retreat and the commerce of men is full of humanity. Civil society is, so to say, a divinity for him on the earth; he honours it by his probity, by an exact attention to his duties, and by a sincere desire not to be a useless or an embarrassing member of it. The sage has the leaven of order and rule; he is full of ideas connected with the good of civil society. What experience shows us every day is that the more reason and light people have, the better fitted they are and the more to be relied on for the common intercourse of life."

Men who regarded civil society as a divinity on earth, and wished to enlist its support in practical reforms, were likely to busy themselves with metaphysical problems only in so far as their free treatment would cause amusement by annoying the ecclesiastical authorities. In any case, all systems of philosophy seemed remote and scholastic to a generation which believed that science could build a new heaven and a new earth.

Almost all the *philosophes* began by studying some branch of science. Voltaire talked of devoting his life to the study of chemistry and worked with enthusiasm both to understand and expound Newtonian physics. D'Alembert was a physicist as well as a mathematician. Montesquieu's first publications were scientific. Diderot dabbled in all the sciences, and even Rousseau wrote a botanical dictionary. In spite of all their differences the party of the *philosophes* was united by their faith in science, their acceptance of Locke and Newton, and their hatred of the Catholic Church.

Writing in 1765, Horace Walpole asked: "Do you know who the *philosophes* are or what the term means here? In the first place it comprehends almost everybody, and, in the next, means men who are avowing war against Popery and aim, many of them, at the subversion of religion." A few years later, Bachaumont noted in his journal that there had been in France for some years " a sect of bold philosophers who seemed to have had a deliberate plan of carrying a fatal clarity into men's minds, of disturbing all belief, of upsetting religion and sapping her very foundations. Some of these, the light troops of the party, armed with sarcasm and irony, began by using transparent allegories and ingenious fictions as a method of covering with ineffaceable ridicule her liturgy and even her code of morals ; others, profound speculative thinkers, armed with learning and bristling with metaphysics, stood out openly attacking her by force. . . . These, being unable to find worthy opponents, have unhappily retained the mastery of the battle-field. To-day, when these unbelievers consider their work to be well advanced . . . they are attacking their adversaries in their last strongholds. They claim to prove that politics has not the least need of religion for the maintenance and government of States."[1]

In the sixties Walpole and Bachaumont could write of the *philosophes* as a united party, engaged in a combined assault on the Church. This unity among the critics of orthodoxy dated only from the middle of the century. During the twenty-seven

---

[1] Bachaumont, *Mémoires secrets*, 22nd September 1768.

years which elapsed between the *Persian Letters* and *The Spirit of the Laws* only Voltaire's *Letters on the English*, published in 1734, was comparable with Montesquieu's work in ability, or in audacity. The other political books of the period—Utopias, for instance, like Morelly's metrical *Basiliade*, or the ceaseless imitations of *Télémaque* by the Abbé Ramsay[1]—were not the kind of books which disturb administrations. Fleury was indeed surprisingly successful in maintaining the relationship of silence between monarch and subject, and even forbade the private meetings of the Entresol club where Saint-Pierre and his friends discussed political principles. In 1748 both Church and State seemed as secure as they had been fifty years earlier; the King was still popular after a successful war, the Jansenists and the *Parlements* were at the ebb of their fortunes in their long struggle with Jesuitism, and the *philosophes* and *libertins* were still disunited, individual critics, apparently as impotent as their predecessors under Louis XIV.

This was the last respite permitted to the champions of the *ancien régime*. *The Spirit of the Laws* appeared in 1748 and the first volumes of the *Encyclopædia* in 1751. The *Encyclopædia*, at first approved by the authorities as a mere bookseller's project, became in the hands of Diderot a central arsenal from which all the apostles of enlightenment could borrow weapons for their combined attack. Against the united forces of the *philosophes* the official attempts to preserve silence were turned to ridicule, and before the death of Louis XV. the Encyclopædic literature had penetrated into all educated sections of society.[2]

---

[1] For the Abbé Ramsay *vide* Cherel's *Fénelon au XVIIIᵉ Siécle*.

[2] From 1750 onwards, Bachaumont's diary bears constant testimony to the "furious epidemic" of Voltairean literature, while Barbier notes with some alarm that all the public had these dangerous books in their hands and were even talking of carrying out the projects suggested in them. D'Argenson declared that though people in the provinces were ignorant and misguided about politics, even they were occupied in discussing philosophy. There is abundant proof that the Philosophic literature was widely discussed outside Paris. The *Encyclopædia* was subscribed for in every part of France, both by aristocrats and bourgeoisie. A striking proof of the influence of the *philosophes* upon the public is to be found in a comparison of the diaries and journals of the period. Men like Marais and Buvat, at the beginning of the century,

2. THE CENSORSHIP—ITS EFFECT ON THE *PHILOSOPHES*

The regulations of the publishing trade remained substantially as Francis I. had laid them down in the sixteenth century. No work could be legally published without the permission of the Director of Publications, and all books were supposed to be submitted to him for examination. In practice, however, the authorities rarely took notice of uncensored books unless they caused offence to someone of importance at Court or among the clergy. In such a case the book would be suppressed, a raid carried out upon the *colporteurs*, and the author imprisoned. If, on the other hand, the author obeyed the law and secured permission to publish, his security was scarcely greater. The Director's permission might always be reversed even after the expense of publication had been incurred, if the clergy or the *Parlement* of Paris or the Sorbonne or the *Châtelet* cared to demand the book's suppression. Finally, it was no uncommon thing for a royal *lettre de cachet* to intervene at the last moment, and condemn an author to the Bastille and his book to the flames. Indeed, remarks Figaro, " Provided I did not write about the Government, religion, politics, morality, officials, or anyone who has any claim to anything, I was at liberty to print what I chose—under the inspection of two or three censors."

In these circumstances most of the bolder books were published under pseudonyms and printed abroad, usually in Holland, and an elaborate secret organization grew up for the distribution of banned or illegally published works. Thus the publishing trade became a game in which the whole of literary France joined. The object of the game was to ensure the circulation of the books of your party, and though hundreds of books were censored all the important Philosophic publications found an excellent market. This constant struggle with authority had two immediate effects upon the Philosophic writing of the century. In the first place the Encyclopædists became a clique.

concern themselves only with the gossip of the Court and with external political events. In Barbier's journal public opinion is a recognized force and the determining factor in every political struggle.

They lost the capacity to laugh at themselves, and were enraged beyond measure or reason when a satirical attack like Moreau's *Les Cacouacs* or a feeble lampoon like Palissot's *Les Philosophe* passed the censorship. They learned to regard every critic as an accomplice of the powers of darkness. In their quarrel with Rousseau, Grimm, Madame D'Epinay and the rest pursued him with the venom of a secret society against a deserter. They lied about his work and his character ; they forged documents to discredit him with posterity. Their inventions were the more remarkable since the truth about Rousseau offered the most bitter opponent ample scope for detraction. The Church itself could scarcely have shown more intolerance or waged more unscrupulous warfare than the *philosophes*. In their long battle with Fréron they treated *L'Année littéraire* and its editor with a contempt and bitterness which often seem quite undeserved. Fréron's defence of the *ancien régime* was based on principles which were implicit in Montesquieu ; and the same principles in Burke's *Reflections on the French Revolution* afterwards proved the most powerful challenge to the Liberalism of the *philosophes*. " Ancient abuses," Fréron wrote, " in the process of growth have become implicated in so many small matters, and are so bound up with the course of affairs, and their roots, in brief, are now so deep and so extensive that to touch them would provoke a serious upheaval. An observer often thinks only of the benefits of the remedy he imagines already applied : and he does not foresee the inconveniences attending their application at the time." " Is not the fanaticism of your irreligion," he asked, " more absurd and more dangerous than the fanaticism of superstition ? Begin by tolerating the faith of your fathers. You talk of nothing but tolerance and never was a sect more intolerant." [1] The *philosophes* usually replied by calling him a scoundrel and a bigot. There was a certain dignity in his declaration : " Pour moi, je ne tiens à aucune cabale de bel-esprit, à aucun parti, si n'est à celui de la religion, des mœurs et de l'honnêteté." Unfortunately, he added, no such party existed in his day.

---

[1] F. Cornou, *Elie Fréron*, 365.

Turgot, perhaps the very greatest of the *philosophes*, contributed to the *Encyclopædia* and did more to advance the ideas of economic Liberalism than Quesnay himself. But he complained that the *Encyclopædia* was " the book of a sect," and always refused to call himself a Physiocrat because he disliked cliques and party labels. There were others, such as d'Alembert, who sought to be above the battle. D'Alembert's desertion from the joint editorship of the *Encyclopædia*, which left Diderot alone to cope with contributors, publishers and authorities, was not due to fear of the Bastille, but to the shrinking of a timid and thoughtful man from a struggle in which science was confounded with politics and personal and party rancour seemed as likely to interfere with truth as religious intolerance itself.

The censorship had a second no less disastrous effect : the *philosophes* were forced to adopt subterfuges harmful both to the reader and to the writer. Outward conformity to a despised creed is not in the long run compatible with clear thought and intellectual integrity, however conscious the inward reservations. When Voltaire criticized the *Encyclopædia*, d'Alembert replied : " No doubt we have bad articles in theology and metaphysics, but since we publish by favour, and have theologians for censors, I defy you to make them any better. There are other articles that are less exposed to the daylight, and in them all is repaired. Time will enable people to distinguish what we have thought from what we have said." [1]

Voltaire's own recipe for evading the censorship was one which he was certainly incapable of following himself. He thought it wise to live on the borders of Switzerland, and amused his friends and annoyed his enemies by attending Mass in his village church. He might publish anonymously or under a false name, but the authorship of his books was always apparent however sturdy his lies. He did not disguise his style. Every new subterfuge only brought more laughter and more readers, since no one else could have written *Candide* or the *Histoire du Docteur Akakia*. Nevertheless it was Voltaire who wrote to d'Alembert to try " if you can, to weaken your style, write

---

[1] D'Alembert to Voltaire, 21st July 1757.

dully, certainly no one will then guess your identity. One can say good things in a heavy way. You will have the pleasure of enlightening the world without compromising yourself; that would be a fine action and you would be an apostle without being a martyr."

The method of disguise adopted in the *Persian Letters* remained one of the most popular. To describe a foreign country possessing all the freedom and good government which France lacked involved no weakening of style and was compatible with the highest literary standards. Sometimes the *philosophes* described the happier conditions of primitive people, who presumably obeyed the laws of nature by instinct or natural reason, unimpeded by the artifices and barriers erected by priests and kings. Sometimes they talked of China, where a benevolent monarch was supposed to rule in the full light of philosophic knowledge; or, again, of a Utopia, where everything suited everybody, including Plato and Sir Thomas More; more often still, the sober freedom of English constitutional government provided a satisfactory foil to the arbitrary ignorance of Louis' ministers.

There were other methods of baffling and teasing the authorities. Ever since the later Middle Ages, men who wished to avoid making up their minds, who disliked committing themselves or who feared punishment, had adopted the doctrine of " double truth." If reason, science and historical evidence came to one conclusion and the unchallengeable authority of Scripture to another, it was safest, and also most effective as propaganda, not to attempt a reconciliation. Bayle had been fond of explaining in a footnote how unlikely the Bible story would have appeared had not we known that with God all things, even contradictions and absurdities, are possible. So an article in the *Encyclopædia* proves with some ease that the cubical capacity of the Ark was insufficient to contain the full bulk of the enumerated inhabitants — another case in which reason would lead astray without the help of revelation. The New Testament story is treated in much the same way. The evidence for the Resurrection is such that it carries proof of the truth of Christianity " to a geometrical demonstration."

Similarly Voltaire adds, after a solemn examination of contemporary evidence of the life and death of Christ, that the
reason why none but Biblical authorities record that the world
was plunged into darkness for the space of three hours, or that
the innocents were massacred by the orders of Herod, is no
doubt that " God did not desire divine things to be written by
profane hands."

Buffon attempted to escape censorship by the same device
in his *Histoire naturelle*. The inadequacy of the biological
theory, hitherto accepted on the authority of Genesis, by which
each species of animals was created in its original and eternal
form at one stroke without relation to any other, became increasingly obvious to him. After a consideration of evidence
which led him to formulate an early evolutionary hypothesis, he
wrote : " if we regard the matter thus, not only the ass and
the horse but even man himself, the apes, the quadrupeds,
and all animals might be regarded as forming members of one
and the same family . . . if we once admit that there are families
of plants and animals, so that the ass may be of the family of
the horse, and that one might only differ from another by
degeneration from a common ancestor (even as the ass and
the horse differ), we might be driven to admit that the ape is
of the family of man, that he is but a degenerate man, and that
he and man have had a common ancestor, even as the ass and
horse have had. . . . The naturalists who are so ready to
establish families among animals and vegetables do not seem
sufficiently to have considered the consequences which should
follow from their premises, for that would limit direct creation
to as small a number of forms as anyone should think fit.
For . . . if the point were once gained that among animals and
vegetables there had been, I do not say several species, but
even a single one, which had been produced in the course of
direct descent from another species—if for instance it could
be once shown that the ass was but a degeneration from the
horse—then there is no further limit to be set to the power
of Nature, and we should not be wrong in supposing that with
sufficient time she could have evolved all other organic forms
from one primordial type. But no ! It is certain from divine

revelation that all animals have alike been favoured with the grace of an act of direct creation, and that the first pair of every species issued full-formed from the hands of the creator."

It was not surprising that the Sorbonne condemned fourteen subversive propositions in the *Histoire naturelle*. Buffon, who was botanist to the King, and anxious not to lose his position nor to have the result of many years' labour destroyed, promptly renounced everything in his book " that might be contrary to the narrative of Moses."

In 1750 Malesherbes was appointed Director of the publishing trade, with the delicate task of steering a course among these conflicting forces. He was himself the most moderate of men and shared many of the sceptical views of the *philosophes*. They overwhelmed him with requests for support. For thirteen years he struggled amid philosophic pique, legal bigotry, court arrogance and religious intolerance. His best efforts did not prevent an extraordinary confusion and constant fluctuations of policy. Savage, and necessarily inoperative, decrees were frequently issued. In 1754, when the attempt on Louis' life by Damiens had frightened the Government, blame was thrown first on the Jesuits, then upon the Jansenists and their supporters in the *Parlements*, and finally upon the *philosophes*. Many arrests were made, and a royal decree was passed announcing that death was the penalty for " all those who shall be convicted of having composed, or caused to be composed and printed, writings intended to attack religion, to assail our authority, or to disturb the ordered tranquillity of our realm." Not only were authors and publishers threatened with execution but also " all those who print the aforesaid works, all booksellers, *colporteurs*, and other persons who shall circulate them among the public."

A decree of this kind was calculated to rouse only laughter, except among a number of obscure men and women who were sent to the galleys for selling books " contrary to good manners and religion."[1] The *Encyclopædia*, which contained all the

---

[1] This occurred comparatively often. *Vide,* for instance, Bachaumont's entry for 2nd October 1768 : Two men and a woman, condemned for "selling books contrary to good manners and to religion" were sentenced "au carcan

subversive doctrines of the century, was at that very moment being published under royal sanction. Arbitrary and uncertain persecution had its usual effect in rendering authority ridiculous and criticism both more subtle in its methods and more effective in its attacks. The propagandist is most blessed when effectively persecuted.

Though this was at times realized by the *philosophes* themselves, they bitterly resented their position. They lived in an atmosphere of constant anxiety, and were never certain from day to day whether they would be courted or imprisoned. Rousseau's *Emile*, which was largely devoted to an exposition of an educational method and which was the most genuinely religious book of the century, was censored by the Archbishop of Paris and burnt by the *Parlement* of Paris. The case of Marmontel, who was at best but a second-rate writer and comparatively orthodox in his views, provides an instructive example of the uncertainty of literary life. Having succeeded with great difficulty in piloting his *Belisarius* through the censorship, nine thousand copies were quickly circulated before the Sorbonne discovered that it advocated the theory of toleration and questioned " the right of the sword to exterminate heresy, irreligion and impiety, and to bring the whole world under the yoke of the true faith." " The thing for me," he remarked while the Sorbonne was considering its verdict, "was to appear neither timid nor rebellious, and to gain time till the editions of my book were multiplied and spread over Europe." In spite of his caution, Marmontel found himself confined in the Bastille. His imprisonment lasted only eleven days. The governor was extremely polite and supplied him with an excellent dinner from his own table. Marmontel gained an adventure with which to amuse the more advanced among his hostesses and friends, but lost both the editorship of the official *Mercure* and his bride, who preferred to marry a man who had not incurred the King's displeasure.[1]

---

pendant trois jours consécutifs," and in the case of the men to the galleys for periods of nine and five years. The woman was confined in the *Hôpital-Général* for five years. The books included Holbach's *Le Christianisme dévoilé* and Voltaire's *L'Homme aux quarante écus*.

[1] The full story is in Marmontel's *Mémoires*.

Prison archives show that most of the Philosophic party spent short periods in the Bastille, and the poorer among them may have found it less comfortable than did Marmontel. Diderot had been imprisoned after the publication of his *Letters on the Blind*, which contained a phrase derogatory to a Minister's mistress. During his editorship of the *Encyclopædia* he was never free from the interference of the Government and the Jesuits, and never knew how long he would be at liberty. When the significance of the first volumes of the *Encyclopædia* was appreciated the Jesuits succeeded in obtaining an order for their suppression. It was typical of the régime, however, that no order was issued forbidding its circulation, and that Diderot was requested by the Government to continue the editorship. The Jesuits indeed confiscated his paper, notes and plates, but, being, as he remarked, unable to confiscate his brains at the same time, they waited for the appearance of the next volumes before again interfering. In 1757, when the struggle between the *Parlements* and Jesuits was at its height, d'Alembert's article on Geneva, indirectly critical of the lives and dogmas of Catholic priests, roused once more a furious opposition. The publication of Helvétius' *De l'Esprit*, in the next year, led to the suppression by the Council of State of numerous Philosophic works, and the sale of past numbers of the *Encyclopædia* was prohibited. No steps however were taken to prevent their circulation, which continued without the least interruption.

On the whole it may be said that during the ascendancy of Madame de Pompadour the royal policy, in spite of many fluctuations, tended rather to flirt with philosophy than to oppose it. Voltaire described the Pompadour as "one of us," and though she was not a very faithful devotee at the shrine of reason, and though her opposition to Jesuitism may have been due rather to personal than to philosophical causes, the Encyclopædists had reason to be grateful to her. After the banishment of the Jesuits the *Parlements* emulated their zeal in banning and burning the work of the *philosophes*; but in the later years of Louis' reign an official ban was most effective as an advertisement.

3. THE *SALONS*—THE SOCIAL ENVIRONMENT

If the *philosophe* had to disguise his argument to placate his enemies he had also to modulate it to please his friends. The *salons* of the eighteenth century were as much the arbiters of taste and the channels of influence as they had been in the days when Society and Letters first met together in the Hôtel de Rambouillet. The eighteenth-century *salon* inherited its characteristics from its seventeenth-century predecessor, and only gradually developed from the preciosity which survived in the drawing-room of Madame Lambert to the free discussions of Holbach's dinner-parties in the sixties and seventies.

Salon leadership was an art which passed on directly from one brilliant woman to another. Madame Lambert and her friends continued to treat psychology in the literary manner of La Rochefoucauld and were scarcely influenced by the scientific trend of thought. She bequeathed her inheritance to Madame de Tencin, who in turn handed on her kingdom to Madame Geoffrin,[1] whose pupil and successor was Madame Necker. The only *salon* which rivalled Madame Geoffrin's in international reputation was Madame du Deffand's. In both the proprieties were strictly preserved, and Marmontel describes how Madame Geoffrin, who had always kept her guests "in leading strings" and politely intimated her displeasure when the conversation tended to grow too free, finally seemed less friendly after his short visit to the Bastille. He was at once able to find more congenial society in the more advanced *salons*, which had begun to spring up about the middle of the century. The first conspicuous break in the old tradition was made when Mademoiselle de Lespinasse, after sharing for many years the house of Madame du Deffand, set up her own *salon* and

---

[1] "Do you know," Madame de Tencin once asked her friends, "what the Geoffrin woman comes here for? She comes to see what she can pick up from my inventory." She was right. Madame Geoffrin picked up not only the arts of rulership but even the subjects themselves. When Madame de Tencin died, Fontenelle, who had been one of her most regular guests for years, took the news calmly. "Ah, well," he is quoted as saying, "then I shall dine with Madame Geoffrin on Tuesday."

took the most distinguished of her friend's guests with her. Though this famous secession began with a personal quarrel, and though Mademoiselle de Lespinasse was not one to disregard convention, her drawing-room really belongs to that second eighteenth century, the philosophic and progressive one, which retained the traditions of the first, but lived, not on the memory of past splendours, but in the hope of the future regeneration of man.

It was not until the sixties that the *philosophes* had so penetrated the *salon* that they could dictate its tastes instead of conforming to them. Until then the *philosophes* had only one public to whom they could appeal. In the absence of an open market for books they were dependent for fame and fortune on the patronage of the earlier and more correct *salons*. Even if one was a philosopher it was necessary to live, and unless one were willing, like Diderot, to work fourteen hours a day in an attic for a hundred pounds a year, or had a sinecure post like Montesquieu, or an official position like d'Alembert or Buffon, one was forced to look for a patron and perhaps a pension. Only the very famous could hope to earn the favour of Frederick the Great or Catherine of Russia; the rest remained at the mercy of society hostesses. To have talent but not the character to succeed might lead to the perpetual humiliations which Diderot describes in *Rameau's Nephew*. Voltaire was ready to accept pensions from anybody, but he early recognized the necessity of independence, spent a good deal of his spare time in accumulating money, and enjoyed his rôle of philanthropic capitalist. And even those who had secure incomes depended upon the *salon* for success; the future of a book was largely determined by its reception in the leading drawing-rooms where the cultured aristocracy of Europe forgathered to discuss, to applaud or condemn. Since Academic Chairs were to be won only by social patronage, intrigue was a natural part of *salon* life. Madame de Tencin, for instance, was not content with obtaining a Cardinal's hat for her brother and supplying the King with mistresses: her greatest triumph was to arrange for an Academic Chair for her friend Marivaux in a year when Voltaire failed to obtain one. Montesquieu's election was due to Madame Lambert, who, said d'Argenson, had at one time created half the living Academicians. D'Alembert owed his Secretaryship of the Academy to Madame du Deffand. A few years later Madame Geoffrin and Mademoiselle de Lespinasse were close rivals for the honour of dispensing the greatest number of Academic Chairs.

"Women," said Diderot, "accustom us to discuss with charm and clarity the driest and thorniest subjects. We talk to them unceasingly; we wish them to listen; we are afraid of tiring or boring them; hence we develop a particular method of explaining ourselves easily, and this passes from conversation into style." This is an admirable summary of the benefits of the *salons*. They had ceased to be pedantic, and they demanded not preciosity but good journalism. But the *salon* had its disadvantages. Montesquieu once remarked that "the society of women corrupts the morals and forms the taste." If morals include intellectual sincerity and the society of women meant the dictatorship of the *salon*, Montesquieu was right. The patronage of literary women did corrupt the philosopher: he was compelled to adjust his style according to the intellectual fashion; he had always to be alert to please his hostess, to write so that she could talk about his book without having read the part which cost the greatest effort and which would constitute its permanent value. He had to adapt himself to the social atmosphere, to sigh over the *effroyable ton* of the Bible and the deplorable lack of taste displayed by the Holy Ghost. If one wished to be caustic about society and manners it was wise to retain the conventions of classical style, and even Mademoiselle de Lespinasse was disgusted when Buffon, whom she had long wished to meet, made use of a word not to be found in the vocabulary of Racine. A judicious philosopher was discreet in phrasing his criticisms, chose a butt who was universally ridiculed, or, if he was bold enough to use his dagger nearer home, stabbed so delicately that each victim, enjoying the treatment of his friend, failed to notice that his friend was secretly delighting in what he believed to be his neighbour's wound.

In this brilliant and restricted society, in which everyone

knew everyone else, and the same people met night after night at each other's houses and contrived, somehow or other, not to be bored, wit, both in conversation and writing, was the key to success. Great reputations were founded on quickness of wit. Duclos, made a member of the Academy before he had published anything, owed his friends and reputation to his turn for *bons mots*. The Abbé Galiani was a leading figure during the ten years in which he was stationed in Paris as Neapolitan ambassador. He had much to commend him; though he was only four feet six inches in height, he was a considerable economist with a European reputation for wit. Everyone enjoyed the story of how he had sought preferment by sending a collection of volcanic remains from Mount Vesuvius to Benedict XIV. with the request, "Holy Father, command these stones to be made bread," and how, as if to prove that the days of the Renaissance were not wholly over, the Pope had laughingly taken the hint and promoted the jester.

In one of the Persian letters Montesquieu describes how two men, complaining that everyone out-talked them, made a compact to ensure their own fame. What was the good, the first asked, of preparing witticisms only to have them lie like old lumber in his head because there was no opportunity of repeating them? If they arranged reciprocal openings, however, they could both shine. " I see that in less than six months we shall be able to maintain a conversation of an hour long composed entirely of witticisms, but we must be very careful to support our good fortune : it is not enough to say a good thing, it must be spread abroad and dispersed everywhere, or else it will be lost. I must confess that there is nothing so mortifying as to have said a smart thing and have it expire in the ear of the fool who heard it. It is true that this is sometimes compensated by having a good many foolish things we say passed over in silence ; that is our only consolation. Act as I have directed you, and I promise you a seat in the Academy in less than six months : your labour will soon be over, for you may then give up your art, since you will be a man of wit in spite of yourself."

The society of the *salon* could not have survived had it permitted itself to be solemn. But if solemnity was impossible, sincerity and seriousness were also difficult. A small circle of persons meeting almost daily in one another's houses, without social obligations or public responsibilities, could avoid both tragedy and tedium only by keeping close to the surface, and strictly regulating the social game which was their exclusive occupation. An old friend of Madame Lambert complained that at the age of sixty she had set up a *Bureau d'Esprit*: " *Bel Esprit* was a disease which struck her suddenly and of which she died incurable." If the conversation in her *salon* had been too serious the less intelligent would have felt slighted. Real differences of opinion would have appeared, and the smooth plane of social life have been ruffled. Where an emotion is genuine there is always danger ; wherever public evils are faced, consciences may play havoc with easy lives and the barren amusements of social intercourse fail to hide their futility. The most popular amusements, therefore, were games which encouraged a super-ficial treatment of matters in which the players were secretly furiously interested. A favourite pastime was to compose elegant character sketches of oneself or others ; these were passed round the circle for comment and emendation. To read these productions to-day is to obtain an intimate picture of *salon* society, but never to learn anything of significance about the individual described. The convention by which physical characteristics were related to mental ones and good and bad qualities placed side by side in antithesis excellently served the purpose of those who wanted an intellectual exercise, and needed a method of wasting time in perfect French. Almost all the *philosophes* at one time or another trained their wit in some such manner and threw off trifles of the moment lest they should be thought unsociable and serious.[1]

Grimm once remarked in his *Mémoires* that it was a good thing there were half-a-dozen people serious enough to discover

---

[1] It is worth while to compare these *tours de force* with the *Mémoire* of Mademoiselle de Lespinasse which d'Alembert wrote after her death. The woman to whom he had been devoted for many years, and whom he believed to be devoted to him, had died leaving him as a parting gift the passionate letters which she had written to two rivals. Technically d'Alembert's performance is similar to the usual *salon* sketch.

their own ignorance. The really important work of the century was done away from the *salons*, though even the greatest books were affected by the irrelevant trivialities which Vauvenargues described as the disease of the age. Montesquieu wrote : " My great work now advances with gigantic strides since I am no longer harassed with Parisian invitations to toilsome dinners and fatiguing suppers." Voltaire's best books were written away from Paris, when the Court patronage for which he had always hankered had been definitely refused him, and he had ceased to need further self-advertisement. D'Alembert was certainly right when he explained to Voltaire that he would merely waste his time in Paris, since he had both fame and the opportunity for serious work in his home on the frontier.

In view of the restrictions and artificiality of *salon* life, it is not surprising that the *philosophes* formed a new type of *salon* of their own. They continued to call on Mademoiselle de Lespinasse until her death, but they began to find a more lively pleasure in a society where literary tradition was not so strict, where the social graces played a smaller part and where discussion ranged over all topics. Rich men, like Dupin and Poupelinière, had become interested in philosophy ; they welcomed Marmontel and other *philosophes*, accepted the new doctrines, permitted freedom of conversation, and themselves provided good dinners and good music. The financier, execrated and ridiculed in plays and lampoons in the twenties and thirties, had become the valued friend of philosophy by the sixties. Best of all, from the point of view of the *philosophe*, however, were Holbach's dinner-parties. It was there that Diderot, unkempt, indecorous, pouring out a stream of exuberant and blasphemous eloquence, was really at home. At Holbach's, too, one might meet others who seldom frequented the Paris drawing-rooms : Turgot and the young Condorcet, and foreign celebrities like Hume, Wilkes, Shelburne, Garrick, Franklin and Priestley all from time to time enjoyed the hospitality of the "Maître d'Hôtel of Philosophy " in the house that was nicknamed the "Café de l'Europe."

In the sixties, therefore, the Philosophic audience had widened, and the opportunity of conversation and the variety

of social experience from which fertile ideas are apt to spring
had greatly increased. If you were a *philosophe* you would be
wise to maintain your reputation in an older world at Madame
Geoffrin's on Monday or Wednesday, you would certainly call
on Mademoiselle de Lespinasse (who received almost every
evening between five and nine), you could discuss Helvétius'
books (for he always wrote them in public) with their author on
Tuesday ; on Friday you could visit Madame Necker, and you
would miss the best part of the week's entertainment if you
did not dine with Holbach on Sunday or Thursday.

Holbach's was an excellent retreat for the philosopher, but
not for the less intellectual persons who were tired of the
artificiality of the *salons* and uninterested in the scientific
pursuits of the Encyclopædists. By the late sixties Paris was
ready for any novelty. Voltaire and his followers had completed
their destructive work, and since the positive implications of
their attack on the Church were as yet seldom understood,
the audiences which had once been thrilled by the *Lettres
philosophiques*, and still found *Candide* infinitely diverting, as
yet remained without any substitute for religion. Into this void
Rousseau stepped.

Rousseau was a *petit bourgeois* whose upbringing and habits
of mind were utterly alien from the conventions and traditions
of the *salons*. Though his entrance into Parisian society brought
him personally nothing but misery, it gave the *salons* new
interest, a new cult, and even in some cases a genuine life. He
was already more than thirty years old when he was first introduced to Diderot and his friends, and his earlier career had
been unusual rather than distinguished. He had left his birthplace, Geneva, an orphan child with a taste for romances ; he
had tried his hand in a notary's office, been apprenticed to an
engraver, been ill-treated and revenged himself by pilfering, had
become a wanderer, had temporarily renounced Protestantism
in order to gain the charity of Catholics, had turned lackey,
roamed Savoy as a tramp, taught music "without knowing
how to decipher an air," and discovered, by failing to teach it,
that he had a genuine talent for composition ; he had been a
luckless teacher of luckless boys, had acted competently as

secretary to a dishonest French ambassador at Venice, returned to Paris, and, after numerous humiliating experiences with women, whose ideal companionship was his constant dream, but whose more intimate favours he could neither resist nor enjoy without terror and a sense of guilt, had settled down with some contentment and a half-witted mistress to earn a precarious livelihood by copying music.

Rousseau was first received as a neophyte of the Encyclopædists, an interesting novelty, whom Diderot and Madame d'Epinay had adopted. Few things require so much social experience, so much poise and self-reliance, as to enter a clique of clever people who share a common experience, laugh at the same things, know each other just well enough and suspect the newcomer of being a bore or a disturbance. Rousseau had none of the necessary qualifications for a *philosophe*. The subversive views of Holbach's circle disgusted him as much as the formalism of the older *salon*. Vain and sensitive, earnest and sentimental, with no sense of proportion and no capacity for trifling, devoid of wit and contemptuous of a smooth society which did not recognize his latent genius, the goodness of his heart and the purity of his intentions, he could do nothing right. Retarded by a morbid inferiority, he was the more eager to be recognized as the central figure ; jealous of his independence, but furious at every hint of patronage ; every word of encouragement led him to assert himself and every slighting glance led him to withdraw precipitately.[1] In excitement he rushed to the centre of the picture, only to retire within him-

---

[1] Rousseau's feeling of inferiority was always increased by his poverty, and it was not as easy to be poor and independent as he imagined. When invited to the houses of the wealthy, and received with cordiality, he assumed that he would be always wanted, and repeated his visits with unwise frequency. Some service would be demanded and his pride would revolt at the thought of his dependence. His replies to those who sent him presents reveal much. *Cp.* his answer to Madame d'Houdetot, when she sent him chickens : " O, Madame, had you only given me news of yourself without sending me anything else, you would have made me rich and grateful. Instead of that the pullets are eaten, and the best thing I can do is to forget them. Let us say no more of them. You see what is gained by sending me presents." And to the Maréchale de Luxembourg he wrote : " Thank you for the butter you sent me. I have willingly received your present, Madame, but I cannot bring myself to touch

self bitterly humiliated. He could not speak his mind or keep silent; "instead of knowing how to hold my tongue," he wrote, "when I have nothing to say, I have a rage for wishing to speak, in order to pay my debt the sooner. I promptly hasten to babble words without ideas, very happy when they do not mean anything. In the wish to overcome and hide my ineptitude, I seldom fail to show it." He was always at a disadvantage. He had none of the easy currency of daily intercourse, and could not "comprehend how anyone could converse in a circle." Neither could he discuss serious matters without the disturbance of personal emotion. Like other men whose puritanism is reinforced by a sense of their own private sensuality he could not tolerate licentiousness in others. He was genuinely religious, convinced by emotional experiences, not by arguments, and altogether unable to let the scoffer go without rebuke. "If it is a fault," he broke out one day when the *salon* was discussing the defects of the Deity, "to allow evil to be spoken of an absent friend, it is a crime to allow anyone to speak evil of his God who is present. And for my part, gentlemen, I believe in God."

The reasons which made Rousseau a social failure also made the friendship he craved impossible. "I have never known," he wrote, "how to preserve a medium in my attachments and simply fulfil the duties of society. I have always been

it. I should think that I took communion unworthily; I should think that I ate damnation to myself."

Rousseau has provided posterity with more material for psychoanalysis than any other great writer. His *Confessions* are designed to give a complete story of his spiritual and intellectual development, and they are determinedly frank in detail. The praise and blame, the explanations and justifications, which he gives for his conduct, are, however, even more revealing than his conscious avowals. A medical diagnosis of Rousseau would not be in place here, but his approach to society is the better understood if one remembers several facts which his biographers usually choose to refer to only obliquely. His first sexual experience, he tells us, was an enjoyment of being whipped by a governess of whom he was fond, and he remained throughout his life a masochist, prostrating himself before women and finding terror rather than satisfaction in adult sexual experience. He was never free from a sense of guilt in relation to any of his several forms of sexuality. In later life his embarrassments were greatly increased by a weakness of the bladder which caused him constant social difficulty, and his adoption of an Armenian costume was a sensible method of disguising this complaint.

everything or nothing." Social ineptitudes would have mattered little if he could have retained any balance in his personal relationships. But he never saw his friends objectively. He was always preoccupied with dramatizing himself before them : he desired desperately to produce some special impression— usually that of an affectionate and natural person who was too independent to mind what others thought of him. A friendly word in response to an advance was enough to convince him that he had begun a lifelong companionship, and that reserve was henceforth unnecessary. It was his fate to pass his life in rushing into intimacy with those who were merely prepared for amicable relations : he strove to break down every barrier in a society which achieved its social success by a nice discrimination in erecting barriers. He was, as he said, "the most sociable and loving of human beings . . . but the truly sociable man is more difficult in his relationships than another ; those which only consist in unreal show could not suit him. . . . He will hate ordinary society, where the rule is a superficial intimacy and an actual reserve."

Humour or even wit might have saved him, but he had none. Voltaire was as sensitive to criticism as Rousseau himself, but he could always work off his spleen in an epigram or a lampoon. Grimm tells a story of a friend who visited Voltaire, and mentioned that he had lately seen Haller, the German scientist. Voltaire broke in with expressions of warm admiration for Haller. " I am glad," said his friend, " that you have so high an opinion of him. Unfortunately, he has not a high opinion of you." "Indeed?" replied Voltaire modestly. "*Then perhaps we are both mistaken.*" In a similar case, if Rousseau had discovered that a man he admired had no corresponding admiration for him, he would have at once been convinced that his friends had been intriguing against him and that he was the victim of malice, ingratitude and treachery. He would have poured out his resentment in passionate language and then, conscious that he had made a fool of himself, have retired to brood upon social corruption, to think out retorts which would have withered if they had occurred to him at the right time,[1]

---

[1] As he explains in the *Confessions.*

and to purge his impotent wrath in vehement letters which only brought him further humiliation. Such incidents were frequent, and Rousseau was driven more and more to seek comfort in the stolid placidity of his Theresa, who never laughed at him, and to seek peace in the wooded countryside, where, after long brooding in solitude, his humiliations lost their intolerable bitterness, mingled in the main stream of his thoughts and reappeared, transmuted into literature.

" A genuine sentiment," wrote a contemporary, " is so rare that when I leave Versailles I sometimes stand still in the street to see a dog gnaw a bone." It was this fact, the extreme artificiality of social life, which gave Rousseau his power with the men and women of the eighteenth century. He brought, it is true, a romantic insincerity even more distasteful to later generations than the polished show of the cultured *salon*. But he also brought something that was simple, and something that was genuine. His roots were deep, alive in a country soil whilst his contemporaries sought an easy popularity by exploiting a dead tradition. His personal relationships might be usually destructive, and always a little ridiculous, but their failure only brought into relief the hidden desire of most men and women for a deeper and more sincere relationship. His ideal of asexual friendship was perhaps largely mythical, and when he described love in the *Nouvelle Héloise* the result is to-day neither attractive nor convincing ; but the sorrows of Julie took society by storm, because they did express in romantic fashion the emotions of which most women were conscious and had been trained to inhibit.

Rousseau's imaginative writing was a novelty to his generation. He could create because he had never been taught to compose. Although writing was a long torture to him, he could not rest until the images which obsessed him had taken an artistic shape. The natural tendencies of his mind were unmodified by any youthful discipline.[1] His ideas came to him,

---

[1] Some of the difficulties of Rousseau's work are explained by his method of study—a method which is usually that of the poet rather than the philosopher. He read philosophy, he tells us, in just the way that he had once read romances as a child, forgetting everything while sharing the emotions and experiences

as he said, unbidden and undesired, flooding him with intense emotion which, after long brooding, could be transmuted into a form which swept away literary conventions, social prohibitions and logical difficulties. In one passage he describes the birth of the *Nouvelle Héloise*. As the conception of the novel grew in his mind, he realized the inconsistency he showed in writing a book "which breathed nothing but effeminacy and love" when he had publicly declaimed against the immoral effects of such novels. " I felt this incoherence in all its extent, I reproached myself with it, I blushed at it and was vexed ; but all this could not bring me back to reason. Completely overcome, I was obliged willy-nilly to submit, and to resolve to brave the *what will the world say of it ?*—except only that I deliberated afterwards whether or no I should show my work, for I did not yet suppose I should ever decide to publish it. This resolution taken, I entirely abandoned myself to my reveries, and by frequently resolving these in my mind, formed with them the kind of plan of which the execution has been seen."

In general, no one was more dependent upon the opinions of others than Rousseau. But he forgot them when he began to write. He wrote without heed of criticism, alike neglectful of orthodox models and of the conventions of the unconventional. He did not tack to meet the winds of fashion ; nor, after his

---

offered him, accepting or rejecting as a whole, making no objective examination or detailed criticism, content with whatever he found of emotional significance to himself.

He composed with extraordinary difficulty. He thus describes his intellectual method : " Two things, very opposite, unite in me in a manner which I cannot myself understand. My disposition is extremely ardent, my passions lively and impetuous, yet my ideas are produced only with much embarrassment and with much after-thought. It might be said that my heart and understanding do not belong to the same individual. A sentiment takes possession of my mind with the rapidity of lightning, but instead of illuminating it dazzles and confounds me ; I feel all but see nothing, I am heated but stupid ; to think I must be cool. . . . When I write my ideas are arranged with the utmost difficulty. They glance on my imagination and ferment. . . . During this state of agitation I see nothing properly, cannot write a single word and must wait until it is over. Insensibly the agitation subsides, the chaos acquires form and each circumstance takes its proper place. . . . Had I always waited till that confusion passed few authors would have surpassed me."

early essays, was his writing a superficial revolt against existing society. His imagination was powerful enough to take him into a world of his own, and he was therefore the most creative thinker of the century. Voltaire and the Encyclopædists led their generation by expressing clearly what men were already beginning to think dimly: Rousseau changed his age by so describing old things that they became new. He was not the first to notice that the grass was green, that common men were capable of passion and the aristocrat of common feelings. He did contrive, however, to make such matters seem interesting to Parisian society, and was largely responsible for the decline in the influence of "philosophy" and the growth of that sentimentalism which is the response of the ignorant and the trivial when an appeal is made to their imaginations.

The constant stream of English visitors who crossed and recrossed the Channel during the last twenty years before the Revolution found the social atmosphere of the *ancien régime* greatly changed. A few of the older *salons* survived; Madame du Deffand lived on until 1780 and philosophical discussion continued at Holbach's until the eve of the Revolution. Both types, however, had gone out of fashion: sentimentalism and politics were taking the place of scepticism and philosophy. For at the moment that Rousseau was leading a movement against rationalism and sophistication a parallel development was taking place. The reaction against a life of social futility led to a "return to nature" cult; with the more serious it also prepared the way for a genuine interest in politics. If the attack on the Church could so far succeed that the censorship failed to prevent the appearance of the most scurrilous blasphemies, was it not possible that philosophy might rule the State as well as destroy the Church? Such hopes took tangible form during the long constitutional struggle which led to the exile of the *Parlement* of Paris and the hated dictatorship of Maupeou. The appointment of Turgot as Controller seemed to justify the most sanguine prophecies, and his speedy downfall, devastating for the moment, only prepared the way for more revolutionary aspirations. For with the advent of the American Revolution the *Contrat Social* became intelligible as well as the

Emile; democracy now seemed a possible alternative to philosophic despotism and politics became, at least for the time,
the fashionable topic of drawing-room conversation.

It was the end of the *ancien régime*. Horace Walpole had
once complained that the *philosophes* were spoiling Paris. How
much worse when the eighteenth-century *salon* had completed
its evolution; it had first been converted by Mr Hume's
troublesome *protégé* to all kinds of extravagances and sentimentalism, and then, not content with Rousseauism, it had
given up its cultured and aristocratic interests and taken to
politics, the most boring and bourgeois of all occupations!

CHAPTER V

THE PHILOSOPHY OF COMMON SENSE

1. THE NEW PSYCHOLOGY—RATIONAL MAN

THE eighteenth-century Church offered men a metaphysic, an ethic, a physical and biological theory, a psychological and a political doctrine, which came from the Middle Ages. Voltaire and the men who shared his philosophy are commonly called sceptics because they expressed the doubts which almost everyone, including most of the ecclesiastics themselves, felt about religious dogma. Yet their work was indirectly constructive; they built a new set of religious and social assumptions upon which a new society was founded.

The form in which the new philosophy was stated was influenced, as we have seen, by the constant necessity of dissembling to escape the censorship and by the requirements of the *salons*. The classical tradition of French literature and a philosophic method inherited from Descartes further limited the *philosophes* to an abstract method of presentation : few of them had patience for induction, and, in spite of their enthusiasm and their experience of science, Montesquieu was almost the only one who tried to apply a scientific technique to social problems. But they were never remote from fact and abstract in argument, in the sense suggested by Taine. Experience played the largest part in the formulation of their theories. They were often dogmatic, because the philosophy they were refuting was dogmatic. Moreover their simple theory of human nature seemed to render detailed social analysis superfluous. Reason—or should we say, common sense—solved all problems.

It is true that the *philosophes* delighted in using abstract terms, such as liberty and equality, reason, nature and humanity. But until the Revolution had transformed them into battle-cries the demand for liberty and equality was generally understood to apply to certain concrete changes, while reason, nature and humanity had more definite significance than has usually been supposed. The *philosophes*, like the mediæval schoolmen, relied on reason to produce valid conclusions from given

117

premises : but whereas mediævalists accepted premises authoritatively provided by the Church, the *philosophes* followed Descartes in repudiating all authoritarian premises and attempting to found their logical structure upon undeniable axioms. Confusion arose from the fact that the *philosophes* used reason to denote the faculty by which these axioms were apprehended. Reason covered both reasoning and intuition. They assumed that reason as driver in the Platonic chariot both controlled the horses and knew exactly in what direction to go. By " natural reason," therefore, men could apprehend the initial certainties and build upon them a firm structure of natural religion and universal ethics. It was also natural reason which led every man to judge of values—to tell good from evil and justice from iniquity. In general, reason stood for a non-authoritarian method of discovering truth of fact or of value.

The *philosophes* were also in general agreement about the use of the word nature, though they differed about what was natural. They all believed that just as examination of physical phenomena showed the existence of certain general laws or principles, so a full understanding of economics and politics would discover natural laws of society. " To follow nature " meant to adjust human conduct to these natural laws, and by positive legislation which harmonized with nature's principles to produce a happy society instead of an unnatural and therefore unhappy one. That they must follow nature's teaching was agreed : unfortunately, it was not always obvious just what nature taught. Some held that men lived " naturally " if left to develop in accordance with instinct ; the American Indian was said to be happy without organization or coercion. Others followed Aristotle in believing that the true nature of man could be developed only in a political and civilized society. Natural, therefore, meant both the primitive and the ideal, the condition before misgovernment had perverted nature as well as the perfect social development which might be the result of good government. Confusions were unavoidable ; both private property and communism, for instance, could be logically defended as natural. All the *philosophes*, however, agreed that eighteenth-century France was unnatural, and that reason could discover the just and ideal order which the law of nature demanded.

Humanity was a simpler conception—an undeveloped form of the principle of utility. The apostles of humanity refused to admit that tyranny, intolerance and persecution could ever be justified : human happiness, therefore, was by implication the supreme value, and the greatest happiness the test of good and evil. To say exactly whose happiness was intended, or in what happiness consisted, or how it was to be attained, was the task of the conscious Utilitarian. But the initial stages were carried out by the " philosophers of humanity."

If reason, tolerance and liberty were to take the place of authority, obedience and asceticism, a new metaphysic and a new psychology were a necessary basis. The *philosophes* had first to substitute a natural for a revealed religion. If men learned to accept Newtonian physics they would cease to be dependent on an authoritarian creed and an inspired priesthood.

In the second place, living in accordance with nature could be defended only if human nature was held to be good and men supposed to be capable of reasonable conduct. If human beings were born in sin, or so foolish that they could not learn how to attain happiness, an authoritarian creed and coercive government were justified.

The *philosophes*, therefore, required an optimistic theory of human nature. They constructed it with materials gathered from several sources. From the Renaissance onwards the *libertins* had always rejected the doctrine of original sin, and in the eighteenth century there was a natural reaction against the gloom of Pascal and a tendency to trust men rather than to shackle them. This optimism was reinforced by science : a pleasing view of human nature seemed to be justified by new observation, by anthropology and by the study of Locke. The *philosophes* were delighted to ask with Bayle whether, in fact, the religious orders lived more moral lives than professed sceptics. Diderot's *La Religieuse* is mainly a declaration that the effect of asceticism is to prevent the natural satisfaction of desire and pervert it into unhealthy channels. In support of the theory of free development the *philosophes* relied far more than has usually been supposed upon travellers' evidence about natural man.[1] "Each fresh start," says Dr Myres, "on the never-ending quest of man as he ought to be, has been the response of theory to fresh facts about man as he is."[2] It is at any rate certain that fresh facts about man as he is have given new impetus and encouragement to political thinkers in quest of man as he ought to be. From the sixteenth century onwards, as Dr Myres shows, current accounts of negroes, of West Indians and North American Indians have influenced European thought. Bodin found support for his theory of political obedience in newly discovered America as well as in classical literature. Hobbes had travellers' evidence for his view that the state of nature was nasty, brutish and short. Locke, who wrote an introduction to Churchill's *Collection of Voyages* in 1704, based his reply to Filmer and Hobbes upon the knowledge that moral principles existed among peoples who had no authorized government. His "state of nature" was in accordance with contemporary accounts of the hunting and food gathering, non-agricultural aborigines of New England, where the Indian's only property was said to be the labour of his body and the deer which he killed. Similarly, when the natural man first "mixed his labour with the earth," it was his by an equally obvious natural law. Presumably there was plenty of land to go round, just as there were plenty of wild animals to hunt. Jesuit accounts of Hurons and Iroquois reinforced the current picture of the amiable Man Friday in *Robinson Crusoe*. Lafitau's comparison of American savages with the primitive man depicted in classical literature lays special stress upon the religious and moral sense everywhere inherent in natural man.[3] Pope's *Essay on Man*,

[1] *Vide* G. Atkinson, *Les Relations de Voyages du xviiie siècle et l'Evolution des Idées* (1924) and *The Influence of Anthropology on the Course of Political Science*, by J. L. Myres (1914).

[2] Dr Myres does not discuss the opposite aspect—the extent to which political thinkers neglected all anthropological evidence which did not suit their general theory. In the eighteenth century de Brosses' remarkable researches into totemism and fetishism were unnoticed by the *philosophes* perhaps because they threw doubt on natural rationality. *Vide* C. de Brosses, *Le Culte des Dieux fétiches* (1760).

[3] *Vide* Lafitau, Le P., *Mœurs des Sauvages Américains comparées aux mœurs des premiers temps* (1723).

one of the most popular books of the century, is based on the
same discovery. In eighteenth-century literature Hurons and
Iroquois everywhere share a place of honour side by side with
the communistic Spartans and Cretans, while the good manners
and mild temper of the natural man, when actually brought
from America and displayed in the Courts of Europe, were
the object of comment in numerous journals and letters.
"Wild Peter," declared by Linnæus to be a natural man,
found in a Hanoverian forest, excited the interest of Buffon
and all his contemporaries. Rousseau and the school which
followed him read and made use of many flattering accounts
of primitive peoples, which included, curiously enough, not
only the attractive races of North America, but also the Caribs
—a tribe of cannibals, who certainly neglected the arts of peace
at the time when the attention of Rousseau was called to
them. In the latter part of the century, accounts of the peaceful
Australasians reinforced the current picture. Polynesia was
represented as a Garden of Eden, and the South Sea Islander,
who could quickly learn English and chess, seemed to prove that
Rousseau had been no dreamer. Hobbes and Bossuet were
both discredited: natural man everywhere possessed an innate
moral sense or natural reason which enabled him to co-operate
freely in society without the aid of an arbitrary despot or of
the Catholic Church.

Finally, the *philosophes* found another even more powerful
support for the view that man was not naturally evil. The
psychology of Locke seemed to furnish a scientific basis for
putting trust in humanity. Locke had denied the existence of
innate ideas: even axioms such as that " the whole is greater
than the part " or that God exists (also thought to be an innate
conviction)were the results of reflection and experience. All knowledge, opinions and behaviour, derived from the senses. This
doctrine was pushed to its extreme form by Condillac, who
argued that even the power of reflection itself was nothing but
transformed sensation.[1] He pictured a statue gradually coming
to life, and showed how the addition of each sense would increase

---

[1] Condillac, *Traité des Sensations* (1754).

its experience and so at length enable it to build up a complete conception of the external world and to formulate beliefs about its nature. The acceptance of the view implied in this illustration constituted a revolution in human thought.

"Can there be anything more splendid," asked Voltaire with reference to Locke, " than to put the whole world into commotion by a few arguments?" The commotion, indeed, was only comparable to that created by Darwin's evolutionary theory. In the latter case men were offered an intelligible explanation of biological development in which the traditional teaching of religion had no share, and with which the current conception of God was incompatible. Similarly in the case of sensational psychology, men were offered an intelligible explanation of the development of ideas from which it followed that all doctrines, even those of the Church, were the fallible and accidental results of a limited experience, and could be tested by the same scientific process. Men, according to the new psychology, were born neither good nor bad, but neutral : blank sheets upon which experience made its individual impression. The divine gift of " grace " henceforth counted for nothing, and human methods of education for everything. The problem no longer was to restrain intractable passions, but to provide knowledge. Ignorance was man's only limitation and science offered unlimited possibilities. Newton had demonstrated that the world was ordered by natural laws, Locke that men were reasonable beings who could utilize their knowledge for their own happiness. As the implications of the new psychology dawned on men's minds there was a new hope and a new feeling of mastery. The Abbé de Saint-Pierre had assumed that reason and science could perfect society. Condillac seemed to have proved it.

It was the new psychology that really separated the eighteenth-century *philosophes* from their predecessors under Louis XIV. They were no longer sceptics in the manner of Bayle. Bayle, as Voltaire said, had been ignorant of Newton, and, he might have added, had thought of Locke as the protagonist of toleration rather than as the author of the *Essay on the Human Understanding*. Thanks to Locke and Newton, the *philosophes* had a positive doctrine to substitute for the orthodox creed. They believed they could demonstrate scientifically that knowledge was the key to happiness, and that it sufficed to enlighten men to make them perfect.

2. DEISM AND NATURAL RELIGION—VOLTAIRE AND ENGLISH RATIONALISM

It is appropriate to date the Age of Reason from Voltaire's visit to England.[1] Until the publication of his *Lettres philosophiques* the new philosophy was confined to a small group of *libertins* and scientists. The works of Newton and Locke had already been translated into French, but Voltaire made it his business to declare the practical implications of these books to everyone. "The example of England," Condorcet wrote, " showed him that truth is not made to remain a secret in the hands of a few philosophers and a limited number of men of the world instructed, or rather indoctrinated, by philosophers : men who smile with them at the errors of which the people are the victims, but who nevertheless uphold these very errors when their rank or position gives them a real or chimerical interest in them, and are quite ready to permit the proscription, or even persecution, of their teachers if they should venture to say what in secret they themselves actually think. From the moment of his return, Voltaire felt himself called upon to destroy every kind of prejudice which enslaved his country."

Voltaire's *Lettres philosophiques* was itself an effective blow at current prejudices. He succeeded in making many thousands of readers see England as he had done—as a land of freedom and opportunity, where common sense reigned. Driven out of France because he had been wronged by a member of the *noblesse*, he had been accepted on his merits in England. He might laugh at its solemn comfort, and declare that suicide was naturally habitual in a country where the wind was always in the east. But the wind of freedom seemed to him a still more

---

[1] Voltaire landed in England in May 1726. His *Lettres philosophiques* appeared in French in 1734. The English version, *Letters on the English*, had been published in the previous year.

potent influence upon the English character. An introduction from the British ambassador in Paris had given him a pass into cultivated society. He had found not only a governing and hunting aristocracy, but a flourishing middle class, a section of which was genuinely interested in scientific, literary and religious discussion. In England the intellect was granted a large measure of both freedom and respect. Although only one form of religious observance was officially favoured, numerous sects existed and, in general, remained unmolested. Religious thinkers were furiously discussing the historical bases of Christianity, and Voltaire was surprised to find that in England God had become so unimportant that one could worship Him and still remain a scientist.[1]

The final bulwark of any orthodox faith is the fear that morality will be undermined and habits of social restraint destroyed if religious authority be impaired. The example of England seemed to Voltaire a refutation of this doctrine. Bayle had shocked his contemporaries by arguing that a society of atheists might exist and even thrive. England seemed at least to prove the less daring thesis that to permit diversity of belief and discussion of the existence of God was not to prevent prosperity or damage morality.

Religion had got to the dangerous point of trying to rebuild its foundations on a basis of reason. Latitudinarian divines, still intent on attacking Catholicism, had ceased to use scriptural texts as weapons, and were arguing that papal doctrines were unreasonable. It was sufficient, as Leslie Stephen remarks,[2] " to substitute Revelation for Rome to make the attack upon Catholicism available for an attack upon all supernatural authority." By this simple process of substitution a number of thinkers now called themselves deists, while others remained unitarian members of the English Church. When once revelation had been discarded a transition from orthodoxy to unitarianism, from unitarianism to deism, and finally from deism to atheism, was

---

[1] Newton's method of reconciling his science and his Anglicanism was not altogether reassuring. Höffding, *History of Modern Philosophy*, i., p. 412, summarizes his position.

[2] *History of English Thought in the Eighteenth Century*, vol. i., p. 77.

unavoidable. Voltaire himself arrived and remained, somewhat precariously, at the deistic stage.

Amongst English rationalists three main positions were in debate. In the first place there was the view held by Chillingworth, and adopted with little variation by Locke, that the Creator had endowed man with a reasoning faculty by which he could discover truth and reject falsehood. Reason everywhere taught him a "natural religion"; he knew that God existed and that it was His will that men should love their neighbours and tell the truth. Reason also showed that God ruled by law and not by caprice. Having established unalterable laws of nature and endowed man with reason, the main part of His work was accomplished. God was a constitutional Monarch who, having made laws, Himself agreed to abide by them. In these circumstances, no revelation which was not in conformity with reason could be accepted, but revelation, if reasonable, might well supplement reason. Locke, and many with him, accepted the main body of New Testament revelation, considered Christ's teaching the perfect expression of natural religion, and were able to remain inside the Church. The next step was taken by Toland, who angered Locke by basing less orthodox conclusions upon the same premises. He declared that for revelation to be merely not unreasonable was insufficient grounds for accepting it. Proof, not probability, was necessary for the scientist. From the secure respectability of All Souls, Tindal went even further; he thought that the scriptural account of a God who redeemed His creatures by permitting them to crucify His Son was scarcely credible. Any personal interposition by the Deity was repugnant to his scientific outlook. "Tindal," said Leland, "makes rewards and punishments the inseparable attendants of virtuous and vicious actions"; so that "I do not see that he leaves God anything to do in the matter at all." When Bishop Butler demonstrated that an argument analogous to Tindal's would lead to atheism, he forced infidelity upon those whose logic was stronger than their fear. Christian deism in fact was no longer Christian and only formally deism.

A century before Voltaire's visit to England, Herbert of Cherbury had reduced the articles necessary for natural religion to five. He was the founder of the third school, the optimistic deists. It was reasonable to believe in a just and omnipotent God Who would some day reward the righteous and punish the wicked, Who had created the world and was fulfilling a good purpose which men in the midst of their sufferings and with their finite outlook were unable to understand. In the early eighteenth century Shaftesbury was the best exponent of this convenient theory. Bolingbroke, more brilliant, and less consistent, supported a similar thesis. Bolingbroke, however, was always haunted by disturbing questions. Why, if God is good and omnipotent, does evil exist in the world? Might it not be man who had created God in his own image? Goodness, Bolingbroke sometimes suggested, is a human conception, which may have no objective existence in heaven. It seemed clear that wisdom and power were attributes of the Being Who had made the world and set the forces of nature in orderly progress, but of other attributes of God men were wholly ignorant. "God is in their notion of Him nothing but an infinite man."

Voltaire never surmounted the difficulties suggested by Bolingbroke. He did not doubt that a creation implies a Creator ; even savages, he gathered, all believed in some god, and this, strangely enough, seemed to him, as it has to many since, a further proof of His existence. The argument from design convinced him, as it convinced most of his generation. The fact that nature worked according to certain fixed principles seemed to argue that an intelligent Being was responsible for them. Anticipating Paley, Voltaire wrote : " I shall always be convinced that a watch proves a watchmaker, and the universe proves a God." This argument always seemed conclusive until the evolutionary idea had found its place in men's minds. It was the discovery that there is maladjustment as well as harmony in the natural world, that decay proceeds side by side with growth, that the appearance of design is rather the result of an elimination of the unfit than a deliberate creation of the fit, that discredited the doctrine that " cork-trees had been created in order to stop beer barrels." Above all, geology, long hampered by the story of the Flood, had not yet given men the idea of development through a vast period of time. A single act of creation was still conceivable, and the eighteenth century had not ceased to think of a law of nature on the analogy of human law—the sole difference being that God's laws were certain and men's arbitrary in their application. It is only in modern times that it has become common to regard a law as a generalization made by men who have observed a regular sequence of events, and therefore assume, until further knowledge disturbs them, that this sequence is universal.[1] In the eighteenth century, therefore, God was necessary as a First Cause, a Being who created the world in six days and had rested ever since.[2] The doctrine of an immanent Deity, a continually active and creative force, was antagonistic to the accepted mechanical explanation of the universe. Rousseau, however, was soon to revive the idea of a living God, and the Catholic revival which followed the Revolution was a natural reaction from philosophic materialism. In England, too, the Methodist revival was a

---

[1] Dealing with the often exposed confusion in the use of the word "law," Bentham compares the laws of men with such a "law" of Optics as that the angle of reflection is equal to the angle of incidence. "We now understand how this matter was brought about. Hark ye (said the author of nature once upon a time), hark ye, you rays. There are some surfaces you will meet with in your travels that when you strike upon them, will send you packing; now when in such case, this is what I would have you do : keep the same slope in *going* that you did in coming. Mind and do what I say : if you don't, as sure as you are rays it will be the worse for you : upon this the rays (finding they should get into bad bread else) made their bows, shrugged up their shoulders and went and did so " (*A Comment on the Commentaries*, p. 32). This, the first of Bentham's attacks upon Blackstone, has been edited by Charles Warren Everett and published for the first time in 1928.

[2] Diderot, like Buffon, at times approached a more modern conception. With reference to the doctrine that a watch implies a watchmaker, he puts up an atheist to argue that there is no real parallel and no reason to think that such " an infinite piece of complexity whose beginnings, whose present condition, and whose end are all alike unknown, and about whose Author you have nothing better than guesses " is in fact a perfect order. "Who told you that the order you admire here belies itself nowhere else ? Are you allowed to conclude from a point in space to infinite space ? You litter a vast piece of ground with earth-heaps thrown here or there by chance, but among which the worm and the ant find convenient dwelling-places enough. What would you think of these insects if, reasoning after your fashion, they fell into raptures over the intelligence of the gardener who had arranged all these materials so delightfully for their convenience ?"

protest against the inertia of the Church, which had become a purely social institution without any distinctive philosophy. Among scientists there was also a reaction against mechanistic theories, which found expression in the biological theory of Lamarck.

Beyond the view that God exists, Voltaire came to no very definite metaphysical conclusions. Like most of the Encyclopædists, he was proud to admit that there were many things about which he knew nothing. His incursions into metaphysical discussion suggest that its vanity was the more obvious to him because he had little aptitude for it. In one of his satires he describes how a " thousand schoolmen arose, such as the unanswerable doctor, the subtle doctor, the angelic doctor, the seraphic doctor and the cherubic doctor, who were all sure that they had a clear and a precise knowledge of the soul, and yet wrote in such a manner that one would conclude that they were resolved that no one should understand a word of their writing. . . . Such a multitude of reasoners having written the romance of the soul, a sage at last arose who gave, with an air of great modesty, a history of it. Mr Locke has displayed the human soul in the same manner as an excellent anatomist explains the springs of the human body. . . . He sometimes presumes to speak affirmatively, but then he sometimes presumes also to doubt."

Plato, Aristotle, Descartes, Spinoza, Malebranche, Leibniz had all of them wasted their time. " I am a body and I think that is all I know of the matter," wrote Voltaire. " I am naturally ignorant what matter is : I guess but imperfectly some properties of it, but I absolutely cannot tell whether these properties may be joined to the capacity of thinking." The problem of reconciling free-will with unalterable law was equally insoluble. He was satisfied with the common-sense reply that men had some liberty, unlike other creatures of God. " I believe," he wrote, " that the Supreme Being has given us a little of His liberty as He has given us a little of His power of thought." Whenever Voltaire ventures further than this into metaphysics he is as inept as Doctor Johnson refuting Berkeley by stubbing his foot against a stone.

The older generation of Encyclopædists remained content with this practical deism. It supported the conception of unalterable law and permitted free scientific inquiry; it repudiated all supernatural interference and gave social morality a tangible sanction. It offered a rational explanation of good and evil and made rewards and punishments the inevitable results of behaviour, not the arbitrary fiats of an external deity. Men shared a common religion—"the universal law," as Diderot called it, "which the finger of God has engraved on every heart." A simple belief in God and a consciousness of good and evil appeared to be common to the whole human race, and all the dogmas of faith and elaborate codes of religious observance were the later inventions of interested priestcraft. Voltaire constantly compared the simple savage, possessing an unclouded knowledge of eternal truths, with the missionary who tried vainly to confuse his mind with subtle questions about the nature and attributes of God, the efficacy of the sacraments, and the history and constitution of the angelic hosts. "What," asked Voltaire, "is a true deist? One who says to God I adore and love you, one who says to a Turk, a Chinaman, an Indian and a Russian, I love you." The untutored savages "take the existence of God for granted and think it natural to adore the Creator Who is the cause of their being, and to offer Him prayers and thanksgivings without being so foolish as to request Him for fine weather when their neighbours are asking for rain." God's will was clear enough to the unsophisticated mind. "I think that whatever gives you pleasure and does injury to no man is very good and very right" is the maxim attributed to the happy Indian, who may "thereby live to be a hundred." Among Christian sects the Quakers only had preserved the simple and reasonable faith of their Master.

Voltaire could appreciate the social value of natural religion and the beauty of the Christian life of his Quaker friends, but he grew increasingly doubtful if God was in any way responsible or interested in what men believed to be good. Were Pope and Leibniz right in thinking that all was for the best? "My poor Pope," he wrote, "my poor hunchback, who told you that God could not have formed you without a hump?" The doctrine that "whatever is, is right " was not optimism but " desperation —a cruel philosophy under a soothing name." The great Lisbon earthquake of 1755 moved him to question the guidance of a Deity who was prodigal of benefits to His children and then rained evils upon them apparently without any discrimination or thought of their deserts.

Voltaire's poem on the Lisbon earthquake roused Rousseau to an indignant defence of God and His apologists. Pope and Leibniz, he declared, had at least offered men a balm for their misfortunes and taught them resignation ; they had represented such calamities as a necessary effect of the divine constitution of the universe, presumably somehow good even if not obviously so to us. Voltaire's scepticism, on the other hand, destroyed faith and led to despair. Voltaire's reply to Rousseau took the form of a novel, published three years later. The doctrine of " the good and sufficient cause " for pain inflicted by a benevolent and omniscient deity has never recovered its prestige since the publication of *Candide*.

Voltaire remained a deist, but by the time he had finished saying what God was not, it was difficult to find any positive attributes left Him. He had derided anthropomorphic conceptions of the Deity, and denounced the sophistries with which men tried to palliate evil by describing it as the goodness of God in disguise. To argue the benevolence, wisdom and power of God from the existence of goodness and order in the world makes it necessary also to argue that God is malevolent, stupid and impotent, in view of the frequent triumph of evil and the prevalence of chaos. Perhaps, then, Candide's friend, Martin, was right, and Manicheism, which leaves it doubtful whether the power of good which one may call God if one likes, or the power of evil which it is then logical to call the Devil, is the more likely to win. " You see," says Candide, when the wicked captain and all the innocent passengers on his ship are drowned, " that crime is sometimes punished? " "Very true," Martin replies, "but why should the passengers be doomed also to destruction? God has punished the rogue, but the Devil has drowned the rest." To the scientist another possibility presented itself; both God and the Devil might be discarded and materialism substituted. In Holbach's *Système de la Nature* the conception of a Creator is discarded, and the view of Lucretius, that the universe is the result of an accidental combination of atoms, resuscitated. It is true that Holbach ended his system with a panegyric to Nature which had insensibly, and in spite of his protests, become personified in the course of his book. Voltaire was nevertheless horrified, for without the idea of a Creator and a final Dispenser of rewards and punishments he feared, as the Church feared, that men would have no incentive for moral behaviour. In the last analysis, Voltaire's view was that of Gibbon, that "all religions were equally true in the eyes of the people, equally false in the eyes of the philosopher, and equally useful to the magistrate." For utilitarian purposes, if God did not exist it would be necessary to invent Him. When the choice between safety and truth was presented to him Voltaire had no trust in ordinary people to save him from apostasy. He was not really willing for frank discussion, and in this he resembled his enemies—who attacked him not because what he said was untrue but because they feared the consequences of free speech.

Voltaire was perhaps the most effective propagandist who ever lived.[1] His defects were not of a kind to interfere with his main task—the destruction of superstitions which men accepted because they had never been permitted to think about them. He exposed the sacrosanct. His wit was the most powerful of weapons: for when he spoke neither cleric nor layman could resist reading, laughing and questioning. It was his unique accomplishment to set a large section of the Church as well as of the laity thinking: since Voltaire, France has been sharply divided into clericals and Voltaireans. If he seems to-day an unsatisfactory and even a shallow thinker that is because he won his battle and forced the Church to

---

[1] There is interesting tangible proof of Voltaire's influence. He amused people so much that everyone who read at all read him. Lanson (*Voltaire*, chap. xi.) cites the booksellers' and publishers' figures of the sale of his works. Between 1778 and 1835 thirty-four complete editions of his works, as well as numerous incomplete ones, were published, and a million and a half copies of his books were sold within one period of seven years.

take its stand on less vulnerable ground than that from which he drove it.

3. CIVIL LIBERTY—NATURAL RIGHTS AND THE ENLIGHTENED DESPOT

The political theory of Voltaire and the older generation of Encyclopædists was, like their religious philosophy, a cautious compromise, based on a common-sense view of immediate social need. When its intellectual foundations were examined it proved far more subversive than its exponents intended. They wished to destroy the superstitions of the Church, not to undermine the religious habits of ordinary men and women. In the same way they hoped to enlighten and to reform the existing State, but were almost as shocked to find their disciples becoming democrats as atheists. The foundation of their politics and their theology had been laid by Locke, whose defence of the English Revolution easily served the turn of more thorough-going revolutionaries, just as his rational Anglicanism proved a step on the way to a rigid materialism.

The demand for civil liberty was supported in the eighteenth century on grounds both of utility and of natural law. Since the time of Bentham the utilitarian argument has proved more fertile than that from nature. To argue that the only justification of the State is its capacity to increase happiness, that happiness consists in the opportunity of freely satisfying desires and developing with the minimum of external interference, and that, therefore, the primary duty of the State is to secure individual liberty—this is a line of approach which made a science of politics a possible aspiration. The conception of utility was valuable because it opened the way for quantitative analysis: men might differ about the things which made for happiness, but utility did offer a more definite basis for argument than the vague and absolute principles which usually prevailed in political controversy. But to condemn the argument from nature as " nonsense on stilts," as Bentham and more modern critics have done, is to misunderstand its value and its basis. The idea of natural rights was not finally discredited because

in eighteenth-century thought the natural was sometimes confused with the primitive and an *a priori* method of argument
commonly adopted. The introduction of the Golden Age and
the social contract as a makeshift support for natural rights was
unfortunate because, when the historical fallacy was knocked
away, the truth embodied in the idea of natural law was easily
overlooked.

The *philosophes* who talked of natural rights were relying
upon the sound assumption that men have everywhere certain
needs in common, and that these are spiritual as well as material.
They had too an historical basis for their claims. They might
profitably have put the matter thus. Society is made up of
individuals who have spiritual as well as economic needs. Now
it is of the very nature of a spiritual existence that it develops
from within, that no outside force can direct it and that its
development will be individual and unpredictable. There is,
therefore, a large part of the life of every man which must not
be regulated by any Government. Any society is self-condemned
which does not give opportunity for the spiritual life to develop,
and we have the long record of history to show that men are
willing to suffer imprisonment and torture, to give up ease
and even life itself, in pursuit of religious freedom. When the
expression of thought is censored, and adherents to any religious creed proscribed, men demand the right of free speech
and religious toleration, just as they demand the right of private
property when the fruits of their labour are confiscated and
economic benefits unjustly distributed. Where justice is venal,
privilege flagrant, and government arbitrary, they demand
equal rights before the law and some form of political liberty.
A Government fails in so far as it omits to recognize and
give scope to these fundamental needs of human nature. In
this sense natural rights, as the *philosophes* argued, are anterior
to the State, since they arise out of the continuous demands of
men ; the preservation of rights remains a principal duty of
the Government, even though the substance of these demands
changes and becomes in part modified through the State's
action. It remains true that the State must be judged by its
capacity to secure the rights of man.

The mistakes of the *philosophes* were due to their failure to realize that natural law has a changing and developing content. When Montesquieu compared the customs of one country with those of another he distinguished permanent underlying principles from superficial differences due to local circumstances ; but he spoke as if the principles themselves were always constant, and as if geography and climate modified their application without any help from the development of social life itself. Voltaire, whose historical perspective was truer, though narrower, could write : " The empire of custom is vaster than that of nature : it extends over manners, over all usages : it covers the scene of the universe with variety : nature spreads unity there, establishing everywhere a small number of invariable principles : the foundations, therefore, are everywhere the same, and culture produces varying fruits." Even here the invariable principles seem static, and the idea that the needs of men in primitive society might not prove an adequate guide to those of modern civilization, totally absent. The Aristotelean conception of the natural as the full development of the potentialities rather than as the original constitution of the organism seldom makes its appearance in the eighteenth century.

In one direction the doctrine of natural law was more serviceable than the current form of Utilitarianism, which suffered equally from lack of historical perspective. The moral appeal in the doctrine of natural law was more immediately effective than an argument based on a balance of pleasure over pain. In the hands of a philosopher, no doubt, a principle established on utilitarian grounds was distinct enough from a temporary expedient. Liberty and justice were words which had meaning for the utilitarian as well as for the exponents of natural law. According to the utilitarian, justice is a principle founded on experience, more important than any passing advantage and always to be recognized by a government, even when the current balance of pains and pleasures would seem to favour its temporary neglect. No doubt this is a more scientific analysis than the conception of natural law, which bases rights on an intuitive apprehension by all men at all times. But in the hands of governments, utility and expediency are so easily interchangeable that men have clung to natural and inalienable rights, apprehending that, in the absence of a moral and absolute claim, their rulers could always find exceptional grounds for violating their liberty. So, when it came to founding a constitution and attempting to preserve the gains of the past from the passing wills of governments and the gusty passions of majorities, the basis of moral law seemed a more secure foundation than a utilitarian argument based on analysis and experience. Natural law was at least a method of forcing authority to recognize principles which transcend immediate expediency.

As employed by its more fervent adherents, the law of nature supports a comprehensive Protestantism. To the Protestant it is intolerable that any authority should stand between the individual and the conclusions of his own reason. Sixteenth-century Protestantism began in this spirit, but failed in courage and set up the Bible in place of the Pope. Only Anabaptists and Quakers accepted the whole faith of Protestantism. In the eighteenth century the arguments which Protestants applied to religion were applied generally to all departments of thought. The methods of science were the only guide to truth : authority could order but it could not prove. Occasionally, therefore, a *philosophe* could speak like a Quaker, though Diderot talked of "natural reason" where George Fox would have spoken of "inner light." But it was left to Paine and a more revolutionary school of thought to declare that the very word "toleration" was an insult, since it implied that any power might possess the right to grant or withhold liberty of conscience.[1]

When the Revolution came, Paine rushed to the defence of the new French Constitution, on the ground that it was "natural." A generation earlier when Voltaire wished to stress the contrast with French government he idealized England as the country where nature was obeyed and the rights of man effectively guaranteed. "Here is the point which English legislation has at last reached : it places every man again in

[1] "Toleration," Paine wrote, "is not the opposite of intolerance, it is the counterfeit of it. Both are despotisms. The one assumes to itself the right of withholding liberty of conscience, the other of granting it. The one is the Pope armed with fire and faggot, the other the Pope granting or selling indulgences."

possession of all those rights of nature of which men are robbed in almost all monarchies. These rights are: entire liberty of person and of goods; the right to speak to the nation through the medium of the pen; to be tried upon a criminal charge only by a jury of independent men; not to be judged in any case except according to the precise terms of the law; to profess peacefully what religion one wishes." An English radical might have pointed out to Voltaire that in fact only a portion of the population in England enjoyed the substance of these advantages. Liberty of person was not secure from the press-gang; political comment could at times be sharply curtailed; Quakers and Unitarians suffered civil disabilities, as well as Catholics; the law was tortuous, antiquated and frequently administered in the interests of the rich against the poor. Even so, the contrast with France was sufficiently striking: the Church did not rule the State, the aristocracy was not wholly irresponsible nor parasitic, and a single legal code, theoretically at least applying to all classes, was some safeguard against tyranny.

The disabilities imposed on Catholics would certainly not have troubled Voltaire. Locke had argued that those whose creed necessarily made them intolerant were rightly excluded from exercising public authority. The French *philosophes* were naturally more Erastian, since their whole experience had taught them the danger of a powerful Church. They were not content with the principle that the State is a secular institution, whose policy should be divorced from religious considerations. Left alone, the Church would be too dangerous. " If," as Diderot remarked, " it is difficult to do without priests wherever there is a religion, it is easy to keep them quiet if they are paid by the State and threatened at the least fault with being hunted from their posts, deprived of their functions and their salaries, and thrown into poverty." Voltaire also advocated the strict subordination of the Church to the State. The State ought not to permit any of its citizens to be troubled with an allegiance to a rival authority. All religious observance should be supervised by the secular power. " If there are in a cult any formulas of prayer, canticles or ceremonies, they ought all to be submitted to the inspection of the magistrate. Ecclesiastics may compose these formulas, but it is for the Sovereign to examine them, approve them, and, if need be, reform them. We have seen bloody wars which would not have taken place if sovereigns had better known their rights." If the instruction of the young remained in the hands of the Church it was for the Government to inspect schools. Marriage, too, should be regarded as a contract, not a sacrament, and priests who performed the ceremony be servants of the State rather than of the Church. Where religion led to obvious abuses it was the duty of the State to restrict even the right of free speech : the Sovereign was justified in preventing the strife of Thomists and Molinists by " imposing silence on both parties and punishing the disobedient." [1]

Voltaire indeed never made any attempt to reconcile his doctrine of sovereignty with his theory of natural rights. Whenever it came to the test he supported the State against the individual and preferred order to freedom. He was even capable of wishing the State to ban an author of whom he disapproved, and was himself responsible for the imprisonment of an opponent. His general position, however, was clear enough. " It is a natural right to use the pen and tongue at one's own peril. I know many books which are boring : I do not know of one which has done real harm." Nevertheless, he could write that there were insulting books which ought to be burnt, because an insult is a civil offence ; whilst a book like *The Social Contract*, an " œuvre de raisonnement," being only illogical, not offensive, ought to be refuted, not suppressed.

Whatever his inconsistencies, Voltaire was successful in spreading the great principle he learnt from England, and from Beccaria, that it was the business of the law to punish criminals, not to supervise morals. It was better to prosecute for libel than to prevent free-thought by a system of spies and censorships.

---

[1] As an evil of clericalism which the State should certainly suppress Voltaire mentions the monastic vows taken by children. "How have governments come to be so much their own enemies, so stupid, as to authorize citizens to alienate their liberty at an age when to dispose of the least part of one's fortune is forbidden ? How can we permit the worst of all slavery in a country where slavery is forbidden ?"

He was nowhere more effective than in his work for the improvement of justice. He protested against the mediæval survivals which still passed as judicial procedure, exposed the barbarity and futility of the *question*—a torture which tried endurance, not innocence, and enabled the guilty to escape, provided they were strong enough, and condemned the weak, whether innocent or not. Bentham's analytic logic had not yet exposed the absurdities of judicial process in England, but, in any case, Voltaire would have been justified in citing English methods as an improvement on those of France, where the magistrate was accustomed "to conduct himself towards the accused as an opponent rather than as a judge," where the accused was not allowed his own counsel, was tried in secret, and not even permitted to confront the witnesses who testified against him.[1] Neither was it possible for anyone in France to know the law, although its endless complications and local variations kept lawyers fat. "Is it not an absurd and frightful thing," asks a litigant in one of his Dialogues, "that what is true in one village is found to be false in another? How strange a barbarism that fellow-countrymen should not live under the same law!"[2]

The idea that punishment should be proportionate to crime and graded according to its deterrent effect was popularized by Montesquieu and Voltaire before Bentham had explained it to lawyers. Voltaire used the case of a young girl of eighteen, who had been hanged for stealing towels from her mistress (who had not paid her wages), as an example of legal inhumanity. What, he asks, is the effect of such punishment? "It is to multiply robbers. For what householder will dare to forswear every feeling of honour and pity so far as to deliver up a servant guilty of so slight an offence to be hanged at his door? He is

---

[1] The Calas case in itself provides an adequate example of judicial method in eighteenth-century France, or at least in Toulouse. A useful and readable account has been published in England, *The Case of Jean Calas*, by F. A. Maugham. Voltaire's work for Calas' wife and family was not only in the cause of toleration but also on behalf of a fairer method of trial.

[2] It has been estimated that there were four hundred different legal systems in pre-Revolutionary France.

satisfied by dismissing him; the thief goes on to rob elsewhere, and often becomes a dangerous brigand." This was an early statement of the truth that, while certainty of punishment may prevent crime, severity may increase it. Further, Voltaire asked, was not the whole penal system founded upon a wrong basis? The main question to be considered was the public advantage; not how to make punishment unpleasant, but how to make it "useful." Beccaria had suggested that the law itself encouraged crime: was it reasonable to expect to "teach men to detest homicide" by making magistrates also commit homicide with pomp and ceremony? Was there, Voltaire wondered, any argument at all for capital punishment, except in the case of a homicidal maniac whom one must kill for the purely utilitarian reason that there was no other means "of saving the life of the greater number"? In every other case the criminal should be condemned to live a useful life, to work "continually for his country because he has harmed his country. He must redress the harm he has done. Death redresses nothing."

Common sense was an excellent weapon for attacking existing French institutions. It enabled Voltaire to establish the principles of equality before the law, civil liberty and freedom of discussion. Beyond these immediate reforms, however, it solved nothing. Montesquieu and Rousseau were exceptions in their period in being seriously concerned with a political philosophy, in realizing that the form of government and the basis of political obedience were important as well as the passing of good laws and the efficiency of their administration. The Encyclopædists were sorry for the poor and hoped that the abolition of privilege and monopoly and the institution of a freer economic régime would bring them a higher standard of life. Diderot was the only Encyclopædist (unless Rousseau is included among their number) who had democratic sympathies or any realization of what poverty meant. The ideal of social equality was seldom taken seriously, though many agreed with Voltaire that something might be done to improve the lot of the indigent by the establishment of hospitals for the sick, the provision of work for the unemployed, and the reorganization of existing institutions like the Hôtel-Dieu in Paris.[1] The division between rich and poor, however, remained unalterable: "it is impossible on our happy globe that men living in society should not be divided into two classes, the rich one which commands, the poor which serves. These two classes, again, divide themselves into a thousand, and among these thousand there are still shades of difference."

By liberty the *philosophes* meant civil liberty, and it was only when men had come to doubt if it could ever be secure without popular government that liberty began to include democracy. It is true that on one occasion, carried away by enthusiasm for England, Voltaire spoke as if the element of democracy in her government was the real safeguard of civil liberty. England, a kind of disguised republic, was free because she taxed herself. The House of Commons was an epitome of the nation; "the King, who is the head, only acts for it and according to what is called his prerogative," while peers and bishops were there merely as their own representatives. "But the House of Commons is there for the people, since each member is deputed by the people. . . . In comparison with this institution the Republic of Plato is an empty dream."[2] It was, of course, a parliament of property-holders to which Voltaire referred. Even when he admitted that a republic might be a good form of government in a small country, he was careful to add that only holders of property could claim a share in legislation. As for the populace, he added, "when it mingles itself with reason all is lost. The populace are oxen, which need a yoke, a goad and hay." A monarchy, in any case, was preferable to democracy. He himself preferred "to obey a fine lion, much stronger than himself, than two hundred rats of his own species."[3]

Voltaire's attitude was not really inconsistent. England seemed a happy accident, a place where a measure of popular government proved compatible with enlightened administration. It was the enlightenment he cared about; whether the power was

[1] Vide *Dic. Phil. Charité.*
[2] *Dic. Phil. Gouvernement.*
[3] *Dic. Phil. Idées Républicaines.*

popular, aristocratic or despotic was of secondary importance. He held with Pope that it was for fools to contest about forms of government, "what's best administered is best." The best Government, he said, was that in which the rights of man were most securely recognized. On the whole, an enlightened despotism seemed more likely to preserve civil liberty than a popular or an aristocratic Government, in spite of the fact that a mixture of all three happened to have served the purpose well in England.

In France the reformer naturally centred his hopes in the King. The King might for the time be controlled by ecclesiastics, just as the mob which had hounded Calas to the wheel was incited by priests, but in the past only kings had ever been strong enough to check the power of the Church, to enforce toleration, and to keep order. The French Constitution had long been destroyed. The *Parlements*, its only remnants, were mainly busied with preserving their own privileges. In 1771, when Chancellor Maupeou exiled the *Parlement* of Paris and set up his own Council to take its place, Voltaire expressed his delight, remarking that the *Parlements* represented no other interests than their own, were useless as a reforming body, and could never, under any circumstances, justify the comparison of themselves with the British House of Commons. To enlighten a single powerful individual seemed comparatively easy, all the more since the *philosophes* found despots throughout Europe ready to buy their books, pay them pensions or compliments, and even on occasion to carry out some of the reforms they suggested. The *philosophes*, therefore, imitated the Jesuits and sought influence through the conversion of the powerful. " I am persuaded," wrote Voltaire to Frederick the Great, " that only a monarch can now crush the seeds of religious hatred and ecclesiastical discord in his kingdom. But he must be an honest man, not priest-ridden : for fools though they be, men know very well in their hearts that goodness is better than religious observance. Under a sanctimonious king, subjects are hypocrites : a king who is an honest man makes his people like himself."

In the thirty years preceding the Revolution the *philosophes* had considerable grounds for believing that European government was profiting by the enlightenment they offered. Frederick the Great, a genuine admirer even if a poor exponent of French literature, had disappointed their earlier hopes. But in spite of his wars and intrigues he had abolished serfdom in Prussia, he worked continuously to improve the honesty and efficiency of his administration, and he persecuted no one on the ground of religious opinion. Catherine of Russia, too, was scarcely as philosophic in practice as she appeared in conversation. She did not learn all the lessons which Diderot endeavoured to inculcate as he sat opposite her, thumping the Imperial knees in his exuberant exposition of Encyclopædist principles. Nevertheless it was much to have an Empress of Russia who patronized philosophy, who called Montesquieu's *L'Esprit des Lois* " her breviary," and who carried out his principles at least up to the point of formally abolishing the use of torture. If Catherine's reforms were often shams, like Potemkin's villages, Pombal in Portugal, Leopold in Tuscany, and, finally, Joseph in Austria, were all genuine reformers, whose inspiration came directly from Voltaire and his colleagues.

In spite of the fact that these remarkable rulers happened to be in power in Europe contemporaneously, enlightened monarchy failed. Its reforms did not make revolution unnecessary, nor prevent the triumph of democracy. Indeed, it was not in the power of the benevolent despot to do for his people all that the *philosophes* asked. A King cannot altogether break with the past traditions of monarchy, free himself from the hampering support of courts and aristocracies, nor suddenly enlighten a populace which has never previously been permitted any kind of education or share in government. The philosophic despots had no constitutional organization to which they could appeal for support in their struggle with feudal privilege and clerical hostility. When Joseph II. attempted, on his own initiative, to carry through reforms which were in advance of public opinion his benevolence led to revolution. The alternative method, attempted by Louis XVI., of appointing enlightened ministers might have been more successful if he had adequately supported them. As it was, the effect was merely to spread a full knowledge of social evils and administrative scandals amongst the populace, to create an impatience with the slowness of reform, and, finally, a demand that if the King could not reform his Government, and get rid of social misery, it was the business of the people themselves to take the matter in hand.

4. *ECRASEZ L'INFAME*—THE WORK OF VOLTAIRE

In *Candide*, Voltaire had given up not only the hope of explaining the universe but also that of reforming the world. His life, however, was a refutation of the doctrine of minding one's own business. Even when human nature seemed to him least worthy of respect, and the mystery of pain most incomprehensible, Voltaire could not lose the belief that there were some things worth doing, and some faith that was rational. "We may believe that industry will always progress more and more : that the useful arts will be improved : that of the evils which have afflicted men, prejudices, which are not their least scourge, will gradually disappear among all those who govern nations, and that philosophy, universally diffused, will give some consolation to human nature for the calamities which it must always experience."

If men were ever to be induced to turn their eyes from unpractical and superstitious beliefs, and choose the common-sense goods which life offered, they must begin by " doubting a little of their own infallibility," as Benjamin Franklin put it, and learn to realize that persecution was never justified by any benefits which it might be supposed to produce. Men have always admitted that the infliction of pain is an evil, but in every age they have believed in some end which seemed to justify it as a means. In Voltaire's day cruelty was justified, not on nationalistic grounds, but on religious ones. The first object of the humanitarian then was to overthrow popular superstitions, and so enable men to see cruelty as cruelty, not as sanctified and necessary suffering.

Voltaire once described how Reason and Truth travelled through Europe, and felt themselves at home only in such enlightened despotisms as Parma and Turin. In England they found that the worst stages of fanaticism and folly were past and a "unique" Government had been set up, in which the advantages of monarchy and the freedom of republicanism were combined. "My daughter," says Reason to Truth, " I think our reign may be just beginning, after our long imprisonment. . . . That will happen to us which has happened to Nature : she has been covered by an ugly veil and completely disfigured during countless centuries. At the end have come a Galileo, a Copernicus and a Newton, who have shown her nearly naked and who have made men almost amorous of her."

In France, however, men were scarcely ready to fall in love with Reason and Truth. When the Jesuit Order was abolished in 1764 Voltaire's prophecy seemed about to be fulfilled. But Jansenist *Parlements* and provincial mobs were as fanatical as Jesuit inquisitors. Already in 1762, Calas, a Protestant tradesman, was condemned by a Jansenist *Parlement* to be broken on the wheel, because of a rumour that his son, who had been found dead, had been killed by him in order to prevent his conversion to Catholicism. There was evidence that made it in the highest degree improbable that Calas had murdered his son : there was no fragment of evidence that he had. Sirven, similarly accused of murdering his daughter, escaped the wheel only by flying to Geneva ; while in a third case, La Barre, who was accused of insulting the Virgin Mary before the *Parlement* of Amiens, was condemned to have his tongue and right hand cut off and then be burnt alive. On appeal, however, the *Parlement* of Paris considered the Virgin's honour sufficiently vindicated by a mere decapitation, and in 1766 La Barre was beheaded.

It has been well said that, while the preacher tells us of our sins, and the magistrate punishes us for social delinquency, the greatest crimes can be dealt with only by ridicule. During the last sixteen years of Voltaire's life there could no longer be any doubt of the serious intention of his mockery. When Frederick wrote to him, taunting him with only coquetting with the "infamous monster," Voltaire replied : "No, I work only to extirpate it." To d'Alembert he wrote : "Here Calas broken on the wheel, there Sirven condemned. . . . Is this a country of philosophy and pleasure? It is rather the country of the Massacre of St Bartholomew. Why, the Inquisition would not have ventured to do what these Jansenist judges have done. . . . Ah, my friend, is it a time for laughing? Did men laugh when they saw the bull of Phalaris made red-hot?"

Putting aside his other work, his plays and history, his epigrams and philosophy, Voltaire devoted himself to the practical task of forcing the authorities to admit that Calas had been unjustly condemned, to ridiculing Catholicism, and to advocating free-thought and toleration. "Like Cato," he wrote, "I always end my harangue by saying '*Deleatur Carthago.*' It is only necessary for five or six *philosophes* to understand in order to upset the Colossus. There is no question of stopping our lackeys going to Mass; it is a question of snatching fathers of families from the tyranny of impostors and inspiring them with the spirit of tolerance." In scores of articles and pamphlets he exposed the barbarities, the immoralities and artifices of papal history, ransacked the works of Bayle and the more militant English deists for examples of discrepancies of Biblical dates and the improbabilities of miracles, described with all solemnity the less savoury stories of Old Testament Fathers and Christian saints, remarking that although according to ordinary standards these would be subjects for incredulity, censure or ridicule, with religious sanction they became matters of faith and inspiration. To doubt or criticize, in these circumstances, was, of course, to deserve an eternity of future punishment, and men who persecuted those who disagreed with them on such matters were, after all, only emulating the vengeance which an All-loving Father wreaked upon them when they did not implicitly believe in His goodness.

In the long run, it was not argument which counted. It was the whole outlook of men, historical, scientific and religious, which Voltaire's appeal was designed to change. In his vindication of Calas he wrote: "Transport yourselves with me to the day when all men shall be judged and when God will render to each according to his works. Imagine all the dead of the past ages and of our own appear in His presence. Are you quite sure that our Creator and our Father will say to the wise and virtuous Confucius, to Solon the legislator, to Pythagoras, to Zaleucus, to Socrates, to Plato, to the divine Antonines, to the good Trajan, to Titus, to all the delights of the human spirit, to Epictetus, and to so many other men, the models of mankind : 'Go, wretches : go down to punishments infinite in their intensity and duration ; may your punishment be as eternal as I am ! And you, My beloved, Jean Châtel, Ravaillac, Damiens, Cartouches, you who have died with the prescribed formulas, you shall share for ever My Empire and My blessedness' ?"

Perhaps, Voltaire suggested in his old age, the new outlook he was offering was not so very un-Christian : it might even be more akin to the New Testament gospel than the teaching of its orthodox interpreters. "Now I ask you if it is tolerance or intolerance which is the divine right; if we wish to resemble Jesus Christ shall we be martyrs or executioners?" In time, no doubt, reason would triumph, and men learn to distinguish Christianity from its counterfeits. "I shall not be a witness of this fine revolution," he wrote, "but I shall die with the three theological virtues which are my consolation : the faith which I have in human reason which is beginning to develop in the world ; the hope that ministers in their boldness and their wisdom will at length destroy customs which are as ridiculous as they are dangerous ; the charity which makes me grieve for my neighbour, complain of his bonds, and long for his deliverance. So with faith, hope and charity, I end my life a good Christian." [1]

---

[1] 13th February 1768, Voltaire to the Comte de Leninhaupt.

CHAPTER VI

THE BRITISH CONSTITUTION

I. *L'ESPRIT DES LOIS*

An enlightened and tolerant State, which guaranteed civil liberty to every individual : a State whose policy was entirely secular, and which was always on its guard against the encroachments of any Church : a State in which the only laws were reasonable applications of a single, universal and evident law of nature—such was the political ideal of most of the *philosophes*. The task of a *philosophe*, therefore, was to enlighten those in authority everywhere, and to persuade them to carry out certain necessary reforms. This policy dominated French thought from the middle of the century, when the first volumes of the *Encyclopædia* appeared, until the downfall of Turgot, the revolt of the American colonies and the vision of Rousseau began to make men doubtful about the possibilities of enlightened monarchy and hopeful about the conception of democracy.

At the beginning of this period, in 1748, Montesquieu's *Esprit des Lois* had appeared. Its influence in stimulating social and political speculation was immediate, and the *philosophes* found many of its doctrines agreeable. Montesquieu's hatred of despotism and clericalism, his demand for toleration, his suggestions for reforming the system of taxation and of civil and criminal justice—all these were common to the philosophic outlook. The more far-sighted *philosophes*, however, recognized him as a dangerous ally, whose arguments might well be used on occasion by the enemy. His approach to politics was a combination of the conservative one usual with lawyers, property-holders and antiquarians and the radical one common amongst sceptics and humanitarians. It is natural to lawyers to hate innovation, but time and again lawyers have aided radicalism because despots are more liable to introduce innovations than revolutionaries. Moreover, the study of antiquity, which formed the basic study of every educated boy in the eighteenth century, exercised its peculiar influence over Montesquieu. His mind, like Rousseau's, was impregnated with an admiration for the

Sparta of Plutarch's *Lycurgus*, for ancient Athens and the Roman Republic. As a lawyer he instinctively shared the views of Fénelon and the later critics of the lawless despotism of Louis XIV., and ranged himself upon the side of the *Parlements* when they asserted their constitutional rights. As a student, d'Aguesseau's theory of divine right made no appeal to him, while he eagerly accepted Domat's interpretation of Roman jurisprudence, based upon the natural law of the Stoics.[1]

Montesquieu had early won a reputation as a radical, a sceptic and a wit by the *Persian Letters*, and he had appealed even more directly to the tastes of Madame de Tencin's *salon* by a fashionable study in polite pornography entitled *Le Temple de Cnide*. He was of the *petite noblesse*, had a sinecure post, a private fortune, and an equable, even a cold temperament[2]; he had written scientific papers[3] and was something of an antiquarian and historian; he had been conventionally successful with women and after his election to the Academy in 1728 seemed well qualified to spend the rest of his life in society, after the manner of Duclos or Marmontel. He preferred, however, to combine an enjoyment of his good fortune with serious work. The results were, first, a Roman history, and, secondly, *L'Esprit des Lois*.

He desired, as his friends desired, to find the simple rules which must surely govern social phenomena, as he had learned from science to believe they governed physical phenomena. But he differed from his contemporaries in several vital respects. It was his peculiar distinction to be alone in his generation in perceiving that both the science and art of free government were difficult. Even so, he imagined them immeasurably easier

---

[1] Dedieu emphasizes the remarkable anticipation of Montesquieu's views in the *Vita Civile* of Doria. Montesquieu, however, does not seem to have been acquainted either with Doria or with Vico's *Scienza Nuova*, though Vico was a contemporary, and his work closely similar. *Vide* Vaughan's essay on Montesquieu in *Studies in the History of Political Philosophy*, vol. i.

[2] Montesquieu's own account of himself was that he had never "had any sorrows which an hour's reading did not dissipate."

[3] He had taken up experimental science just at the time when Fontenelle had begun to popularize it, and wrote papers upon physics, botany and natural history between 1717 and 1723.

than they have since proved. But from the beginning he could not confidently accept the easy universality of Lockean individualism. Unlike most of his contemporaries he was primarily an observer, and of that comparatively rare type of mind which is more interested in understanding things than in praising or deploring them. He was more detached and less subjective in approach than his friends. He set out to study social variations by the inductive method, convinced that in social as in physical phenomena the fashionable deductive method of Descartes led to premature " systems " and false simplification.

The division between natural law and actual law seemed to Montesquieu less definite and complete than the *philosophes* were accustomed to suppose. Actual law was admittedly defective since it sprang from the passing wills of individuals rather than from the permanent principles of justice. Yet even existing conventions and laws were not wholly arbitrary. There had been natural limitations upon the will of the legislator. Laws differed in different countries, not only because law-makers had willed variously, but also because the needs and conditions of countries had varied. Now, if this was true, a single uniform application of natural law would not everywhere produce the same result, and justice and liberty would be achieved only by a scientific adjustment of universal principles to special conditions. These special conditions included psychological as well as physical factors. The political thinker was forced to take into account the spirit as well as the substance of the law, and remember that the formal recognition of the rights of man did not in itself ensure individual liberty. New and complicated questions were thus introduced : the content and application of the law of nature might vary with varying material conditions and human opinions, and the reformer must begin to study, to classify and to compare the infinite variety of human habits and social institutions.

Montesquieu set about this task without appreciating its immensity. He believed that the results of a comparative study would be easy to classify and that final generalizations would be obtainable from the mass of facts he was collecting. " If serious people require some other work of me of a less frivolous nature," he wrote only a few years before his death, " I can easily satisfy them. I have been labouring thirty years at a work of twelve pages, which will contain all that we know of metaphysics, politics and morality : and all that the greatest authors have forgotten in the volumes which they have published on these sciences."

The claim was not very extravagant. *L'Esprit des Lois* was not frivolous though it contained passages that were, and, if it did not summarize all that was known of metaphysics, politics and morality in twelve pages, it at least added to that knowledge in thirty-one books. *L'Esprit des Lois* is the most formless of all masterpieces.[1] Its brilliant generalizations are scattered among countless ill-divided and ill-sorted chapters containing illustrations from ancient and modern history, contemporary observation and gossip, travellers' tales and spicy anecdotes, descriptive and analytic economics and politics. The natural assumption was that Montesquieu had not mastered his material but the material him. His friends in the *salons* were amused by the passages put there to amuse them and thought, like Madame du Deffand, that his book was really nothing but *de l'esprit sur les Lois*. Curiously enough, Madame du Deffand's *mot* is still quoted as though it were genuine criticism. Montesquieu may have weakened his argument by trivialities, but it was his critics who substituted wit for understanding. Voltaire, indeed, as Montesquieu himself remarked, had too much *esprit* to understand such a lengthy, formless and philosophic piece of work.[2] He was shrewd enough to see that

---

[1] Some of the confusion of *L'Esprit des Lois* is perhaps due to the fact that it was actually written over a period of seventeen years, the first ten books being written in 1731-1732 and the last five in 1747-1748. Montesquieu had travelled in Europe before he wrote the first ten books : his English visit came before the composition of the eleventh book, and all the remainder of his work was affected by his enthusiasm for England.

[2] " As for Voltaire," wrote Montesquieu, " he has too much wit to understand me. He reads no books but those he writes, and he then approves or censures his own progeny as the wind takes him." Voltaire's complaint, in his dialogue between A, B and C, that *L'Esprit des Lois* lacked arrangement, and that its gasconades were often irrelevant, nevertheless remained true. He was justified, too, in attacking Montesquieu for his easy acceptance of any contemporary or

the book undermined the current interpretation of Locke, and, though he once uttered a splendid panegyric on Montesquieu, he made two efforts to discredit his work and criticized isolated passages with customary shrewdness, but without attempting to appreciate Montesquieu's general intention or the book's significance. Helvétius, to whom Montesquieu submitted the MS. for criticism, joined with several friends in requesting him not to ruin his reputation by publishing it, though after its appearance he took the trouble to criticize it more intelligently. Most of the Encyclopædists failed altogether to understand its intention and contented themselves with incorporating undigested fragments from it in their own writings. Diderot, however, had an unlimited capacity for absorbing new ideas and new groups of facts, and finally reached political conclusions similar to those of Montesquieu.[1] Rousseau, already impatient with the standpoint of his Encyclopædist friends, attempted, at the price of some confusion, to bring his own views of the ideal to terms with Montesquieu's description of the actual. Between Montesquieu's conservative and concrete method and Rousseau's revolutionary and abstract one there could be little or nothing in common. At the Revolution, therefore, the legal and constitutional view of Montesquieu remained distinct, forming the basis of a third school which would not blend either with the declamatory egalitarianism of Rousseau or with the mathematical utilitarianism of Helvétius and Condorcet.

Montesquieu's immediate influence in France was chiefly exerted upon the *Parlements* and the antiquarians who sought on

---

historical anecdote which suited his argument. As an historian, Montesquieu was inferior to Voltaire in this respect at least : he paid less attention to Bayle's instruction as to care and accuracy in sifting historical evidence. For Voltaire's list of Montesquieu's inaccuracies *vide* his *Sur l'Esprit des Lois.*

Some of Voltaire's criticisms are obtuse, *cp.* his accusation that Montesquieu is Machiavellian in suggesting that the fear of attack by another nation is a justification for aggression. Montesquieu was surely ironic.

[1] Diderot was always too good an observer and too much a scientist to accept the abstract or "geometric" approach to politics. *Cp.* his attack in his *Pensées sur la Nature* and his insistence that a universal æsthetic is impossible in his article *Beau* in the *Encyclopædia.*

their behalf an historical basis for freedom. For Montesquieu revived the ancient French Constitution and transformed the struggle of the *Parlements* with the King from being a mere struggle to retain inherited privileges into a broader and more objective attempt to restore to the nation the ancient safeguards of its rights on which the seventeenth-century monarchy had trampled. It was this conception that inspired early leaders of the Revolution, like Mounier, in their efforts to make France a constitutional monarchy; had the royal family of France itself understood and been faithful to this conception it is at least possible that the Jacobins would not have had the chance to apply the idea of popular sovereignty which they had learned from Rousseau and Mably. The idea of popular sovereignty would then have played only the part it played in England—the people would have been regarded as ultimately sovereign, but the task of exercising their sovereignty would have been left to their representatives.

Outside France, Montesquieu's influence was equally great. The school of Blackstone and of Burke was directly inspired by him, while the Federalists modelled the American Constitution upon his interpretation of Locke and his observation of England. Nor was Montesquieu's influence exhausted in the eighteenth century. With his contemporary, Vico, he may fairly be called the founder of the comparative method of politics, and the whole study of historical jurisprudence dates from *L'Esprit des Lois*. Montesquieu changed the traditional outlook upon law; it became with him a concrete study, based on examination of facts rather than upon *a priori* principles. Moreover he made the discovery that whole groups of facts which had hitherto seemed to have no relevance to law were really essential to its understanding. He first showed that laws were not the arbitrary fiats of their makers, but were the formal recognition of customs which were themselves the results of economic and geographical facts. In maintaining that law is only the formal superstructure built upon a basis of tradition and economic and physical fact, Montesquieu was a forerunner of Marx, as well as of Savigny and Henry Maine.

THE BRITISH CONSTITUTION

2. THE COMPARATIVE METHOD OF MONTESQUIEU

Voltaire once remarked that Montesquieu was Montaigne turned legislator. The remark, meant merely as a jesting criticism of Montesquieu's irrelevant gasconades,[1] called attention to an important aspect of *L'Esprit des Lois*. Montesquieu did, indeed, share Montaigne's eager interest in the diversity of things; he enjoyed collecting and relating the various customs of men, and pointing the moral of understanding and tolerance in a world where good and bad were so mixed and our knowledge so fragmentary and imperfect. But Montesquieu, bitten by the scientific virus of his generation, could not remain an essayist or a sceptic: he was forced to attempt for the modern world the task which Aristotle had performed for the ancient. The facts of society had to be collected, not because they were curious or amusing, but in order that they might be classified and explained. Montesquieu sought to discover the basis of law and to trace the causes of social diversity.

He at once encountered a difficulty which has always haunted social philosophers—and which has led many altogether to deride the idea of a science of politics. He had learned that the physical world follows certain ascertainable and unchanging rules which by their joint action produce the variety of natural phenomena. If we look for similar rules behind social events, do we not imply that the movements of men, who believe themselves responsible for social institutions, laws and customs, are really just as much predetermined as those of material objects? How could one believe at the same time in free will and in the possibility of discovering all the causes of human behaviour and social institutions?[2] When *L'Esprit des Lois* appeared, Jesuit critics at once denounced its deterministic tendency and described him as a disciple of Spinoza and a

---

[1] Montaigne and Montesquieu were both born in Gascony.

[2] In one passage of his *Pensées*, Montesquieu admits that much appears to be purely accidental. If the Turks had conquered Europe and shut up all women in harems would it not have seemed obvious that such was the "natural" state of women? "It is not," he adds, "reason or nature that governs men, but pure chance."

materialist. Montesquieu, who had in fact dealt with this difficulty at the outset of his book, replied in a manner which satisfied the practical reader, if not the metaphysician.

In the first place, he had admitted the existence of God, and had argued that one of the causes of social phenomena was the moral intelligence of human beings. Materialism was antithetic to his whole outlook. "Can anything," he asked, "be more absurd than to pretend that a blind fatality could ever produce intelligent beings?" The world displayed a progressive manifestation of intelligence. The Creator had ordered that the material world should conform to certain invariable sequences. In the case of animals Montesquieu was doubtful how far they had been given the power to adjust themselves consciously to their environment. Men, on the other hand, clearly had the power to apprehend natural laws, and to control their adjustment, well or ill. In this scheme of things the word "law" is the difficulty and the key. A law is a relation; God's relation to the universe is the law of His being. The laws of the material world are the invariable relationships between inanimate bodies. The laws of men are also "necessary relations," arising from their relationship to each other and the physical world. But, as they are "intelligent beings," they become conscious of this relationship and can modify it to suit their needs. They have in fact laws, or relationships, of their own making. Such adjustments were always possible; when men had become conscious of a relationship they formulated it in deliberate laws. "Before laws were made there were relationships of possible justice. To say there is nothing just or unjust but what is commanded or forbidden by positive laws is the same as saying that before the describing of a circle all the radii are not equal." In other words, a law is a recognition of a relationship which had hitherto been unnoticed, not the arbitrary creation of a new relationship. All laws are, in Montesquieu's unsatisfactory definition, "the relations which necessarily flow from the nature of things."

The first book of *L'Esprit des Lois* was thus a reply to Hobbes and Spinoza. Hobbes had imagined that society was instituted by contract when the individuals who composed it found anarchy intolerable. Men, Montesquieu thought, had never been isolated creatures; they were naturally related, bound together by common wants, common fears, sexual attraction and social consciousness.[1] This natural sociability in men has led them everywhere to unite their common force in political States and their common will in civil laws. Social life, being now more deliberate, brings a greater consciousness of common wants, and ideas of justice and morality, always innate in individuals, become recognized. Hobbes is therefore mistaken in identifying justice with the dictates of authority, in confounding sin with crime, and in speaking of laws as the arbitrary invention of kings, appointed to regulate the actions of men who would otherwise merely war against each other. Even savages, who ate their prisoners, had international and political regulations: their habits were founded on less true principles than those of civilized societies only because they had less knowledge of their true relationships with other peoples.

So far then Montesquieu had refuted Hobbes and Spinoza, and, at the same time, criticized and expanded Puffendorf and Locke. Law has a double origin: it is not purely the result of human will, but of reason acting upon causes which men cannot control. Now these external factors have varied in different places, and laws have therefore varied even though human nature has been essentially the same everywhere at all times. Montesquieu did not entertain the idea that natural man himself may have varied. Race was a complication introduced by later writers. "As men have in all ages been subject to the same passions," wrote Montesquieu, "the occasions which produce great changes may be different but the causes are always the same." If, then, human nature remains constant, two factors are left to account for varieties in social institutions: the first is environmental difference; the second is the varying success and degree of understanding of legislators in adapting their laws to these different environments.

Montesquieu's task, therefore, was to examine past and present forms of government and political institutions, and to

---

[1] *L'Esprit des Lois*, Bk. I., chap. ii. Men in .Montesquieu's state of nature are moved to form societies, not because they tyrannize over one another, but because they fear the unknown.

disentangle the permanent physical factors from the variable effects of human will. History was obviously one starting-point. Montesquieu, unlike almost all his contemporaries, thought of the Middle Ages not as a barbarous gap between the civilization of Rome and that of Louis XIV., but as the clue to existing French institutions. He brought, too, a new spirit into the fashionable study of Roman history. Machiavelli and numerous subsequent historians had been content to cull moral and political maxims from the story of Rome's growth, grandeur and decay. Bossuet's *Universal History* had indeed a more philosophic import. God ruled: the facts of history, Greek, Roman or French, must be arranged to support the axioms of Providential guidance. Montesquieu, however, wished to find the causes of development and decay by examination of the facts. " It is not chance," he wrote, " which rules the world. There are general causes, some moral, some physical . . . accidents are secondary to these causes. . . . In a word, the principal movement carries along with it all the particular accidents." From the history of Rome he developed one of his most famous generalizations. Rome, beginning with a small territory, attained strength as a republic founded upon the virtue of its citizens. When its territory had been everywhere extended, the old methods of government were no longer adequate, the spirit of the Republic was corrupted, and new vices accompanied the growth of Imperialism. Constitutional monarchy soon degenerated into despotism, relying no longer on virtue but on force and fear. It seemed then that certain fundamental characteristics of a country made a particular form of government suitable; if this government was to be successful it must adhere to its nature and principle—must maintain, that is, the essentials of its form and constitution, and keep alive the spirit which animated it. If, on the contrary, laws were passed or a policy was pursued which undermined this natural adjustment or changed the emotional bond which united Government and people, it must deteriorate and collapse.

In *L'Esprit des Lois* Montesquieu developed this idea in detail. European travel gave him many new illustrations and confirmed his belief that different forms of government might

be suitable to different countries, and that their laws were
not to be judged absolutely good or absolutely bad, but only
in relation to their environment, history and traditions. The
environmental factors which Montesquieu perceived were the
climate of a country, the quality of its soil, its situation and
extent[1]; these, in turn, occasioned the growth of certain
occupations, religious beliefs, manners and customs among its
inhabitants. A particular form of government was evolved,
more or less suitable to these conditions. "From different
wants in different climates have come different ways of living,
and these different ways of living have resulted in different
kinds of laws." Thus each country had its own variant of the
law of nature : the purpose of the legislator should be to keep
the positive laws consistent "with their origin " and, when
making any change, to consider them in relation to all these
factors.

So far, Montesquieu's sociological basis is clear. Two
difficulties of application obscure many of his pages. Being
completely unable to trace the relative importance of these
factors in any country, he picked out any single factor which
caught his attention and made it responsible for the whole. All
sense of proportion and all sense of historical development
disappear. In *Considérations sur les Romains* the material and
psychological had been blended and presented in a complex and
changing unity. In *L'Esprit des Lois*, climate and geographical
situation are often spoken of as if they were immediate and
sufficient causes operating in the eighteenth century, directly
and obviously. He saw that what may be right in one place may
be wrong in another, but he seems to have altogether forgotten
that what may be right at one time may be wrong at another.
For this reason his examples and arguments are often unreal :
the uncivilized inhabitants of North America, the ancient
Athenians, the eighteenth-century French and the sixteenth-
century Russians are compared without allowance for variety
of epoch, while the difference between the climates of Germany

---

[1] The importance of climatic and geographical factors in the formation of
institutions was not a new idea. It is in Aristotle, and, among more modern
writers, in Bodin.

and Spain is enough to excuse a custom in one country which is repudiated in another. He notes the fact that in the northern part of Europe, where the climate is comparatively cold, republics and Protestants flourish, while in southern and warmer parts of Europe kings rule over Catholic countries. He leaps to the conclusion that a spirit of liberty is the result of a cold climate. Voltaire found it easy to refute generalizations of so sweeping a character; any exception—Catholic Ireland, for instance—was a sufficient answer.

In the second place, Montesquieu does not make it clear when the legislator should conform to the existing character-istics of the nation and when he should attempt to modify them. If, for instance, drunkenness is the natural result of some climates, is the Government right in encouraging or discouraging alcohol? Montesquieu does not explain, but he apparently means that these natural predispositions are an important and ineradicable factor, always to be taken into account when making laws. Climate and geographical factors form the basis on which the political structure rests: if in-stitutions do not conform to them and harmonize with them they will certainly fail. Peter the Great attempted too much —he could not change the eternal character of Russia: Solon was right when he gave the people " the best laws they could bear."

On this basis Montesquieu approaches the problem of govern-ment. Its form should be determined by the size of the nation. A small nation might, in Montesquieu's opinion, be republican, a large country could be ruled only by a single man, with or without constitutional checks. He was clearly influenced by Aristotle's analysis of the three types of government, each liable to degenerate by the loss of its moderating principle. The types in eighteenth-century Europe were a little different. Firstly there were monarchies which Montesquieu thought better described as despotisms. Here " a single person, with-out law or regulation, directs everything by his own will and caprice." Secondly, there were monarchies in which a single person governed " by fixed and established laws." Thirdly, there were republics, which might be either democratic or aristocratic. Each of these types of government, Montesquieu saw, demanded a different disposition on the part of the rulers and the ruled. A despotic government would survive only as long as its subjects were intimidated : fear must be its ruling principle. The despot's power depends upon the humiliation of his people : he begins by "making a bad subject in order to make a good slave." Thus education is contrary to the principle of despotism. "Everything must depend upon two or three ideas : therefore there is no need for any new notions to be added. When we want to break in a horse we take care not to let him change his master, his lesson or his pace. Thus an impression is made on his brain by two or three motives and no more." Despotism is, therefore, a crude, simple and destructive form of government : "when the savages of Louisiana want fruit, they cut down the tree to the root and gather the fruit. *Voilà le gouvernement despotique.*"

The principle of a republic, on the other hand, was far more difficult to attain : those who ruled, whether a few or the whole mass, must be imbued with "virtue," they must be filled with love of their country, and willing to subordinate their own interests to the public good. Successful democracies like those of ancient Greece and contemporary Paraguay were all small, based on economic equality, and animated by public spirit. Inequality bred class hatred and was fatal to virtue. The distinction between the propertied *noblesse* and the humble landless workmen is one that fits a country whose principle is one of status and function, but it is fatal where all are required equally to love the republic. Equality, therefore, is the necessary counterpart of political liberty. There may be advantages in a warring state of classes, where rivalry, honour and ambition lead men to great achievements, but they are incompatible with democracy. A repudiation of self-seeking and a real devotion to the public interest alone can make democracy a working institution. Thus frugality, encouraged by sumptuary laws and restriction of inheritance, is a good thing in a republic.[1] Private fortunes in trade, however, may even be good for morals, because they

---

[1] *L'Esprit des Lois*, Bk. V., chap. v.

are the result of frugality and hard work : they are dangerous because they may lead to the formation of an aristocratic class, and when " excessive wealth destroys the spirit of commerce the inconveniences of inequality begin to be felt." [1]

If despotism rests on fear and republicanism on virtue, monarchies are best supported by the motive of "honour." By honour Montesquieu means a rivalry for distinction and a jealousy of rank among the classes who make up the social hierarchy. Each class must be anxious to guard its privileges ; from this rather than from the highest motives it may be induced to perform its function. "Philosophically speaking, it is a false honour which moves all parts of the government." Nevertheless, "by this useful motive men can be induced to perform the most difficult actions, requiring a great degree of fortitude and spirit, without any other recompense than the fame and reputation arising from the actions themselves." France, Montesquieu seems to have believed, had once been such a monarchy : Louis XIV. had ruined his country by neglecting the nature and principle of its government. France is clearly referred to when he writes of " a certain country degenerating into despotism." The great kings of France ruled constitutionally, retaining the services of the aristocracy and the *Parlements*. They kept the affection of their people by a policy of moderation —a quality which is essential to a constitutional monarchy. In the first ten books of *L'Esprit des Lois*, Montesquieu is always thinking of France when he writes of monarchy.[2]

Montesquieu's interpretation of French history had an

---

[1] Montesquieu believed that luxury was good for trade ; in democracy, however, equality was more important than wealth. He approves the economics of Mandeville, but sees that luxury and *laissez-faire* are incompatible with public spirit.

[2] Montesquieu appears to have thought that France was too large to be a successful republic or democracy. It should have been a constitutional monarchy, but he feared that the essential principle of honour in the aristocracy as well as moderation in the government had been lost in the eighteenth century. He described the courtier as combining "ambition with idleness and baseness with pride, while wanting to be rich without work, hating truth and neglecting the duties and virtues which should characterize a citizen " ; and Louis XIV. had turned all the *noblesse* into courtiers."

immediate effect in France. The champions of the *noblesse* and the *Parlements* had not altogether overlooked the value of an historical argument against the absolute pretensions of the King. Saint-Simon had complained that the King refused to recognize the right of the peerage to advise the Crown and Boulainvilliers had advanced a learned but untenable thesis that the *noblesse* of France were the descendants of the conquering Franks, and that the King was a usurper claiming autocratic powers which had never been accorded the tribal chieftain. Montesquieu also went back to Tacitus and championed the Teutonic against the Roman view of monarchy; the "beautiful system" of constitutional monarchy was, he said, invented in the forests of Germany. His argument was less extreme than Boulainvilliers', and based on a national rather than a class outlook. Even among the *noblesse* its effect was to stimulate the idea of service and function rather than that of rights and privileges. The contrast between the class-grumbling of Saint-Simon and the enlightened feudalism of Mirabeau in *L'Ami des Hommes* is, at least in part, to be explained by the publication of *L'Esprit des Lois*. But it was the lawyers rather than the *noblesse* who availed themselves of Montesquieu's championship of the rights of the ancient "orders" of France. From 1753 onwards, when the first ill-considered criticisms of Montesquieu had died down, numerous works by antiquarians and legalists appeared, giving documentary proof that mediæval kings had governed with the aid of the Estates, and that in France as well as England they had frequently respected a recognized constitution.[1] When, in 1770, the struggle reached its climax, when the King had exiled the *Parlements* and abolished the last remnants of the French Constitution, the lawyers and their supporters could bring forward a mass of evidence to prove that he was an innovator and that Maupeou's Government was illegal. That view was reinforced on the popular side by Mably, who also looked back to mediæval history, but argued that it was the States-General, and in particular the Third

---

[1] *Vide* Carcassonne, *op. cit.*, for an account of these legal and historical books. One of the most interesting is *Théorie des Lois politiques de la France* (1792), by Mademoiselle de Lézardière.

Estate, who should govern France. When the Revolution itself arrived, various interpretations of Montesquieu were in competition : the *noblesse* and the lawyers held that the Estates should vote separately—a provision which gave privilege the dominant voice ; while the Third Estate, protesting that numbers should outweigh rank, argued that the lower chamber, like the House of Commons, should have the decisive voice. For Montesquieu had not only championed the ancient Constitution of France, but also the whole idea of constitutional monarchy and, in particular, its English pattern. Until the advent of Republicanism, in 1792, it was Montesquieu who dominated the discussions of the Assembly. The nature and extent of his influence becomes clear only when his interpretation of the British Constitution is understood.

3. THE SEPARATION OF POWERS—THE INFLUENCE OF MONTESQUIEU

Montesquieu's visit to England in 1729-1730 probably occurred between the composition of his tenth and eleventh books. The discovery of the English Constitution had almost as great an effect upon him as the discovery of English philosophy had upon Voltaire. Many things in England disgusted him. He agreed with most visitors about the climate, and Voltaire's quip about the coincidence between the east wind and suicide assumed with Montesquieu the dignity of serious sociology. He found the English aloof and money-grubbing ; their roads too were execrable, although he admired their enthusiasm for landscape-gardening. English politics were at their meanest under Walpole ; each politician seemed to him anxious only to get the better of the others, and the whole country was endangered by the universal passion for making money. Religion, he saw, counted for little, though the Church was a great social institution to which all the respectable paid court. In nothing was he so far-sighted as in his observation of the characteristics of the aristocracy. The landowners were, he saw, the rulers of England, and their motive was " honour." What would happen if they turned increasingly to commerce and lost their sense of responsibility?

The monarchy would certainly decline and England become a nation of merchants and shopkeepers. Her natural resources, disposition and geographical position would then make her extraordinarily powerful. But her spirit would be transformed.[1]

In spite of jobbery and self-seeking, Montesquieu found in England what Voltaire had found—individual liberty. The rights of man were guaranteed by the Revolutionary settlement, by laws such as *Habeas Corpus* and by the common law, which made "outward acts" alone amenable to punishment. There was no sovereign except the law. The Government ruled according to a reasoned application of natural law, embodied in the positive laws of the country. This happy state of affairs was perpetuated by the nature of English government. The Government was mixed. In form England was a monarchy which retained the intermediary bodies, the aristocratic support and the legal checks which were proper to it. The aristocracy were still, in part at least, actuated by the ancient motive of honour. The Government was also in some degree democratic, and the common people were imbued with at least a portion of the republican virtue.[2]

The explanation of English liberty was now clear. The rule of law was maintained because authority was divided. No single authority could impose its will upon the whole, and each of the three functions of government was given just the requisite power to prevent the other functions from being abused. "When the legislative and executive powers are united in the same person," writes Montesquieu, "or in the same body of magistrates, there can be no liberty. . . . Again, there is no liberty if the power of judging be not separated from the legislative and executive powers." All liberty would be at an end if all three functions of government were concentrated in one person or body of persons. Here then was the secret of liberty—the separation of the powers or functions of government.

---

[1] For Montesquieu on England cp. *Pensées diverses, Œuvres,* vii. 167; *L'Esprit des Lois,* VI. vi. ; XIX. xxvii. Also *Lettres Persanes,* 104th letter.

[2] Montesquieu considered the liveliness of English politics a good sign. He contrasted the popular interest in England with the silence of France under Louis XIV.—the silence of a town which the enemy has just occupied.

The three functions of government were separated but not isolated, they were related by a nicely adjusted system of checks and balances. "England is the finest country in the world," wrote Montesquieu, " I do not except any of the republics. I call it free because the Prince has not the power to do any conceivable wrong ; his power is curtailed and limited by statute. Similarly the legislature is harmless, being divided into two parts. One checks the other by the mutual privilege of veto. They are both checked by the executive power, as is the executive by the legislative." The whole therefore "naturally forms a state of repose or inaction. But as there is a necessity of movement in the course of human affairs, they are forced to move, but to do so in concert." [1]

It was not the Revolutionary settlement of 1689 which Montesquieu misunderstood, but its recent development. He could not perceive that the growth of the Cabinet system at the very time when he was in England was actually establishing the unity of authority which he feared. Liberty, he said, would be lost if "the same people shared in the legislative and executive power." The Constitution of 1689 was already gone ; the ministers of George II. were, in fact, responsible less to him than to the House of Commons, and, in spite of the efforts of George III. to destroy this new Cabinet responsibility, sovereignty was becoming firmly established in a single authority, the "King in Parliament." Montesquieu had foreseen that the power of the House of Commons would increase at the expense of the King and the House of Lords,[2] though he had not understood the mechanism by which this

---

[1] Locke had already noted that the executive power (under which heading he included the judiciary) required different capacities from those needed by the legislator, and had argued that they ought not to be confounded in the same authority. When Locke wrote he was of course unable to foresee the future development of Cabinet government : everything pointed to a system in which the King would remain the executive power, to whom ministers were in fact responsible. If Sir William Temple's scheme had been carried into effect, or George III. had succeeded in establishing departmental government, the American Constitution would have been an accurate copy of the British.

[2] "If the Lower House [of the legislature] became mistress," he wrote, "its authority would be unlimited and dangerous, because it would have at the same time the executive power."

transference was to take place, and had imagined that the loss of an independent executive would be the end of civil liberty. Curiously enough, English constitutional lawyers, like Blackstone, accepted his description of the British Constitution without hesitation or inquiry, and indulged in unqualified panegyrics of a separation of powers which had ceased to exist.

Montesquieu's interpretation of the English Constitution had even more important results. The fathers of the American Constitution borrowed from him one of their central ideas. The fixed Constitution, enshrining the gains of the past, in a sacred document liable to interpretation only by an independent judiciary, was an effort to base the government of a newly-born nation upon the conception of a law of nature which no government was competent to abrogate. The provision which excludes Cabinet ministers from Congress was the work of the Federalists under the influence of Montesquieu. They were really not copying the British Constitution, but the "departmental system" which George III. strove to establish. When they made the President of the United States "a fossilized George III." they were carefully excluding the distinctive and most important feature of the British Constitution—the dependence of the executive on the legislature and the leadership of the legislature by the executive. As a result, the story of American constitutional development consists largely in a series of efforts to find some method of overcoming its central characteristic. No device was ever so hampering as the separation of powers; no device has been so generally praised or so ingeniously evaded. It is a sober fact that Montesquieu's interpretation of the British Constitution resulted in constant antagonisms between Senate and President: he may be said to be ultimately responsible for the non-participation of the United States in the League of Nations.[1]

---

[1] The numerous constitutions inspired by the revolutionary movement in the late eighteenth and the first half of the nineteenth centuries were all haunted by the same fear of giving any one too much authority. The separation of powers, therefore, appeared in the French Constitution of 1791, the Prussian Code of 1792, the Spanish Constitution of 1812 and the various models of 1848. The best aspect of the separation of powers was the independence

Montesquieu's constitutional theory was based on Newtonian physics. In his early work he appears to have had a firmer grasp of the organic idea of the State than any other eighteenth-century writer, but his final political theory, in which each power is separate and related to the others only by a system of checks and balances, is entirely mechanical. The whole phraseology and conception is taken from mechanics : the State is a vast piece of engineering in which each joist is kept in place and made to do its work by an exact calculation of strains and stresses, held in place by a balance here, itself checking another joist, correctly attached and related to its neighbour. Since there is no animating principle, no directing head or organic life, the result would seem to be a motionless equilibrium. Sheridan might even have had it in mind when he constructed the scene in his play, *The Critic*, where each member of the cast desires to stab his neighbour, but is prevented by his neighbour's attempt to stab him, the whole remaining in tableau, each unable to act because the balance of forces is precise. A State in which no one has the chance to do harm will scarcely have much vitality.

Nineteenth-century Liberals naturally canonized Montesquieu. No writer had expressed a more fervent hatred of clericalism and despotism nor championed the cause of toleration more forcibly nor indicted slavery more splendidly. As an opponent of unified sovereignty and an advocate of the rule of law, Montesquieu could be invoked wherever individual liberty was threatened by irresponsible power. Yet Helvétius and Voltaire were right in fearing the conservative uses to which *L'Esprit des Lois* could be put, and the direct line of Montesquieu's influence runs from Burke to Maine. The com-

---

of the judiciary. Even here the effort to make it free from both legislative and executive interference has led in some cases to the adoption of popular election of judges. The belief that the separation of powers was a source of English freedom has never quite died, and the system of checks and balances is still praised both in England and America. This English model was already extinct in the eighteenth century, but some writers on political theory apparently imagine that it exists in England to-day. For a distressing example *vide* Sir John Marriott, *The Mechanism of the Modern State*. By way of contrast, *cp.* Robson, *Justice and Administrative Law*.

parative school of which he was the founder has been generally conservative. His aim was descriptive, but, like other political theorists, he found it beyond his capacity to keep distinct the division between the real and the ideal, to avoid confusion between his descriptions of what was and his views of what ought to be. The confusion was easily made. If a law was the recognition of a relationship which necessarily existed, it was easy to assume that it was itself the only possible law. If institutions are based upon a traditional adjustment necessitated by fundamental and unalterable conditions, then legal and social change must certainly be dangerous. Unlike his contemporaries, Montesquieu was always conscious of the complexity of society and the interrelation of its parts, and he was therefore more inclined than they to hesitate before advocating changes which might have far-reaching and unexpected effects. He was almost the only *philosophe* who regarded the fact that an institution or law was *a priori* unreasonable as an insufficient reason for abolishing it.[1]

For a Frenchman to champion the British Constitution in the eighteenth century was to side with the party of reform. To explain, however, that the perfection of British institutions arose from the nice balance of forces and powers which they had miraculously achieved was to give Burke the opportunity of denouncing all reformers. Henceforward every suggestion of change, every denunciation of corruption or declaration that a rotten borough was in fact rotten, could be represented as an effort to destroy the equilibrium of man's supreme architectural achievement. When Burke led the reaction against the Revolution he based his championship of the British Constitution upon the principles of Montesquieu. " Our Constitution," he wrote, " preserves an unity in so great a diversity of its parts. We have an inheritable Crown ; an inheritable peerage ; and a House of Commons and a people inheriting privileges, franchises and liberties from a long line of ancestors. This

---

[1] Note Condorcet's criticism of Montesquieu's eulogy of " moderation " in a monarchy such as the British : " By a spirit of moderation does not M. Montesquieu mean that spirit of uncertainty which permits a hundred little irrelevancies to modify the indispensable principles of justice ? "

policy appears to me to be the result of profound reflection; or rather the happy effect of following nature, which is wisdom without reflection, and above it. A spirit of innovation is generally the result of a selfish temper and confined views." The conclusion commonly drawn from such premises was that existing institutions had a sanctity necessarily containing an element of the mysterious, and that when the individual found himself in conflict with them it was his duty to " venerate where he was unable presently to comprehend."

These were not the conclusions of Montesquieu, who was attempting to form a science of politics and was not in search of a mystical justification for existing abuses. He would have agreed with Burke that " those people will not look forward to posterity who never look backward to their ancestors." He was even willing to argue that institutions like the Catholic Church, polygamy and slavery, though bad in themselves as he knew them, might have had, and might still have, some justification under certain conditions. The contemporary *philosophes* naturally feared any such concessions. They held the contrary view, at least equally justified by experience, that people who look backward to their ancestors frequently lose the capacity for looking forward to posterity. To the *philosophes* it seemed obvious that some things were bad and others were good, and that to discuss origins, past adjustments and balances of forces, was to seek an excuse for neglecting immediate duties. So Helvétius wrote to Montesquieu, complaining that the result of so much theorizing seemed likely to emphasize the difficulties and throw doubt upon the possibilities of desirable change. " I believe, nevertheless, in the possibility of a good government where the liberty and property of people will be respected, and where one may see the general good necessarily emerging without your balances of particular interests." To those who believed that men were reasonable and the path to happiness simple, Montesquieu seemed to be spreading darkness rather than light when he suggested that men were not altogether free to alter their institutions just as they liked, that there was no clear-cut issue between good and evil, but only a difficult problem of changing, with due circumspection and regard to circumstances, things which were in some respects bad and in others relatively good.[1]

---

[1] With regard to Christianity, Montesquieu explains that it is not of course to be judged rationally like other religions. Such remarks, which are frequent in his work, and may be considered partly as gibes for the benefit of his friends and partly as defences against the persecution of his enemies, did not prevent him from discussing Christianity as one religion among many, with good and bad points, mostly the latter, which needed analysis.

Montesquieu laid himself open to the charge of being an apologist for the *ancien régime* when he justified the use of patronage and purchase as methods for obtaining posts in his own profession. His own position as *Président à Mortier* was gained by the system of *venalité des charges*, and there was always a personal bias in his outlook upon legal reform. *Cp.* Helvétius' *Lettre à Saurin* about Montesquieu : " He adhered to the prejudices of the lawyers and *noblesse*—this is the source of all his errors. . . . Deprived of his title of Wise Man, he will become no more than the lawyer, the nobleman, and the fine genius. I am distressed for him and for humanity."

CHAPTER VII

UTILITARIANISM : THE END OF THE COMPROMISE

I. THE PHILOSOPHY OF THE ENCYCLOPÆDISTS

THE bulky volumes of the *Encyclopædia* contained a large variety of doctrines. For the most part, however, it accepted both the principles and compromises of Voltaire. D'Alembert's *Discours préliminaire*, which introduced the first volume, was written while the Encyclopædists still hoped to avoid a clash with the authorities ; it summed up the practical objects of the *Encyclopædia* and revealed its positive faith, even though it evaded the less obvious intellectual difficulties. It was to be a " reasoned " dictionary, designed to make what was known on every topic accessible to educated Frenchmen, to explain the relationship between one science and another and to serve as an introduction to current theory and philosophy.

D'Alembert was as willing as Voltaire to leave a sphere for the Church and to acknowledge a God who did not interfere with scientific research. The scientist's task was to investigate the nature of matter : metaphysics could be set on one side and the censorship kept quiet by what seemed harmless admissions. That done, d'Alembert could proceed to his main task. Firmly based on the Lockean principle that sensation is the only source of knowledge, he shows the scientist steadily advancing, confident, as Fontenelle had been, that all the sciences are ultimately one, and implicitly denying Pascal's proposition that there is " a domain set aside, which human intelligence may not penetrate."

At the outset all knowledge was classified, after the manner of Bacon, according to the mental faculty brought into play by its pursuit.[1] This method emphasized the purely sensational

---

[1] This method of classification, which places each branch of science under one of man's three faculties, instead of taking account of their subject-matter, led to most curious results. History, according to the *Discours*, results from memory ; science, theology and gardening from reflection, and metaphysics and the *beaux arts* from imagination. In the same way, in the *Encyclopædia* itself the classification all turns upon the utility of the subject for human purposes.

Morley (*Diderot*, i. 203) selects some interesting examples of the resulting confusions.

origin of knowledge, even if it was not satisfactory in other respects. The tree of knowledge had grown amazingly since Bacon's outline more than a century earlier. Descartes, d'Alembert suggested, though useful because he had repudiated external authority, had on the whole delayed advance. His followers had been slow to learn the folly of system-making. " It is only within the last thirty years that people have begun to renounce Cartesianism," d'Alembert wrote ; " our nation, singularly eager for novelties in all matters of taste, is in matters of science extremely attached to old opinions." Newton's splendid example, however, had now shown everyone the way ; science was rapidly progressing, and man learning to understand Nature, to make her his ally and fellow-conqueror.

The preliminary discourse and the *Encyclopædia* itself were throughout imbued with a practical spirit. The Encyclopædists did not realize their own assumptions or the difficulties they left unsolved. They hid things from themselves as well as from the censor. Their metaphysics, ethics and politics were all more dangerous than they knew. If God was to be reduced to a First Cause someone was sure to point out that He was unnecessary, and indeed fatal, to clear thinking. The empiricism of the *Encyclopædia* led naturally, though not inevitably, to the rigid materialism of Holbach.[1] In the same way, in ethical matters the Encyclopædists found a belief in natural religion useful in saving the sceptic from the charge of undermining morals as well as religion. But natural religion was precariously allied to a psychology which made men's ideas depend entirely on experience. Morality, in that case, was a matter of convenience, a social code which could be changed if forbidden freedoms were found after all to be compatible with social happiness. Natural religion easily developed into utilitarianism. And, in politics, utilitarianism led to democracy. For if both ability and character were the result of experience, social distinctions were arbitrary or accidental. By nature one man was as good as another—a doctrine which undermined the established order

---

[1] Holbach's most extreme conclusions had been anticipated by La Mettrie, vide *Histoire naturelle de l'Ame* (1745) and *L'Humane Machine* (1748). For a vigorous vindication of La Mettrie *vide* Lange's *History of Materialism*.

and was promptly seized upon by those who claimed that all were equally entitled to happiness and power.

It was inevitable that someone should draw these logical conclusions. Men like Diderot and Condillac had already shown the dangerous implications of the fashionable physics and psychology. Helvétius and Holbach, however, went further: *De l'Esprit*, *Le Système de la Nature* and *La Politique naturelle* were systematic as well as bold, uncompromising as well as dangerous. Holbach is one of the few writers who can justly be called a "materialist." He left none of the loopholes and omitted all the modifications which usually make classification difficult. Helvétius was equally unafraid of a crude and complete utilitarianism, and both writers were prepared to accept representative government as the natural inference from sensationalist psychology.

2. MATERIALISM—LOGICAL PHYSICS—DIDEROT AND HOLBACH

Diderot's letters to Mademoiselle Voland have left a record of the conversations at Holbach's where the intellectual basis of these books was hammered out in the frankest discussion. Diderot describes the conversation that arose when someone declared that even "if a single supposition explained all phenomena it would not follow from this that it was true. For who knows whether the general order allows of only one reason?" God, they decided, was scarcely worth discussing; in any case it was impossible "to introduce him into nature or discussion without darkening them." Galiani indeed took up the cudgels on behalf of the Deity, asking how the *Iliad* or the physical universe could be accounted for by the chance throwing of dice. Considering the complexity of "that well-contrived piece of villainy, the world," did it not seem probable that nature's dice were "loaded, and that there is a big Rogue up there who takes delight in cheating you"? It was Diderot who replied that, if the number of throws were infinite, accidental combinations of molecules might account for the world or anything else, and went on to refute the current argument for God's existence, pointing out that to rely upon wonders of adaptation and order in nature is to forget its failures, wastefulness and misadaptations. In his *Lettre sur les Aveugles*, published as early as 1749, he applied the argument from natural adaptation in an unusual way, and suggested that the apparent perfection of many existing organisms might be the result of a sifting process involving the destruction of numerous species of badly adapted monsters so that an evolution had taken place ; " all the faulty combinations of matter had disappeared, and those only had survived whose mechanism implied no important misadaptation (*contradiction*) and which had the power of supporting and perpetuating themselves." [1]

Diderot's promising approach to the theory of evolution by natural selection bore no immediate fruit. Speculation was mainly concerned with physics, not biology. The general principles of physics already familiar in Hobbes and Spinoza were now supported by scientific experiment rather than by philosophic speculation. The most plausible view seemed to be that put forward by La Mettrie, that men, animals and plants were all combinations of molecules, only quantitatively different, since thought and consciousness were themselves nothing but the movements of material particles. Diderot, it is true, had his doubts, arguing that the consciousness of a complex organism could not result from a mere conjunction of material particles, even if the particles themselves were endowed with a potential capacity for receiving sensations.

In 1770 Holbach published *Le Système de la Nature*. The storm it raised was comparable only with that which Helvétius' *De l'Esprit* had produced twelve years earlier. Indeed the works of Holbach and Helvétius are complementary to one another : taken together they form a single system of philosophy. Holbach was primarily concerned with metaphysics, Helvétius with ethics and psychology, whilst both made incidental applications of their theories to politics. Holbach, too, dealt at some length with ethics, but his psychology differed from that of Helvétius in emphasis rather than in substance. As writers, they are in sharp contrast. Helvétius interlarded his psychological

---

[1] Translation taken from Morley's *Diderot*, i. 94.

analysis with anecdotal illustrations, which are successful as anecdotes rather than as illustrations. There is no trifling in Holbach. His temper at times is revolutionary, and an elaborate system of argument is capped with vehement declamation against every existing institution and current superstition. Justice has never been done to the political insight of Holbach or to his power as a social critic. Few writers of the century have either his force or his sincerity, and beside him Helvétius reads like a promising undergraduate with a theory. The theory, however, was a good one, and Bentham, who spent most of his life in developing and applying it, acknowledged his debt to Helvétius, while Holbach has been almost completely forgotten.[1]

Holbach's contemporaries were appalled by his temerity. He swept away all compromises; permitted no evasions; and included priests, kings and gods in a single majestic anathema. His system had no place for free will or immortality. Voltaire was horrified, and lost no time in composing a refutation. He feared atheism scarcely less than Rousseau did, but whereas Rousseau thought that it destroyed the spirit and denied the most sacred emotions, Voltaire was afraid that to deprive the poor and uneducated of the consolation of superstitions would endanger society. God as a Creator and Dispenser of rewards and punishments was surely an essential deterrent, an omniscient Policeman who must be invented should He happen not to exist.

Holbach cared for none of these things. Science seemed to him to reveal a closed universe composed of material particles which follow inevitable laws. Matter is the word we use for the condition of existence. Of its nature we are totally ignorant, though we discover its qualities, such as motion and extension, by observation. All phenomena, conscious and unconscious, are bound together in an unbreakable chain of causation: their diversity results from innumerable changes caused by the energy

---

[1] It should be remembered, however, that translations of Holbach's works sold widely in England in the early nineteenth century and were only less effective instruments of free-thought than Paine's *Age of Reason*. For the part they played in the battle for free speech waged by Richard Carlile *vide* Wickwar, *The Struggle for the Freedom of the Press*.

inherent in matter itself. There is no room for chance or final causes or free will. Man is but one combination of particles and thought a particular kind of molecular motion, a peculiar quality of the brain, hitherto unexplained.[1] The words which men have invented to cover their ignorance of these mysteries become actively harmful to the advance of knowledge. Scientific habits of mind grow so slowly that the civilized man, who has left off seeing hobgoblins in every bush, still finds comfort in superstitions such as deity, soul, immortality and free will. Unfortunately, such inventions, which offer no rational explanation themselves and hinder the progress of knowledge, are fostered by priests and despots who profit by them. Existing religion is nothing but "the fruit of a very deep and very interested theological policy. . . . If we go back to the beginning we can always find that ignorance and fear have created gods : fancy, enthusiasm or deceit has adorned or disfigured them : weakness worships them, credulity keeps them alive, custom respects them and tyranny supports them in order to make the blindness of men serve its own ends."

The discovery that man is infinitely small, an ephemeral being, as much subject to unchanging law as any other creation, does not lessen the need or the value of knowledge. For knowledge itself may be the most powerful of the forces compelling him[2] : when he has learned that the spiritual and the material are one, and has come to rely on science and not on theories of the supernatural, he will be able to make use of his knowledge for his own happiness. He will be able, for instance, to cure what are now known as mental diseases by physical means. He will be able so to arrange political society that sympathy, understanding and affection become the dominant motives, and scientific knowledge

---

[1] Since all thoughts are only modifications of matter, and so many of them find place in one brain, La Mettrie had argued that thoughts must be very small in size.

[2] See *Système de la Nature*, i. 387 ff., for a striking passage dealing with the futility of hoping to change human nature by religious teaching rather than by knowledge. " To tell an ambitious man not to desire power and greatness is to order him to reverse at a blow the habitual system of his ideas ; it is to speak to a deaf man. To tell a lover of impetuous temperament to stifle his passion . . . is to combat realities with chimerical speculations."

of Nature be used to serve the purpose of human happiness. When men understand Nature they will adjust their lives to her laws. The contrast of that future society, the approach of which Holbach did not doubt, with the existing authoritarian State dominated by ancient superstitions, moved him to a generous apostrophe of Nature. For Nature had become personified ; in destroying the malevolent deity of the priests, Holbach had substituted a new one, whose purposes are good and wise but not past finding out. Holbach's materialism is a gospel of hope, not of despair. " Nature invites man to love himself, incessantly to augment the sum of his happiness : Religion orders him to love only a formidable God who is worthy of hatred ; to detest and despise himself, and to sacrifice to his terrible idol the sweetest and most lawful pleasures. Nature bids man consult his reason, and take it for his guide : Religion teaches him that this reason is corrupted, that it is a faithless, lying guide, implanted by a treacherous God to mislead His creatures. Nature tells man to seek light, to search for the truth : Religion enjoins upon him to examine nothing, to remain in ignorance. Nature says to man : 'Cherish glory, labour to win esteem, be active, courageous, industrious ': Religion says to him : 'Be humble, abject, pusillanimous, live in retreat, busy thyself with prayer, meditation, devout rites ; be useless to thyself, and do nothing for others.' Nature proposes for her model, men endowed with noble, energetic, beneficent souls, who have usefully served their fellow-citizens : Religion makes a show and a boast of the abject spirits, the pious enthusiasts, the phrenetic penitents, the vile fanatics, who by their ridiculous opinions have troubled empires. . . . Nature says to man ' Thou art free and no power on earth can lawfully strip thee of thy rights ' : Religion cries to him that he is a slave condemned by God to groan under the rod of God's representatives. Nature bids man love the country that gave him birth, serve it with all loyalty, bind his interest to hers against every hand that might be raised against her : Religion commands him to obey without a murmur the tyrants that oppress his country, to take their part against her, to chain his fellow-citizens under their lawless caprices. . . . If politics, which supernatural ideas have so shamefully depraved, were to take account of the nature of man, it would contribute far more than all the religion in the world to make communities happy, powerful and prosperous under reasonable authority. . . . Nature herself would teach princes that they are men and not gods; that they are citizens deputed by their fellow-citizens to watch over the safety of all. . . . Instead of attributing to the divine vengeance all the wars, the famines, the plagues that lay nations low, would it not have been more useful to show them that such calamities are due to the passions, the indolence, the tyranny of their princes, who sacrifice the nations to their hideous delirium?"

3. THE GREATEST-HAPPINESS PRINCIPLE—LOGICAL ETHICS—HELVÉTIUS

Bentham tells us that it was in the works of Helvétius that he first read that the " greatest happiness of the greatest number " was the criterion by which individual and governmental action should be judged. The idea of utility, the conception that actions are to be judged good or bad by their effect upon human happiness, had been of course implicit in the works of irreligious social theorists throughout the history of thought. In the eighteenth century almost all the *philosophes* may be considered utilitarians. Saint-Pierre had laid down the utilitarian principle in exact terms.[1] Hutchison, Hume and Priestley, and even the pious Paley, had all founded their systems of morals on utility, while the constant appeal to humanity in the works of Voltaire, Turgot, and other Encyclopædists, in itself constitutes a recognition of the utilitarian principle.[2] In Helvétius, however, it was explicitly laid down for the first time that if we would judge rightly of laws " it is indispensable to be able to refer them all to a single principle, such as that of the utility of the public—that is to say, of the greatest number of men submitted to the same form of government: a principle of which no one realizes the range and possibilities; a principle that

---

[1] *Vide supra*, p. 61.
[2] For the sources of Helvétius' views *vide* Keim, *Helvétius*, p. 222 ff. *Cp.* also Halévy, *La Formation du Radicalisme philosophique* : i. *La Jeunesse de Bentham*.

contains all morality and legislation, which many people repeat without understanding it and of which even legislators have still but a superficial idea, if, that is, one may judge by the unhappiness of almost all the peoples of the earth."[1]

Helvétius desired to found ethics and politics on a scientific psychology. "If poetry, geometry, astronomy, and, in general, all the sciences advance more or less rapidly towards perfection, while morality seems scarcely to have left its cradle, it is because men, being forced to unite in society to give themselves laws, were obliged to form a system of morality before they had learned from observation its true principles." Montesquieu, who had investigated and classified various types of government, had begun at the wrong place, for he had neither established the principles which legislators ought to recognize in common nor tried to construct a science of human nature. He had succeeded in giving hints to the legislator, not in founding a sociology. His contribution was rather to the art than to the science of government. If, as he admitted, human nature was essentially the same everywhere, why discuss the accidental vagaries of men, born of prejudice and ignorance, before being in a position to understand them? Helvétius thought, as Chastellux put it, " that before examining systems of legislation and comparing them, man himself must be studied, and the structure of institutions to which he should be subject must be based on the nature of man himself. Such was the object of his book *De l'Esprit*, which, though later than *L'Esprit des Lois* in order of chronology, immediately preceded it in order of ideas."[2]

This difference in outlook between Montesquieu and Helvétius could scarcely be better illustrated than by contrasting their methods of dealing with religion. Ethical systems and religious cults differ in different countries for local reasons although human nature is substantially the same everywhere. This was common ground to both writers. Montesquieu, however, was interested mainly in the differences, Helvétius concerned with essential similarities. Montesquieu thought that local varieties

---

[1] *De l'Esprit*, Discourse 2. [2] Quoted by Keim, *op. cit.*, 234.

would remain even though reforms might improve the natural adjustment in each case; Helvétius could not see why there should not be a universal religion deliberately constructed to suit everyone alike. " An universal religion," he wrote, " cannot be founded except on principles that are eternal and invariable, that are drawn from the nature of men and things, and that, like the propositions of geometry, are capable of the most rigorous demonstration." Are there such principles? " Yes, if they vary, it will be only in some of their applications to those different countries where chance has placed the different nations." [1]

The basis for a new psychology had already been laid down by Condillac and other disciples of Locke. At the very time that Hartley was developing the principles of mental association, La Mettrie was writing that development consisted in multiplying desires : the higher the organism the more sensations, and therefore the more cravings, it possessed. Helvétius began by assuming that man was a purely physical organism capable of receiving sensations and of forming ideas and mental habits, as a result of remembering and associating them. Descartes should have written " I feel, therefore I am," since our only certainty is the fact that we have sensations. Some of these are pleasant, some painful ; we try to repeat the former and avoid the latter. " The simple recital of what I feel," he writes, " forms my judgment." Judgment, that is, is the memory that one sensation is preferable to another ; this memory may in time become a mental habit and develop into a passion. Helvétius and Holbach were both explicit in asserting that there was only one possible spring of human action : " there is no other motive than the hope of a good or the fear of an evil." From this statement it would seem to follow that all affectionate conduct in private life, as well as public service and political obedience, is the result of a calculation that good conduct is rewarded and bad punished. It does not, of course,

---

[1] Helvétius insists that his method is the scientific one. *Cp.* preface to *De l'Esprit* : " It is by facts that I have ascended to causes. I imagined that morality ought to be treated like all other sciences and founded on experiment, as well as natural philosophy."

imply that every particular action is based upon such a calculation for, in adult life, habits and passions have been developed.
Analysis nevertheless reveals a basis of self-interest in every
action. We call our actions altruistic when they happen to
benefit other people as well as satisfying ourselves. Sound
virtue consists in finding one's own happiness in the happiness
of the greatest number.[1]

In a civilized society it remains true, then, that men can only
search for pleasure and avoid pain, but they may have learned
to do so in indirect and surprising ways. The desire to gratify
the senses, for instance, may lead to a passion for money in a
society where money is the only channel through which so many
gratifications may be obtained. Power, in the same way, is not
a thing which men desire for its own sake, and in a society
which provided men with more freedom and satisfaction without
forcing them to fight for it the desire for power, as well as the
craving for money, would cease to exist. The moral or altruistic
passions prove on examination to have a similar indirect basis.
Men want a just society because they fear the consequences to
themselves of existing injustices, while a virtue like saintliness
arises from a mistaken belief that asceticism will be rewarded
in the next life—a form of selfishness far-sighted enough to
look beyond the grave.[2] In any case, men can only search for
pleasure, and everyone secretly knows that his kindness,
generosity or self-sacrifice is really due to a hope that it will
be repaid by similar favours from others, or that he will get a
reputation for virtue, and so enjoy a more comfortable life.[3]

A virtuous action is one that promotes the greatest happiness,
and truly virtuous men, like Lycurgus and Jesus Christ, have
acquired "the habit of performing actions that are of use to their
country." They have discovered that they are most happy when

---

[1] In all this Helvétius was almost certainly indebted to Mandeville. For a
full account *vide* Kaye's introduction to his edition of *The Fable of the Bees*.

[2] "If a hermit or monk imposes on himself the law of silence, flogs himself
every night, lives on pulse and water, sleeps on straw, offers to God his nastiness
and ignorance, he thinks by virtue of emaciation to make a fortune in heaven"
(*De l'Homme*, 1772).

[3] It was this that Madame du Deffand had in mind when she said that
Helvétius "had told everybody's secret."

other people are happy, and that their pleasure lies in public service. The hero is a man who enjoys heroics, the saint one who finds asceticism pleasant, and the kind man one to whom benevolence is attractive. These statements seem to amount to a tautology. It is true that men prefer what they prefer, but the problem for the utilitarian moralist is to explain why some find pleasure in the gratification of the senses and others in the general welfare. The next stage was to give an account of the pains and pleasures actually at work in society, but the task of classifying human motives was one that Helvétius left to Bentham. It is conventional to say that the hedonist denies the altruistic impulses of men, offers no basis for social actions, and degrades all morality into enlightened self-seeking. Helvétius is, indeed, more open to this criticism than most utilitarians : he seems even to forget at times what he is at others at pains to emphasize—that in the course of education a desire which was originally purely selfish may have been transformed into a habit of social action. On occasion he writes as if man was a purely rational and calculating creature, who, before taking any action, considered whether the gratitude and public esteem which he would earn by kindness and generosity were, on balance, preferable to the immediate advantages to be won by brutality and fraud. Yet he argues that men need a universal religion, extols the Christianity of the gospels in contrast to current popery, and ends by asking why we should not " deify the public good."

Now how can a purely egoistic creature, who has, in some unexplained way, become part of an organized society, ever be inspired with a desire to serve the general good ? To this question hedonists have given three main answers. Shaftesbury, followed for a time by Diderot, believed in a moral sense, a capacity for sympathy, the origin of which may be explained by the fact that it is unpleasant to watch other people suffering.[1] Bentham himself seemed to accept this view in several passages. In the second place, it was possible to rely on the

---

[1] Diderot later abandoned this doctrine, and he seemed often to hold that morality as we know it is simply a trick of the ruling classes to keep the common people in order.

theory of natural harmony; "to do unto others as you would they should do unto you" is only common sense. Hartley had argued that Christianity itself needs no support except that of reason, since it always pays to do good to your neighbours. Though, as we have seen, there are traces of this doctrine in *De l'Esprit*, Helvétius is concerned mainly with the third solution, which was later to occupy Bentham's attention. In the absence of a natural harmony, it seemed possible to create an artificial harmony by the scientific development of education and by legislation designed to make honesty the best policy. It seemed wisest to assume that men would always behave selfishly and then so to weight the scales that enlightened selfishness would lead to the same results as genuine altruism. "Every man," said Hume, "should be held to be a knave," and Helvétius declared that it was "necessary to expect little from men in order to love them." Goodness, then, depends on the provision of the right incentive: men would be lovable only if taught to obey the Golden Rule from self-interest. Human beings are donkeys: if you hold the carrot in the right place they will walk the right path. The problem is to find the suitable carrot and present it so skilfully that from infancy onwards the child will be always lured into behaving nicely. And as all children are the same at birth the same carrots will do for everyone.

Helvétius was as contemptuous of Rousseau's theory that men are born good as he was of the clerical view that they were naturally wicked. They are not born, he said, with any "innate principle of virtue" or "natural compassion," but they may learn both, when they see the punishment that society inflicts on injustice and cruelty. Originally, their minds are blank sheets upon which the educationist can write whatever he thinks best, and "morality, law-making and pedagogy" are consequently a single science.

The differences between men are therefore due to variety of experience, of education, of physical and political environment. Some children, Helvétius admits, may be born with more energy than others, but in gifts all are identical. Nature, he says, "never made a dunce," while genius is the result of some accident which directs an individual's mind strongly and continuously to a particular subject. Under a good system of education and laws, therefore, creative ability can be manufactured. " It is certain," he writes, " that great men, who now appear haphazard, will in the future be produced by the legislature, and the abilities and virtues of the citizens in great empires need not be left so much to chance : by really good education they may be infinitely multiplied."

If character and ability are the product of education and law, Rousseau was wrong in suggesting that the child should be left alone to develop good habits. At times he had written as if all knowledge except that picked up in the course of daily life was actually harmful. Helvétius thought, on the contrary, that the more knowledge could be passed on to the child from the experience of the past the more virtuous he was likely to become. For virtue was intelligent self-interest, the result of knowing that honesty was the best policy. In a good State it would really be so : the child would see the solid advantages of goodness instead of hearing it extolled in a conventional manner and supported by supernatural sanctions, the unreality of which it soon discovered. It was no good to teach children the gospel of altruism if they soon learned that it actually paid to be avaricious, intolerant and cruel. The discrepancy between education and laws accounted, in Helvétius' view, for much of the misery as well as the hypocrisy of the world. " The majority of the people of Europe," he wrote, "honour virtue in theory ; this is the effect of their education. They despise it in practice, which is the effect of their governments. . . . No one in any case has concurred in the public good to his own prejudice, so that the only method of forming virtuous citizens is to unite the interests of the individual with those of the public." If the laws were made with this object in view, that "nobility of soul" which is the habit of finding one's own happiness in the public welfare might become the rule, not the exception, among men.

4. REPRESENTATIVE GOVERNMENT—LOGICAL POLITICS

Helvétius' political system followed logically from this psychological basis. He laid down the utilitarian premise that no government ought to have "any other object than the happiness of the majority." Now happiness is a personal thing, the result of the individual's own seeking. The business of the State is therefore to promote freedom. If the right penalties are attached to unsocial conduct, men will freely seek virtue. The right laws will ensure both happiness and righteousness.

"Every country," wrote Helvétius, "always counts among the gifts of nature the virtues derived from the form of its government." Thus the Englishman who "thinks himself a being of superior nature and takes the French for a giddy-brained trifling people" ought to recognize that "his fellow-countrymen owe their spirit of patriotism" to the civil freedom of England.[1] In England the security of individual rights makes men happy. The rights of man should be everywhere guaranteed, not because they are natural, except in the sense of arising from natural desires, but because they are useful and conducive to happiness.

The utilitarian reasons for granting men the rights they demand are clear enough. They should, for instance, be free to worship as they please. There is only one case, remarks Helvétius, "in which toleration can be detrimental, and that is when it tolerates a religion which is intolerant, such as the Catholic, which causes universal destruction if it gets the upper hand." Liberty of thought and of expression, on the other hand, can be almost absolute. "To publish the truth can never be harmful," and truth, Helvétius argued, anticipating John Stuart Mill, could be discovered only by open discussion. "Truth is a method of increasing happiness, the silence that

---

[1] Helvétius went as far as to admit that the insular situation of England might have in some measure contributed to her freedom, but he did not grant Montesquieu's thesis that climate could have been a serious factor. "The Englishman, who feeds on bread and meat and breathes a foggy air, is certainly not less intelligent than the lean Spaniard, who lives on garlic and onions in a very dry atmosphere."

is enforced by authority is the principal cause of the miseries of nations."

Helvétius' principles seem naturally to lead to some form of democracy. If ability and character are not the result of inherited differences, but of artificial privileges, the usual justification of despotism or aristocracy disappears. What answer could be given to those who claimed that all were equally entitled to happiness and equally able to exercise power? If men are born with substantially the same faculties, if their ideas are the result of their education and environment, if they must seek their own interest and are capable, with instruction, of perceiving the right way of attaining it, the argument for social and political equality is unanswerable. Any minority group which rules must necessarily be swayed by what Bentham termed " its sinister interest." It will find, that is, that its own pleasure results from a partisan policy and not from pursuit of the happiness of the greatest number. If the majority itself is in control, however, it follows that the search for its own interest will result in the greatest happiness for the greatest number. Bentham was to reach this conclusion with reluctance, when experience had taught him the strength of the " sinister interest " of the aristocracy. Abstract argument sufficed for Helvétius. Where a single individual or an aristocracy was in control " the equilibrium of forces " resulting from democracy was disturbed, and a struggle of group interests was inevitable. The worst of all sinister interests was, of course, the Church, and Helvétius remarks that " the real crime of the Jesuits was not the depravity of their morals but their constitution, riches, power, ambition, and the impossibility of reconciling their interests with those of the nation."

Helvétius, then, was, within limits, a democrat, and in favour of representative government. Amongst the greatest number who were to rule he did not include the uneducated and the poor. Without education or property a man could not be expected to see any advantages in moral conduct; indeed Helvétius admitted that the poor were necessarily immoral, and argued that private property was an essential without which a man " had no country." "Have not the poor," he asks, " too many wants to be virtuous?" The poor were haunted by jealousy of the rich, and mistakenly convinced that to possess riches was to be happy.[1] It seemed, then, that Montesquieu and d'Argenson had been right in thinking that a complete democracy was possible only where there was economic equality. Where riches or birth carried with them the privileges of idleness there would necessarily be divisions and unhappiness : " the labourers will die of happiness and the idlers will not be more happy."

Money, he agreed, was bad for virtue, and in a State governed by good laws men would not acquire a passion for wealth but would find "honour" a better substitute. Money, however, was a great source of happiness, and luxury, so far from being in itself an evil, was, as Montesquieu and Melon insisted, good for trade as well as pleasant. As a hedonist, Helvétius could scarcely take the ascetic view of the Utopian communists. The ostensibly economic argument for and against luxury in the eighteenth century is really only one aspect of the essential conflict between religious repression and austerity, on the one hand, and the Renaissance assertion of the right to happiness and freedom, on the other. While admitting therefore that wealth is a source of disharmony in society, Helvétius does not suggest the suppression of private property and money-making. Communism, he said, had always failed when it had been tried and private gain was a necessary incentive. He therefore came to an intermediate conclusion. The good State would " assign some property to each individual," would relieve the poor of the terror of penury and the rich from the misery of excessive wealth. Until such a redistribution of wealth was made, society would always live precariously. What, Helvétius asked, could prevent the poor some day realizing their strength and declaring themselves heirs to all the land and owners of all the wealth? He suggested that the wise course was to take the matter in hand in time, to tax the highest incomes out of existence for the benefit of all, and through legal means bring about sub-

---

[1] "O ye indigent, you are certainly not the most miserable of mortals ! To alleviate your sufferings, behold the idly opulent, whose passions provide almost all their amusements, and who cannot divest themselves of discontent but by sensations which are too poignant to be frequent."

stantial equality. To combine private property with taxation of the rich in the interests of the poor seemed the best solution.

Finally Helvétius took the usual eighteenth-century view that large democracies become corrupt, and that the best sanction of social conduct, the fear of public disgrace, diminishes proportionately with the size of the country. Internal federalism was the solution. Men will search for the greatest happiness of only a limited number of fellow-citizens. Internationally, small republics should retain their own individuality, but form themselves into a federal league, thus safeguarding themselves against tyrannical neighbours. France would do well to divide herself into thirty provinces or republics of about equal size. Each provincial republic would have its own law, its own police and elected magistrates, and would send its own deputies to a superior council, whose business would be external relations, and supervision of the provinces only when important changes were under consideration by the constituent members of the federal whole. Helvétius, like a number of other eighteenth-century writers, was in revolt against the centralization of French administration and, like Rousseau and, to a lesser degree, Turgot, an early apostle of regionalism.

Although not a federalist, Holbach reached political conclusions substantially similar to those of Helvétius. The political theory of his *Politique naturelle* is like his metaphysics—bold and systematic rather than original. In his treatment of the causes of decay in states, there are traces of Montesquieu's theory of the principles of governments; he speaks of the separate interest of intermediary bodies and of the general will in a manner faintly reminiscent of Rousseau.[1] He reproduces Locke's theory of the basis of political obligation: a government was legitimate only if it sought the public good, or, in his alternative phraseology, legislated according to the guidance of nature. Such a government would always keep the social compact: it would legislate by consent, since the people would always desire their own happiness. "Only the consent of the nation," he wrote,

---

[1] Holbach speaks throughout of the Sovereign as identical with the ruling government, and thus avoids all the philosophic difficulties involved in the conception of final and unlimited authority.

" makes the Sovereign legitimate," and he was less willing than Locke to assume that apathy denotes consent. The populace should not constantly interfere with the executive, but might demand that the government should be the kind they desired, and should revolt against arbitrary government. Consent constitutes "a supreme will, an indelible charter, an inalienable right, a right anterior to all other rights." Holbach constantly emphasizes the need for " public spirit," which he describes as a " reasoned attachment to the laws, the fatherland and the government." No State can be happy which is not animated by virtuous pursuit of the public interest on the part of its citizens, and this seems most likely to be obtained by a democratic system of government. Holbach fears, as Montesquieu had done, that popular government tends to degenerate, sectional interests to be formed, and the power to pass into the hands of demagogues.[1] The mass of the people he thought too ignorant for self-government. On the whole, he favoured a system of representative government, in which the right to vote would be confined to men of property, who are alone likely to feel their responsibility, since they alone have a stake in the country.

Holbach's use of natural law is not simply that of Locke. He accepts Helvétius' formula, and in fact tests every suggestion by referring it to "the greatest-happiness principle." He thus represents a half-way house between Locke and Bentham, and though he begins with Locke's phraseology his conclusions are substantially those of the " Constitutional Code." At first, indeed, he seems to anticipate nineteenth-century Benthamism with surprising completeness. He has the same belief in the State's power to influence the motives and behaviour of its citizens. Intelligent laws, education, and a peaceful and careful administrative system, can make men happy. On the political side the State may be a positive factor in producing the greatest happiness of the greatest number.

---

[1] It should always be remembered that eighteenth-century writers who speak of democracy are seldom thinking of representative government, but have Aristotle's warning in mind and associate democracy with the demagogy of Athens as described by the Greek writers of the fourth century.

In economic affairs, however, Holbach was not as optimistic as Bentham, and left it to Adam Smith and his disciples to develop the doctrine of the "invisible hand" which turns the selfishness of men into public beneficence. He was himself content to argue that free trade was obvious common sense, since nature had decreed that the surplus of one nation would supply the deficiency of another. Governments should repudiate the remnants of mercantilism, and seek prosperity and plenty instead of money and power. The less direct part the government attempted to play in trade the better. The government, he wrote, "could do nothing for the merchant, except leave him alone. No regulations can guide him in his enterprises so well as his own interest. . . . The State owes commerce nothing except its protection. Among commercial nations, those which allow their subjects most unlimited liberty may be sure of soon excelling all others."[1] Holbach, however, was aware of the dangers as well as the advantages of universal *laissez-faire*: the industrial revolution had not yet taught men to think commercial prosperity synonymous with happiness. He proved himself still a man of the eighteenth century when, like Montesquieu and d'Argenson, he uttered a warning against allowing the prosperity which may come from the abolition of privilege, monopoly and restraint of trade, to swamp real happiness, which depended on other factors in addition to economic welfare. He did not assume that for a man to be successful in business in itself constituted him a public benefactor, or that production was all-important, and that distribution would automatically prove perfect if left alone. He suggested that, "other things being equal," it is as well for a nation to live off its own soil, to retain some independence, and not to multiply its needs unnecessarily. Great wealth, he thought, was apt to create an unreal demand for the new and fantastic. Moreover the State should be concerned "to enrich its subjects as equally as possible." The labourer, the manufacturer, the sailor and even the savant play a part in production and distribution. A wise government would not

---

[1] *Pol. Nat.*, ii. 7, xxviii.

permit "wealth to be concentrated in the hands of a small number of citizens. . . . Governments seem to have altogether neglected this important truth. In almost all nations more than three-quarters of the subjects possess nothing. . . . Yet it is property which binds the individual to his country. . . . When all the citizens can procure themselves ease by moderate work the State can rely upon them for support, when a small number of men absorb all the property and wealth in a State they become the masters of that State, and it cannot without the greatest difficulty afterwards take away from them the wealth they have amassed." [1] There comes a point, too, when commerce ceases to be an advantage ; luxury has caused the ruin of many empires, it leads to strife and rivalry : " the globe ceases to be large enough " for the merchant who, " in his delirium," finds " a desert island an object of importance " ; in time " nations are ready to cut each other's throats " for possession of " some heaps of sand " where greed already imagines treasure. " Entire nations," he continues, " are the dupes of the avarice of hungry business men, who beguile them with the hope of wealth, the fruit of which they gather for themselves only. States are depopulated, taxation piled up, and nations impoverished, in order to satisfy the avarice of a small group of citizens who enjoy themselves because of their fellow-citizens' folly. Thus wealth has become the signal for war between Powers. There is one people who in the transports of their greed seem to have formed the extravagant project of usurping the commerce of the world and making themselves owners of the seas—an iniquitous and mad project, whose execution, if it should be possible, would hastily bring the nation which is guided by this frenzy to certain ruin." [2]

Holbach's analysis of the evils of his own day led him at length to prophecies which are more likely to attract attention after a century of industrial development. The pursuit of riches, he argued, has a natural limit. " If one might read in the future the effects of this unbridled passion for trade which now divides the nations one would see, perhaps, that when they had destroyed

---

[1] *Pol. Nat.*, ii. 7, xxx. [2] *Ibid.*, ii. 7, xxxii.-xxxiii.

each other under this pretext, the peoples would severally end by confining themselves to farming their own land, engaging only in that trade which proved essential for each. Governments more humane, just and sensible will perceive that money does not make the true happiness of society any more than of individuals. They will get to dislike sending armies of citizens to perish annually in scorching climates, in fighting and on the seas. At last, perhaps the day will come when Indians, having learned the art of war from Europeans, will hunt them from their shores, where their greed has inevitably made them odious."[1]

D'Alembert remarked that Holbach's system would be excellent if there were no such thing as history. And this, the orthodox plea of conservatism, contains an important if hackneyed truth. Helvétius and Holbach understood much of the needs of man : they saw that he could be rendered happier by a more reasonable social organization and that he would behave more reasonably under a happier one. But their temper was absolute and unhistorical. Just as they thought of each newborn child as a new slate to write upon, so they thought of society at any moment as a slate on which certain stupid things had been written which could be wiped off without leaving any permanent marks. Even Turgot, who recognized some of the power of inheritance and the inertia of accumulated tradition, could write to the King that the results of universal education would be that " in ten years your nation will be no longer recognizable." In that time every child would have become an enlightened citizen serving the public interest. Sensationalist psychology opened the way for an enormous optimism. The Encyclopædists never dreamed that if men were offered the truth they would not leap for it, that if they were told ugly facts they would prefer pleasant lies, that if reasonable ideals were offered them they would continue to act as their fathers had done ; they did not see that the follies of the past were not only imposed but ingrained, that men carried their history not only on their backs but in their heads.

---

[1] *Ibid.*, ii. 7, xxxiv.

CHAPTER VIII

DEMOCRACY

I. NATURAL RIGHTS AND POPULAR SOVEREIGNTY

UNTIL late in the eighteenth century the word "democracy" was still commonly used in its strict Aristotelean sense : it meant a form of government under which the assembled populace voted their own laws in the market-place and appointed their own administrative officers to enforce them. It was a system which the individualist feared, holding that mob rule was even more tyrannous than personal despotism. Democracy was objectionable as an alternative to the bureaucracy of Louis XV. for two reasons. First, believers in the rights of men disliked any system which located sovereignty in a single body ; the sovereignty of the people was repugnant because, like personal despotism, it put will above law and assumed that law proceeds from the transient wills of men, not from the eternal and irrevocable ordinances of God and nature. Secondly, it was not a system applicable to a modern State, and it was therefore discussed mainly for the sake of logical completeness and in deference to Aristotle. Rousseau declared that democracy was suitable only in the city-state, and added that in any case it was a system for gods, not for men. Yet it was he more than any other man who gave the idea of popular sovereignty its vogue : it was he who provided the slogans and the arguments which enabled the founders of nineteenth-century representative government to describe their system as democracy.

To most eighteenth-century French observers the British Constitution, as interpreted by Montesquieu, seemed the one practical alternative to despotism. In England, individual liberty was secured by institutional checks upon the abuse of executive power. Such a system had nothing to do with democracy : it was described as "republicanism"[1] or "mixed

---

[1] *Cp.* Kant's *Essay on Perpetual Peace.* He refers (in 1795) to "the common error of confusing the republican with the democratic constitution . . . the form of government is either republican or despotic. Republicanism is the political principle of severing the executive power of the government from

government," being aristocratic in substance, monarchical in form and popular only in so far as it permitted some plebeian persons to assist in electing its aristocratic House of Commons. Its essential feature was the separation of powers and the absence of sovereignty : it was " a government of laws, not of men." The *philosophes* knew the value of an independent judiciary and believed the English common law, based on nature and experience, to be secure from essential alteration by King, Parliament or people. They did not see that personal rights could be easily overridden in England when the landlords who dominated Parliament cared to exercise their effective sovereignty ; they did not grasp the significance of the Enclosure Acts, which in a few years swept away the ancient property rights of the English peasantry. Nor could they anticipate the repeal of the Habeas Corpus Act and the political persecutions which were soon to prove that the reputed separation of powers was but a frail protection for an unorthodox minority who insisted upon the right of free speech even in time of war.

The British Constitution, however, was a symbol of freedom on the Continent. It is an odd fact that when England and France went to war in 1792 both sides believed themselves to be fighting for the British Constitution. There was not a squire in England who would not have said that the cause of England against France was the cause of freedom and the British Constitution against French tyranny and revolutionary innovations. In France, meanwhile, revolutionaries were setting up a Constitution in direct imitation of the British. Paine was right in his answer to Burke : the principles of 1689 were at work in France, not in England.

When the era of revolutions, inaugurated by the revolt of the American Colonies, arrived, two sets of ideas and phrases were current : revolutionaries talked of the rights of man and thought them best guaranteed by the separation of powers

the legislature. . . . Democracy, in the proper sense of the word, is of necessity despotism . . . 'the whole people,' so-called, who carry their measure are really not all, but only a majority ; so that here the universal will is in contradiction with itself and with the principle of freedom " (Kant's *Perpetual Peace*, Miss Campbell Smith's translation, pp. 124-125).

and the British Constitution : they also acclaimed democracy and the sovereignty of the people. Now both these concepts—indefeasible rights and unlimited sovereignty—are legal fictions, not descriptions of reality, and the recognition of the one idea in absolute form would make the adoption of the other logically impossible. Constitutions and their makers, however, are not bound to adhere to any single logical system, and the numerous revolutionary constitutions of the later eighteenth and of the nineteenth centuries all show the marks of conflict between the two concepts. The new constitutions were therefore based on the sovereignty of the people, while they evaded its implications by the separation of powers ; they declare rights inalienable and indefeasible, and leave their practical limitation to the wills of peoples and parliaments. Sometimes there is more democracy and less stress upon rights ; sometimes Montesquieu and the separation of powers play a more prominent part than Rousseau and direct democracy.[1]

The type of government which was called democracy in the nineteenth century was therefore a mixture of two systems which the eighteenth century had kept distinct, and indeed regarded as antithetic. Even where, as was commonly the case, new institutions were based on the English pattern they were defended by phrases and arguments for which Rousseau, as well as Montesquieu, was responsible. Although Rousseau despised the British Constitution, and ridiculed the whole idea of representation, his followers could adapt his theory of democracy in support of both. In *The Social Contract* revolutionaries found that incompatibles could be combined and men

---

[1] It is to be noticed that the sovereignty of the people was open to a less exact interpretation than Rousseau's : Locke had avoided the phrase while justifying the Revolution of 1688 as a legitimate exercise of the ultimate rights of the people—a theory which conceded the whole principle of government by consent and therefore, by an unavoidable further step, of self-government. In the nineteenth century any form of government which included a form of popular election was described as democracy. It would have saved much confusion if the British system had been called representative government and democracy reserved for systems which at least attempted to approach Rousseau's ideal of direct government by providing for the popular election of executive officials and for plebiscites and referenda.

retain their natural and absolute rights while submitting to a sovereign authority. Rousseau's conception of the General Will turned what had hitherto seemed a contradiction into a truism. Popular government no longer appeared as the antithesis of individual freedom, but was assumed to be its necessary condition. This assumption was so general in the nineteenth century that men like de Tocqueville and John Stuart Mill were forced to explain at length to nineteenth-century democrats what everyone had taken for granted before the Revolution—that without safeguards democracy might be repressive to individuality. The voice of the people was no longer the untaught folly of the mob but the vehicle of divine revelation.

Crucial though Rousseau's argument was in the development of political thought, it was the spirit which infused his life and work which was the secret of his immense influence. The attack of Voltaire and the Encyclopædists was directed mainly against clericalism and scarcely tinged with democratic passion. The *philosophes* were critics : Rousseau spoke as one of the common people. He wrote not as a satirist or a humanitarian but as a man who himself suffered under an intolerable sense of injustice. His books were attempts to objectify his own conflicts—conflicts which commonly originated within himself but which always seemed to be, and sometimes in fact were, the outcome of social corruption and State intolerance. Thus the key to Rousseau's philosophy lies in the *Confessions*, where he portrays himself as a man of good instincts, good intentions and friendly disposition driven to knavery, buffoonery and misanthropy by the artificiality and falsehood of society. Each of his books is therefore an attempt to explain and resolve the miseries and humiliations of thwarted men—and Rousseau assumed that his own difficulties were typical—in an unjust and unequal society. His books contain numerous formal inconsistencies which are explicable only in the light of his emotional experiences. The clue to Rousseau's works is his own psychological history.

Each of Rousseau's attacks on the existing social system, each of the remedies he proposed for its transformation, sprang out of his own passionate misery and his consciousness of the miseries of others. And in every case he wrote with so much power and insight that he expressed the discontent and the aspirations of multitudes of men who had no other spokesman. Beginning as an anarchist in revolt against all social coercion, he came in time, as Plato had done, to a conclusion which made the State everything and the individual nothing. In the *Discourse on the Influence of the Arts and Sciences* he declared that social misery and individual depravity were the results of artificiality and sophistication. In the *Discourse on Inequality* he argued that the institution of private property was the curse of civilization. The first period of Rousseau's writing was thus devoted to denunciation of existing society; it ended spectacularly with his formal break from the *philosophes*, who attacked not society but religion. This rupture was signalized by two letters—one to Voltaire, defending God against the charge of injustice and indifference, and a second to d'Alembert, who had dared, in his article on Geneva, to praise Rousseau's birthplace for the wrong reasons, belittling its Puritanism and commending its theatre. Then came the great epoch of Rousseau's life, when he turned his face from Paris and sought in the peace of the country to objectify his personal revolt and to expound its real implications. In the *Nouvelle Héloise* he idealized the conception of friendship which he had always failed to realize in his own life and insisted that happiness is to be found in trusting to the instinctive goodness of men and women. In the *Emile* he explained that if human relationships were ever to be satisfactory the existing system of education would have to be transformed, and he pictured the happy results of a natural education which would give men mastery and freedom, save them from the miseries which he had himself undergone and which could alone serve as a basis for a natural society of free and happy men and women. Finally, long brooding over the problems of government led him to begin a full-length work upon the relation of the individual to the State. Of this only one part—known as *The Social Contract*—was completed. Its thesis was that although natural simplicity and economic equality had gone for ever, a strong State could still make men substantially equal, and could offer them that higher type of freedom and happiness which comes from voluntarily sacrificing self to the public good. In the last period of Rousseau's life, persecution, both real and imaginary, overthrew the precarious equilibrium in which he lived : in the *Letters from the Mountain*, however, he was able to vindicate himself against the authorities who persecuted him, and in his *Confessions*, *Dialogues* and *Reveries* to explain and justify his life against the attacks of the *philosophes*.

2. THE INDIVIDUALISM OF ROUSSEAU—THE EARLY DISCOURSES

Rousseau's first published work already foreshadowed his later rupture with the *philosophes*. It was a challenge to the main trend of the century, an attack upon the rationalism and sophistication which was its special pride. What, asked the Academy of Dijon, had been the moral effect of the rebirth of the arts and sciences? Had the Renaissance, and by implication every increase of knowledge and culture, had good or bad effects upon humanity? The question answered itself in Rousseau's mind. How happy and care-free he had been as a wanderer in Savoy, or when living an instinctive life in the society of Madame de Warens! How morose, how conscience-stricken he had become, and how suspicious of those who offered him friendship and hospitality in Paris! If his life had been poisoned by contact with sophisticated persons, were not the *philosophes*, and all the brilliant society he met, in the same case? The form of his answer came to him as a sudden flash of illumination. " If ever anything resembled a sudden inspiration, it was the commotion which began in me as I read this. All at once I felt myself dazzled by a thousand sparkling lights ; crowds of vivid ideas thronged into my mind with a force and confusion that threw me into unspeakable agitation ; I felt my head whirling in a giddiness like that of intoxication. A violent palpitation oppressed me ; unable to walk for difficulty of breathing, I sank under one of the trees of the avenue, and passed half-an-hour there in such a condition of excitement that when I arose I saw that the front of my waistcoat was all wet with tears, though I was wholly unconscious of shedding them. Ah, if ever I could have written a quarter of what I saw and felt under that tree, with what clearness should I have brought out all the contradictions of our social system; with what simplicity I should have demonstrated that man is good naturally, and that by institutions only is he debased."[1]

The theme of Rousseau's essay was that of Genesis, a restatement of the Protestant doctrine of the Fall of Man in the speculative terms of eighteenth-century anthropology. Man, born for goodness and innocence, had tasted the fruit of the Tree of Knowledge, had learned to think of interest rather than spontaneously to follow his natural instincts; Rousseau himself, hitherto almost care-free and conscienceless, had been tempted, if not by Eve at least by Madame d'Epinay, and lost both his innocence and his happiness.[2] Before art, knowledge and culture had corrupted man his "morals were rude, but natural." "In our day, now that more subtle study and a more refined taste have reduced the art of pleasing to a system, there prevails in modern manners a servile and deceptive conformity; so that one would think every mind had been cast in the same mould. Politeness requires this thing, decorum that; ceremony has its forms and fashion its laws, and these we must always follow, never the promptings of our own nature. We no longer dare seem what we really are, but lie under a perpetual restraint; in the meantime the herd of men, which we call society, all act under the same circumstances exactly alike. . . . Ignorance is held in contempt, but a dangerous scepticism has succeeded it." Physical health as well as moral integrity had been sacrificed

---

[1] Second letter to M. de Malesherbes. Vide *Confessions*, Bk. VIII. *Cp.* Morley, *Rousseau*, i. 134, note.

[2] In a note upon the influence of women, Rousseau remarks "we are not sufficiently sensible of what advantage it would be to society to give a better education to that half of our species which governs the other. Men will always be what women choose to make them." In his letter to d'Alembert, written in violent reaction against Madame d'Epinay and her circle, he says that the manners of the French are the opposite of those of the ancients: ". . . lâchement devoués aux volontés du sexe que nous devrions protéger et non servir, ils ont appris à le mépriser en lui obéissant, à l'outrager par leur soins railleurs; chaque femme de Paris rassemble autour d'elle un sérail d'hommes plus femmes qu'elles, qui savent rendre à la beauté toutes sortes d'hommages, hors celui du cœur dont elle est digne."

to artificial eloquence. " It is beneath the homespun of the labourer, and not beneath the gilt and tinsel of the courtier, that we should look for strength and vigour of body." Virtue had suffered as much as happiness and health ; the art of printing had merely perpetuated corrupt philosophies like those of Hobbes and Spinoza ; men had banished the gods (whom, in the days of innocence, they had kept in their huts) to magnificent temples where they could no longer witness the viciousness of their devotees ; a false education, which could not produce genius but which turned the man who would have been an excellent clothier into a bad versifier, had prevented men from recognizing the teaching of their hearts. "Virtue, sublime science of simple minds, are such industry and preparation needed if we are to know you? Are not your principles graven on every heart? Need we do more, to learn your laws, than examine ourselves, and listen to the voice of conscience, when the passions are silent? " [1]

D'Alembert's preliminary discourse was the answer of the *philosophes* to this declaration that virtue was more important than intellect, and that the character of individuals and society suffered from the progress of science. In 1753 Rousseau denounced civilization again in his *Origin of Inequality*.[2] The book has been generally described as too " abstract." Rousseau has been accused of a total disregard of facts and is supposed to have believed in the historical existence of a mythical " state of nature." In fact he explicitly denies the possibility of knowing the story of human development, though he did his best to get what hints he could from the accounts of primitive peoples which missionaries and explorers had recorded.[3] His use of the " state of nature " is, in the main, as he says, a hypothetical one, a way of illustrating his view of human nature and his diagnosis of society's ills. " Let us begin, then, by laying facts aside, as they do not affect the question." It was the basis of

[1] This and subsequent translations are taken from the Everyman Edition.
[2] A discourse, also written as a prize essay for the Academy of Dijon, and dedicated to Geneva. Unlike the first discourse it did not win the prize.
[3] *Cp.* the notes and references which he makes in *The Origin of Equality*, *vide* Vaughan's edition of the *Political Writings of J.-J. Rousseau*.

right in which he was interested, not the historical facts, and he exposed the fallacy shared by Hobbes and Locke of attributing social vices and virtues to men before the existence of organized society. He pictures man evolving through stages from an animal ancestry, and possessing two unique faculties —a capacity for learning by experience and an ability to sympathize—from which all his good qualities have sprung. After a long process, in which the pressure of population gradually drove men from their primitive isolation to a life of co-operation, family life began. Hunting, fishing, and then agriculture, took the place of promiscuous food-gathering. During this the happiest phase of human development men learned to co-operate in tilling the soil, and so learned the rudiments of morality. As long as there was ample produce for all there was no need for private property and no social difficulties. The time came, however, when the first man enclosed a piece of ground, "bethought himself of saying *this is mine* and found the people simple enough to believe him. This man was the real founder of civil society. . . . From how many crimes, wars and murders, from how many horrors and misfortunes might not someone have saved mankind, by pulling up the stakes, or filling up the ditch, and crying to his fellows, 'Beware of listening to this impostor; you are undone if you once forget that the fruits of the earth belong to us all, and the earth itself to nobody.'" From this original misfortune all other evils developed. Through private property the harmless inequalities which were the outcome of natural differences gave way to social inequalities. As a result of the inheritance of wealth one class was able to tyrannize over another. From private property moral evils sprang. "It now became the interest of men to appear what they really were not." On the one side insolent display and insatiable ambition, on the other servile trickery and corrupting jealousy. "In a word, there arose rivalry and competition on the one hand, and conflicting interests on the other, together with a secret desire on both of profiting at the expense of others." Men no longer worked to satisfy real wants, but to get more than others. There was permanent war between the rich and the poor, between those who were strongest by nature and those whose right was founded on the artificial institution of private property. In this society the natural inequalities of merit and capacity were subordinated to those of riches, which could be used "to purchase every other distinction." It was useless to say that there was a natural harmony of interests, "that every man gains by serving the rest." This, Rousseau saw, might be ultimately true. Unfortunately, as things were, men appeared to be able to gain still more by injuring others. "There is no legitimate profit so great that it cannot be greatly exceeded by what may be made illegitimately; we always gain more by hurting our neighbours than by doing them good."

The Origin of Inequality ends with an invocation to the god of simplicity, but despairs of a return to simplicity after the corruption of civilization had done its work. If Rousseau had ceased writing at this point, he would have been rightly acclaimed an apostle of the simple life, and a pessimist who was certain of human degeneracy and of the impossibility of regaining natural happiness. His mind, however, was already at work upon a more constructive conclusion; it appeared in an incomplete form two years after his second discourse, as an article on political economy in the *Encyclopædia*, and, after six years of brooding, he fully developed his ideas in *The Social Contract*.

3. THE COLLECTIVISM OF ROUSSEAU—*THE SOCIAL CONTRACT*

At the basis of the two discourses there is a complete individualism, a hatred of all authority and all institutions which prevent a man from freely following his instincts. Rousseau knew, however, that such an individualism was incompatible not only with the State but with society, and since it was impossible to desocialize man and revive a condition of amoral innocence it was now a question of finding a method of organization which would preserve moral and spiritual freedom, even at the expense of other forms of liberty. The social chains which restricted the development of man's instinctive freedom could not be altogether discarded. Yet the essence of freedom which lies in obedience only to oneself might be retained in

society. "The problem," he wrote, "is to find a form of association which will defend and protect with the whole common
force the person and goods of each associate, in which each,
while uniting himself with all, may still obey himself alone, and
remain as free as before."

Leaving aside the conception of an anarchic community as
a dream of the past, now for ever irretrievable, Rousseau sets
out to follow his master Plato and found a society based not
on instinctive freedom but on moral freedom and, therefore, on
justice. He begins with the explicit assurance that his object
is a philosophic, not a practical one; he is in search of the
principles of "political right," not of the methods by which
the best political compromise can be reached in any particular
instance. Natural law is mentioned only to be discarded, and
the social contract introduced merely as a method of informing
the reader that Rousseau is now dealing with the socialized
man we know, not with the abstract individual of *The Origin
of Inequality*.[1] Men had gained in society more than they had
lost from the state of nature. In primitive isolation " our whole
happiness would consist in not knowing our misery. There would
be neither kindness in our hearts nor morality in our acts. We
should never have tasted the sweetest feeling of which the soul
is capable—the love of virtue." [2] The moral self was more
important than animal freedom. Rousseau's own Puritan self-
analysis easily led him to the Pauline conclusion that there are
in every man two natures, a higher and a lower, and that to
abase the lower and surrender to the higher is to be free. In

---

[1] It was a misfortune, as Vaughan points out, that Rousseau did not decide
to call his work by its sub-title, *The Principles of Political Right*, instead of by
the highly misleading one which became so famous. The introduction of a
social contract and of a " Legislator " are devices for getting over a logical
difficulty. In the absence of any evolutionary principle, Rousseau had to
explain how the amoral man of the state of nature (devoid as the latter was of
" reason, duty, justice and humanity ") could ever have come to set up a law
at all. This, as he remarked, implied a miracle. The miracle is the Legislator,
an idealized version of Lycurgus, a man who can force his fellows to accept the
society which they could not themselves perceive to be in accordance with
their own general will (*Social Contract*, Bk. II., chap. vii.).

[2] *Social Contract* (Geneva MSS.), quoted by Vaughan, vol. i. 27.

himself, he explained, there were two souls, that of the voluptuary and that of the Puritan, which gained successive mastery over him for periods of about a fortnight. The one condition was freedom, the other slavery: liberty is obedience to a law which we prescribe to ourselves. Thus the conclusion reached in *The Origin of Inequality* is exactly reversed: the good society is one in which men are virtuous and do not suffer from the tyranny of animal freedom.

Rousseau was now in a position to solve his problem. If individual freedom consists in virtue, then social freedom is present where men are subject only to those laws they have imposed upon themselves. The legal system will then embody the "general will"—that is, the altruistic, moral and rational desire for the general good. The general will is not merely the will of all but the sum of all the wills which make for the common good: it is public spirit, not public opinion: the spirit which Montesquieu called virtue, which subordinates private interests to public ones, the spirit without which democracy cannot live. A society animated by this corporate spirit gives every man his moral freedom, since the laws which restrain him represent his own moral triumph over the despotism of his lower nature. The law coerces the selfish individual and thereby gives him freedom, just as conscience coerced Rousseau and gave him the sense of spiritual freedom in the reaction after an unsuccessful struggle against his sexual appetite. A man whose actual will conflicts with the law, which embodies the general or moral will, may appear to be constrained, but is, in fact, "forced to be free."

Where the general will is fully operative there will no longer be conflicting units kept within bounds by an external force, but a single corporate whole, composed of members each of whom commands and each of whom obeys.[1] Each plays a part

---

[1] The organic theory of the State had been already stated by Rousseau in his *Political Economy*. His debt to Hobbes was obvious: "The body politic, taken individually, may be considered as an organized, living body, resembling that of man. The sovereign power represents the head; the laws and customs are the brain, the source of the nerves and seat of the understanding, will and senses, of which the Judges and Magistrates are the organs; commerce, industry

in the activities of the body politic, and the whole society is a harmonious macrocosm of each individual. In such a State " we see at once that it can no longer be asked whose business it is to make laws, since they are acts of the general will ; nor whether the Prince is above the law, since he is a member of the State ; nor whether the law can be unjust, since no one is unjust to himself ; nor how we can be both free and subject to the laws, since they are but registers of our wills."

Rousseau had now clearly established his basis of right. The only legitimate State is one in which the laws are made by the whole body of citizens, acting, not as units with particular desires and private passions, but as altruistic members of the body politic, solely concerned with the good of the community. In these circumstances every member of the community is free, but Rousseau's admission that there may be individuals who refuse " to obey the general will," and who must be " compelled to do so by the whole body," might seem to invalidate his argument. For, if the only legitimate rule is self-rule, what happens to the basis of right which has been established if some individuals are coerced? Is it not, in fact, a mere juggle of words to assume that an individual who differs from his fellows is being " forced to be free " when he is being compelled against his actual will? Is this anything but a muddled way of saying that the best compromise is to accept majority rule, and that this form of government will satisfy men's desire for a share in government as long as there is sufficient underlying agreement about fundamental issues to induce the minority to give way until their own opportunity of rule arrives? [1]

and agriculture are the mouth and stomach, which prepare the common subsistence ; the public income is the blood, which a prudent economy, in performing the functions of the heart, causes to distribute through the whole body nutriment and life : the citizens are the body and the members which make the machine live, move and work ; and no part of this machine can be damaged without the painful impression being at once conveyed to the brain, if the animal is in a state of health " (trans. Everyman Edition, p. 252).

[1] Contemporary critics seized upon this point. In plain language Rousseau's argument for sovereignty was a plea for the right of the majority to coerce the individual. *Vide*, e.g., *Anti-Contrat Social*, by Gerdil : " It is a dangerous maxim that the community cannot impose an inviolable law upon itself ; it is to

DEMOCRACY

Majority rule is the only practical application of *The Social Contract*. Rousseau makes no such admission. Since it is impossible that the body of citizens should not desire their own good it is clear that, even if they are sometimes mistaken in the methods by which they hope to achieve it, their decision is infallible in the sense that they alone have the right to make such a decision, and that no one can know their own will except themselves. If the fundamental condition of popular sovereignty be observed, the citizen may be assumed to give " his consent to all the laws, including those which are passed in spite of his opposition, and even those which punish him when he dares to break any of them." [1] In such circumstances to ask how a man can be both free and coerced is " to put the question wrongly." " The constant will of all the members of the State is the general will; by virtue of it they are citizens and free. When in the popular assembly a law is proposed, the people are not exactly asked whether they approve or reject the proposal, but whether it is in conformity with the general will, which is their will. Each man, in giving his vote, states his opinion on that point; and the general will is found by counting votes. When therefore the opinion that is contrary to my own prevails, this proves neither more nor less than that I was mistaken, and that what I thought to be the general will was not so. If my particular opinion had carried the day I should have achieved the opposite

---

submit public and fundamental law to variations and changes, often unjust and always pernicious. It is to excite revolutions in the heart of the country. . . . I read with pleasure that one may be free and coerced at the same time. I have long looked for a way of reconciling these two irreconcilables. I admit that I have never rightly understood how liberty can be the effect of constraint . . . soon being and not being, war and peace, the infinite and the finite will live under the same roof." Rousseau, says Gerdil, has really destroyed his whole basis of right. Government by consent has passed into government by force, and the morality, at first described as innate, has disappeared and become equivalent to such conduct as the existing government and public opinion approves.

[1] This argument leads to the position that in a democratic State a man who is hanged for breaking the law is hanged voluntarily. *Cp.* Vaughan, vol. i. 113, note, and *Social Contract*, Bk. II. v. : " his will is chained by his own permission, his past consent set off against his present refusal, and the obligation laid upon him to punish himself for having acted against his own deliberate intentions."

205

of what was my will; and it is in that case that I should not have been free." [1]

You cannot escape from a dilemma by a vehement denial of its existence, and Rousseau was forced to admit that his theory was applicable only to ideal conditions. He saw that wills would in fact conflict even in a democracy. Where public spirit is lacking, the transitory "will of all" may be confused with the permanent "general will," and private interests prove more influential than considerations of the public good. Particular associations within the State endanger the whole, since they have particular interests: they may, as Hobbes had put it, become parasitic, "like worms in the entrails" of the body politic. Such associations, indeed, may be general as regards their own members, but particular as regards the State: they may make a man "a devout priest or brave soldier," and yet prevent his being anything but "a bad citizen." "It is therefore essential, if the general will is to be able to express itself, that there shall be no partial society within the State, and that each citizen shall think only his own thoughts," without any intermediary associations to remind him of particular interests.

Even if these conditions are observed the perfect form of government in which the people would unite in themselves executive and legislative powers is an unrealizable ideal. In this strict sense, Rousseau remarks, "there never has been a real democracy and there never will be. . . . It is unimaginable that the people should remain continually assembled to devote their time to public affairs, and it is clear that they cannot set up commissions for that purpose without the form of administration being changed." Such a perfect form of government "is not for men. Were there a nation of gods their government would be democratic."

This being so, what remains? The people are still sovereign and must exercise their sovereignty. Rousseau exposes the error, made by Locke and earlier exponents of the "social contract," of imagining that there could be a contract between

---

[1] *Social Contract*, Bk. IV. ii.

DEMOCRACY

people and government. The people cannot, even if they
would, alienate their ultimate right to govern themselves;
in imagining that they could do so, and thereby bind their
successors to a future obedience, Hobbes was even more
obviously wrong than Locke. The only contract admitted by
Rousseau was the one made among all the original constituents
of a society, the arrangement that they would co-operate in a
single community. If it is, as a rule, impossible that everyone
should take part in government, the people retain the right
to appoint what executive they please, and to change its
character and personnel as often as they like. When Rousseau
discusses forms of government, therefore, he is merely comparing the merits of different forms of executive, which must
in any case be directly responsible to the people, and should
be so intimately controlled by them that it never has any
opportunity of manifesting " a particular will " of its own in
opposition to the general will of the community. An hereditary
aristocracy is obviously the worst of all forms of executive,
since it is certain to exercise its power in its own private
interest: " an elected aristocracy," which is what writers
often call a democracy, consisting of magistrates duly elected
by the people and responsible to them, is commonly the best.

Elected persons may, then, perform executive duties satisfactorily as long as their authority is derived from and continuously exercised by the whole people. Legislative authority,
however, can never be delegated or represented. Representation
is no substitute for direct democracy. " The lukewarmness
of patriotism, the activity of private interest, the vastness of
States, conquest and the abuse of government, suggested the
method of having deputies or representatives of the people in
the national assemblies." Sovereignty, however, " cannot be
represented; it lies essentially in the general will, and will
does not admit of representation ; it is either the same or other ;
there is no intermediate possibility. . . . Every law the people
has not ratified in person is null and void—is, in fact, not a law.
The people of England regards itself as free; but it is grossly
mistaken ; it is free only during the election of members of
Parliament. As soon as they are elected, slavery overtakes it,

and it is nothing. The use it makes of the short moments of liberty it enjoys shows indeed that it deserves to lose them."

4. THE PRACTICAL POLITICS OF ROUSSEAU—FRANCE, POLAND AND CORSICA

So far, Rousseau's argument has been devoted to establishing the basis of political right. When he turned to the complex question of the art of government the result was surprising. Few writers in the eighteenth century had studied and grasped *L'Esprit des Lois* to such effect. The whole trend of Montesquieu's thought, with its Whig assumption that change is permissible only as a result of careful adjustment to historic tradition and unchangeable environment, with its stress on the relativity of good and evil, and its consequent acceptance of compromise—this whole method of thought seemed the antithesis of Rousseau's abstract philosophy and revolutionary Protestantism. Yet so imbued with Montesquieu's caution had Rousseau become that even in his *Social Contract* he applies his principles with an unexpected timidity. Rousseau was revolutionary only in theory, and when he was called upon to suggest practical reforms Burke himself could scarcely have considered his proposals extravagant.

In his political writings two strands lie side by side : on one page we are dealing with absolutes and on the next making compromises and exceptions which seemed to undermine his most cherished principles. What are we to say of a philosopher who opens his treatise by declaring that " the terms of the contract . . . are everywhere the same and everywhere tacitly admitted and recognized," and then proceeds to tell us that there are " unfriendly and barren lands " where all political society is impossible ; that " liberty not being the fruit of all climates is not within the reach of all peoples," that Montesquieu was right in thinking that considerations of territory and climate sometimes justify a monarchy, that democracy suits only States that are small and poor and that no one can say " what sort of government is absolutely the best " ? In the same way, when Rousseau, who had opened *The Social Contract* by saying,

" If I were a Prince or a Legislator, I should not waste time in saying what wants doing ; I should do it or hold my peace," was actually offered the opportunity of becoming a legislator, the main burden of his advice was to move cautiously and to practise moderation.

In *The Social Contract* he had admitted that the ideal conditions for which he sought were no longer attainable anywhere, and certainly not in most European countries. For " legislation is made difficult less by what it is necessary to build up than by what has to be destroyed ; and what makes success so rare is the impossibility of finding natural simplicity together with social requirements. All these conditions are indeed rarely found united, and therefore few States have good constitutions." In one country, however—Corsica—all the conditions for the foundation of a good society still existed. "The valour and persistency with which that brave people has regained and defended its liberty well deserves that some wise man should teach it how to preserve what it has won. I have a feeling that some day that little island will astonish Europe."

In 1764, Buttafuoco wrote to Rousseau reminding him of this passage, and suggesting that he himself was the wise man who could legislate for independent Corsica.[1] " Corsica has never yet borne the true yoke of the Law ; it has no fear of being crushed by a sudden invasion : it can do without the aid of other nations : it is neither rich nor poor ; it is sufficient to itself. Its prejudices will not be hard to overcome ; and I venture to say that the simplicity of nature will be found there to go hand in hand with the needs of social life."[2] Rousseau responded by a project of government which follows the principles of *The Social Contract* closely. Every citizen was to take an oath " in the name of Almighty God " to join himself, "body, goods, will and powers," to the Corsican nation, " granting to her full ownership of myself and all that depends upon me." In the

---

[1] In 1768 Choiseul annexed Corsica to France, and the hopes of creating a Utopia were thus destroyed.

[2] This is a summary of the conditions laid down by Rousseau which would render a people "a fit subject for legislation"—vide *Social Contract*, Bk. II. x., and *cp*. Vaughan, vol. ii. 296.

new State of Corsica there was to be social equality and a recognition of the "fundamental principles of prosperity." "No one should be rich," everyone should produce according to need, agriculture should remain the principal industry, and there should be no capital town, such as Paris, wealthy and corrupt, to undermine the simple happiness of a people who still spontaneously enjoyed their liberty and equality. When it came to more practical matters, however, Rousseau did not forget that the legislator should follow Montesquieu, and he requested Buttafuoco to provide him with all the facts—political, industrial and social—which could serve "to reveal the national character." He decided, consistently enough, that the island was too large to be an unmixed democracy, and suggested that the executive should be chosen, and changed frequently, by as many of the people as could effectively meet together in a congress at the same time. He was also cautious in his treatment of the Church, and, in spite of the anathemas he had pronounced upon "the religion of priests," did not advocate the abolition of church tithes, but only suggested the addition of a civic tithe to be paid to the State. As to the institution of private property, he held that the ideal would be State socialism. " So far from wishing the State to be poor I should wish on the contrary to see it the sole owner ; the individual taking a share of the common property only in proportion to his services." [1] He was content, however, with the practical suggestion that the State should have the right to confiscate or bestow property when it desired to punish or reward.

In 1769 the Polish Convention resolved to ask the French *philosophes* to make suggestions for a new Constitution for Poland. In the next year Polish liberty was destroyed by the neighbouring despots, whose philosophic principles did not prevent them from dividing among themselves the territory of an independent people. Voltaire enthusiastically approved of this example of enlightenment. Rousseau and Mably, however, had already made suggestions for the reorganization of a free Poland. Rousseau decided at once that the situation and tradi-

---

[1] *Vide* Vaughan, vol. ii. 151-152.

tions of Poland made anything like an ideal Constitution out of the question. Montesquieu himself could not have been more statesmanlike. The most important thing was that Poland should be animated by the spirit of liberty, that every citizen should think only of his country, her independence and moral greatness. But the spirit of liberty was dangerous : " High-souled and holy liberty ! If these poor men could only know thee, if they could only learn the price at which thou art won and guarded ; if they could only be taught how far sterner are thy laws than the hard yoke of the tyrant ; they would shrink from thee a hundred times more than from slavery, they would fly from thee in terror as from a burden made to crush them." Thus the Poles, and especially the serfs, should be moderate both in obtaining and using their liberty. " In thinking of what you would wish to acquire, do not forget what you may lose. Correct, if you can, the abuses of your Constitution, but never despise a Constitution which has made you what you are." Nevertheless, since " repose and liberty are incompatible . . . I will not say you ought to leave things as they are, but I will say that you must touch them with the greatest caution."

In accordance with these principles, Rousseau outlined a scheme of reforms. Poland, again, was too large for the democratic severity of ancient Sparta : " Your vast provinces will never admit the stern administration of a small State." Rousseau suggested, therefore, that the monarchy should become really elective ; that taxation should be equitably administered and levied upon landed property ; that the power should continue to reside in the aristocratic Senate. He offered the Third Estate no part in government and was opposed to anything more drastic than a very gradual scheme for freeing serfs, who might so easily misuse liberty when it was given them. He put his trust for the future of Poland in two things : education and the development of the principles of federalism. The education he recommended closely followed the precepts of *Emile* : it was not to proceed from books, not to aim at intellect, but to be a training for a useful life, rooted in virtue and inspired by patriotism. " Your citizens must learn to guide their tastes and opinions so that by inclination, by passion and by necessity they will be patriots." True patriotism and public spirit seemed to Rousseau to go only with a small State, where everyone could actively share in the duties of government. He pointed out to the Polish people that almost all the small States prospered because they were small, while " all the large nations, crushed by their own immensity, either grow like you into anarchy or sink beneath the petty oppressors whom their kings are compelled to give them." Poland, therefore, could hope to avoid the worst evils, though not to obtain the perfect society, by resolving herself into a Confederation consisting of Lithuania, Great and Little Poland. Each of the three would have its own Government, but would be united by a " legislative bond " and " subordinated to the Republic as a whole." " In one word, set yourselves to extend and perfect the system of federal government : the only one which unites the advantages of the large and the small State, and, for that very reason, the only one which is suited to your needs. If you disregard this advice I doubt whether your enterprise will ever come to good."

The apparent confusion between the absoluteness of Rousseau's principles and the caution with which he applied them is explicable by his doctrine of human nature. In both his early *Discours* he was certain that man, uncorrupted by human institutions, is naturally good. He could only hope that good institutions might redeem him from his actual wickedness. The doctrine of the social contract was an eighteenth-century reproduction of the sixteenth-century creed which he had first learned in Calvinist Geneva. Man, once innocent in the Garden, had been corrupted by the Fruit of the Tree of Knowledge, but a means of grace was offered him through which he could obtain regeneration and reach a far higher state than he ever could have attained before the Fall. Rousseau wrote *The Social Contract* to explain the social means of grace, by which civilized man could be saved. Redemption was possible, given the right political institutions. When, however, Rousseau was offered a repentant State clamouring for conversion, its heritage of sin seemed so overwhelming that an immediate attempt to find salvation in a wholehearted acceptance of the perfect life seemed out of the question. For Rousseau did not overlook the instinctive and passionate nature of man. Montesquieu had seen that there were environmental limitations, and these were fully appreciated and accepted by Rousseau. But he knew that they were less serious obstacles than human nature itself, since the men who suffered by the present institutions would have to work those which were substituted for them. Like the other *philosophes* he relied ultimately upon education; but whereas they meant by education simply the destruction of existing superstition, and the teaching of scientific truths, Rousseau saw that the mind was not synonymous with the intellect, and that it was possible to use knowledge for bad as well as good purposes. Conscious of the strength of human passions, Rousseau could not attribute the same importance to institutions as did his contemporaries, and even in *The Social Contract* the essence of his teaching is not that any democracy we can institute can be perfect, but that it is the only form of government which can ever be good at all in the long run, since it is the only one that offers men and women freedom, and which may in time regenerate them, and lead to the formation of a truly social community.

It was therefore Rousseau who supplied the answer to the Physiocratic doctrine that there was a single natural system, the observation of which would solve all social problems. He wrote to Mirabeau: " It seems to me that compelling evidence is never to be found in natural and political laws, unless when we consider them in the abstract. In any given government, composed, as it must be, of very diverse elements, this evidence is necessarily wanting. For the science of government is a science purely of combinations, applications and exceptions, which are determined by time, place and circumstance. And the public will never detect with intuitive certainty the relations and workings of all that. . . . Moreover, even supposing this certainty of evidence . . . how can philosophers who know anything of human nature assign to it such influence upon the actions of men? Can they be ignorant that men guide themselves very seldom by the light of evidence and very often by their passions? My friends, allow me to tell you that you give too much weight to your calculations, and not enough to the promptings of the heart and the play of passion. Your system is excellent for Utopia. For the children of Adam it is worth nothing."

5. THE INTERPRETATION OF ROUSSEAU

This last aspect of Rousseau—the cautious reformer, the respectful disciple of Montesquieu, the revolutionary who even hesitated to abolish serfdom—has been usually forgotten, but other parts of his teaching have had long, complicated and surprising histories. No one can be as fairly quoted in support of opposite theories as Rousseau. His doctrines were capable of extension and elaboration in directions which would have astonished him. His influence was probably increased by the fact that some passages in his works were mystical and obscure: *The Social Contract* could be treated like the Bible and *Das Kapital*—it could be variously interpreted by enthusiasts, endlessly commented on by scholars, and triumphantly quoted by rival schools, each certain of possessing the true milk of the master's teaching.

To some, Rousseau is an extreme individualist, hating all forms of social coercion, and denying the right of State or Church to impose its will upon any individual. The ideal of both the early *Discours* was a simple life, in which property would be held in common, and each man would be able to live as he pleased, earning his own living by his labour under the coercion of hunger only, untroubled by governments and heedless of conventions. Rousseau's own life and expressed inclinations supported this interpretation of his main teaching, and the apostles of the simple life, as well as the philosophic anarchists and early Utopian communists, found inspiration in his work. Godwin's *Political Justice* is a logical continuation of *The Origin of Inequality*. *The Social Contract* was equally useful to the exponents of an opposite theory of government. For them the State, the result of the general wills of all the individuals who compose it, is everything, and the individual whose actual will is recalcitrant counts for nothing. He has ceased to have rights of any sort against the State, he must be content with his opportunity to contribute to the general will. So far from being an exponent of natural rights, Rousseau is fairly quoted by authoritarians as a precursor of an extreme collectivism, in which neither private property nor religious liberty is free from the interference of government. Rousseau's division between the actual and real wills of individuals, the assumption that moral purposes can be fully developed only in the ideal State, led to nineteenth-century Idealism. Kant could base an individualist theory upon it, but the followers of Hegel easily used it to support a transcendental theory of the State, which, as the embodiment of the highest and best in the community, became valuable in itself and was alone able to give value to individual life. The confusion between the ideal democracy—in which the general will should give effect to the highest aspirations of individuals—and the actual dominance of class government in Prussia was the more easily made because the division between the ideal and the actual is never very clear in *The Social Contract* itself. The application of Rousseau to the more democratic conditions of England made by the Oxford idealists was more logical, but it resulted in a denial of individual rights as complete as that in the German followers of Hegel.

The truest interpretation of *The Social Contract* is some form of federalism: the Commune of 1870 is so far the nearest approach to a practical realization of Rousseau's theory. He had expressly said that the ideal freedom at which he aimed was attainable only in a small community, and had added that no freedom was possible in a large State unless it were divided into districts and given a federal constitution. The Girondists were attracted by this theory; nineteenth-century communists based a revolutionary philosophy upon it; syndicalists gave a new twist to its development by applying it to industrial groups instead of geographical areas. Exponents of mediæval federalism have found support in Rousseau's refusal to admit the validity of representation and have developed for their own purposes his argument that a social group other than the State may embody the will of its constituent members in relation only to the purpose for which the particular association has been formed.[1] Those who accept the corporation theory of the State are therefore indebted to Rousseau, as well as their bitterest opponents, the idealist protagonists of unified sovereignty.[2]

In the Revolution itself much of Rousseau's theory was inevitably misunderstood or neglected. For Rousseau had solved the problem of reconciling liberty and authority by postulating a State so small that the practical difficulties of reconciliation scarcely arose. He had himself seen that his argument applied only to the small community. He knew what economists have often forgotten—that, while the consideration of a simple case may sometimes elucidate the nature of a complex problem, it cannot provide a solution for it. The economic problems of a million persons are not those of Robinson Crusoe multiplied by a million, nor can the political problems of a modern community of men be solved by a statement of conditions which would be ideal for a small community of gods. If you simplify both your people and your conditions the result may be logical, suggestive, and even inspiring, but it cannot serve the purposes of the legislator and administrator. So much Rousseau had himself implicitly admitted when asked to apply himself to the art of government. When his followers,

---

[1] It is worth while to notice that Mr G. D. H. Cole, the principal exponent of guild socialism, began as an Oxford idealist, and wrote an introduction to Rousseau's political works (Everyman Edition) on orthodox Hegelian lines before he had developed his federalist theory. For his later use of Rousseau's doctrine of representation, and the position of particular associations, *vide* his *Social Theory*, p. 51. The argument that every modern State is really federal, and draws its authority from the fact that particular associations and corporations all play their part in the composition of any genuine community, is not of course confined to those whose federalism is mainly economic, but is equally found in Maitland, Figgis and Laski. This position is really first stated in Rousseau's *Political Economy*.

[2] The influence of Rousseau's remarks about particular associations in the State provides a curious example of the elasticity of political terms and of the ease with which the same theory can be utilized for opposite purposes by rival parties. The Chapelier Law of 1791, which prohibited all professional organizations in France, was passed in accordance with Rousseau's doctrine : with equal logic, modern theories of internal federalism appeal to Rousseau for justification of the thesis that authority is rightly exercised only where every member of the State is also organized in a professional association.

steeped in his phrases, tried to transform them into constitutions the only mechanism to their hand was that of representation. They could not stop to consider Rousseau's view, that the human will could not be represented and that representation really involved a different form of government. They did not consider the problem of how the " general will " could be made effective in a modern State : there is no hint in their writings or speeches of the need for organized parties or of an independent civil service.

Robespierre could not wait for a democratic meeting before taking action. He assumed, as naturally as Louis XIV. had assumed, that his own will represented the general will of the community. Rousseau's federalism, embodied in the Girondist proposal to give power to the communes of France, appeared political madness when foreign enemies were at the door. When the need for autocracy had passed away the only possible interpretation of *The Social Contract* seemed to be representative government and majority rule. Rousseau had supplied the populace with the cry of popular sovereignty, and in the French Revolution this could only mean the right to vote. Orators who quoted Rousseau were never tired of reminding their audiences that the people themselves were now sovereign, every common man exercising his share of the divine right of the French monarch. For the moment there seemed no difficulty. In the enthusiasm engendered by the struggle against the aristocrats and the Austrians, both the patriotism and the democratic virtue which Rousseau had acclaimed as the true basis of a political society seemed to be realized throughout France. Sebastian Mercier, a fervent disciple of Rousseau, expressed his astonishment, in 1791, that Rousseau could have imagined that democracy was only applicable to a State the size of Geneva, while the Abbé Sièyes popularized and gave effect to *The Social Contract* by his pamphlet *Qu'est-ce que le Tiers Etat ?* He saw none of Rousseau's difficulties, had no objection to representation, no view that the only valid legislation is of a purely general character which affects everyone equally ; he was content to expound the doctrine of popular sovereignty in a form which people could understand. "What is the Third Estate ? " the

first page of his pamphlet asks, and the reply is : " Everything."
"What has it so far been in the political order?" "Nothing."
"What is its demand?" "To be something." In the event, as
the result of revolutionary movements in many countries, the
Third Estate of Europe became something, and the arguments
which led to a middle-class franchise were available for a
later generation which urged that a property qualification was
inconsistent with democratic theory.

Rousseau's disciples were easily reconciled to the exclusion
of the working class from its theoretical share in government.
They were also persuaded by utilitarian arguments to tolerate
representation. The elected representative would maintain his
constituents' liberty because his interest would lie in obeying
the will of his masters. Those who respected British practice
more than democratic theory were content that the representative should retain some independence and owe his constituents,
in Burke's phrase, "not his industry only, but his judgment."
Sterner democrats, who feared that representatives would
develop "sinister" or "particular" interests (here Bentham
and Rousseau meant the same thing), were anxious to make
them delegates liable to frequent re-election. Jeffersonian
democracy, directly inspired by Rousseau, had little influence
on the Federal Constitution; it was more successful in the
case of some State constitutions which ensure administrative
inefficiency by providing for the annual or biennial elections
of their legislatures and officers. Further instalments of direct
democracy have been added in many parts of the world, and
Rousseau's influence is to be traced wherever civil servants
and judges[1] are directly elected and liable to recall, and
where referenda and plebiscites may override the authority
of parliaments.

These were later victories of the democratic principle. At the
Revolution itself the task of interpreting democratic doctrine
was in the hands of men of property. The peasantry and the

---

[1] The election of judges was tried during the French Revolution, and is still
the usage of some American States, which also elect many of their civil servants.
The institution of an independent civil service chosen by examination was
perhaps the most fortunate of all British contributions to the art of politics.

urban middle class, which controlled the Revolution except when the Parisian mob was out of hand, had long been burdened by an arbitrary executive which did not respect any rights of property, person or thought. They desired political power commensurate with their economic power; the practical method of obtaining it was the one which the great landowners of England had discovered in the seventeenth century. A Parliament elected by themselves should make the laws and see that they were enforced by a responsible executive. Thus European States in the nineteenth century were commonly governed by parliaments which represented the energetic and wealthy middle class : this class claimed to be " the people " ; its sovereignty was the sovereignty of the people and middle-class government was therefore democracy.

To mention the schools of thought that paid homage to Rousseau and to explain the developments of political practice which have been influenced by him is enough to show the varied possibilities of his teaching. But in truth Rousseau was a genius whose real influence cannot be traced with precision because it pervaded all the thought that followed him. Rousseau was the originator of a religious movement of which the Catholic revival was only one of the beneficiaries. He paved the way for men as various as Bernardin de Saint-Pierre, Chateaubriand, Victor Hugo and Lamennais. Everything anti-rational, whether it was religious, romantic or merely sentimental, profited by his teaching. Men will always be sharply divided about Rousseau ; for he released imagination as well as sentimentalism ; he increased men's desire for justice as well as confusing their minds, and he gave the poor hope even though the rich could make use of his arguments. In one direction at least Rousseau's influence was a steady one : he discredited force as a basis for the State, convinced men that authority was legitimate only when founded on rational consent and that no arguments from passing expediency could justify a government in disregarding the claims of individual freedom or in failing to promote social equality.

CHAPTER IX

EQUALITY AND PROPERTY

I. THE DEMAND FOR EQUALITY

EQUALITY, like other abstractions of political controversy, has been used as the standard and rallying cry of the battlefield, not as the measurable condition of a good life. There is no absolute equality, just as there is no single condition of liberty. Analysis shows that with each group and period the substance of the equality claimed has varied, though the emotions of the struggle always prevented any adequate analysis being made, either by those who claimed new rights or by those who defended old privileges. When men demand equality their desire for justice is stimulated by the hope of effecting concrete social changes, and it is only by examining the proposals which accompany the demand, and the use made of greater equality when it is obtained, that any light is thrown upon the political theory of the period.

In eighteenth-century France equality was the demand of the middle class, and eventually of the peasantry, for the abolition of privilege. They protested because the *noblesse* were not subject to the same courts, did not pay any share of the taxes which oppressed them, and added to their burdens an even greater toll of feudal dues. They asked for the unhampered right to work, the right to enjoy the fruits of their labour and the abolition of the powers which the idle possessed to levy toll upon it. Feudalism was a system of legalized inequality based on rank and function. When the functions were no longer performed the privileges stank. Equality, therefore, meant that nature gave no sanction for legal inequalities : that all men were entitled to the same rights, having equal needs and being able to perform the same functions.

A theoretical basis for this claim was evolved by moralists, psychologists and economists. Firstly, moralists of the school of Rousseau declared that men were naturally equal. They were once more expressing the Christian idea that men, being all children of God, were of the same intrinsic value. Secondly, at the opportune moment, sensationalist psychology seemed to offer a scientific basis for what had hitherto been a religious doctrine intuitively apprehended. Starting from Condillac's elaboration of Locke, the politician was able to declare that men were by nature equal, not only in value but in intelligence, capacity and gifts. If the child's mind was a blank sheet at birth, and there was no original sin nor original merit, the presumption of hereditary superiority was merely a trick to support aristocratic privilege. If men were indeed all "perfectible" by the right education and environment, then there was no justification for social inequality.

Thirdly, the economists now produced arguments for abolishing privilege. The land, Locke taught, though originally "common to all men," became private property through individual work. "Whatsoever, then, a man removes out of the state that nature hath provided and left it in, he hath mixed his labour with it, and joined to it something that is his own, and thereby makes it his property." Men labour in order that they may enjoy the fruits of their labour : they are entitled to do so since "it is labour indeed that puts the difference of value on everything." "As much land as a man tills, plants, improves, cultivates, and can use the product of, so much is his property." Thus natural law and common sense seemed the same thing, and the peasant had a theoretical justification for claiming the ownership of the land which he tilled. The Physiocrats accepted Locke's basis of natural law as well as his argument for private property, though they emphasized the land itself rather than the labour expended upon it as the ultimate source of value. Providence, they believed, had so arranged society that the grant of equal property rights and trading opportunities would produce the greatest social well-being.

Avarice, for centuries repudiated by the Catholic Church as a sin, became in the new philosophy a virtue whereby the indulgence of each man's desire to do the best for himself proved also to be best for the public welfare. Even before the Revolution, however, there were some who thought this right to struggle on equal terms for private possessions an inadequate guarantee of social harmony. Locke's doctrine, moreover, was open to different interpretations. Like the Physiocrats, he had thought in terms of an agrarian community, and in the eighteenth century there were groups of town wage-earners whose claim to the whole product of their labour challenged middle-class employers rather than feudal landlords. Locke had assumed that Nature was beneficent and her gifts plenteous. A man's labour, he wrote, " being the unquestionable property of the labourer, no one but he can have a right to what that is once joined to, *at least where there is enough, and as good left in common for others.*" Men submitted to unequal distribution of land, "having, by consent, found out and agreed in a way how a man may, rightfully and without injury, possess more than he himself can make use of by receiving gold and silver." But what if this arrangement proved to be not " without injury," and " right and conveniency " failed to go together? What if a property owner, in spite of Locke's assurance, did not regard it as " useless, as well as dishonest, to carve himself too much, or take more than he needed "? What if the institution of private property actually led to inequality instead of making all men equal? Would not communism then be the fulfilment of the law of nature?

In the second half of the century, therefore, we may distinguish several distinct schools, united in attacking the social and legal inequalities of the *ancien régime*, but basing their opposition on widely different philosophies and looking forward to opposite alternatives. The Church and the *noblesse* defended their privileges against the King, whose financial needs tempted him to assert his sovereign right to tax all the orders equally. Driven by bankruptcy, the monarchy undermined the feudal structure and initiated the Revolution. Encyclopædists and economists took sides with Louis, appealing to him to recognize openly the iniquity of all privileges, to abolish economic restrictions and levy taxes, when necessary, only upon the land, which they thought was the sole source of wealth. Above all, the King should establish equal rights for all descriptions of property. Communists, on the other hand, planned Utopias in which private property had been altogether abandoned and a life of co-operative service substituted. More directly revolutionary writers were concerned less with the moral degradation of society than with the physical miseries of the Fourth Estate, and suggested Liberal reforms which would produce greater equality, though they shrank from the practical results of advocating a socialist revolution. Two men are especially interesting here : Linguet, because he alone submitted society to a purely class analysis and prophesied a future revolution of the poor against the rich ; and Babeuf, because, unlike his fellow-theorists, he was unsatisfied with limited political democracy as a substitute for the economic equality he had preached and was willing to put his socialistic faith to the test of action. When the Revolution came, the grievances of the town worker and the communistic visions of theorists were alike unheeded. Babeuf's socialist rising was quickly suppressed ; the peasants had gained the free ownership of their land and the middle classes had destroyed the social superiority of the *noblesse* and won the right to trade freely without the restrictions of the *ancien régime.* But political equality as well as economic equality was refused to the town worker and the nineteenth-century State was a middle-class affair, governed by men of property. Even equality of opportunity was but partially established, since inheritance of wealth remained to form the basis of a new aristocracy.

2. PRIVILEGE—THE SURVIVAL OF FEUDAL THEORY

The establishment of a Liberal economic régime in France meant, as the Physiocrats well knew, sweeping away the privileges of all the ancient corporations. It meant attacking not only the *jurandes* and *maîtrises*, but also the aristocracy and the Church. Turgot confronted these vested interests with arguments ultimately derived from Locke. "I do not think," he wrote, after describing the reforms which he hoped the King would bring about, "that such useful plans would be opposed on the great principle of the respect due to property." Such opposition would indeed be "a very strange contradiction," since corporation property was, in its origin, "almost all founded on usurpations." Yet those who possessed it were

" permitted, on the pretext of a very badly understood right, to steal the property which is most sacred of all, that which can alone be the basis of all other property "—a man's right " to the fruit of his labour." [1]

Ancient corporations, however, become habituated to the possession of property, and seldom see the necessity of justifying their title-deeds. When Turgot was at length given his short opportunity of reform, all the corporations opposed him. His edict suppressing the *corvée* which fell exclusively on the poor, carried with it the threat of more equable taxation. In its remonstrance on behalf of the privileged orders, the *Parlement* of Paris reminded the King that all his subjects were " obliged to contribute to the needs of State," but " by this very contribution order and harmony will always be maintained. The personal service of the clergy is to fulfil all functions relating to education and religious observance and to contribute to the relief of the unfortunate by alms. The noble consecrates his blood to the defence of the State and assists the Sovereign by advice. The last class of the nation, which cannot render such distinguished services to the State, contributes industry and manual labour. . . . By freeing the last class of citizens from the *corvée*, to which it has hitherto been subjected, the edict transfers this charge to the two orders of the State which have never been subjected to it. The difference between your subjects disappears, the noble and the ecclesiastic become liable to the *corvée*, or, what is the same thing, they become liable to contribute to the tax which must take the place of the *corvée*. This is not, as people have tried to persuade you, Sire, a battle of the rich against the poor. It is a question of State and one of the most important ; for it is a question of knowing if all your subjects can and ought to be treated in the same way ; if there must be an end of admitting different conditions, ranks, titles and pre-eminences amongst them."

Certainly the case for class as an institution could scarcely have been more clearly expressed ; it would have been a stronger case, however, if the Church had, in fact, organized any general

---

[1] *Collection des Economistes*, t. iii. 253.

system of education or poor relief, or if the *noblesse* had really been the principal sufferers in Louis XV.'s numerous wars. Indeed, the defence of feudalism on the ground that privilege was the reward of service was out of date in an age when feudal services had long ceased to be performed.

After the Revolution, de Maistre attacked the *philosophes* on the ground that they had undermined that spiritual authority without which society is merely a chaos of conflicting groups and individuals seeking their own advantage, heedless of social outlook or Christian purpose. This is a sound line of defence for the mediæval Church : it seems scarcely applicable to the eighteenth century, when a resident bishop was a rarity, a large part of the clergy were free-thinkers and the struggle between Jansenist and Jesuit filled France with discord. The seventeenth century had produced ecclesiastics like Claude Joly, who were not afraid to speak freely, and during the age of Louis XIV. Fénelon, Massillon and Bossuet had at least reminded the rich of their Christian duty to the poor and warned the King of the dangers of misrule and arbitrary government. But in the eighteenth century the clergy left social criticism and public instruction to the *philosophes*. Marmontel describes a conversation between a *philosophe* and de Broglie, Bishop of Noyon, in which the Bishop complained of the impudence of the *philosophes*.

" ' It is true, Monseigneur,' I replied, ' that they take it upon themselves to usurp some of your noblest functions, but only when you fail to fulfil them.' 'What functions?' he asked. ' Those of preaching from the roof-tops the truths that are too rarely told to sovereigns or their Ministers or to the flatterers who surround them. Since the exile of Fénelon, or perhaps since the touching little course of moral instruction given by Massillon to Louis XIV. as a child, useless because premature, have the clergy once protested boldly against public crimes and vices? ' " [1]

There were, however, some clerical protests against social evils in the century.[2] Poucet de la Rivière declared that " all men are

---

[1] Quoted by Roustan, English trans., p. 262.
[2] For these *vide* Lichtenberger, *Le Socialisme au XVIIIᵉ Siècle*, 349 ff.

only depositories and administrators of those goods of which God, who has put them into their hands, always remains proprietor and master," and approved the maxim of Saint Ambrose that to give alms to a poor man is only to give him back part of that which is already rightly his ; in any case, the poor man possesses spiritual riches, while the rich man obtains earthly possessions instead and runs the risk of suffering the fate of Dives hereafter. Popular orators like the Abbé Poulle and the Abbé de Cambacérès reflect current sentiment in insisting on the right to happiness rather than the duty of mortifying the flesh ; and Father Griffet warned rich men that they owed their wealth to the accident of birth, and should share it with the poor. God might not hold the rich guiltless if poor men were driven to blasphemy and wickedness by the injustice of their lot. Some preachers even praised the ideal of Christian communism. The wickedness of usury still formed an occasional theme for clerics, one of whom, Père de Gasquet, went so far as to assert that interest is " a tax imposed by the idle or unintelligent owner upon the industrious cultivator and hard-working merchant. . . . Moneylenders gnaw and devour the best citizens, as insects fasten upon the best fruit ; hidden under a mysterious veil of bills drawn upon the borrower they amass criminal wealth without giving him the sad satisfaction of knowing whose is the unjust hand which gathers the fruits of labour." This section of society, consisting of all the useless persons in the State, lives on the cultivator's knowledge and the business man's toil, but contributes least to the taxation levied on the nation because it occupies all the privileged positions. "The rich never pay in the same proportion as the poor," because their wealth can be carried in a pocket-book and so cannot be assessed.

An occasional churchman might still remember that Saint Thomas had denounced trade for mere gain, saying that " it is justly scorned since in itself it serves the lust for wealth " ; and the early years of the Revolution were to show that Rousseau's picture of the Savoyard vicar, beloved of his flock and teaching the gospel of Christ rather than the doctrines of Catholicism, was not an imaginary one.

The greater clergy, however, had become indistinguishable from the rest of the higher *noblesse*. Bossuet had been of middle-class origin, but the great churchmen of Louis XV.'s reign usually owed their position to their families, as in the case of a Rohan or a Montmorency, or alternatively to intrigue, as in the case of a Dubois or a de Tencin. The general view presented by the eighteenth-century Church is that of a feudal corporation grasping a great inheritance, free from recognized obligations or service, absorbed in a struggle nominally due to dogmatic differences, but actually concerned with temporal power, and willing at every opportunity to crush with violence and cruelty any rival faction, heretic or critic.[1]

The clergy were not, therefore, a popular body, and when the Clerical Assembly protested against the King's demand for a twentieth the royal lawyers found immediate public support.[2] They declared that the sovereignty of the Monarch was not restricted by past immunities and that all property was held at the King's pleasure. Pamphleteers supported the theory of absolute sovereignty, making *raison d'état* the final test and denying all rights against the State. The churchmen were reminded that even in the original feudal contract, by which they had gained their immunity, the Crown was " the first proprietor of all goods," that they, like other men, were subject to the social obligations that arose from the existence of the State and the facts of sovereignty. The entire goods of the State belonged to the Sovereign, one writer declared; individuals had only the usufruct of them. "Property," he wrote, "ought to be respected; yes, certainly: but only in this sense, that one ought not to alienate it unnecessarily, and without a necessity arising from the actual condition of public affairs." The safety of the State is the final law. " All means are good, according to the circumstances in which a State finds itself." Even taxation

---

[1] The landed property of the clergy is estimated at five to six per cent. of the whole territory of France. The annual revenue of the Church was some 80 to 100 millions livres in rent and about 123 millions in tithes. For all this *vide* the summary in Sée, *La France économique et sociale au XVIIIᵉ Siecle*, 55-57.

[2] For this controversy *vide* Lichtenberger, *op. cit.*, 383 ff.

which would break up the property of families would be justified on occasion, but obviously the goods of the clergy can be
confiscated with less dislocation to society. In this controversy
the revolutionary struggle is already foreshadowed ; the clergy
were soon to find themselves attacked by the Jacobins in the
name of the sovereign people who sat crowned upon Louis'
throne. Popular support of despotism has always arisen where
it alone is sufficiently strong to check greedy and powerful
corporations.

3. LIBERAL ECONOMICS AND NATURAL HARMONY—THE PHYSIOCRATS AND THE BOURGEOISIE

Conditions were in every way favourable to the rise of a
Liberal school of economists. The King's financial embarrassment, the burden of oppressive and arbitrary taxation, the
restraint of trade and the absurdity of surviving feudalism,
the agricultural depression and miserable condition of the
peasantry, all added point to criticism and led to the growth of
a group of economic thinkers who expanded and systematized
the views already expressed by Vauban and Boulainvilliers in
the reign of Louis XIV. It was natural that this school should
have been primarily concerned with attacking Colbertism and
emphasizing the importance of agriculture as the source of
wealth.[1] The form which this doctrine took, however, was
greatly influenced by current philosophy, and its most important
generalizations applied not only to France but to all States
which adopted a basis of free contract and private property.

In the thirty years which followed the death of Louis XIV.
there was frequent but spasmodic discussion of economic theory.
Controversy raged around John Law's luckless scheme of in-
flation ; Cantillon's *Essai du Commerce* (1715) did for economics

---

[1] Holding that land was the only source of wealth, the Physiocrats believed
that the only just tax was a land tax. Unlike any other kind of property, land
yielded a rent, a net product. The landlord could pay a tax on this without
the right of private property being infringed and without the productivity of
the land being impaired. The State would always leave the landlord as much
revenue as he could have acquired in any other kind of business, and by the
impôt unique the State and the landowner would become partners.

what Voltaire's *Letters on the English* did for "philosophy," summarizing English political economy and introducing Locke's economics to a wider audience. Melon's *Essai politique* (1734) and Dupin's *Mémoires sur les Blés* (1742) both struck at mercantilism and advocated the removal of restrictions upon the transport of corn in France, though neither Melon nor Dupin reached the point of suggesting complete freedom of trade. Montesquieu's *Esprit des Lois* (1748) was the signal for a great outburst of economic discussion, and by 1760 a group of economists had been formed, holding a common doctrine and advocating a common policy. Quesnay was safely installed at Versailles as Madame de Pompadour's doctor; the official *Gazette du Commerce* was converted to the new economic doctrines in 1765, and the hitherto hostile *Ephémérides* became the organ of the Physiocrats two years later. The publication of the *Tableau économique* signalized the unity of the new group whose abilities were openly pitted against the royal policy. The Government indeed played into the hands of its critics, sometimes admitting its conversion by passing reforming edicts and then advertising its weakness by new surrenders to private interests. In 1754 it passed an edict to facilitate the transmission of corn from one province to another, but neglected to remove the feudal rights which actually prevented its passage. Physiocratic influence reached its height when Turgot, who, as *intendant*, had already attempted to apply Physiocratic principles in his own province, became Controller-General of France. His dismissal eighteen months later was an admission that though the King might be Liberal in sentiment he was not powerful enough to carry reforms in the teeth of the aristocracy. Disappointment was increased when, after Turgot's dismissal, the *Parlements*, once more secure from attack, initiated an obviously reactionary policy. Instead of edicts designed to promote free trade and social equality, Turgot's successors passed decrees excluding all who had not four degrees of nobility from holding military commissions, forbidding anyone to cut grass or corn with a scythe, and demanding that in future all pocket-handkerchiefs should be exactly as broad as they were long. The Commercial Treaty with England in

1786, though believed to be unfavourable to France, seemed to be a further vindication of the Physiocrats, and reinforced their view that it was bad government, not natural poverty, which made the State bankrupt. But the direct influence of the Physiocrats really ends with Turgot's dismissal, and when Liberal economics revived with J. B. Say, Adam Smith had taken Quesnay's place as the patron saint of economists.

The starting-point of the Physiocrats was that of eighteenth-century philosophy in general. The scientific notion that the material world was not subject to the arbitrary caprice of a personal deity, but was governed by fixed and ascertainable laws, was applied by them to the organization of society. Quesnay's conviction that a natural order of society lay within our reach, if the Creator's ordinances were followed, was built, just as Locke's had been, upon his training and experience as a doctor. He believed, as one of his disciples put it, that " natural laws extended far beyond the bounds hitherto assigned to them," and applied to the circulation of money just as they did to the circulation of the blood. The order of nature was merely the physical constitution which God Himself had given the universe, " its laws," said Mercier, another disciple, " are irrevocable, pertaining as they do to the essence of matter and the soul of humanity ; they are simply the expression of the will of God." In the organization of society, therefore, just as in the physical order, there are unalterable processes, the understanding and observation of which lead to salvation, the neglect to destruction. Thus the art of government is not to make or administer new laws but to maintain a condition in which the laws of nature freely operate. Social life must follow nature—that is, must be regulated by an intelligent adherence to divine law. Therefore, in Dupont's words, " there is a natural judge of all ordinances, even of the sovereign's." This judge, who recognizes no exceptions, is simply the evidence of their conformity with, or opposition to, natural laws. The Chinese, the Physiocrats believed, had so far been alone in appreciating this truth, " for," said Baudeau, they speak of " the order or voice of heaven and reduce all government to a single law to conform to the voice of heaven."

The Physiocrats were therefore left with the task of discovering the law of nature and persuading the rulers of France to conform not to their own wishes but to the dictates of Heaven. Fortunately the natural laws of society were much easier to discover than their counterparts in the physical world. Newton had established the truth of a natural law only after many years of arduous calculation, but the formulæ of social gravitation were believed by the Physiocrats to be immediately " evident," since the supply of apples and other commodities always came in response to men's demands. " The order," said Mercier, " obviously most advantageous to each nation only needs to be known to be observed." Man had only " to examine himself, to find within him an articulate conception of these laws." A simple process of introspection was conclusive, though an empirical investigation might be necessary for scientific demonstration.

Descartes and Locke together offered the psychological basis for this confident conclusion. "Evidence," declared Mercier, " is a clear and distinct discernment of sentiments which we have and of all perceptions which depend on them." The " evidence " here is Cartesian : the " rational intuition " which is corroborated by " the witness of the senses." " It would be a great enterprise," wrote Thomas, in an *éloge* on Descartes in 1765, " only to judge of all customs, usages and laws after the great maxim of Descartes, according to the evidence. A truth exists by itself and is in nature, and the act of judging is nothing else than the talent of opening the eyes." The influence of Locke was in the same direction. The social truth became more certain when innate ideas were abolished. Condillac, himself a notable economist, had already argued that the child's only instinctive tendency was to repeat some sensations called pleasures, and to avoid others called pains. " Love of pleasure and aversion from pain are the two great springs of humanity," said Mercier, long before Bentham had arrived at the same formula. Unhampered by the false teachings of morality, men would soon find that this simple tendency led them to happiness ; being endowed with a capacity for reflection, they would quickly discover their dependence on one another, would avoid giving offence to those who could inflict

pain in return, and realize that their own happiness lay in the
welfare of others. Christian ethics could easily be deduced from
self-interest, since, as Mercier put it, " not to do to others what
we should not wish them to do to us is an invariable law of
reason."

The task of the economist, therefore, is to work out the
detailed application of principles which are evident to every
reasonable human being who cares to reflect upon his experience.
Since these principles are part of the law of nature, and everywhere valid and invariable, economics must cease to be a matter
of opinion, of probabilities and surmises, and become a science
whose conclusions are as reliable as those of the physicist. Once
the information is obtained and the laws known, the calculus
can do the rest. Economics then becomes a question of
mathematics. The amount of taxation, for instance, which the
Sovereign is right in demanding can be discovered by simple
" addition and subtraction." His calculation may be wrong :
if so, his error is easily demonstrable, for, with the *Tableau
économique* as a basis, anyone may check him, and his conclusion
must, like a proposition in Euclid, be either right or wrong.

By an easy transition the whole service of government seemed
to the Physiocrats capable of the same mathematical treatment.
The warning of Montesquieu that the application and development of natural law vary with place and circumstance was
altogether neglected. The *a priori* habits of classical thought
were reinforced by a mathematical approach, and political and
economic problems were all capable of simple and final solutions.
" It will suffice to have that amount of capacity and patience
which a child who is good at arithmetic employs, to become
a good politician or a truly good citizen," wrote another
economist.[1] Mirabeau declared that politics, on the basis of
natural law, was more exact than any of the physical sciences.
To collect particular facts and deduce principles from them
might be a " very good or even the only method " in other
sciences, such as chemistry or physics, but it was quite unnecessary to establish the truths of politics and economics,

---

[1] *Vide* Weulersse, *Le Mouvement physiocratique*, vol. ii., p. 123.

which were " everywhere susceptible of decisive demonstration."
The Physiocrats, believing in the universality of natural law,
could cast all caution to the winds. Bentham, who repudiated
the whole conception of natural law, was scarcely less optimistic
about the possibility of founding an exact science of politics.
Bentham saw, however, that such a science was possible only
—even theoretically—if the pleasures and pains which moved
men to action could be classified. The " felicific calculus " was
an indispensable supplement to the " *tableau économique*." But
Dupont anticipated James Mill's arithmetical political science
without the least attempt at psychological analysis. " If the
different powers [in the State]," he wrote, "are equal, there is no
authority ; if one among them is superior, that is the authority,
the others are nothing." Historical considerations seemed as
futile to the Physiocrats as to the early utilitarians. The past
is to be remembered only to be condemned. " All human legislation has been only the institution of legal disorder, excited
by the particular interest and excused on the ground of the
public interest."

The task of the enlightened ruler in the eighteenth century
was, therefore, a godlike one ; as " a living image of the most
high " he could harmonize all things by simply substituting
natural order for existing chaos. The first and most evident
teaching of natural law was the mutual interdependence of men.
In a natural society men and nations would freely exchange
their superfluous products, and all would gain, since some were
rich in one thing, some in another. Particular interests would
then automatically serve the public well-being. This would
always be the result if the natural right to private property
were recognized. A man who worked had the best title to the
fruits of his industry, and would hardly work well unless pricked
by the incentive of personal gain. The first duty of the State,
therefore, was to abolish all hampering restrictions and feudal
contracts which kept men from enjoying the property which
was naturally theirs. If men were to benefit by their mutual
interdependence, private property must be coupled with freedom of contract and equality of opportunity. Both production
and distribution were best served by freedom of the market,

in which supply and demand swing upon their eternal balance. Though it was left to Adam Smith to make the full deductions from the theories of division of labour and natural inter-dependence, the need for international peace and its connection with international free trade finds a prominent place in Physio-cratic writing. If it is desirable for individual men to exchange freely, it is equally important that there should be no barriers between provinces, and, since " each nation is only a province of the great Kingdom of Nations," universal free trade will result in universal prosperity.

The prospect was certainly bright. Mercier wrote : " Each of us, by favour of this full and entire liberty, and pricked by desire of enjoyment, is occupied, according to his state, in vary-ing, multiplying, perfecting the objects of enjoyment which must be shared amongst us, and thus increases the sum of the common happiness by increasing his private happiness. And so each in the sum total of the common happiness would take a particular sum which ought to belong to him. We must admire the way in which every man becomes an instrument to the happiness of others, and the manner in which this happiness seems to communicate itself to the whole. Speaking literally, of course, I do not know if in this State we shall see a few un-happy people, but if there are any, they will be so few in number and the number of the happy will be so great that we need not be much concerned about helping them. All our interests and wills will be linked to the interest and will of the Sovereign, creating for our common good an harmony, which can only be regarded as the work of a kind Providence that wishes the land to be full of happy men."

This is the very apotheosis of optimistic Liberalism. In an age of feudal privilege, dynastic war and arbitrary taxation, the removal of legal and customary barriers appeared to be all that was required for happiness and prosperity. It was easy to believe in the existence of a natural harmony when so much misery was obviously caused by artificial maladjustment : freedom and *laissez-faire* seemed the same thing to a generation fettered and choked by unreasonable methods of interference. Agriculture and trade could never prosper while the feudal superior, the monarch and the tax-gatherer took from the peasant and the merchant the best fruits of their industry. England seemed to the Physiocrats a model only less to be imitated than China : they praised the system of peasant proprietorship in England just at the time when England was in fact ceasing to have peasant proprietors and when the land was being absorbed by great landowners who had often as little interest in agriculture as the French *noblesse*. But the comparison served for the time. The demand for freedom of contract and for private property involved the reversal of the whole social system in France ; and the Revolution itself gave the land to the peasants, who, having won it at the expense of the private rights of their feudal superiors, have adhered steadfastly to a belief in the absolute rights of property ever since.

4. SOCIALISM AND UTOPIA—MESLIER, MABLY AND MORELLY

In an agricultural society property and equality are naturally associated. To the French peasant they were coincident. In a community of small farmers, all who own are equal, and, where there are no differences of rank, degrees of prosperity do not give rise to social problems. The freeholding peasant is not directly in the power of any capitalist, and feels himself the superior, rather than the inferior, of the merchant, while the views of the landless labourer are seldom expressed and almost always unheeded. In an urban civilization, on the other hand, where land and inheritance play a smaller part, property and equality seem contradictory conceptions. Distinction depends on money, not on land, and in an industrialized community money means power and carries with it social superiority. When the town worker demanded equality, therefore, he was not asking for a change of legal status, but for a different distribution of the product of industry. Socialist theory has always suffered, and still suffers to-day, from a failure to distinguish between two contradictory views of what this new distribution should be. The worker might claim his right to a just share in the product of industry : in this case he was using the orthodox argument that since every man is entitled to the reward of his own labour a system which gives the capitalist and the shareholder the first claim on profits is inequitable. But since it was in fact impossible to apportion exactly what was produced by labour and what by capital in an industrial society, the worker might demand that the whole product of industry should be vested in the State and then equally divided among producers. Even before the Revolution some writers declared that all profits were the result of labour, and one, Simon-Henri Linguet, anticipated the theory of "surplus value" and the "iron law of wages." Communism, however, does not depend on the Marxian argument, and consistent egalitarians, alike innocent of dialectic or of economic science, demanded that the social product should be divided according to need, not according to productive capacity.

France was a land of peasants, not of industrial workers, and the main current of revolutionary economics was therefore in the direction of equal rights of ownership, and not of equal distribution. The demand for property and equality meant quite simply that all should have the legal right to free economic activity—a claim that would have been fairly described as "equality of opportunity" only if there had been a universal system of free education and if all rights of inheritance had been abolished. This theory assumed the existence of a natural harmony. But even in the eighteenth century some observers were unfavourably impressed by the effects of the growing capitalist organization, and doubted whether the interests of employers and employed were identical. And before the rise of these early urban socialists there were moralists who, being moved to pity by the misery of the poor, and haunted by the precepts of the gospels, recalled the canons of the mediæval Church and the ideal republic of Plato. They denied the right of the individual to act without consciousness of social obligation, and described enlightened self-interest as the sin of avarice. Eighteenth-century socialism sprang from a moral objection to the theory that luxury is socially beneficial. It was in origin a Puritan attack on economic hedonism.

Thus, although the results of *laissez-faire* economics could be only dimly foreseen in the eighteenth century, a number of writers, who joined with the Physiocrats in criticizing the *ancien régime*, repudiated the remedy they offered. They denounced the existing order because rights were divorced from service : it seemed to them no remedy formally to recognize a practical evil and to substitute irresponsible competition for irresponsible privilege. The search for money and for possessions was in itself bad. Private vices, they declared, could never be public benefits : no moral, communal nor happy life was possible upon the basis of individual self-seeking. A community implied a common effort. The individual ownership of property in an unorganized society would lead merely to an aristocracy of wealth founded on the destruction of an aristocracy of birth : a new struggle between rich and poor would take the place of the existing one between the privileged and the Third Estate.

Socialism in the eighteenth century was primarily moral, and only incidentally economic. It found its inspiration in the conception of a natural state of communism, and supported it by accounts of the primitive virtues of the American Indians whom Jesuit missionaries described. It looked to Plato and to Stoicism for its theory and the Sparta of Lycurgus became its stock example of an egalitarian society. The Christian Church, too, though in the main ready enough to find the usual moral justification for institutions condemned in the New Testament, gave birth to occasional priests who contrasted the political Church of the eighteenth century with the simple life of the early Christians.

The moralist believed that the love of money was the root of social evil : it was bad that some should live as parasites on the labour of others, worse that most people should want to do so. As long as men based their society on self-interest, struggle and chaos were inevitable. Socialists agreed with Physiocrats that in a natural society men would help one another without pain or effort, but were sure that this desirable result would not automatically follow from the encouragement of selfishness and the removal of State regulation. Harmony would take the place of chaos only if society were deliberately organized on a moral basis. It was absurd to expect a harmony from the absence of order, or a guiding hand to bring universal peace and prosperity to men engaged in cutting one another's throats.

Even in the first half of the century, men like Montesquieu and d'Argenson agreed that democracy implied socialism. Montesquieu had argued that a democracy must be inspired by civic virtue, and it was rare " for there to be much virtue where men's fortunes were unequal." D'Argenson also treated property, not as a natural right, but as a matter of utility, and criticized Montesquieu for thinking that economic inequality was ever desirable, even in a monarchy. He held, on the contrary, that " a legislator, like a doctor, ought to aim at banishing inequality and luxury," and declared that the extravagance of private individuals in France was one of the usual signs of decadence. He complained of monopolists, compared great financiers to drones in a hive, and proceeded, in a remarkable passage, to attack the whole theory of capitalism. Why, he asks, this elaborate method of enabling a few to accumulate all the power and money? Are big merchants really good for the country? Would it not be better if the State lent money to small cultivators rather than to merchants who made themselves monopolists? "The question comes down to this : does the well-being of a pond demand the existence of huge pike which grow fat on all the little and moderate-sized fish?"[1]

This was an isolated view. The main stream of eighteenth-century socialism begins in 1755 with Rousseau's attack upon private property in the essay on *The Origin of Inequality*. The simple and carefree state of nature had been destroyed by the introduction of private property, and from this fatal departure from natural (that is, primitive as well as ideal) conditions came all the crop of social evils and unjust laws which the usurpers of the common stock of property imposed on the others. The present institution of private property could not be defended by Locke's argument that it was the natural result of labour. When there ceased to be enough land for everyone ownership changed its character : the owner used his strategic advantage to make others do the work for him. Thus Rousseau's

---

[1] The whole passage is quoted by Lichtenberger, *op. cit.*, 98-99.

whole attack on wealth could be deduced from a mere hint in the *Essay on Civil Government*. The wealthy, Rousseau argued, not having either good arguments or superior physical strength, conceived " the profoundest plan that ever entered the human mind." They made allies of their adversaries, persuading them to institute rules of justice, to stabilize the *status quo*, and thus safeguard their ill-gotten gains. So did the rich persuade the poor to run " headlong to their chains in the hope of securing their liberty." Society is therefore founded on fraud, and a revolution, followed by a return to primitive communism, seems the natural conclusion of Rousseau's argument. Rousseau, however, explicitly repudiated this inference. " What then is to be done? " he writes. " Must society be totally abolished, must *meum* and *tuum* be annihilated, and must we return again to live among bears? " No, that was impossible, unless for any fortunate individuals whose passions were still uncorrupted and who could subsist on plants or acorns and live without laws and magistrates. Those who had once learned the moral law " will respect the sacred bonds of their respective communities, they will love their fellow-citizens, scrupulously obey the laws, although they will never lose their contempt for a constitution which is only rendered tolerable by so much good government." [1]

Other more logical writers held that, if private property had been unjustly acquired and was upheld by class legislation, it must be abolished.[2] Among those who reached this position the Curé Meslier was the least compromising. He was an obscure country vicar, who, after forty years' labour in his parish, struggling, as it seemed in vain, on behalf of his flock against the extortions of their overlords, is said to have starved himself

---

[1] *Vide* Appendix II. of *The Origin of Inequality*.

[2] One learned Benedictine, Dom Deschamps, tried to escape from the dilemma by the same idealistic device as Rousseau. Indeed his conclusions were more extreme than those of *The Social Contract*, and in many particulars he anticipated Hegel. In his *Letters on the Spirit of the Age* (1769), and later, in *The Voice of Reason against the Reason of the Time*, he looked forward to a society in which individual personality is absorbed in that of the State. He built a Utopia akin to that of Plato, but founded on the doctrines of Catholicism : the Church had been originally right in regarding individual property as the result of original sin.

to death, only taking the precaution of ensuring that several manuscript copies of three bulky volumes in which his real convictions were stated should reach the hands of the sceptical *philosophes* in Paris. He preferred, as he said, to be roasted after than before his death. His attack was primarily directed against organized religion, which in practice upheld private property and other social evils which theoretically it condemned. He ridicules the conception of a personal or spiritual deity, is convinced that there can be no life after death, and regards French institutions, including the Church and the monarchy, as a single fraud perpetuated by the propaganda of religious and political superstition.

In his sixth book he deals especially with the social failure of the Church, which " suffered and authorized the abuses, vexations and tyranny of the great," and made no protest against the un-Christian condition of society. For the social order was morally evil, and at its root was private property. Instead of a society of Christian parishes, where men and women co-operated as brothers and sisters, one actually saw the workers starving because their produce was devoured by the idle and the useless. The rich were proud, ambitious and arrogant. What could the poor feel but hatred, envy and lust of revenge? How hardly could either rich or poor enter into the kingdom of heaven, where love and mutual service reigned! How could Christianity and social inequality co-exist? Christ had taught that blessedness was service : the religion which adopted His name supported conditions of privilege and class hatred.

The ruling class based their power upon successful robbery, and secured their stolen property by unjust laws. They lived as vermin preying on the lives of those who worked. The greatest of all vermin were kings. Samuel had vainly warned the people against setting up a monarchy, and from Saul down to Louis XIV. kings always used their subjects as chattels, stealing their goods and calling it taxation, laying waste their homes and driving them to slaughter in the name of the Prince of Peace. *Le Grand Monarque* was the perfect type of ruler, living in luxury, flaunting his concubines, "great at least in love." Indeed, adds Meslier, he was certainly not surnamed the Great " for great and praiseworthy actions . . . but for great injustices, robberies, usurpations, desolations, ravages and massacres of men on all sides."

While the aristocratic vermin thrive under his protection the priests of the Christian Church frighten the people with stories of an imaginary Devil to prevent their revolting against the ladylike and gentlemanly devils who live upon them. Worst of all are the great clergy themselves, who dwell in palaces, and the religious orders, who wear ridiculous costumes to prove that they have taken sacred vows which they have not the least intention of keeping. Finally, to complete their hypocrisy, they lead the people to church, and there, in " lugubrious tones," ask God " not to deal with them according to their infirmities nor remember their iniquities . . . but to help them to slaughter their enemies with success, thanking Him for their prosperity, and ending the whole ceremony with a pious *Te Deum*."

Such a world, Meslier declares, cannot be the work of an all-powerful God, unless, indeed, God and the Devil are one. If there is a good God the malice of men must have thwarted His intentions. On the one side the rich in paradise, on the other the poor in hell; between them is a great gulf fixed—a social gulf which cannot be passed until there is community of goods and equality of service. The myth of religion, the political myth and the myth of property are all part of the same fraud. Even the social institution of the family is evil.

In a natural society men and women would live together and part again on inclination. The miseries of domestic life would disappear and children would be brought up together in communal schools. No one would fear poverty; " equal sharing of moderate work for all " would take the place of idleness on the one side and excessive toil on the other. Social hatred, class contempt and the cries which arose from them would cease. The true doctrines of Christ would at length be practised ; men would once more return to the ideals set them by the early Church, when " all things were in common " and distribution was regulated by the needs of the weakest, not the might of the strongest.

Who could wonder if the poor attempted to overthrow such a system by force ? When the people were told the truth would it not be a reproach to them if they did not entirely destroy "the odious yoke of their tyrannical Government"? "Where are the Jacques Clément and the Ravaillac of our France? Are there none still alive in our days to stun and to stab all these detestable monsters, enemies of the human race, and by this means to deliver the people from tyranny?" When the great political and religious fraud was discovered, would not injustice and iniquity be quickly overthrown and the equal and free communities of the ancient world be re-established? Would not the people make all goods common in every parish and all share equally in the fruits of their common labours? "Dear people, your safety is in your own hands, your deliverance would depend only on yourselves if you could but understand."

Meslier indicted the economic and social order on the ground that it was fundamentally immoral and un-Christian : he suggested that communism was the natural order to be established after the probable revolution. The future society was described in more detail by Meslier's younger contemporaries, Morelly and the Abbé Mably. Morelly described the communist society in both prose and verse,[1] while Mably preached a similar gospel of equality in his *Entretiens de Phocion*, his *Doutes proposées aux Philosophes*, his *De la Legislation* and his *Du Gouvernment de Politique*. Morelly and Mably completely rejected the current individualism and declared that happiness is to be found only in an organized society where individual satisfaction is deliberately subordinated to the public good. Voltaire's irreligious Deism, the natural order of the Physiocrats, the pleasure-pain psychology of Helvétius and Holbach—all these would alike lead to anarchy. Did not the advocates of natural harmony really admit this themselves? They did not altogether trust to Providence. They argued that to serve one's own economic pleasure automatically secured the public welfare ; but they had not the courage of their convictions and made constant calls upon the legislator to supplement the work of the Deity. Sometimes they seemed to hope that men would

---

[1] Very little is known of Morelly, and his principal works, the *Basiliade* and the *Code de la Nature*, have been attributed frequently to Diderot.

realize that unselfishness was the true path to happiness, but even Holbach admitted the need of laws to restrain the unenlightened. Reason, Mably thought, might indeed show that nature " unites and confounds the general happiness of society and the particular happiness of each citizen," but reason alone was certainly not powerful enough to curb the passions of individuals to whom chance desire would often seem more important than ultimate happiness. The Encyclopædists' mistake was to emphasize happiness rather than virtue. Happiness was only the incidental result of virtue, and it was virtue which laws should foster. " Is it not certain," Mably wrote, " that the polity ought to make us love virtue and that virtue is the only object which legislators, laws and magistrates ought to have in view?"[1]

Morelly took the trouble to describe in detail the polity which could make us love virtuously. His true pattern of natural legislation is remarkable in many respects and closely anticipates the proposals of Fourier. Three fundamental and sacred laws will make all the familiar social evils impossible, and under their protection it will be " impossible to be depraved." Firstly, no private possessions beyond those which are necessary for the individual's daily comfort will be permitted; secondly, every citizen will be a public servant and his needs supplied by the State; thirdly, he will himself contribute to the general welfare in accordance with his powers, talents and age, performing his duties under a strict and elaborate economic code.

The nation will be divided into families, tribes and garden-cities of the same size; each city will have a public square, round which " uniform and agreeable " shops and assembly halls will be grouped. Beyond these will begin the residential quarters of the city, of the same size and shape, regularly divided by parallel streets. Each tribe will occupy one quarter, and each family a spacious, convenient and uniform building. On the outskirts of the city, beyond the workshops and special houses in which the agricultural workers will live, there will be a public hospital, a workhouse and a prison, in which any citizen who is unfortunate enough to be ill, decrepit or criminal

---

[1] *Entretiens de Phocion* : *Œuvres*, t. x. 511.

in these ideal circumstances will be looked after. Still further off will be the "burial field," a strongly fortified place for the perpetual imprisonment of anyone who has deserved to be " civilly dead."

All buying and selling will be communal, durable goods housed in public stores will be rationed and distributed daily to the public. The citizens may, however, exchange their surplus agricultural produce in the market square. The city will be surrounded by cultivated land sufficient for the needs of the inhabitants, and all the youths of the city from twenty-one to twenty-five years of age will be obliged to help in farming.

In every profession one master will watch over ten workmen, each master taking turns to be head of the whole profession for one year. The chief of the profession will direct all the labour and, in consultation with fathers of the families, see that the standard dress of each trade is worn "without any superfluous adornment " by each worker during his hours of labour, though every citizen will have a different holiday dress of a " modest and serviceable kind." " All vanity " will be suppressed by the ruling fathers. At the age of ten every child will learn a profession which appeals to him, at fifteen or eighteen he will be married, and after his agricultural period take his turn as a master. At the age of forty, having satisfactorily passed through these various stages, he will retire, doing only voluntary work, happy in the knowledge that in the event of becoming old and infirm " convenient lodging," nourishment and entertainment will be provided.

The nation will be divided into multiples of ten, and composed of federations of families in tribes, cities and provinces, and will be governed by a senate, composed of fathers who have reached the age of fifty. Each subdivision of the nation has its own council of fathers, who will send representatives to its superior council. The supreme senate is to guard the constitution and to prevent the city senators ever contravening the fundamental laws. Within this limit the councils of fathers have absolute power. Any individual loss of liberty will be atoned for by the formula which begins every public order : " Reason wishes, the law orders."

Every kind of excess will be prevented by education, marriage laws and the penal code. No celibacy is permitted after forty and marriage will usually be early. A marriage ceremony will take place in public at the beginning of each year, when each eligible young man, in the presence of the senators and public, will choose the girl who pleases him, and after obtaining her consent take her for his wife. Marriage is indissoluble for ten years, after which divorce is permitted on adequate grounds, but made absolute only after a period of six months, during which the partners may not meet. This last provision appears to be the only proposal of Morelly which the modern world has adopted.

Mothers will tend their own children up to the age of five, after which the city will take care of them and provide them with all they need, including an exact uniform education. Parents who have special interest in education will look after them, all the boys in one building and the girls in another, where they will learn the laws of the community and be introduced gradually to their future occupation. They are then passed on to the care of a professional master until they are old enough to enter their agricultural period. The whole process is to be most carefully supervised by the fathers, lest any suspicion of the spirit of property should corrupt the young and " any fables, stories or ridiculous fictions " should warp their natural love of truth.

Morelly recognizes that there may be individuals who will not immediately approve of such a system. Like Plato he feared the critical habits of the young, who may be ignorant of the laws of nature. He is especially anxious to encourage scientific research and to give studious children every opportunity of indulging their curiosity and improving the resources of the State, but no one may be allowed to question the simple tenets of the prescribed religion. The existence of a just Creator, the natural operation of His laws, the working of His intelligence in the world, must be accepted, and the hopelessness of attempting any further inquiry into the eternal mysteries acknowledged. The sacred laws are to be engraved on columns in the public square, where every child may read them : he will also learn to celebrate the simple, happy and unheroic story of his nation and its distinguished citizens in eloquence, poetry and painting.

If, in spite of this education, any citizen should be so unnatural as to kill his fellow, plot against the sacred constitution, or introduce "detestable property," after conviction by the supreme senate he would be shut up for the rest of his life in a specially constructed cell in the place of public burial. Other crimes—adultery, lack of respect to elders or assaults involving "outrageous epithets or blows"—would be punished with shorter periods of imprisonment.

Both Morelly and Mably assumed that a very moderate amount of labour would produce sufficient for human wants. If nature were more bountiful men would have less reason for association, and the value of co-operation might never have been discovered. "The world is a table amply furnished for every guest." No one has the right to assume control or to take more than his share: all are hungry and all may be satisfied. But Mably knew that chaos, not harmony, would reign at the table, however well stocked, unless men learnt to curb their appetites. Quarrels might arise in the distribution of plenty just as in the sharing of a little, unless virtue had supplanted greed in men's minds.

Happiness can never come from libertinism, nor from an excessive asceticism, but only from virtue, which is mental harmony, "the peace of the soul, which is often troubled by the revolt of the senses. Virtue ought to fly excess and all human morality to consist in a wise moderation which can reconcile the sublimity of reason and the folly of passion. In a word, morality, if it is to open the way to virtue and happiness, must begin by diminishing needs, since it is in these needs that the passions of men find their source and their nourishment."

The most destructive of all the passions is "avarice." The other vices are its offspring. "It is the Proteus, the mercury, the basis, the vehicle of all vices. Analyse vanity, pride, ambition, knavery, hypocrisy, villainy; all resolves itself into this subtle and pernicious element which you will find in the very hearts of disinterested people." Avarice is not a necessary part of human nature, but is developed by an immoral society. Men are naturally affectionate and full of compassion, and reason co-operates with natural goodness in showing men the "happy necessity of being beneficent." The question then arises how men ever came to behave as they do. Mably thinks that no one can explain the origin of evil, but Morelly gives a similar answer to that of Rousseau.

When the growth of population made land scarce, new societies took the place of the primitive family. Individuals were allowed to " usurp possessions which ought to belong to humanity." When Mercier de la Rivière talks of just laws and then defends the private ownership of land and capital he has destroyed the basis of the natural order which would admit only personal property. Where a man may add to his posses-sions at the expense of another, avarice triumphs, and the very heart of the community is corrupted.

In his *De la Législation* (which appeared in the same year as *The Wealth of Nations*) Mably stages a debate upon the ethics of private property between an Englishman and a Swede. The Englishman is aglow with the new Liberal doctrines. He has no doubt that freedom makes England the greatest country in the world : its glory, strength and wealth are the direct result of its flourishing trade. When mistakes occur (as in the recent case of the American Colonies) it is because the principles of free trade and international unity have been imperfectly grasped. On the whole, however, he is sure that there can be nothing seriously wrong with a country whose wealth is so great and whose Constitution is so wonderful. But he is more open-minded than most patriots. In the course of two volumes of argument the Swede is gradually able to convince him that Sweden is a better country than England. In Sweden, it seems, there is no longer a search for glory (Charles XII. is happily forgotten), and no preoccupation with money-making. Contentment and discipline are the rule—the effect of a moderate prosperity, a sufficiency of work and a comparative equality of wealth. Happiness is found to arise from virtue of manners, not from abundance of material goods. In Sweden character comes before renown and contentment before property. " In our poverty," says the Swede, "we can still hope to make citizens: you by increasing your riches will make only mercenaries."

England has been led by the search for wealth to forget the true ends of life. Happiness, however, comes from restricting needs, not from multiplying possessions. This is why sumptuary laws are wise, why Lycurgus was the greatest of legislators, and Plato of political thinkers. It is a mistake too to believe that money means liberty. England is wealthy, but liberty lives only in the hearts of such of her poor as have not learned to want to be rich. For the most part rich and poor are alike corrupted: the rich grow arrogant and grasping through success; the poor envious and rebellious through failure. The boasted perfection of the Constitution offers no remedy: Magna Charta may have destroyed political tyranny, but it did not make England as happy as North America, where primitive communism was still to be found.

Montesquieu had been right in saying that an aristocracy would govern well only if it were animated by a sense of honour and in prophesying that the British aristocracy would degenerate if it took part in commerce. Avarice would increase and the disasters attendant upon private property grow and overwhelm the nation. "As for us," says the Swede, "who see the infinite evils which have come from this fatal Pandora's Box, ought we not, if the least ray of hope gleams upon us, to aspire to that happy communism which the poets have so much praised and so much regretted: a state which was established by Lycurgus at Sparta, one whose revival Plato hoped for in his Republic, and which, thanks to the degradation of manners, can be only a chimera in the world?"

Mably easily dismisses the objections usually raised to communistic proposals. The Englishman, though at length convinced that a communist society is theoretically the best, argues that the motive of acquisition is so deeply engrained in society that it cannot now be discounted. Existing society is held together by the hope of reward and the fear of punishment; men no longer want equality and are spurred to industry by self-interest and ambition. The Swede replies by recommending the study of history, quotes the example of Sparta and mentions that primitive peoples are untroubled by avarice, which is the offspring, not the progenitor, of the institution of private property. "I think," he says, magnificently begging the question, "that no one will contest the obviousness of this proposition, that where no property existed there could not be any of its pernicious consequences."

Men need no such spur to industry. In a natural society their necessities force them to work until their simple wants are satisfied. The corruption of civilization is nowhere better illustrated than by the fact that men are constantly induced to desire new luxuries and to put a fictitious value upon the artificial distinctions which money brings. Communism, not competition, is the way of nature. " In place of the essential order of nature," writes Mably, in replying to the Physiocrats, " I am much afraid that we are given the natural order only for avarice, greed and folly." The only test of a good law is whether it adds to the substance of equality : everyone should be ensured a subsistence wage and laws should be passed prohibiting luxury and guarding against avarice. How absurd " to ruin everyone on the plea of enriching property owners. . . . What man could be so unreasonable as to claim that a sane policy should not lay down for the rich the conditions under which they may enjoy their fortune and prevent them from oppressing the poor?"

Mably is scarcely more hopeful than Rousseau of a return to a natural society, and is almost as cautious as Rousseau when the practical question of rebellion is mooted. " Perhaps," he says, " men are now too depraved ever to be able to have a wise polity," though he elsewhere admits that the people are sovereign and have the right to rebel if they wish. " Choose," he cries in one passage, " between revolution and slavery, there is no half-way house."

Mably, in fact, agreed with Rousseau in thinking reason a weak bulwark against passion. If the corporate feeling which alone would support his communistic society should ever come, it would be the result, not of self-interest, but of a fervent religion. He argues that men have an intuitive knowledge of God and a consciousness of right and wrong, and that atheism and Voltairean deism are only " fashionable cults," natural reactions from the superstitions of Catholicism. Materialism is as fatal to humanity as "war, famine or plague." The true legislator will stimulate the innate religious feeling in man by insisting on a simple religious ceremony, emphasizing the lesson of God's condemnation of the wicked and reward of the good. Moreover, Mably differs from Rousseau because the community he imagines is not national but world-wide. Patriotism must be a subordinate virtue: only a universal sentiment of brotherhood will prevent jealousy between States destroying the harmony resulting from economic communism. Three things are essential if men are to live the good life: internal equality within the State, political organization of States into a world federation and, lastly, a religion to reinforce the teaching of reason and to keep private and group passions at bay. Mably was an international socialist, and he remained an abbé and a Christian in spite of his free-thinking.

5. THE FOURTH ESTATE——REVOLUTIONARY THEORY——LINGUET TO BABEUF

The communist theory of men like Morelly and Mably had little practical application to eighteenth-century conditions. They were moralists, content to praise a natural order remotely staged in the past or the future. During the last ten years of the *ancien régime*, however, the condition of the landless proletariat was the subject of numerous pamphlets, and many reformers, among whom Necker is perhaps the best known, at least talked as if they were socialists. They were not content to attack the Government and to demand an equal system of taxation, but went on to repudiate the whole institution of private property. When the time came to make definite suggestions, however, the majority of them were satisfied with demanding a guaranteed living wage. Babeuf was alone in making any serious attempt to establish socialism when the middle-class character of the Revolution had disappointed the hopes of his party.

The Fourth Estate stormed the Bastille, but it had few spokesmen in the States-General and but little voice in its election. An occasional pamphlet, like that of Devérité, was significant of

much submerged feeling.[1] As " a working man " he complained
that he would have no chance of expressing his views in the
States-General. He recounts the " grievances of a poor devil "
who can only play the part of an " army mule " bent beneath
the weight of the baggage, while the battle between the privileged classes and the bourgeoisie raged about the rights of
property. "How will laws of property help a poor labourer? "
His limbs are his only capital. Out of his precarious earnings
he pays away a large share in taxes to the rich. Under a wise
government great fortunes would be limited and " taxes would
be increased in geometric proportion as fortunes increased."
Under the existing system the more luxury the less taxation.
The effect of agricultural and industrial machinery was to leave
the labourer at the mercy of the rich: those who laboured
received an ever smaller share in the product of industry. The
destruction of machinery as a whole would perhaps be too drastic
a step, but its operation should certainly be stopped where it
caused distress and unemployment. Other spokesmen of the
Fourth Estate declared that the demands of the peasants failed
to meet the needs of those without land, that mere reform of
the iniquitous system of taxation and the abolition of feudalism
were inadequate. One of the clauses of the civil compact is that
no one should be condemend to die of hunger.

Many of the later leaders of the Revolution went far in the
same direction before they obtained power. Carra, the future
Girondist, remarked, some years before the Revolution, that
there were limits to the patience of the poor: they had strong
arms, and if they could not look after themselves by cultivating
part of the land as their property they could do so " by purging
it of the monsters who devoured it."[2] His practical advice, however, was that they should claim their natural rights, including
that of an adequate livelihood. A number of other writers,
equally violent against the injustice of poverty and equally
willing to argue that democracy might ultimately involve a
more equal division of wealth, still agreed that, as things were,

---

[1] *La vie et les doléances d'un pauvre diable pour servir de ce qu'on voudra aux
prochains Etats-Généraux* (1789).
[2] *Vide* Lichtenberger, *op. cit.*, 394-395.

the existing institution of private property was useful and unalterable.[1] Distributivism seemed a more hopeful doctrine than communism.

There were others less easily contented. Gosselin declared that the happiness of man does not demand the sacrifice of wealth or the repudiation of the pleasures of social life or the neglect of agriculture. And what then does it demand? Simply an organization which guarantees to those who work a sure means of subsistence. "Land belongs to the whole community" and should be taken, though not without compensation, from the big proprietors and shared out until France is " filled with happy people who will ever bless the bold mortal who carries out such a revolution, and becomes the artisan of their happiness and the author of their prosperity."[2]

In the same spirit Boissel, after the usual commendation of Rousseau's analysis of economic inequality, points to the weakness of his political solution. "He only considered the origin of evil and did not trouble to look for any remedy or for the origin of good."[3] He deplored the first theft of communal property, but accepted its disastrous results as inevitable. Yet a remedy must be found. Violent revolution could still be avoided, Boissel argued, if communist schools were established and industry nationalized. A sound and moral revolution might then be peacefully accomplished.

Brissot de Warville's *Philosophic Researches on the Right of Property and on Theft in their Relations to Nature and Society* appeared in 1780.[4] His main argument is that, since property is a social not a natural institution, theft is not a crime against natural law, and should not be punished by death. Property is justified by nature only in so far as it fulfils essential needs. Thus, as Proudhon was later to urge, where property is unjustly divided it is not the thief who breaks the moral law but the man who has seized more than his share. There is no " sacred right of property to travel by carriage while we have legs, or to eat the food of twenty men when one man's share is enough." In a

[1] Lichtenberger, 426-427. [2] *Ibid.*, p. 438.
[3] *Ibid.*, pp. 448-449. [4] *Ibid.*, p. 413 ff.

subsequent book [1] Brissot spoke of the laws " as a conspiracy of the stronger against the weaker, the rich against the poor, authority against humanity." Yet his conclusions were only mildly revolutionary. He felt, as Rousseau had, that though the institution of private property had originated in injustice it could not be overthrown—theft might be morally justified but it could not be tolerated : it should be considered a minor offence, not a crime punishable by death. During the Revolution itself Brissot was attacked by Morellet for having defended robbery : he replied by pointing out the moderation of his programme, and pleaded that in any case his writings of twelve years earlier had been only schoolboy essays, not to be taken seriously.

All these writers advocated economic change before the Revolution, and were satisfied with political democracy when they found themselves in power. Linguet is a unique and neglected figure. He was a barrister, who was early disbarred as a result of an attack upon law and property, published as early as 1763. During the final decade before the Revolution he poured into the journal of which he was editor a constant stream of brilliant social analysis mingled with invective. His position was unusual, but logical. He was a conservative who saw through the shams of society and exposed them, who stated the Ricardian theory of the iron law of wages and anticipated Marx in declaring that there was a class war, and that it would be fought out on the issue of private property. He argued, however, that since property rights were now the basis of the whole social system, the struggle would destroy society itself : it was therefore best to keep things as they were as long as possible. His unflinching analysis of social injustice, however, was scarcely likely to aid conservatism. The most sincere of pessimists, he saw no remedy for fundamental social abuses except a communist revolution. Yet he hoped nothing from such a revolution : it would destroy existing injustice, but not make human happiness. He therefore stuck to analysis and eschewed advice. Nevertheless he was imprisoned in the Bastille

---

[1] *Théorie des Lois criminelles*, 1781.

and exiled to London : after the Revolution itself had broken
out he returned to France and spoke before the Assembly
on behalf of the insurgent blacks of San Domingo. He was
guillotined in 1794.

Law, he declared, was the chief instrument by which those
who had won their possessions by force or by fraud retained
their spoils and their power. The institution of private
property "was not set up to hinder the poor from losing
anything," but to safeguard the rich man. "Laws are destined,
above all, to safeguard property. Now as one can take away
much more from the man who has than from him who has not,
they are clearly a guarantee accorded to the rich against the
poor. It is difficult to believe, and yet clearly demonstrable,
that the laws are in some respects a conspiracy against the
majority of the human race." Property turns society into a
vast prison, where a few warders control the mass of prisoners
who "groan in the disgusting rags which are the livery of
poverty. They never have any share in the plenty which
their labour creates." In these conditions, was the suppression
of slavery a benefit to the slaves? "I say it entailed as much
suffering as liberty : all that they have gained is to be constantly tormented by the fear of starvation, a misfortune
from which their predecessors in this lowest rank of humanity
were at least exempt." Slaves, after all, were worth keeping
alive and feeding all the year round ; the modern labourer,
whose work was only seasonal, had to find his own fodder. If
he begged for food it was a crime : "the crime of having a
stomach and no money."

Linguet proceeded to state the main tenets of Marxian
theory—the class war, the doctrine of surplus value and the
inevitable communist revolution. "Society is divided into two
parts : the one consists of the rich, owners of money who, since
they are consequently owners of commodities, also claim for
themselves the exclusive right to tax the reward of the industry by which the commodities are produced ; the other is
composed of isolated labourers. Since they are no longer
anyone's property, and no longer have masters, they no longer
have guardians with an interest in protecting them or relieving

them; they are helplessly delivered over to the mercy of avarice itself. "The rich are even saved the pain of hearing the cries of the poor, who die silently in their huts." Linguet regarded the Liberal programme of the Physiocrats with contempt.[1] There is no natural harmony between the interests of worker and employer : when profits are increased wages do not rise simultaneously, nor is the price of food proportionately lowered.[2] There is always a "lag" period, terrible to the labourer. Any benefits he may ultimately reap from general prosperity are but part of the capitalist's surplus—a surplus created by the work of the labourer. It is an error to think the rich benefit the poor by providing them with employment. On the contrary "it is the life of the hireling which builds up the rich man's wealth." Streams maintain the river, not the river the streams.

The economic system gives rise to a competition between the right to life and the right to private property. Where the latter involves the destruction of the former, where the wealth and power of the few are destroying the vitality of the State and the happiness—the lives even—of the mass of citizens, individual property rights would justly be subordinated to the general welfare. He compared a rich man denouncing slavery to a bird of prey screaming "while it rends a pigeon in its talons." To speak of progress and liberty in such circumstances was hypocrisy. A philosopher might counsel patience on the ground that a destruction of all organization and return to natural anarchy would be even worse, or he might encourage revolt, but if he were honest he could not preach the usual optimistic doctrine of the Physiocrats. For his part, Linguet leaves little doubt as to his own view—the poor have the right to revolt, and some day will have the power, though he could not counsel them to attempt it. They could console themselves, however, with the thought that their rights had been stolen, and that "if they or their posterity had the courage one day to seize upon them again, nothing could prevent them." Providentially,

---

[1] *Réponse aux Doctrines modernes.*
[2] *Ibid.*, vol. ii., pp. 83-84.

Linguet remarks, despair seems to make men inert, not violent. Yet inertia could not last for ever. "Never," he wrote, "has want been more universal, more murderous for the class which is condemned to it : never, perhaps, amidst apparent prosperity has Europe been nearer to a complete upheaval. . . . We have reached, by a directly opposite route, precisely the point which Italy had reached when the Slave War inundated it with blood and carried fire and slaughter to the very gates of the mistress of the world." [1] Perhaps, he suggested, Spartacus was already preparing for a war of liberation.

When the Revolution arrived it was a middle-class affair. The Third Estate was represented mainly by lawyers : there were also some merchants and even a few peasants. The Fourth Estate was scarcely represented, and the revolutionary politicians were generally and enthusiastically agreed, first, that all existing feudal property rights should be abolished, and, secondly, that all private property was sacred and inalienable. Property was even considered a necessary qualification for the vote, and proposals for social equality never went further than attempts to regulate food prices and relieve urgent distress. Confronted with the disappointment of the Fourth Estate, and challenged to make good the promise of equality to the poor, both Danton and Robespierre deliberately appealed for the support of the peasant and the tradesman. "It seems to have been thought," said Danton, in 1792, "excellent citizens have held, that friends of liberty may do harm to the social order by exaggerating their principles. Well, let us now eschew all exaggeration : let us declare that all territorial, individual and industrial property shall be for ever maintained." In the following year Robespierre put the matter more argumentatively but equally definitely. "Certainly a Revolution is not necessary to convince us that the extremes of wealth and poverty are the source of many evils and many crimes, yet we are nevertheless convinced that equality of wealth is a chimera. For myself, I think it even less necessary for private good than for public happiness. It is much more important to make poverty honour-

---

[1] *Annales*, t. i. 345.

able than to proscribe riches. The cottage of Fabricius need not envy the palace of Crassus. . . . Let us therefore honestly declare the principle of the rights of property." [1]

Babeuf's communist rising of 1796 was a reply to Robespierre. Sylvain Maréchal had written, before the Revolution itself, that society was a huge slave market, where men were daily bought and sold. "The chaos which preceded the Creation was certainly nothing in comparison with that which reigns on the surface of this earth now that it has been created, and hell, with which I am threatened after death, cannot be worse than the life one leads in a society where the individuals are all free and equal and where, however, three-quarters are slaves and the rest master." What if the servile class should refuse to continue to serve their rulers and answer: "We are three to one. Our intention is to re-establish for ever things on their ancient footing, in their primitive state—that is, upon the basis of the most perfect and legitimate equality. Let us divide the earth once more among all its inhabitants. If any of you is found to have two mouths and four arms, it is quite fair: let us assign him a double portion. But if we are all made on the same pattern, let us share the cake equally."

Maréchal's draft for the "Manifesto of Equals" elaborated the same principle. "Since civilized society began, this finest possession of humanity has been unanimously recognized, yet not once realized; equality was only a fair and sterile fiction of the law. To-day, when it is more loudly demanded, we are answered: Silence, wretches! real equality is but a chimera: be content with constitutional equality; you are all equal before the law. *Canaille*, what more do you want?"

The time had come for open recognition of the principle that "the earth belongs to nobody, while its fruits are everybody's." The French Revolution, Maréchal wrote, "is but the precursor of another revolution, far greater, far more solemn, which will be the last. . . . Let there be no difference now between human beings except in age and sex! Since all have the same needs and the same faculties, let there be one education

---

[1] Quoted. Postgate, *Revolution*, 1789-1906, pp. 41-44.

and one standard of life for all. . . . On the morrow of this true revolution men will say 'What! Was the common good so easy to achieve! We had but to will it!'"[1]

Unlike most of his contemporaries, who were revolutionary before the Revolution and quickly frightened by its development, Babeuf began with a careful social analysis and with cautious recommendations, and pushed his theory of equality to its logical conclusion only when he saw that France was becoming a land of peasant proprietors and that economic equality was not part of their programme. He pushed it to the point of abortive revolt and his own execution. His principles were clear enough. Land should be divided equally for the purposes of occupation, but ownership should be national. No one, he wrote in 1796, " can, without committing a crime, appropriate for his exclusive use the goods of the earth or of industry." His full programme included the abolition of all inheritance and the nationalization of the land. He declared that the Revolution was not at an end, because the rich absorb all valuable products and exclusively command while the poor toil like real slaves, pine in misery and count for nothing in the State. Babeuf's own attempt to establish communism failed, but both he and Maréchal were more far-sighted than their contemporaries when they declared that the Revolution was not ended and that the poor were not likely to be satisfied, nor society rendered harmonious, by the establishment of legal equality without the further bestowal of the substance of economic and social equality. If the Commune of 1870 was, on its political side, the logical development of Rousseau's philosophy, on its economic side it was a fulfilment of the prophecies of Linguet, Maréchal and Babeuf.

---

[1] Postgate, *op. cit.*, 54-56.

CHAPTER X

PEACE, FRATERNITY AND NATIONALISM

I. INTERNATIONAL ANARCHY IN THEORY——MACHIAVELLI AND GROTIUS

"Hugo Grotius, Puffendorff, Vattel and others—Job's comforters all of them—are always quoted in good faith to justify an attack although their codes, whether couched in philosophic or diplomatic terms, have not—nor can have—the slightest legal force, because States, as such, are under no common external authority" (KANT's *Essay on Perpetual Peace*).

INTERNATIONAL as well as social peace seemed to be the natural result of the Revolution. Just as the destruction of privilege and the victory of the middle class removed the immediate causes of social conflicts in the eighteenth century, so the downfall of the divine monarchy and the establishment of popular government abolished the type of warfare which had devastated Europe for two centuries. At the end of an age of religious and dynastic wars it was easy to assume that wars would cease when States became secular and popular.

In 1648 the Treaty of Westphalia gave a legal sanction to international anarchy. The Pope's claim to rule over a united Christendom had ceased to have any meaning in the sixteenth century : the modern State was established as the recognized and final Sovereign, subject to no moral law, without obligations or responsibilities to its neighbours. Machiavelli had exposed the practices of mediæval diplomacy, and advised the Renaissance Prince to adopt similar methods on behalf of the nation-state, undeceived and undeterred by the religious maxims and moral purposes professed by the rulers of Christendom. Perhaps this advice was unnecessary ; in any case, kings and ministers pursued a policy of war and aggrandizement, of intrigue and faithlessness, exactly in accordance with his suggestions.

With the Reformation the theory of the modern State became complete. Bodin evolved the doctrine of royal sovereignty, while Sully's *grand dessein* was based on a conception of European States legally equal as juristic persons, entitled to enter into a permanent alliance if they wished without consideration of religious differences. Richelieu's domestic and foreign policy

259

was founded on the same principles : the State was a territorial unit ruled by a Monarch, absolute at home and abroad. The objects of the Sovereign's policy were internal unity and foreign aggrandizement, resulting from war or from alliances which he was as free to make with Protestants or Turks as with Catholics. But the most striking assertion of juristic sovereignty was not made by a despotic Monarch but by the rebellious Dutch. William the Silent appealed to Europe against Philip II. on the ground that he too was a sovereign Prince : when the rebellion succeeded, Holland became a fully fledged nation, claiming a Sovereign's right to make alliances and wars and to oppress her own minorities and conquered people just as Spain had oppressed her. By the end of the sixteenth century the new moral disorder of Europe was complete.

To assert one's own sovereignty, however, does not in fact make one independent of extra-territorial obligations, and to declare that one's own interest is the final criterion does not get rid of the consciousness of a moral relationship. It was this fact that Hugo Grotius perceived, and which is the basis of his *De Jure Belli*. Machiavelli assumed that individuals are amoral units, kept together only by fear of their rulers : similarly he regarded States as amoral units which had no external authority and which were therefore in perpetual conflict with one another. As a generalization about sixteenth-century Europe this account of the relationship of States was roughly true. But just as Machiavelli neglected the fact that men were bound together, not only by force but also by a sense of moral obligation, so he overlooked the existence of a rudimentary desire for an international morality. The opponents of the Machiavellian view that society rests only on force have commonly founded their case on the Stoic doctrine of natural law and of the contract implicit between fellow-members of a society. Grotius transferred this doctrine from the national to the international sphere, and founded international law upon the law of nature. Ultimately national States were the outcome of the individual's consciousness of moral obligation. An analogous development between States should some day lead to international government.

Grotius of course was far from reaching such a conclusion. He accepted the facts of his age. He assumes the territorial sovereignty of nations and the international anarchy which is its consequence. Every State, whatever its size, religion or form of government, is an equal juristic personality, and Europe, if united at all, even in the manner suggested by Sully, would be held together only by treaty obligations voluntarily incurred. So much Grotius takes for granted. He argues, however, that these facts do not destroy the law of nature : that moral obligations exist even between persons juristically separate. Thus there is no external sanction to coerce a State which breaks a voluntarily made treaty on grounds of *raison d'état*. But there is a moral obligation, universally binding, to keep faith. The natural law which forbids treachery and cruelty also imposes an obligation not to break one's pledged word, even in dealing with an enemy, and not to make war on non-combatants. International law, therefore, begins with Grotius as a system of rules which nations are morally bound to obey. It is concerned with laws of humanity and decency whose public recognition would mitigate somewhat the horrors of international anarchy.

2. INTERNATIONAL ANARCHY IN PRACTICE—THE DENUNCIATION OF WAR IN THE EIGHTEENTH CENTURY

This tentative beginning of international law did not materially modify the behaviour of kings in the seventeenth and eighteenth centuries. Yet in days of mercenary armies it was valuable to have rules for the protection of non-combatants, even if they were only occasionally observed. Civilian populations which had experienced every kind of abomination during the Wars of Religion did find some slight measure of protection from these rules in the eighteenth and nineteenth centuries. It was only in the twentieth century that the rules of war ceased to have any significance. Yet the main effect of the attempt to institute rules of international behaviour was to change the excuses made in breaking them. Phraseology changed, if practice did not. The policies of Henry VIII. in the sixteenth century, of Louis XIV. in the seventeenth, and of Frederick the Great in the eighteenth, were in essentials similar : all were obedient disciples of Machiavelli and all showed their obedience most faithfully when they publicly denounced his precepts. The only important difference was that whereas Henry and his contemporaries were close to the Middle Ages, and found it best to justify their policy and their wars on religious grounds, Louis XIV. based his claims on legal fictions and broke rules of international law, supported by his pledged word, on high grounds of national honour. International law became itself an excuse for war : an alleged infraction by your enemy of a rule you did not expect him to keep and did not keep yourself would serve as a *casus belli*. Frederick the Great used the same subterfuges on occasion, but could more easily dispense with hypocrisy and boast that national expansion was the justification of his policy and force its sufficient sanction. Both the ends pursued by States and the means of pursuing them remained in any case the same.[1]

National aggrandizement, the increase of power, prestige and territory at the expense of neighbours, was the object of State policy. Every statesman from Louis XIV. to Talleyrand would have agreed with Catherine the Great that "he who wins nothing, loses." It was a competition for power, which involved stealthy annexations of territory, constant wars and general plunder and destruction. The practice of diplomacy was aggrandizement by any means at the disposal of the diplomat, however contrary to the ethics of ordinary human intercourse.

---

[1] The right of self-defence provided an excuse for aggressive war in the eighteenth century as well as later. Montesquieu raised the problem of defining aggression when he wrote that the natural right of self-defence sometimes carried with it the right to attack, since, if a people fear that another Power intends to attack them, their only means of saving themselves from destruction may be to strike the first blow. Voltaire's comment (article *Guerre*, in *Dic. Phil.*) is always valid against this argument. You could not, he remarks, find a more obviously unjust reason for war. It would be impossible for you to attack your neighbour on the excuse that he intended to attack you unless you were yourself prepared to attack him—which meant, on your own argument, that you had given him the right to attack you. "This is to kill your neighbour (who is not attacking you) for fear that he should be in a condition to attack you : you must, that is, risk ruining your country in the hope of ruining another's country without any reason."

The pursuit of power through alliances which might lead to increases of territory and prestige without war was commonly known as the "Balance of Power." In practice, however, it led to war. For, since the object of each party was always to weight the balance in its own favour, the equilibrium could scarcely be permanent, and constant war was necessary to preserve a balance which had been invented in order to maintain peace. By the balance of power, Mercier remarked, "people arm against each other and cut each other's throats according to a system invented to prevent throat-cutting." Throat-cutting was continually resorted to when diplomacy failed to gain its end by chicane.

Much of Europe and most of Germany had been devastated by the Wars of Religion. A generation after Westphalia, Louis XIV.'s dynastic ambition carried the work of destruction further. Under Louis XV. matters were little better, and the moral, economic and political criticism of writers like Fénelon, Boulainvilliers and Saint-Pierre was renewed and repeated in many of the philosophic writings of the eighteenth century. From 1740 onwards Europe was an armed camp. Montesquieu speaks of the international competition of armaments as "the new malady" which "has spread itself over Europe; it has infected our Princes and induces them to keep up an exorbitant number of troops. The disease increases in virulence and of necessity becomes contagious. For as soon as one Prince increases his troops the rest of course do the same; so that nothing is effected thereby but the public ruin. Each Monarch keeps as many armies on foot as if his people were in danger of being exterminated; and they give the name of peace to this general effort of all against all. Thus Europe is brought to such a pass, that were private people to be in the same situation as the three most opulent Powers of this part of the world, they would be below subsistence level. We are poor, while we possess the riches and commerce of the whole universe; and if we continue to increase our troops at this rate, we shall soon have nothing but soldiers, and be reduced to the very same situation as the Tartars."

This was the philosophic view of eighteenth-century war. Seen from the council-chamber it looked very much the same to a sensitive statesman. Bernis had become Foreign Minister in France after his successful negotiation of the Franco-Austrian Alliance. He had embarked on the struggle with Frederick the Great willingly enough, but in his letters to Choiseul at Vienna he made a gradual repentance as disillusionment came upon him. He was a man of exceptional honesty, genuine humanity and only fluctuating ambition. Not many months after the commencement of the war he told Kaunitz that there was no hope of success. It was not, he explained, a question of good or bad luck next year or the year after, since success would always be impossible "without generals or well-disciplined troops." As to the generals, their chief motives were avarice and ambition. They thought only of "what will be said at Versailles," and were always willing, if they thought they could hide their incompetence from the King, to run away from the battlefield, leaving behind them, as they actually did on one occasion, half the artillery and 20,000 wounded or sick men. As to the troops, how could discipline prevail when the officers had " the manner of *grisettes*," and the men themselves neither pay nor food?

" The misery of the soldier," wrote Bernis, " is so great that it makes one's heart bleed. . . . The army has neither food nor shoes, half of it is without clothes, part of the cavalry is without boots. The troops have plundered terribly and done great mischief. The reason for all this is the excess of misery in which the officers find themselves, so that they send the soldiers out to pillage or buy bread and meat for them as cheaply as possible."

Bernis found that he could neither stop the war nor reform the Administration. The Government was controlled by the King's latest mistress. "The King is not at all upset by our anxieties nor embarrassed by our embarrassments." Empire, trade and prestige were vanishing under an indolent routine administered by " little spirits and narrow heads." "We live like children : we shake our ears when the weather is bad and we laugh at the first ray of sunshine." "We expect money like dew from heaven . . . every day we are on the eve of bankruptcy." Every week Bernis had " to spend a day coaxing Montmartel, the financier, to lend the King money," and was

so dependent upon him that " he could always force our hand."
" It is not," wrote Bernis, " the state of affairs which frightens
me ; it is the incapacity of those who conduct them : it is not
the misfortunes which crush me ; it is the certainty that the
right means of remedying them will never be employed. The
only remedy is a better Government. Give me this condition
and I will advise the continuance of the war, but it is precisely
that which we lack, and that which no one can give me—I mean
a Government." " God keep us," he wrote, " from light heads
in the management of grave affairs." Bernis knew that the
populace hated him, believing him responsible for a disastrous
war, which he was only too anxious to bring to an end. His situation became intolerable : he begged Madame de Pompadour
to accept his resignation. " She tells me sometimes," he
wrote, " to enjoy myself, and not to look gloomy. It is as if
a man with a burning fever were told not to be thirsty."
Finally, after urging " peace at any price," Bernis persuaded
the Pompadour to submit a letter to the King giving a full
account of his own illness, weakness and inefficiency, and suggesting that his friend Choiseul would be a more energetic and
capable Minister. The King regretted to hear that State affairs
had proved too great a strain for his Minister's health, accepted
his resignation, made Choiseul a Duke and appointed him
Bernis' successor. Bernis was made a Cardinal, and, after a vain
attempt to remain without portfolio in the Cabinet from which
he had resigned, retired to the country, in order, as he said,
" to cultivate cabbages."

At the very time that Bernis was taking this decision Voltaire
was composing *Candide*. The horrors of war and misgovernment in Europe brought him to the same conclusion, that in a
world so terrible, so inexplicable and so fortuitous, the only
course for a sensible man was to cultivate his garden.

Yet he could at least tell people what war was like, and
expose the sophistries by which despots excused themselves
when their ambition ruined their subjects.[1] Voltaire could pay

---

[1] For a detailed example of a case in point *vide* the account of the war
between Frederick II. and Joseph in *Frederick the Great and Kaiser Joseph*, by
Temperley and Reddaway.

equivocal compliments to Frederick the Great on his victories, but he left Frederick in no real doubt about his views upon his foreign policy. In his *Philosophical Dictionary* he described with unpleasant accuracy the origin of a dynastic war: "A genealogist proves to a Prince that he is the direct descendant of a Count whose parents had made a family compact three or four hundred years before with a House whose very memory is now forgotten. This House had distant claims on a province whose last possessor had died of apoplexy. The Prince and his council see his unmistakable right. This province, which is some hundreds of leagues away from him, in vain protests that it does not know him, that it is not at all anxious to be governed by him, that a people cannot be given laws without at least consenting to them : this talk never gets beyond the ears of the Prince whose right is incontestable. He straightway finds a large number of men who have nothing to lose ; he dresses them in a coarse blue cloth at a hundred and ten sous the ell, trims their hats with a coarse white ribbon, turns them to the right and to the left and marches to glory.

"The other Princes get wind of this preparation, they all take part according to their strength, and cover a section of the country with more mercenary murderers than Gengis Khan, Tamerlaine or Bajazat trailed behind them. . . . These multitudes rage against each other, not only without any interest in the proceedings, but without even knowing what it is all about. . . . The marvellous part of this infernal enterprise is that each leader of murderers has his flags blessed and solemnly invokes God before going out to exterminate his neighbour. If a chief is only lucky enough to get two or three thousand men's throats cut he does not thank God for it : but when he has got ten thousand of them exterminated by fire and sword, and as a crowning mercy has completely destroyed some city, then a pretty long part-song is sung, written in a language unknown to all those who fought and quite full of barbarisms. The same song serves for marriages and births—as well as murders— which is unpardonable, especially in a nation greatly renowned for new songs. . . .

"A certain number of spouters are paid to celebrate these

days of murder . . . they all talk for a long time, quoting what
was once done in Palestine.

" During the remainder of the year these people denounce
vices. They prove by three points and antitheses that women
who lightly spread a little carmine on their fresh cheeks will be
the eternal objects of the eternal wrath of the Eternal . . . that a
man who has two hundred crowns' worth of fish on his table one
day in Lent is assured of salvation, while a poor man who eats
mutton worth two and a half sous is going for ever to all the
devils. . . . The wretched spouters unceasingly talk against
love, which is the only consolation of humanity and the only
way of improving it; they say nothing of these abominable
efforts which we make to destroy it."

3. THE IDEA OF PEACE—SAINT-PIERRE—ROUSSEAU AND KANT

Voltaire made no constructive suggestions for the abolition
of war. Indeed he remarked that it was unfortunately inevitable. His hope lay only in the enlightenment of monarchs,
who might in time realize the claims of justice and humanity.
He was always a practical man, and it was only men who did
not fear ridicule who seriously considered schemes for attacking the institution of war and substituting law for anarchy
between States. And the politician could afford to tolerate
the dreamer: the statesman, as Kant remarked at the end of
his *Perpetual Peace*, " looks down upon the theorist as a mere
pedant whose empty ideas can threaten no danger to the State."
Why, then, should the philosopher not be permitted " to knock
down his eleven skittles at once without the worldly-wise statesman needing to disturb himself "? In any case, philosophers can
never be kings, and they can do no harm amusing themselves
with schemes for social improvement.

Some philosophers actually did address themselves to the
problem of war. They relied for the most part on the operation
of natural law, upon the results of free trade and upon the
dissipation of ignorance.

According to the doctrine of natural harmony the removal

of artificial restrictions would show men that their real interests were the same, and that all war was really civil war, and ruinous to the victor as well as to the vanquished.[1] If men could see that the world was becoming economically united, that the gain of one man was also another's gain and not his loss, self-interest would dictate a policy of free trade, peace and plenty, instead of protection, war and power. Kings, Mercier pointed out, already addressed one another as brothers, an excellent recognition of the law of nature, which meant States to be fraternally useful to each other. The very kings, however, who thus paid a ceremonial tribute to their common fatherhood proceeded to organize their people into robber bands in order to spoil one another's property and destroy one another's subjects. The natural order was clearly a general confederation of all States. In this idea there was nothing chimerical, since each State had what another lacked and all would gain by mutual service. To think of enriching oneself at another's expense was the most obvious fallacy of international economics. "This false policy has cost us very dear : its supposed advantages occasion wars which threaten the safety of the State. These advantages vanish ; as soon as one understands them they are found to be losses. . . . After all, each nation is only a province in the great Kingdom of Nature."

According to the doctrine of natural harmony international peace would follow inevitably from the advance of knowledge. If it could be demonstrated that men's interests were not

---

[1] That free trade would in itself bring peace was a natural assumption for a rationalist who had realized the economic advantages of free interchange of commodities between nations. After the publication of *The Wealth of Nations* this view became a regular part of Liberalism, and was the centre of Cobden's political philosophy. Bentham stated it in classical form in his *Universal Peace* (*Works*, vol. ii., pp. 557-558) : "Conquer the whole world, impossible you should increase your trade a halfpenny ; it is impossible you should do otherwise than diminish it. Conquer little or much and you pay for it in taxes." When popular ignorance is dispelled by publicity, peace, free trade and prosperity would be the choice of everyone. In the twentieth century Norman Angell still found it necessary to prove that war and conquest did not pay, though, with the history of the later nineteenth century behind him, he was too intelligent to imagine that considerations of self-interest would be sufficient to prevent men from fighting.

antagonistic but reciprocal, war would be swiftly outlawed by the operation of self-interest. The majority of philosophers who accepted the current rationalistic philosophy were therefore ready to assume that the growth of international commerce, the discovery that it was more advantageous to trade than to fight and the gradual linking up of the world as an economic unit would shortly abolish war. They hoped that the enlightened despot would soon see that it was to his interest to lead his subjects in the way of peace.

Rousseau could be relied upon to oppose any view which assumed that reason was more powerful than passion or that despots could be enlightened. His hatred of war was as intense as Voltaire's or Holbach's, and he was equally convinced that bad government and the false ambitions of Princes were its cause. But whereas Voltaire and the other *philosophes* hoped to convert the Princes to a peaceful policy, Rousseau thought that peace would come only through democracy. He had met the Abbé de Saint-Pierre in his old age, and knowing that his work was neglected because of its length and heaviness of style he undertook the task of editing and abridging it. His short edition of *La Paix perpétuelle* appeared in 1761. Nowhere is Rousseau more surprising—here are all the unromantic qualities which he is supposed to lack. No book of the century is more logical, definite or persuasive, and none has a stronger grip upon reality.

The fundamental cause of war, Rousseau pointed out, was international anarchy: men had learned to co-operate within the State while they remained " in the state of nature with the rest of the world ": " we have prevented private feuds, only to fan the flames of public wars, which are a thousand times more terrible; in short, mankind, by gathering itself into groups, has become its own enemy. If there is any means of getting rid of these dangerous contradictions it can be only by a confederative form of government, which, uniting nations by bonds similar to those which unite individuals, submits them all equally to the authority of the laws." Such a government is preferable to all others, since " it comprehends at one and the same time the advantages of both large and small States "; its basis already

exists in European culture. Christianity had been a social
bond sufficient to keep alive an underlying unity in Europe
after the last traces of Roman organization had disappeared.
Every part of Europe was necessary to every other, so that
Europe was not merely a collection of peoples, with nothing
but a name in common, like Asia and Africa, but a real community with its own religion, its manners, its customs, and even
its laws. Nevertheless the nations remained in a state of war,
and their partial treaties could be no more than truces, " either
because these treaties had generally no other guarantee than
that of the contracting parties, or because the rights of the two
parties were never thoroughly settled. These unextinguished
rights . . . would infallibly become sources of new wars as
soon as the trend of circumstances gave new strength to the
claimants."

A Confederation of Europe is the only possible solution :
no single ruler can ever be strong enough to impose his own
peace on all the other Powers, and if two or three States attempted to combine for the permanent subjection of the others
they would only quarrel amongst themselves when it came to
dividing the spoils. A Confederation, however, of so general a
character " that no considerable Power would refuse to join it,"
with its own judicial tribunal and rules for enforcing its will
on a recalcitrant member by the common forces of the rest,
would have a considerable chance of permanence. As a basis,
the *status quo* in Europe, however unjust to those who had been
despoiled in the past, would have to be accepted ; any Power
which attempted to alter it would be declared a common
enemy. The Presidency of the new Confederation would fall in
rotation between the different Powers, and all disputes would
be submitted to arbitration.

Once established, Rousseau believed all parties would find
such a Confederation to their advantage, and there would be
no fear of revolt. The only obstacle was the nature of the
sovereigns themselves. The Abbé de Saint-Pierre had relied on
the fact that " the true glory of Princes consists in securing the
public good and the happiness of their people " ; Rousseau
pointed out that this was small comfort if they were actually

in the habit of disregarding their true glory and preferring the false splendour of conquest and self-aggrandizement. How could you take away from sovereigns "the precious right of being unjust when they please"? There was the alternative possibility that Princes who would not consider the public good might be convinced that peace would pay them better than war. Would they never realize that after a war the victor himself is weaker than he was before it, and that "he has only the consolation of seeing the vanquished more enfeebled than himself"? A list of the advantages of peace to the Prince, drawn up by the Abbé de Saint-Pierre, seemed to establish beyond question that if Princes consulted their true interests his project would be adopted. "The only thing we assume on their behalf is enough intelligence to see what is useful to themselves, and enough courage to achieve their own happiness. If, in spite of all this, the project is not carried into execution, it is not because it is chimerical; it is because men are crazy, and because to be sane in the midst of madmen is a sort of folly."

Saint-Pierre's project of perpetual peace, Rousseau declared, was no vain speculation, but "a solid sensible book." If Princes did not adopt its conclusions that was not the fault of the project, but of the Princes. They valued war, not only in order to extend their rule abroad, but because it alone enabled them to preserve their tyranny at home. "Any other view is either subservient to one of these objects, or a mere pretext for obtaining them. Such are the 'public good,' 'the welfare of the people,' or the 'glory of the nation,' words always banished from the King's closet, and so clumsily used in public edicts that they seem to be warnings of approaching misery; and the people groan in advance when their masters speak to them of their paternal care."

Saint-Pierre, therefore, was a little simple-minded in thinking to persuade tyrants to abandon their tyranny. As long as monarchies lasted, the Confederation could be set up only at a time when there happened to be a number of kings as wise and enlightened as Henry IV., every one of whom had learned "to see in the good of all the greatest good he can hope for himself. Now this demands a concurrence of wisdom in so many heads and a fortuitous concurrence of so many interests, such as chance can hardly be expected to bring about." Finally, therefore, Rousseau concludes, there is no prospect of an international Confederation being established except by general revolution. Even a bold man would hesitate to say whether a European League is more to be desired or feared at such a price. The immediate destruction might outweigh any good that it could produce in the course of centuries to come.

The Revolution came, and with it a new type of warfare, in which the mercenary armies of the Allies were continually worsted by an enthusiastic nation in arms. During the armistice of 1795 Kant wrote his *Essay on Perpetual Peace*. He laid down as one of the positive rules for preventing war that every State must have a republican form of government. Under popular constitutions he thought war unlikely. "And the reason is this. If, as must be so in a Republic, the consent of the subjects is required to determine whether there shall be war or not, nothing is more natural than that they should weigh the matter well before undertaking such a bad business. For, in decreeing war, they would of necessity be resolving to bring down the miseries of war upon their country. This implies that they must fight themselves; that they must hand over the cost of the war out of their property; that they must do their poor best to make good the devastation which it leaves behind. On the other hand, in a country where the subject is not a citizen holding a vote, plunging into war is the least serious thing in the world. For the ruler is not a citizen but the owner of the State, and does not lose a whit by the war, while he goes on enjoying the delights of his table or sport, or of his pleasure palaces and gala days. He can, therefore, decide on war for the most trifling reasons, as if it were a kind of pleasure party. Any justification of it that is necessary for the sake of decency he can leave without concern to the diplomatic corps, who are always only too ready with their services."

Men who attack an existing evil naturally assume that it will cease when the circumstances with which they have always seen it associated are changed. Rousseau and Kant saw that the wars of the eighteenth century were made by politicians to the ruin of common people : give the power to the people and war would cease. Experience, indeed, proved them right in part : under popular governments, elected rulers do not declare war as if it were a game ; they have to persuade the people that war is both necessary and right. This, however, has proved surprisingly easy, and the very same moral reasons by which eighteenth-century diplomats excused themselves have served to justify the wars of a more democratic Europe.

For the Revolution did not change the nature of States though it changed their rulers. Kant argued that there were certain preliminary principles which must be observed if war was to cease. These preliminaries included the abolition of standing armies and the provision that when peace was signed it should be real peace, not merely a temporary armistice in which each country made a " secret reservation " to fight again when a favourable opportunity arrived. Such preliminaries would have been carried out only if the advent of democracy had meant a change in the objects of State policy as well as in its institutions. States still remained armed and sovereign, and the same causes of war therefore remained in operation.

With the Revolution the sovereignty of the State formally passed from the King to the people, but its character changed little in the transference. The King, as Kant protested, treated the land as his private *patrimonium*, an estate for which the common people were obliged to fight as the feudal serf had once fought for his lord's fief. In the nineteenth century the State still remained an estate, sacred territory whose defence was a supreme duty and whose extension was always desirable. Patriotism was not weakened but reinforced by the Revolution : the people, now sovereign lord of their own territory, volunteered to overthrow the invader, and were ready enough to become invaders themselves if they could believe the old excuses that they were fighting in self-defence, for the balance of power or for the integrity of international law.

Thus a new patriotism was born. The aristocracy had never been patriotic in the modern sense, though, as owners of the soil and the State, they had been willing to fight or hire mercenaries in its defence.[1] At the Revolution the soil of France became the private property of the peasantry, and every property holder learned to regard himself as exercising part of the sovereign power. Even in countries where the number of patriots and property holders has been smaller than in France democracy has had the same result—the bestowal of power and property on a new class and therefore an enormous extension of patriotism. For patriotism is the sentiment of ownership extended to the nation : its virtues and vices are those of private ownership. Its virtues are affection for the countryside and desire for the welfare of its inhabitants, its vices the pursuit of imagined greatness and the vulgarity which enjoys size, show, and a cheap superiority over others.

Those who believed that international hatreds would end with the *ancien régime* were deluded by a psychology which neglected the whole of man's instinctive nature. They thought that a change of rulers, and a clear exposition of the economic advantages of peace and of the moral evils of war, would suffice to change human behaviour. In fact the occasions rather than the causes of war were changed. Greed, ignorance and the lust for power were potent in the era of democracy and industrialism as they were in the days of despotism and mercantilist economics. Rousseau and Kant, however, were not mistaken in thinking that democracy had released new forces making for peace. Vice has had to pay more extravagant homage to virtue : the nineteenth-century citizen was an easy victim of propaganda, but it was at least necessary to persuade him that he was acting rightly when he did all those things which his usual code of ethics forbade. The strength of this reluctance to settle disputes by force has grown in the nineteenth century, and the number of

---

[1] Voltaire had commented (*Dic. Phil.*, art. *Patrie*) on the value of their patriotism, and on the mockery of expecting patriotism from the dispossessed. As for the luxurious Parisian who had never journeyed farther than "to Dieppe to eat fresh fish, who only knew his smart town house, his pretty country villa, the champagne that came to him from Rheims, and his rents"— of course he loved his country. No doubt financiers, officers and soldiers who preyed on it had the tenderest love for the peasants they ruined, but you could hardly expect the worker, a slave to a superior's orders, without any property or share in government, to be an enthusiastic patriot.

persons who hold that national ends can no more justify war than personal ones justify murder has steadily increased. Kant stated an essential truth when he based his hope of a European Federation upon the growing desire for moral relations in international affairs : the moral revolt against the European anarchy grows side by side with and reinforces the repulsion against the horror, waste and futility of war.

" In all these twistings and turnings of an immoral doctrine of expediency," says Kant, "which aims at substituting a state of peace for the warlike conditions in which men are placed by nature, so much at least is clear—that men cannot get away from the idea of right in their private any more than in their public relations ; and that they do not dare (this is indeed most strikingly seen in the concept of an International Law) to base politics merely on the manipulations of expediency and therefore to refuse all obedience to the idea of a public right. On the contrary, they pay all fitting honour to the idea of right in itself, even though, at the same time, they devise a hundred subterfuges and excuses to avoid it in practice and regard force, backed up by cunning, as having the authority which comes from being the source and unifying principle of all right. It will be well to put an end to this sophistry, if not to the injustice it extenuates, and to bring the false advocates of the mighty of the earth to confess that it is not right but might in whose interest they speak, and that it is the worship of might from which they take their cue, as if in this matter they had a right to command."

Kant saw that there could be no solution to any problems of social justice while nations continued to claim their own sovereignty. If their own interest was the final good, morality and politics must necessarily be divorced. Every representative of the nation was confronted with an insoluble problem ; he was appointed to further the ends of his State, whether they were, viewed from outside, moral ones or not. He was therefore constantly in the dilemma of having to act immorally or disloyally. The only solution was an international federation which would create an ethical relationship between States and thus release the statesman, and indeed every individual, from the necessity of repudiating his moral code and his sense of decency in his dealings with foreign nations. Kant believed that an international government might be realized in the future after a long evolution—it was an " idea of reason " which accorded with the trend of evolutionary forces and which could be accomplished when men saw the need for it and willed its realization.

CHAPTER XI

PROGRESS

I. THE NEW RELIGION

THE distinctive feature of European thought since the French Revolution has been its attitude towards time. Liberty, equality and fraternity, nationalism and internationalism, democracy and toleration had been the subject-matter of political discussion in earlier periods of history. Neither were the *philosophes* on unexplored ground in substituting a secular for a religious outlook. Anti-clerical writers had always urged that the object of life was terrestrial happiness, not eternal salvation. But the *philosophes* made a new and surprising synthesis when they combined a belief in the goods of this life with a doctrine that they were to be judged good only if they contributed to a better future. This was to join the advantages of hedonism with those of Christianity. The creed of the *libertins* had the practical advantage that it concentrated upon actual human satisfactions rather than upon conventional obligations to act morally and believe unreasonable doctrines. It was unsatisfactory as a religion because it was almost wholly individualist : however much its best thinkers might urge that the highest happiness came from altruism, it provided no spur to social conduct. It saw the value of human development and of individual freedom in contrast with the Church's insistence on abnegation and obedience. Hedonism was usually sterile because it treated men as separate units whose nature was to find pleasure ; it forgot that society existed because men were naturally social beings. The mediæval Church had built a wall round human life in the belief that men would be lost if left to find their own way : the hedonists assumed that, if the wall were broken down, men would need no guidance except their own desires. Hedonism emphasized the value of the moment : Christianity, the vanity of temporal happiness. At its best, mediæval Catholicism had put before men an ideal of service and had attempted to inspire every part and aspect of common life with social purpose. The new doctrine of progress, soon to be christened " the religion of humanity," accepted the terrestrial values of the hedonist : it stressed the importance of individual happiness, the practical satisfaction of human desires, the solution of earthly problems and the utility of increased knowledge. But, like mediæval Christianity, it subordinated these to social ends, and judged them valuable only in relation to an ultimate standard. This social and religious aspect had almost wholly disappeared from eighteenth-century Catholicism and the *philosophes* were the true religious teachers of their generation. The French Revolution was a religious revival : the articles of its creed were liberty, equality and fraternity, its ideal was social happiness and its deity was the future of the race. Like most religions, progress could be defended by reason and was considered the very embodiment of reason. Comte took from Condorcet the motto : " Live for others : it is only then one lives for oneself " ; and this recommendation to lose your life in order to find it was sound utilitarianism as well as sound Christianity. But the most competent utilitarian philosopher could show no reasonable grounds for including the unborn as well as the born among those for whom one was to live. The generation for whose welfare the present was to be lived might never be born, and could not in any case repay the consideration of its ancestors. In the event, indeed, it might prove that their forethought had been misdirected and their sacrifice futile. Progress was a religion because it offered men a vision which they could follow irrespective of utilitarian considerations, an ideal in whose service they were prepared to do most unreasonable things.

All religions decay, and the sceptic is quick to profit by the widening gap between profession and practice. Indeed, there is nothing more worthy of ridicule than the religious attitude which remains after the inspiration has gone : the conventional phrases and reverent posturings which accompany commonplace conduct. It was not long before the religion of progress had degenerated into a gospel of acceleration : before ends were often confused with means, and change of any sort welcomed as advance. Rapid movement was exhilarating and men forgot, in the midst of scientific discovery and industrial change, to ask in what direction they were hurrying. The philosophy of progress is a serviceable one as long as the better future it assumes is clearly imagined and deliberately willed. It is essentially a moral philosophy, continuously concerned with the effects of action —the creation and enjoyment of beauty fits only with effort into its scheme and programme. The artist has naturally objected to this emphasis on the future : time and moral preoccupations are alike his enemies. In his view the men of the nineteenth century spent their time and energy pouring out the wine of the present as a libation to the future.

The habit of judging the past and the present by their contribution to the hypothetical future is the child of modern science. A few scientists in the ancient world had approached the modern attitude, and Lucretius had emancipated himself from the legend of the Golden Age, but his scientific evolutionary theory was not a regular ingredient of classical thought or literature. The Middle Ages were almost wholly free from the notion of progress. Knowledge of essentials was complete ; time and space were both fixed and defined in Catholic cosmogony. The boundaries of Christendom were limited and the date of the millennium known, at least to the best authorities. In any case, it was no business of the ordinary man to hasten or retard the Second Coming. Secular improvement was of only secondary importance in the estimation of the Church, and the structure of society, based on social orders with appropriate functions, seemed not fluid and wilful, but static, divinely ordained and final. The mediævalist might concern himself with his own and his neighbours' salvation, but time and space and the future of the world were God's mysteries, not man's. Most moderns, with an endless vista of time ahead and an unalterable assumption that human wills are important in shaping future history, appreciate with difficulty a literature and a philosophy which were indifferent to the temporal effects of actions, and judged them by their contribution to the glory of God. A charmed circle surrounds the Middle Ages : none may enter it who are preoccupied with the religion of progress.

With the advance of scientific habits of mind after the Middle Ages, the past began to seem absurd, the present hopeful and the future glorious. If uniform and unalterable laws of nature could be everywhere discovered, man could adjust himself to them for his own advantage : knowledge gave him the power to control his own destiny. This view could be fully effective only when it had replaced Catholic cosmogony in the minds of ordinary men and women. Scepticism of past dogmas and religions was an inevitable stage towards the new faith. Above all, the doctrine that men came into the world already burdened with an unalterable inheritance of sin was repugnant to a progressive theory. If progress is to be effective as a religion, man's fate must be, at least to some extent, in his own hands, and knowledge his sufficient means of grace. By the end of the seventeenth century the new psychology combined with the rapid advance of scientific discovery had enabled Saint-Pierre to preach a doctrine of human perfectibility.

At first sight the doctrine of progress seems complete in Saint-Pierre. He believed in the indefinite possibilities of human improvement (which is the accurate translation of *perfectibilité*) through the power of reason applied by governments and scientists. His faith was so pure as to be completely uncontagious. He wrote infelicitously and at enormous length, and it was only after a period of administrative breakdown, religious struggle and philosophic propaganda that men were ready to listen to the new religion. When Saint-Pierre boasted of man's perfectibility the facts seemed to contradict him. Things seemed to get worse rather than better. Men were unlikely to believe in progress unless they could see it. History was still commonly presented as a decadence, not an advance. The Renaissance had assumed without question that the world of classical antiquity was a peak from which men had permanently descended. Without any conception of historical evolution, Saint-Pierre and his contemporaries had the material for generous speculation and philosophic hope : they could still argue that science and reason might one day triumph, but they could not convince the sceptic or excite the enthusiasm of the common man. The driving force of religion in the West has usually been the conviction that the ideal is already in process of development and that its arrival can be hastened by human agency. The believer needs a God who is omnipotent and yet in need of his help.

Saint-Pierre offered men a religion without a God : a century later philosophers had discovered a teleology in natural develop-ment and learned to regard man as the climax of a divine purpose which utilized human effort for the attainment of an ultimate perfection.

2. HISTORICAL INTERPRETATION—VOLTAIRE, TURGOT AND CONDORCET

The doctrine of historical progress means, when strictly used, first, that there has been in history an increase of things con-sidered good at the expense of those considered bad ; secondly, that this desirable trend may be expected to continue indefinitely. If such a belief is to stand criticism the historian must provide a philosophy and interpretation of the past, he must be able to generalize about what has happened and to explain why it has happened, to state laws of development and show what forces, physical and psychological, have been and are at work. Without a doctrine of historical causation there can be no confidence that an increase in the good, even if evident one day, will con-tinue. The historical philosophy which best suits the religion of progress is one which suggests that advance is inevitable and yet dependent upon human will.

The idea that the historical process might be a record of improvement rather than of degeneration was first clearly conceived in the seventeenth century ; the effort to explain this development, to apply the intellect to the record of the past as a whole, did not begin until the eighteenth. The humanists of the Renaissance, inspired by the writings of classical antiquity, assumed that the age which had produced Seneca was an un-assailable summit of civilization. Bacon struck one of the first blows at this conception when he suggested in his *Novum Organum* that the title of antiquity was properly used not of ancient Greece, when civilization was young, but of "the time in which we live." Knowledge and experience belong to the present : we stand on the shoulders of the past and can see farther. Pascal, in an almost equally famous passage, wrote that those whom we call "*anciens*" were in fact "*nouveaux*."

"The whole succession of human beings through the whole course of the ages may be regarded as a single man, ever living and ever learning." Fontenelle pushed this conception even further. He successfully transformed the literary battle between the ancients and moderns from a sterile conflict of pedantries into a serious discussion of an intelligible question. Did historical evidence support a theory of degeneration? If the trees of antiquity were no larger than those of the eighteenth century neither were the men : the sap of nature had not run dry, but remained precisely the same. Knowledge, however, had increased, and we might therefore look forward to improvement. Fontenelle contributed to the doctrine of progress the idea of an indefinite advance, resulting not from a change in human nature but from the accumulation of knowledge and experience.[1] The world, he said, would never degenerate because the "best minds" would always contribute to each other's wisdom.

The problem for the eighteenth-century historian was to show this improvement at work. How did men pass on their social heritage from one generation to another? What, in other words, was the mechanism of historical change? There were several possibilities. Was the sequence of events the result of an external Providential plan, as Bossuet declared? Were historical forces purely material or did human reason and organization play a part? The eighteenth century did not discuss these factors scientifically or realize their possible combinations, but it stated this central problem of history and provided a variety of answers.

Most history Voltaire regarded as a " parcel of tricks we play on the dead." For his part, historical writing served two purposes. It was primarily a method of propaganda and a reply to Bossuet. Bossuet's *Universal History* was not, as Voltaire urged, either universal or very good history ; it was, however,

---

[1] In *Dialogues of the Dead* Fontenelle seems to express just the opposite view—that of the sceptics—that men behave instinctively, not rationally, and never learn from experience. Montaigne is made say to Socrates : "Little silly birds, they suffer themselves to be taken in the same nets that have caught a hundred thousand of their kind already : the follies of the fathers are lost upon the children, and do not seem to instruct them at all."

an effort to apply the intellect to history, to interpret, not to list, events. Bossuet's doctrine of Providence marked a clear stage towards a philosophy of secular progress. It set events in a time-sequence, and pictured the march of man, under the guiding Hand, towards a future goal. It enabled men to accept doctrines which seemed at first contrary to Christian conceptions and still to remain believers : it prepared the way for the creed of natural harmony and reconciled many of the orthodox to scientific discoveries. God ruled by law, and man might legitimately inquire into His mysteries and thus serve as a more efficient instrument in His hand.

Voltaire pictured the amazement of a Chinaman who bought the *Universal History* and found no mention of the great civilization of the Chinese, while the Jews, " an ignorant and barbarous people "—" a race of pedlars "—were represented as the pivot of history. Voltaire found this an excellent starting-point for an account of historical evolution which put the Jews in their proper place, which justified the persecutions of Diocletian on political grounds, which found natural causes where orthodoxy sought for miraculous ones, which praised the statesmanship of Julian the Apostate, which exploded the sanctity of saints and the heroism of heroes, and which suggested unflattering parallels between ancient abuses and modern methods of government.

Voltaire's history attempted more than this. He made a genuine effort to envisage the pageant of history, to see the story of man as a unity. He was no mere chronicler, recording picturesque details of wars and courts, but an historian selecting his facts in obedience to a conscious philosophy. " Laws, manners, arts,—these," he writes, " have been my principal concern ; paltry facts shall not enter into this work except where they have produced important results." Art, literature and philosophy were the only important social products, and they had flourished in four great epochs of good government and enlightened opinion. History was the story of man's long martyrdom, occasionally relieved by wise rule and favourable circumstances. War and religion were the two principal enemies of mankind ; when they were destroyed by the onslaught of reason an age of greater happiness and culture might arrive. Voltaire's sociology stopped at this point. His interpretation of history was more rational than Bossuet's, but equally partial. He saw only political causes where Bossuet saw only Providential ones, and when politics seemed not to explain everything he fell back on Chance. The great epochs of which he writes remain unexplained : they hang so precariously upon personal genius or accidental circumstance that there seems no security for their continuance or recurrence. He saw that there were natural tendencies usually outside human control, but that a genius at the right moment could do much to utilize them.[1] " Almost all laws," he wrote, " have been instituted to meet passing needs ; like remedies applied fortuitously they have cured one patient and killed others." Voltaire resembled Gibbon not only in his ironic treatment of Christianity but also in his lack of all sociological interpretation, his contentment with political events and ostensible motives. Like Gibbon again, his treatment is flat : he judges all institutions good or bad irrespective of place or period. All religions are equally harmful at all times ; he admits no contribution to civilization in any period when science was not dominant. Voltaire admitted improvement and hoped for progress : he believed that reason was valuable but saw nothing to ensure its triumph.

Montesquieu was in point of accuracy and method Voltaire's inferior as a historian, and he had none of Voltaire's sense of the pageantry of the past. But from Aristotle, Harrington, and perhaps from Bodin, he had learned that political explanations are usually inadequate, and he had too scientific a bent to fall back upon Chance when knowledge was lacking. In the *Décadence des Romans* he had shown an admirable sense of historical perspective, and even in *L'Esprit des Lois*, when he wrote as if all constitutions and institutions were to be judged and explained by a few invariable physical factors, he was over-emphasizing and misapplying a truth, not stating a falsehood. He at least saw that the record of external politics is intelligible only against an economic and social background.

---

[1] *Cp.* his article, *Chaîne des Evènements*, in the *Dic. Phil.*

Two years after the publication of *L'Esprit des Lois* Turgot gave the first of his remarkable discourses on history at the Sorbonne. He was only twenty-three years of age, and his essays were rather suggestions for others to work out than finished products. He combined Montesquieu's idea of underlying causes with a conception of human will and social evolution. He begins by comparing the futility of mere animal and vegetable change with the fruitful development of man's history. Natural phenomena are " enclosed in a circle of revolutions that remains the same for ever "; successive generations of vegetables and animals perpetuate themselves and " time does nothing more than continually produce replicas of that which it has just thrown aside." Humanity, unlike the rest of nature, acquires knowledge and transmits experience : it steps outside the circle to which all other forms of life are condemned, and consciously improves itself. Physical phenomena may be precisely explained if we know the preceding events and the laws which apply to them : an historical event depends on mental and social factors as well as physical ones. The historian must trace a succession of social states causally connected but explicable only on the assumption that mechanical factors play a diminishing part and the intelligent control of man an increasing one. The growth of knowledge is the key to progress.

The whole human race moves slowly forward. Unlike his contemporaries, Turgot felt that even the Middle Ages had not been altogether retrogressive—something was learned, even if only the fact that religious domination was evil. There is no real retrogression though there may be periods of maladjustment : the suffering involved forces men to new efforts, acts as a stimulus to better government, and proves, in the long run, progress too. Humanity is a baby tumbling upstairs. " I search for a progress of the human mind and I find almost nothing but the history of error." Nevertheless, the evidence of anthropology (and Turgot naturally assumed a lineal and similar development of man everywhere), showing at the same moment all the shades of advance from barbarism to civilization, discloses to us in a single glance " the footprints of all the steps of humanity, the measure of the whole track along which it has passed, the history of all the ages."

How could it be otherwise? Natural laws are invariable ; man controls his life by experience and knowledge. When knowledge is complete man will be able to make an exact adjustment to natural forces, his tumblings and strivings will cease and a static Utopia be achieved. The day of the scientific Utopia had begun. The imagination of men dimly saw that mechanical power would transform the face of the world : they ceased to dream of a Platonic Republic built neither in space nor time and proposed to establish a modern Utopia in Paris itself, renewed, reorganized and scientifically managed. In the future State the scientist, not the philosopher, is King.

When, in his second *Discours* on universal history, Turgot came to trace the epochs of past development and to account for human institutions, he anticipated Comte's famous division of intellectual evolution into three stages. Man gradually passed from primitive animism and anthropomorphism into the stage of philosophical guesswork—from the religious to the metaphysical stages, in Comte's phraseology. Each of these earlier stages continued, unfortunately, in some degree to retard the growth of the scientific age which had superseded them.

During the forty years that elapsed between Turgot's essays and Condorcet's elaboration of a similar thesis in the *Prospectus for an Outline of the Progress of the Human Race*, the idea of historical evolution from a barbaric past to a scientific and perfect future was expressed in numerous books. In his *Public Felicity*, published in 1772, Chastellux contrasted different historical epochs, with the object of discovering in which men had been most happy. He concluded that even ancient Greece, the one period not dominated by the priest and the despot, was made wretched by the existence of slavery. In the modern world there was hope : war, superstition and tyranny were at least dying before the attack of science. Other Utopias of the later part of the century are influenced by the same hope. Such predictions as Mercier's *Year 2440*, Volney's *Ruins*, and Restif de la Bretonne's play *The Year 2000* are new in the history of Utopia-making, not because the worlds they suggest are more attractive

than those of earlier ideal republics, but because they assume
that moral and political improvement are necessary by-products
of mechanical science.

When during the Revolution itself Condorcet wrote a fuller
outline of the history of human progress, his perspective and
interpretation were substantially those of Turgot. His *Tableau*
is one of a long series of refutations of Rousseau's early essays.
He aims at showing that knowledge, not simplicity, is the key
to happiness and morality, that society moves not from primitive
excellence to sophisticated misery, but from bondage and superstition towards an ultimate perfection of freedom and reason.
Condorcet began, as his predecessors, Turgot, d'Alembert and
Chastellux had done, with a dogmatic explanation of sensationalist psychology. And if the individual formed his ideas and
regulated his conduct as a result of knowledge and experience,
so did the race as a whole. The general laws which are to be
observed in the development of an individual's faculties govern
the progress of the race. For the race advances only because a
great number of individuals develop together. The process is
cumulative, each period knowing more than the last, and passing
on that knowledge and also a wider power to utilize it. Indeed,
had not the time come when there might be a science of society
itself, when it would be possible " to foresee the progress of
humanity, to direct it, to hasten it "? If so, we must begin
by understanding the part and discovering the mechanism by
which error and superstition had been induced to give way to
truth and science. When this was accomplished, and the strength
of the directing forces better appreciated, a provisional answer
might be given to the further question—whether there were
obstacles which still barred the way to ultimate perfection.

Condorcet divides the past of the human race into nine epochs,
stretching from the dawn of history up to the Revolution itself,
through long ages when men first learned to hunt and then to
plough, to write and at last to print and so to spread and pass
on the knowledge they had gained. In Condorcet's as in Turgot's
treatment the story of progress is identical with that of knowledge ; it is a long struggle with error and with the priests and
despots who opposed truth for interested reasons. In early

periods the progress of knowledge was slow; men had "a natural attachment to opinions acquired in infancy and to the customs of their country"; ignorance and superstition made men averse from every kind of novelty; laziness of body, and even more of mind, prevailed over their early curiosity, and often kept primitive society almost stagnant. To these natural obstacles must be added "greed, cruelty, corruption and the prejudices of civilized peoples." The vice and unhappiness of the powerful, the educated and the cultured, "with their eternally restless passions, always active and always unsatisfied," had not been due to the growth of knowledge itself, but to its struggle with ancient errors and prejudices which it had not yet been able to overcome. Enlightenment had been confined to the few: its power to promote happiness depended on its extension over the whole society where superstition still reigned. Rousseau had misunderstood the symptoms: knowledge was not a sign of decadence nor misery its result, but humanity was in the course of "a struggle and painful passage from a rude society to a state of civilization . . . a necessary crisis in the gradual advance of the human species towards absolute perfection." [1]

In spite of hindrances, however, man had gradually acquired the art of civilization, and the beginnings of science had appeared in the ancient world. Unfortunately, Rome had failed to stem the invasions of the barbarians, on the one hand, and of mystical religions, on the other. Many warring sects from the East were gradually merged in a common worship of "a Christ, a messenger sent by God to redeem the human race. . . . The time, the place of his appearance, his human name were all matters of dispute, but the claims of a prophet said to have appeared in Palestine under Tiberius eclipsed all the others, and the new fanatics rallied to the standard of the son of Mary." The spirit of the new sect suited the conditions of the decaying Empire so well, and it learned so effectively to organize itself as a political force, that it triumphed in spite of the wise and courageous efforts of Julian the Apostate to deliver the Empire from the religious plague he saw settling down upon her.

---

[1] *Deuxième Epoque.*

Every religion demands the acceptance of miracles and other absurdities from its adherents, but the particular characteristic of Christianity was its contempt for the humane sciences. " Thus the triumph of Christianity was the signal for the total decadence of the sciences and of philosophy." Without printing there was no way of preserving knowledge : the barbarians and the Christians had their own way, and the Dark and Middle Ages began, when men could not distinguish between authority based on knowledge and self-constituted authority which exists only because none dare contradict. Condorcet, summarily dismissing a thousand years of history, reverted to the theory of Voltaire. Unlike Turgot he did not think progress continuous : it began again at the Renaissance. The eighteenth century did not define knowledge widely enough to include mediæval contributions to art and literature, to moral perception and to political ideas. The Middle Ages were a period of " slavery of the mind," harmful not only directly but still more "by reason of its corruption of the method of studying "—a period in which men learned to adopt " a proposition not because it was true but because it was written in a particular book and had been accepted in a particular country or since a particular period."

The discovery of printing, at the close of the mediæval period created a new tribunal of public opinion. The authority of the priesthood was undermined and men were able to accumulate knowledge and profit by experience. The revival of classical literature and the discovery of America completed the foundations of the new era. The Reformation, instead of leading to the general destruction of Christianity, was seized upon by kings for their own advantage and a new form of State tyranny instituted. Science, however, made great strides in spite of persecution. Religious toleration and freedom of thought were granted, if at all, " not to men but to Christians." Consequently the history of this period was marked by " little real progress towards liberty but more order and strength in governments and in the nations a stronger and, further, a more just consciousness of their rights. Laws were better put together : they seemed less often the shapeless work of circumstance and caprice : they were made by *savants* if not yet by *philosophes*."

Moral, political and economic sciences were in process of
formation: International Law came into existence, founded,
unhappily, "not on reason and nature," but "on established
customs and the opinions of the ancients." Science, reason and
humanity grew in isolated places where "pure and strong souls,
of fine character, united to unusual gifts, appeared here and
there amidst scenes of fanaticism, hypocrisy, corruption and
bloodshed. . . . The human race is still disgusting to the
philosopher who contemplates the scene it presents: but it no
longer humiliates him and it offers him hope not so far distant."

In the ninth epoch, opened by Descartes' *Discourse on Method*
and ending with the Fall of the Bastille, political liberty advanced
side by side with scientific discovery. The slavery of the old
world had disappeared even if the liberty of the most advanced
countries was still imperfect. Under enlightened despots the
illumination of science spread and "the practice of governments
followed slowly and as if regretfully the march of opinion and
of philosophy." The ideas of equality, rights and democracy,
the discovery of economic laws and the universal dissemination
of the new philosophy with "its battle-cry, reason, liberation
and humanity," were the work of the epoch leading to the
Revolution itself. Thought had become international as well
as humane and free. "Animated by a universal philanthropy,
the *philosophes* fought injustice wherever they saw it at home
or abroad, both Englishmen and Frenchmen calling themselves
friends of the negroes whom stupid tyrants scorned to count
among the number of men." Russians and Swedes were taught
by the French to praise toleration, while Beccaria, the Italian,
exposed the barbarity of French jurisprudence. "Frenchmen
sought to cure the Englishman of his commercial prejudices, of
his superstitious respect for the evil of his Constitution and
laws," while English philanthropists, like Howard, applied the
new philosophy to the task of social reform. Philosophy, letters,
art and science all advanced, and with the success, first of the
American Revolution and then of the French, the influence of
the new doctrines was spread far and wide. Even after the
Declaration of Rights, however, only a small proportion of the
world was enlightened: most of it was still "vegetating in

the infancy of the early epochs." The number of men with real understanding appears almost nothing "in comparison with the mass of mankind, still bound by prejudice and ignorance." "We see that the labours of these last periods have done much for the progress of the human mind, but little for the improvement of the race : much for the glory of man, something for his liberty, but almost nothing yet for his happiness."

3. THE FUTURE—THE TENTH EPOCH AND THE ASCENT OF MAN

By the end of the eighteenth century men, Condorcet thought, had discovered how to acquire knowledge, how to learn nature's secrets, and therefore how to be happy. That they were not generally happy was because this knowledge was confined to a few. Progress, the increase of knowledge, and therefore the beginnings of happiness, had been due to the almost accidental adoption of useful inventions and discoveries made by occasional men of genius who had contrived to survive in a society inimical to new ideas. Now however that men knew that the laws both of external nature and of the human mind were constant, a science of society was possible and men could learn consciously to co-operate and control their future. Man's happiness was within his grasp : he could destroy traditional barriers and set up institutions which would give his capacities full scope. Nature set no limit to progress.

Condorcet based his hopes on three main lines of advance. First, he could see no reason why all nations should not reach "the same point of civilization at which the most enlightened, free and emancipated nations, such as the French and Anglo-Americans," had arrived. He could see no reason to think that any people were congenitally incapable of learning to reason. In the second place, he asked, was it not possible to remove most of the inequalities which existed within each nation? The differences of education, opportunity and wealth which had hitherto divided society into classes were mainly the result of the "*imperfections actuelles de l'art social.*" The aim of the *art social* should be to remove all unnecessary and harmful inequalities. Thirdly, Condorcet hoped for the indefinite improvement of man himself: "May it not be expected that the human race will be improved by new discoveries in the sciences and arts and, as an unavoidable consequence, in the means of individual and general prosperity?" It could scarcely be doubted: there would be " progress in the principles of conduct and in practical morality " and a continuous improvement in " the intellectual, moral and physical faculties," as well as in " the instruments which increase the intensity and direct the use of these faculties." The thought that general prosperity might not be an " unavoidable consequence " of scientific advance scarcely occurred to him. That men would know and still act as if they were ignorant, that they might be creatures of heredity even more than of environment and might disregard the clear teaching of science and follow instinct even to disaster, that their values might be wrong when their knowledge was accurate—these did not seem real difficulties in the eighteenth century. As long as freedom and knowledge spread everywhere, all was well: they could be extended by democracy, economic reform and education.

" The principles of the French Constitution are already those of all enlightened men ": now that democracy had destroyed the power of despots and priests in France, truth must soon find its way even " into the hovels of slaves." Released from their long humiliation even the slave would respond to the call. So far the white colonist, with his " commercial monopolies, treacheries, bloodthirsty contempt for men of another colour or another faith, his insolent plundering and religious fanaticism, had not made a good impression, and had destroyed the natural respect of the black man for the white's superior intelligence and the benefits of his commerce." Democracy has changed all this: some English " friends of humanity " had already begun to attack slavery, and now that the advantages of free trade were known, tariffs and monopolies would cease. Colonization would proceed peaceably and white men, " too enlightened about their own rights to trifle with those of others, would respect the independence of backward peoples and instead of sending monks to spread shameful superstitions among them would themselves become colonists, anxious to teach them the truths useful to their happiness." Eventually, it might be after a period of misery and distrust, natives everywhere would learn to look to their "brothers among the Europeans" and to become their friends and disciples. Their progress could be swifter and more certain than ours had been because they could benefit by our experience. "It will come at last, this moment when the sun will shine upon a world in which all men are free and recognize no master save reason; when the tyrants and the slaves, the priests and their stupid or hypocritical tools will no longer exist except in history or on the stage"; when men will know how to "recognize and stifle with the force of reason the first germs of tyranny and superstition, should they ever dare to reappear!"

The backward peoples then offered no permanent barrier to progress. What of the struggle between classes, the social and economic inequalities within each nation? One may summarize Condorcet's economic aspirations by saying that he was not a socialist but that he was a somewhat advanced twentieth-century Liberal. He accepted the Physiocratic theory of natural harmony with reservations and admitted the necessity of government regulation on behalf of the weak: he thought that "nature's inevitable evils" might be lessened by public foresight and wise State action. Like the Physiocrats, therefore, he emphasized the injurious effects of trade monopolies and tariff barriers which interfered with the free flow of commodities and the formation of the world into a single economic unit. But he went further. If the market was to be really free, he saw that the small man must be protected against the big capitalist, whose monopoly might be none the less injurious because it was the result of his own efforts and not of a royal gift. Condorcet had all the economist's belief that most evils may be remedied by statistics and scientific forethought: "the application of the calculus" should enable men to devise social safeguards against the greed of rich men and to discover ways of releasing industrial and commercial progress from its dependence upon great capitalists.

Some of the worst miseries of poverty might, he thought, be provided against by an increase of every form of insurance. All those who were unable to compete on fair terms—the sick, the old, women and children—should be protected not only by private insurance but also "by social authority." He had certainly departed from any principle of *laissez-faire* when he remarked that under good institutions " riches would no longer be the means of satisfying vanity and ambition," and that men would cease to work mainly for money and be content with a more moderate and equable distribution. Condorcet looked forward to a distributivist State in which there was no proletariat and little luxury, and in which government guarded the interests of small property holders of every type, commercial as well as agricultural. Some natural inequalities would remain, but their evil social effects could be abolished.

Together with democracy and economic reform must go education. The State could ensure that " the entire mass of the people are instructed in what each man needs to know for the management of his private affairs, the free development of his industry and talents. He need not be a stranger to any of those lofty sentiments and delicate feelings which are mankind's distinction : he can know his rights and defend and make use of them." Thus education was the way to substantial equality, since men feel injured not by inequality of talent but by inequality of opportunity. Class distinctions were based on the contrast between refined and uneducated speech and on similar social distinctions ; they resulted from a system of education which increased natural inequalities instead of correcting them. And every argument for male education was equally one for female, just as every claim for the rights of man was also one for the rights of woman. Condorcet, as the friend of Mary Wollstonecraft and Thomas Paine, was not likely to suffer from the usual inconsistency and imagine that democracy could exist without equality of the sexes.

Condorcet had a practical opportunity of advancing the cause of education. He opposed the communist proposal in the Convention to educate all children, boys and girls, at the public expense, taking them from their parents and providing them with " the same clothes, the same food, the same teaching and the same care." But his own proposal, so effective in nineteenth-century France in obliterating class divisions of speech and outlook and in cultivating a specific French culture, could scarcely be termed an individualist solution. Every child should be " *un élève de la patrie*," provided with a sound grounding of elementary knowledge and enough teaching about religion, politics and economics to make him safe against the wiles of charlatans and demagogues.

Condorcet believed that education should aim at diminishing rather than encouraging the spirit of rivalry : " the habit of wishing to be first is a ridiculous one, a misfortune for those who have acquired it and a real calamity for those whom fortune condemns to live near it." A school should teach practical co-operation as well as the principles of commercial, political and moral science. Both pupils and masters should, however, be encouraged to form and expound their own opinions, and the only views proscribed should be the dogmas of religious cults. In the same way, the teaching of political science would not aim at making men admire a complete legislative system or form of government, but at " making them able to appraise its value." Even the French Constitution and the Declaration of Rights, he said, should not be taught as if they were " tables come down from heaven which must be adored and believed." Fearful of State propaganda, he devised an educational hierarchy to secure the independence of teachers and, above all, to guarantee complete freedom of opinion in higher education. In the event, the Convention accepted the bulk of Condorcet's educational proposals—his division of education into primary, secondary and superior, the provision of free elementary education for both sexes and the opportunity of comparatively cheap higher education. And though the Revolutionary system of education did mean that during the nineteenth century class distinctions in France have depended less on differences of speech and culture than elsewhere, French teachers and professors have not been altogether free from State interference or owed their position entirely to non-political considerations.

Good laws and a free educational system could altogether end the social inequalities which destroyed men's happiness and could provide against natural and inevitable inequalities in such a way that they were humiliating to none and advantageous to all. The only final authority would be that of science, an authority based not on arbitrary power but upon reason, one whose claims could be rationally examined and rationally supported. As scientific precision grew it would be increasingly possible to order society for the general good : men themselves may or may not improve in their innate capacity, but the same effect must result from the improvement of scientific instruments, and the growth of accurate and perfect machinery will release men from most of the labour which now occupies their time, exhausts their energy and retards their progress.[1] If we remember that, " even in enlightened countries, scarcely a fiftieth part of those to whom nature has given talents receive the necessary training to develop them," the possibilities of future improvement in all the arts and sciences seem unlimited. The production and distribution of commodities will be scientifically controlled, each country producing what best fits its soil and receiving what its populations most need. Population will increase, enabling more to be produced and the needs of all to be more fully satisfied.

At this point Condorcet was confronted with the objection which seemed to Malthus and his followers a complete refutation of his hopes. Will there come a time, he asks, when the increase in the number of men will be too great, when the well-being of the population will commence to deteriorate— " a retrograde movement, at least a kind of oscillation between good and evil "? Will such a period " mark the point past which all improvement becomes impossible, the limit to human perfectibility which it will reach in the vastness of the ages, without being able to overcome it "?

Condorcet's answer has been commonly misunderstood. It is true that he brushed aside the fundamental and ever-present difficulty of adjusting food supply to population as a distant and scarcely relevant speculation. " It is equally impossible," he wrote, " to pronounce for or against the future reality of an event which would be realized only in an enlightened age—an epoch when the human species had acquired intelligence almost

---

[1] Both Helvétius and Condorcet emphasized the dependence of a real social science on the possibility of finding a language in which one word would mean one thing.

beyond our powers of imagination." In any case, if over-population did ever become an actuality, men would have learned by that time that their obligation to their children was not to " give them existence but happiness . . . they would have lost the childish notion of filling the earth with useless and unhappy beings." Indeed Condorcet's view was sound enough on the assumption that the society of the future would be scientifically regulated and public morality rationally guided. " Is not a wrong understanding of interest the most frequent cause of actions that are contrary to the general good? Would not a consciousness of dignity—which belongs to free men—and an education based on a deeper knowledge of our moral constitution, inevitably fertilize in almost all men the principles of a rigorous and pure justice : would it not lead men to act habitually from the motives of a lively and enlightened benevolence, of a delicate and generous sensitiveness? The germ of all these things has been placed in our hearts by nature : it awaits only the sweet influence of knowledge and liberty to develop." The reason for unsocial actions will disappear when institutions based on science make the common interest also the individual one. " Is not the aim of politics to destroy their apparent opposition? Man is capable of indefinite improvement because he changes with his environment and may change that too as his knowledge grows. Nature therefore has made a chain of which truth, happiness and virtue are all inseparable links." In particular we may hope for the entire destruction of the prejudices which hinder equality between the sexes. The effect of the emancipation of women will be to transform family life, and its effect on men will be scarcely less great than upon the women themselves. War, the most fatal scourge and the greatest of crimes, will be known for what it is, conquest will be thought futile and unprofitable, and a permanent confederation of nations will cease to be the dream of a few philosophers and become the natural way of organizing the world. A simple universal language will make knowledge accessible to all and overcome national divisions. Art and science will be seen to be only in their infancy and political science, now the monopoly of a few, will be generally understood.

Finally there is good reason to think that the natural capacity of men will improve. All species either improve or decay, and with the improvement in medicine, with saner methods of living, and the destruction of the two most active causes of degradation—poverty and riches—better bodily and mental health will be assured. The length of life will be increased, and, though immortality may be impossible, man's life may be lengthened to a degree which we cannot conjecture. We do not yet know enough science to be sure whether there is any limit to the possible duration of human life. Intellectual and moral improvement is equally within our reach. Parents transmit physical traits and perhaps " they may transmit also that part of the physical structure which is responsible for intelligence, strength of mind, energy of spirit and moral feelings." And if education can improve these qualities, will it not modify and improve the inheritance we pass on?

Condorcet was not far from the scaffold when he wrote the concluding words of his *Tableau*. The philosopher, however, could take courage amidst present misery, not in the thought of a personal paradise but in the imaginative conception of future human happiness. " Cette contemplation," he concluded, " est pour lui un asile, où le souvenir de ses persécuteurs ne peut le poursuivre ; où, vivant par la pensée avec l'homme rétabli dans les droits comme dans la dignité de sa nature, il oublie celui que l'avidité, la crainte ou l'envie tourmentent et corrompent ; c'est là qu'il existe véritablement avec ses semblables, dans un élysée que sa raison a su se créer, et que son amour pour l'humanité embellit des plus pures jouissances."

CONCLUSION

PROGRESS was the religion of the nineteenth century, just as Catholicism was of the Middle Ages. In both a great gulf was fixed between practice and precept. But if men confused progress with magnification and acceleration it was no more the fault of Condorcet and his allies than the degeneration of the mediæval Church was the fault of Augustine. The *philosophes* gave men a creed whose phraseology has been readily adopted even when its social implications have been ignored.

The *philosophes* taught that by reason man may be the master of things, that he can imagine a society in which all men enjoy freedom and happiness, and that he can deliberately create the society he has imagined. They directed their most powerful blows against the traditional and clerical view that " our lives are in His hands," that man is a creature fallen and perverse, who cannot be saved from self-destruction except through the gift of grace and must bow his individual reason before the sublime authority of Church and State.

Ultimately no doubt a question of values is involved. One phase of a perpetual conflict was heroically staged at the Revolution. For the moment victory appeared to belong to the party which preferred reason to dogma, liberty to authority and the individual to the State. But in this conflict there is no permanent victory. The serviceable doctrines which reason offered have in their turn become dogmas. Those who demanded liberty have set themselves in the seats of authority. The nation-state which seemed under democratic rule the complete guarantee of free individual development is now almost as great a barrier to the realization of the ideals of the Revolution as it was when men toppled kings from their thrones in the name of humanity.

The religion of the Revolution may be rejected for a variety of reasons. It must be opposed at every point by those who believe that truth is revealed, not to be discovered, and who regard temporal happiness as trivial in comparison with eternal salvation. But even those who approve its philosophic and social ends—who accept individual development as the justification

299

of political organization, who believe in liberty and hope for a future in which a world-order takes the place of an international anarchy—even these may fairly dissociate themselves from the presumptuous enthusiasms of the Revolution. For the contemporaries of Condorcet attributed the same universal validity to the institutions they founded, and to the scientific and social theories they formulated, as their opponents had to the atrophied convention which passed for religious observance in the eighteenth century. They understood none of the difficulties : their all-absorbing task was one of clearance, and the fact that the decaying lumber they condemned to the fire was the remains of what had once been a stately building did not concern them. The Catholic Church as they knew it was an instrument of tyranny and a purveyor of lies : it must be destroyed. Man had been denounced as the victim of his passions : he was extolled as the embodiment of reason. They had been told that the poor were always with us : they declared that the total abolition of poverty was immediately at hand. They had found privilege and monopoly everywhere hampering men's energies and corrupting their relationships : they acclaimed that economic freedom and the absolute rights of property would lead to universal harmony. Absolute kings had ruled and inefficiency and cruelty had stalked the land : the people should be absolute and political problems would be solved. It was a generous and fighting creed, not the elaboration of a programme of social organization.

This faith had been built up during a century of struggle. At every stage in the battle and in every aspect of thought, theological, ethical, economic and political, the *philosophes* had taken advantage of the breakdown of government and the conflict of classes to substitute reasonable and practical theories for traditional and moribund ones. Under the influence of seventeenth-century science a god who conformed to universal law took the place of the providential and personal deity of the Old Testament. Deism then passed by easy stages into materialism, which should logically have been a deadening creed but which was actually in practical matters an invigorating one. Ardent materialists, like Holbach, were apt to reintroduce teleology in the guise of a personified Nature, a beneficent guide who intended our interests and activities to be harmonized and mutually advantageous. The doctrine of Natural Harmony was a support, though not a necessary one, for the new religion of Progress.

Ethical theory underwent a parallel development. The *libertins* had long protested against the clerical doctrine of sin and asserted the right to happiness : hedonism, the protest of the individual against clerical domination, developed into the positive creed of " humanism," which makes the full development of human faculties the only goal worthy of pursuit. Natural religion was its immediate outcome : men of all races and colours had the same needs and capacities and could therefore be rendered happy by the same rights and the same instruction. As a sensationalist psychology was substituted for an intuitional one, humanism developed into scientific Utilitarianism. In its completed form Utilitarianism threw off its individualist inheritance and declared that men should find happiness not in the search for pleasure but in the improvement of society and of human nature itself.

In social and economic questions the critics of atrophied feudalism and of inefficient mercantilism began by demanding that governmental policy should aim at popular welfare and economic freedom, not at State power and private monopoly. The demand for specific administrative reforms gradually took a more general aspect and led to the theory that if artificial restrictions were removed, and the rights of property fully recognized, natural harmony would ensure peace and prosperity both internationally and within the State. Economic laws were easy to formulate from the axioms of human nature : it seemed, curiously enough, that if men followed their selfish impulses the result would be exactly the same as if they were actuated by Christian principles. This dominant theory was challenged by a school of thinkers whose analysis was more realistic, even if their constructive proposals were no less Utopian. These early socialists held that the right of property must be strictly limited if social happiness was to be diffused among the population, and that *laissez-faire* would bring a renewal of strife not an era of peace. The battle between the privileged and unprivileged would be succeeded by the even more bitter contest between the rich and the poor.

Finally political theory passed through a similar development. The first stage was the declaration that the monarch should not rule arbitrarily but in accordance with the traditional Constitution of France and with the fundamental laws of nature. The king might be absolute, but he must also be enlightened and tolerant and promote the happiness of his people. The subject, however, had no security unless the power of the Crown was limited, and its responsibility enforced. The British Constitution offered a model of responsible government and the separation of powers was a practical method of safeguarding rights against the sovereign's claim to irresponsibility. The British Constitution appeared to be the best practical expression of the social contract between government and people: it guaranteed by an ingenious mechanism the eternal superiority of the moral law to the wills of governments. Rousseau, however, unable to contemplate a divided State, hoped to solve the problem of liberty by transferring the sovereignty of the monarch to the people themselves: the difficulty of making the State responsible to the subject was thus evaded by the facile assurance that in the ideal community they would be identical, every citizen being at the same time sovereign and subject. Faced, however, with the practical difficulties of applying such a doctrine in the modern nation-state, Rousseau and the more far-sighted of his contemporaries learned to look to Federalism for a solution. Indeed their ideal of complete individual development was compatible only with a more complex society than they had imagined—one in which men were not only members of a self-governing State but associates of many groups, both national and international.

Thus the temple of liberty, equality and fraternity was supported by an elaborate structure of doctrine. If its framers had not so loudly declared that their work was final and indestructible a later generation might have watched its collapse without so much ironical satisfaction. For the physics, biology and psychology of the eighteenth century have been largely superseded, and in so far as they still form a background for twentieth-century thought they serve mainly to impede

inquiry and to increase the difficulties of those who are attempting to construct a social philosophy out of the accumulating
fragments of more modern science. Moreover, it did not occur
to the men of the Revolution that liberty as they understood
it—meaning the security of private rights—might not be easy
to pursue at the same time as equality as they understood it
—meaning the same opportunity of self-development and of
happiness for all. They were too thick in the fray to pause:
they dealt in absolutes and knew nothing of quantitative
thinking. To the modern critic the *philosophes* seem somewhat
naïve: they were quite unconscious of being moved by any
but disinterested motives though it has subsequently become
clear that many of the theories they thought final were distorted by the violence of their revolt against the conditions
in which they lived. Physiocrats and utilitarians, for instance,
desired a strong political State to put an end to privilege:
they also constructed elaborate philosophic arguments to show
that State interference in economic matters—in all that touched
on property rights—would necessarily be harmful to the general
welfare. Indeed the eighteenth-century State was so inefficient,
and its control of trade and industry was so hampering, that
laissez-faire seemed to be an immediate corollary of the
principle of utility. The connection however was historical,
not logical, and even at the Revolution itself men like Paine
and Condorcet saw that the State must engage in positive
social and economic activity if equality and liberty were not to
be the sole perquisites of the propertied class. In the event,
however, the original argument for private property that the
peasant who tilled the land had a natural right to the product
of his industry was forgotten and the industrial *rentier* often
defended profits which were no more the natural result of
social service than those of the landed *rentier* whom he had so
vehemently denounced. Indeed, though the "accident of birth"
was less powerful in the nineteenth century than it had been in
the eighteenth it remained the most striking proof that the
ideal of equality, like that of liberty, had been given a partial
and a class interpretation at the Revolution. Yet liberty and
equality remained ideals to which society had formally pledged

itself: property has made many subsequent concessions to them, and the conflicts of the twentieth century turn upon the acceptance of their fuller implications.

But there is a more serious charge made against the men of the Revolution. It is said that the history of the nineteenth century is a sad commentary upon their individualism: that they stressed the rights of the individual instead of emphasizing his social duties, and by their negative view of the State they led men to lose sight of its organic unity.

It is of course true that in the struggle with Leviathan and *l'infame* it was individual liberty, not social organization, which seemed of overwhelming importance, and that the growth of the "Great Society" has necessarily involved an ever-increasing degree of State activity and an ever more closely knit and elaborate effort of social organization. The *philosophes*, moreover, were led in part at least by mechanical analogies of contemporary physics to regard society as a machine rather than as an organism and the individual as an isolated unit related to his fellows not by common purposes and sympathies but by the automatic propulsion of self-interest. From the theories of the *philosophes* agrarian categories of property and contract passed into an industrial age whose need was not so much a statement of individual rights as a conception of purpose and a principle of social organization. But it was not the men of the Revolution who were responsible for the commercial selfishness which actuated the drab era of early industrialism: they could not anticipate its arrival nor know that their championship of individual liberty against Church and State would be used to justify the commercially powerful in oppressing the weak. It was not the *philosophes* who substituted a mechanical for a purposeful State: they found a society which had no informing principle of justice; in which there was no longer any relation between function and position; which was, in fact, nakedly a class domination even if its forces and its religious phraseology bore witness to a time when the aristocracy served as well as owned, and the Church taught as well as persecuted. They made no vain effort to recall the dead. Even had they desired, they could not have revived the Church. It had once given mediæval

society significance as a microcosm of a universal whole and informed a social order with purpose by relating men's activities
to their functions in the corporate unity. The *philosophes* were
attempting to offer that spiritual leadership of which the Church
was no longer capable. They told men of their great inheritance
and opportunity: they emphasized their unity and their progressive development towards perfection and urged them
deliberately to hasten the advance towards a happier, freer
and more equal society. Without this conception "the march
of science" was a meaningless accumulation of the less interesting kinds of knowledge. This religion of humanity—the
development of the individual within and through the developing social organism—has, in spite of its misinterpretations,
inspired the most fruitful work which has been done since the
Revolution.

BIBLIOGRAPHY

Editor's Foreword:

The following works are important for an understanding of the 18th century in its many aspects: P. Hazard, *La Pensée Européenne au XVIIIème Siècle. De Montesquieu à Lessing*, 3 vols., Paris 1946; see particularly the volume *Notes et Références*. The same author's *La Crise de la Conscience Européenne (1680-1715)*, also in three vols., Paris 1935, is equally an invaluable study. E. Cassirer, *Die Philosophie der Aufklaerung*, Tuebingen 1932, American edition under the title: *The Philosophy of the Enlightenment*, Princeton 1951, is probably the best work on the philosophy of this epoch. Carl L. Becker, *The Heavenly City of the Eighteenth Century Philosophers*, New Haven 1932, is a short but brilliant book. Basil Willey, *The Eighteenth Century Background*, London 1949, is indispensable. Cf. also L. Gershoy, *From Despotism to Revolution*, 1763-1789, New York 1944, with valuable annotated bibliography. A. Chérel, *De Télémaque à Candide*, Paris 1933 is immensely suggestive.

FRENCH LIBERAL THOUGHT IN THE EIGHTEENTH CENTURY.

General orientation:

Gustave Lanson, *Manuel Bibliographique de la Littérature française. III. Dix-Huitième Siècle*, Paris 1911. Jeanne Giraud, *Manuel de Bibliographie littéraire pour les XVIème, XVIIème et XVIIIème siècles français*, Paris 1939, brings Lanson up to date. See also the volumes VII, 1, 2 and 3 of the series *Clio; Le XVIIème Siècle* par Edmond Préclin et Victor L. Tapié, Paris 1949 and *Le XVIIIème Siècle* by the same authors, Paris 1952. Henri Sée's *Histoire économique de la France*, Paris 1948, edited by Robert Schnerb is fundamental. See also the same author's: *La France économique et sociale au XVIIIème Siècle*, Paris 1925; *L'Evolution Commerciale et Industrielle de la France sous l'Ancien Régime*, Paris s.a.; *Les Idées politiques en France au XVIIème Siècle*, Paris 1923; *Les Idées politiques en France au XVIIIème Siècle: L'Evolution de la Pensée Politique en France au XVIIIème Siècle*, Paris 1925. Cf. the important work by Fr. Olivier-Martin, *Histoire du Droit français des origines à la Révolution*, Paris 1948; D. Mornet, *La Pensée française au XVIIIème Siècle*, Paris 1932, is a useful summary. M. Leroy, *Histoire des Idées sociales en France de Montesquieu à Robespierre*, Paris 1946; H. J. Laski, *The Rise of European Liberalism*, London 1936. Philippe Sagnac's two volumes: *La Formation de la Société française moderne*, Paris 1945-1946,

BIBLIOGRAPHY

are masterly. The recent volume by R. Mousnier and R. Labrousse, *Le XVIIIème Siècle*, Paris 1953, is a suggestive synthetic effort. Cf. also Bernard Fay, *La Franc-Maçonnerie et la Révolution intellectuelle du XVIIIᵉ Siècle*, Paris 1935.

Chapter I.

Georges Lefevbre's *La Révolution française*, vol. XIII in the series *Peuples et Civilisations*, Paris 1951, is a veritable Summa of the work done until now on the French Revolution. Its rich bibliographical indications should prove of great value to the student. See also my edition of Tocqueville's *Ancien Régime et la Révolution* in two volumes, Paris 1952 and 1953. (In vol. I, pp. 354-355, of this edition, I have given a short summary bibliography of more recent studies on the pre-revolutionary and early phase of the French Revolution.) *Les Origines intellectuelles de la Révolution française. 1715-1787*, by Daniel Mornet, Paris 1947, though somewhat pedestrian, contain very rich material.

Chapter II.

Cf. G. Lacour-Gayet, *l'Education politique de Louis XIV*, Paris 1923; R. von Albertini, *Das politische Denken in Frankreich zur Zeit Richelieus*, Marburg 1951. Rébelliau's *Bossuet*, Paris 1900, is still a standard-work. See also: Gustave Lanson, *Bossuet*, Paris 1894; and J. Calvet, *Bossuet. L'homme et l'oeuvre*, Paris 1941, with valuable bibliographical indications. For Fénelon, see A. Chérel, *Fénelon au XVIIIème Sièle en France. Son Prestige, son influence*, Paris 1917; see also the same author's edition of Fénelon's *Oeuvres choisies*, Paris 1930. E. Carcassonne's small volume *Fénelon. L'Homme et l'Oeuvre*, Paris 1946, is admirable and contains instructive bibliographical material. On Vauban, see Daniel Halévy's *Vauban*, Paris 1923. Vauban's *Projet d'une Dîme Royale* has been edited by E. Coornaert, Paris 1933 (with important bibliography). See also Ch. W. Cole, *French Mercantilism. 1683-1700*, New-York 1943. On Bayle: Cf. A. Cazes, *Pierre Bayle*, Paris 1905; E. Faguet, *Pierre Bayle* in *Dix-Huitième Siècle. Etudes Littéraires*, Paris s.a.; Jean Delvolvé, *Religion, critique et philosophie positive chez Pierre Bayle*, Paris 1906. On Fontenelle, see *La Philosophie de Fontenelle*, by J. R. Carré, Paris 1932.

Chapter III.

Cf. the bibliographical indications given in my edition of Tocqueville's *Ancien Régime I.*

Chapter IV.

See Barckhausen's and Carcassonne annotated editions of Montesquieu's *Lettres Persanes*. On the *salons*, there is now the suggestive

BIBLIOGRAPHY

volume by Roger Picard: *Les Salons littéraires et la Société française. 1610-1780*, New-York 1943.

Chapter V.

Leslie Stephen, *English Thought in the Eighteenth Century*, two vols., London 1881. A classic. Cf. also Ch. Bastide, *John Locke*, Paris 1907. On Voltaire: Cf. G. Lanson, *Voltaire*, Paris 1919; see H. N. Brailsford: *Voltaire*, London 1935, and Raymond Naves, *Voltaire. L'Homme et l'Oeuvre*, Paris 1942. The latter volume gives precious bibliographical indications. Cf. also: René Hubert, *Les Sciences sociales dans l'Encyclo-pédie*, Paris 1923. See also *Origines de l'Esprit encyclopédique*, in Brunetières' suggestive volume *Etudes sur le XVIIIème Siècle*, Paris 1911. Voltaire's *Lettres Philosophiques* should be studied in Lanson's fine edition or in H. Labroue's more recent one.

Chapter VI.

On Montesquieu: the best book so far is probably Joseph Dedieu, *Montesquieu. L'Homme et l'Oeuvre*, Paris 1943. Dedieu gives also a short and admirable bibliography. *De l'Esprit des Lois* has recently been edited in an American edition by Franz Neumann who has added to the old translation by Thomas Nugent a well-informed introduction: Montesquieu, *The Spirit of the Laws*, Hafner Classics, New-York 1949. See also the recent French edition *De l'Esprit des Lois*, edited by Jean Brethe de la Gressaye, *Les Textes français*, Paris 1950. Amongst the older studies on Montesquieu the following are still indispensable: Albert Sorel, *Montesquieu*, Paris 1887; H. Barckhausen, *Montesquieu. Ses Idées et ses Oeuvres d'après les papiers de La Brède*, Paris 1907; *Montesquieu*, by Joseph Dedieu, Paris 1913; *Montesquieu*, by Victor Klemperer, Heidelberg 1914-1915. Meinecke's *Die Entstehung des Historismus*, Munich and Berlin 1936, contains a fascinating chapter on Montesquieu. Cf. also Dedieu, *Montesquieu et la tradition politique anglaise en France*, Paris 1909, which ought to be read in conjunction with G. Bonno, *La Constitution britannique devant l'Opinion française. De Montesquieu à Bonaparte*, Paris 1932. Important with invaluable bibliography. E. Carcassonne, *Montesquieu et le problème de la Constitution française au XVIIIème Siècle* is indispensable. See also F. T. H. Fletcher, *Montesquieu and English Politics. 1750-1800*, London 1939. The most convenient recent edition of Montesquieu is the one done by Roger Caillois in Gallimard's admirable series *La Pléiade* in two volumes. Caillois' introduction is brilliant. Emile Durkheim's famous thesis has recently been re-edited: *Montesquieu et Rousseau, Précurseurs de la Sociologie*, Note introductive par G. Davy, Paris 1953. A fine and scholarly complete edition of Montesquieu's

BIBLIOGRAPHY

works is in progress, edited by André Masson. Vol. I and II have already been published (Paris 1950 and 1953). See also D. C. Cabeen, *Montesquieu; A Bibliography*, New York 1947.

Chapter VII.

Elie Halévy, *The Growth of Philosophic Radicalism*, London 1938, a classic study. (With invaluable bibliography.) W. H. Wickwar, *Helvétius and Holbach* in *The Social and Political Ideas of some great French thinkers of the Age of Reason*, edited F. J. C. Hearnshaw, London 1930; cf. A. Keim, *Helvétius, Sa Vie et son Oeuvre*, Paris 1907; on Holbach see Pierre Naville, *D'Holbach*, Paris 1943.

On Diderot: Jean Pommier, *Diderot avant Vincennes*, Paris 1939; Daniel Mornet, *Diderot. L'Homme et l'Oeuvre*, Paris 1941; Henri Lefèbvre, *Diderot*, Paris 1949; John Morley's *Diderot and the Encyclopaedists*, London 1878, 2 vols. is still useful.

Chapter VIII.

For a recent interpretation of Rousseau's totalitarian democracy, see the important volume by J. L. Talmon, *The Origins of totalitarian Democracy*, London 1952. (With valuable notes.) On Rousseau see Albert Schinz, *La Pensée de Jean-Jacques Rousseau*, Paris 1929; Alfred Cobban, *Rousseau and the Modern State*, London 1934, an important book. Cf. also Robert Derathé, *Jean-Jacques Rousseau et la Science politique de son temps*, Paris 1950, an admirable study; see the same author's *Le Rationalisme de Rousseau*. There are two suggestive essays by Ernst Cassirer in *Rousseau, Kant, Goethe*, Princeton 1945. Amongst older studies two should be mentioned: E. Champion, *J.-J. Rousseau et la Révolution française*, Paris 1909; and Richard Fester's important work: *Rousseau und die deutsche Geschichtsphilosophie*, Leipsic 1890. Vaughan's edition of the *Political Writings of Rousseau* in two vols. is still not superseded. Cf. also Bertrand de Jouvenel's edition of the *Contrat Social*, Geneva 1947.

Chapter IX.

André Lichtenberger, *Le Socialisme au XVIIIème Siècle*, Paris 1895, is still fundamental. On Mably and Morelly, see *Morelly and Mably* by C. H. Driver in *The Social and Political Ideas of some great French thinkers of the Age of Reason*, with bibliography.

On Physiocrats, see the classic work by G. Weulersse, *Le Mouvement physiocratique en France de 1756 à 1770*, two vols., Paris 1910; and by the same author *La Physiocratie sous les ministères de Turgot et de Necker (1774-1781)*, Paris 1950 (with important bibliographical references). Cf. also M. Beer, *An Inquiry into Physiocracy*, London 1939. On

BIBLIOGRAPHY

Babeuf see the valuable little book by David Thomson: *The Babeuf Plot*, London 1949.

Chapter X.

On Saint-Pierre see P. Vaucher, *The Abbé de Saint-Pierre* in *The Social and Political Ideas of some great French Thinkers of the Age of Reason:* J. Drouet, *L'Abbé de Saint-Pierre*, Paris 1912. On Bernardin de Saint-Pierre see Albert Duchène, *Les Reveries de Bernardin de Saint-Pierre*, Paris 1935. On Kant cf. K. Vorlaender, *Immanuel Kant. Der Mann und das Werk*, two vols., Leipsic 1924. Cf. also E. Hoffmann-Linke, *Zwischen Nationalismus und Demokratie. Gestalten der franzoesischen Vorrevolution*, Munich 1927. Meinecke, *Die Idee der Staatsraeson*, Munich and Berlin 1929.

Chapter XI.

J. B. Bury, *The Idea of Progress. An Inquiry into its origin and growth*, London 1928. On Condorcet, see L. Cahen, *Condorcet et La Révolution française*, Paris 1904; the best edition of the *Esquisse d'un tableau historique des progrès de l'esprit humain* is by O. H. Prior; with bibliography. See also John Morley, *Condorcet* in *Critical Miscellanies*, vol. II, London 1892 and J. S. Schapiro, *Condorcet and the Rise of Liberalism*, New York 1934.

Conclusion.

Cf. Léon Brunchvicg's great work: *Le Progrès de la Conscience dans la Philosophie occidentale*, 2 vols., Paris 1927.

Supplementary Bibliography for the revised Impression.

A. Adam, *Histoire de la Litterature française au XVIIe Siècle*, 4 vols., Paris 1948-1954. An outstanding and important work.

J. Bertaut, *La vie littéraire au XVIIIe Siècle*, Paris 1954. Suggestive.

L. Ducros, *Les Encyclopédistes*, Paris 1909. This classic study should have been listed in our previous bibliography.

G. Grente, Editor, *Dictionnaire des Lettres françaises. Le XVIIe Siècle*. Invaluable. Paris 1954.

P. Vernière, *Spinoza et la pensée française avant la Révolution*, two vols., Paris 1954. A classic.

I add now a number of studies on individual thinkers:

On Diderot see: G. May, *Quatre Visages de Denis Diderot*, Paris 1951; P. Mesnard, *Le Cas Diderot*, Paris 1952; J. Lough, *The Encyclopédie of Diderot and D'Alembert*, Cambridge 1954.

On Leibniz see now the admirable study: W. H. Barber, *Leibniz in France. From Arnauld to Voltaire. A Study in French Reactions to Leibnizianism. 1670-1760*, Oxford 1955. Fontenelle's *Entretiens sur*

BIBLIOGRAPHY

la pluralité des Mondes has been edited with a valuable introduction by R. Shackleton, Oxford 1955.

Andre Masson's monumental Montesquieu edition is now complete. As a valuable addition to this edition see: L. Desgraves, *Catalogue de la Bibliothèque de Montesquieu*, Geneva 1954.

On Helvétius there is now a fine recent study: Ian Cumming, *Helvetius: His Life and Place in the History of Educational Thought*, London 1955.

The volume by M. Souriau, *Bernardin de Saint-Pierre. D'apres ses manuscrits*, Paris 1905, should have appeared in our previous lists.

On Rousseau cf. now: E. Cassirer, *The Question of Jean-Jacques Rousseau*, New York 1954. F. C. Green, *Jean-Jacques Rousseau: A Study of his Life and Writings*, Cambridge 1955, must be regarded as the most up to date and solid standard work in the English language.

On Voltaire see Th. Besterman's admirable edition: *Voltaire's Notebooks*, 2 vols., Geneva 1952.

Condorcet's *Esquisse* is now available in an excellent English edition: Condorcet: *Sketch for a Historical Picture of the Progress of the Human Mind.* Introduction by Stuart Hampshire, London 1955.

These bibliographical references do not aim at completion. They merely intend to give some guidance for further study.

J.P.M.

FURTHER BIBLIOGRAPHY 1962

A REVISED edition of the present volume was published in 1956. Since then quite a number of new studies concerning the general traits and individual thinkers of the period, analysed in this book, have appeared.

General:

Adam, A., *Histoire de la Littérature française au XVIIᵉ Siècle*, vol. v, Paris 1956. This volume concludes what is probably the best French work on the subject. Barber, E. G., *The Bourgeoisie in Eighteenth Century France*, Princeton 1955. Cobban, A., *In Search of Humanity. The Role of Enlightenment in Modern History*, London 1960. Crocker, Lester G., *An Age of Crisis. Man and World in Eighteenth Century France*, Baltimore 1959.

FURTHER BIBLIOGRAPHY

Grente, Cardinal, ed., *Dictionnaire des Lettres Françaises: XVIIIe Siècle*, 2 vols., Paris 1959. An indispensable mine of information. Krauss, W., and Mayer, H., ed., *Grundpositionen der franzoesischen Aufklaerung*, Berlin 1955. A Marxist interpretation. Lough, J., *An Introduction to Seventeenth Century France*, London 1954. Lough, J., *An Introduction to Eighteenth Century France*, London 1960. Both volumes will prove useful. Manuel, F. E., *The Eighteenth Century Confronts the Gods*, Cambridge, Mass., 1959. An admirable study. Mauzi, R., *L'Idée du Bonheur au XVIIIe Siècle*, Paris 1960. Encyclopedic. Stankiewicz, W. J., *Politics and Religion in Seventeenth Century France*, Berkeley and Los Angeles 1960. Suggestive. Spinks, J. S., *French Free-Thought from Gassendi to Voltaire*, London 1960.

Studies on Individual Thinkers:

Pierre Bayle, *Le Philosophe de Rotterdam*, ed. Dibon, P., Amsterdam and Paris 1959. Wilson, A. M., *Diderot. The Testing Years*, New York 1957. Standard work. Althusser, L., *Montesquieu, la politique et l'histoire*, Paris 1959. Kassem, B., *Décadence et Absolutisme dans l'œuvre de Montesquieu*, Geneva 1960. With important bibliography. Spurlin, P. M., *Montesquieu in America*, Louisiana 1940. Fundamental. Shackleton, R., *Montesquieu, A Critical Biography*, Oxford 1961. Scholarly, but fails to grasp the creative genius of Montesquieu. Starobinski, J., *Jean-Jacques Rousseau. La Transparence et L'Obstacle*, Paris 1957. Admirable and breaking new ground. Weil, E., 'J.-J. Rousseau et sa Politique', in *Critique*, Paris January 1952. Important essay. Manuel, F. E., *The New World of Henri Saint-Simon*, Cambridge, Mass., 1956. A classic. Brumfitt, J. H., *Voltaire Historian*, Oxford 1958. Gay, P., *Voltaire's Politics. The Poet as Realist*, Princeton 1959. With a suggestive bibliographical essay. Pomeau, R., *La Religion de Voltaire*, Paris 1956. Valuable and original. Wade, I. O., *Voltaire and Candide*, Princeton 1959. Standard work.

These bibliographical references do not aim at completion. They merely intend to give some guidance for further study.

J. P. M.

INDEX

313

INDEX

INDEX

69 70 71 72 73   12 11 10 9 8 7 6 5

Revised December, 1967

harper ⚜ torchbooks

HUMANITIES AND SOCIAL SCIENCES

American Studies: General

LOUIS D. BRANDEIS: Other People's Money, and How the Bankers Use It. ‡ Ed. with an Intro. by Richard M. Abrams   TB/3081
THOMAS C. COCHRAN: The Inner Revolution. Essays on the Social Sciences in History   TB/1140
HENRY STEELE COMMAGER, Ed.: The Struggle for Racial Equality   TB/1300
EDWARD S. CORWIN: American Constitutional History. Essays edited by Alpheus T. Mason and Gerald Garvey △   TB/1136
CARL N. DEGLER, Ed.: Pivotal Interpretations of American History   Vol. I TB/1240; Vol. II TB/1241
A. HUNTER DUPREE: Science in the Federal Government: A History of Policies and Activities to 1940   TB/573
A. S. EISENSTADT, Ed.: The Craft of American History: Recent Essays in American Historical Writing
                        Vol. I TB/1255; Vol. II TB/1256
CHARLOTTE P. GILMAN: Women and Economics: A Study of the Economic Relation between Men and Women as a Factor in Social Evolution. ‡ Ed. with an Introduction by Carl N. Degler   TB/3073
OSCAR HANDLIN, Ed.: This Was America: As Recorded by European Travelers in the Eighteenth, Nineteenth and Twentieth Centuries. Illus.   TB/1119
MARCUS LEE HANSEN: The Atlantic Migration: 1607-1860. Edited by Arthur M. Schlesinger   TB/1052
MARCUS LEE HANSEN: The Immigrant in American History.   TB/1120
JOHN HIGHAM, Ed.: The Reconstruction of American History △   TB/1068
ROBERT H. JACKSON: The Supreme Court in the American System of Government   TB/1106
JOHN F. KENNEDY: A Nation of Immigrants. △ Illus.
                                                         TB/1118
LEONARD W. LEVY, Ed.: American Constitutional Law: Historical Essays   TB/1285
LEONARD W. LEVY, Ed.: Judicial Review and the Supreme Court   TB/1296
LEONARD W. LEVY: The Law of the Commonwealth and Chief Justice Shaw   TB/1309
HENRY F. MAY: Protestant Churches and Industrial America. New Intro. by the Author   TB/1334
RALPH BARTON PERRY: Puritanism and Democracy
                                                         TB/1138
ARNOLD ROSE: The Negro in America   TB/3048
MAURICE R. STEIN: The Eclipse of Community. An Interpretation of American Studies   TB/1128
W. LLOYD WARNER and Associates: Democracy in Jonesville: A Study in Quality and Inequality ¶ TB/1129
W. LLOYD WARNER: Social Class in America: The Evaluation of Status   TB/1013

American Studies: Colonial

BERNARD BAILYN, Ed.: Apologia of Robert Keayne: Self-Portrait of a Puritan Merchant   TB/1201
BERNARD BAILYN: The New England Merchants in the Seventeenth Century   TB/1149
JOSEPH CHARLES: The Origins of the American Party System   TB/1049
HENRY STEELE COMMAGER & ELMO GIORDANETTI, Eds.: Was America a Mistake? An Eighteenth Century Controversy   TB/1329
CHARLES GIBSON: Spain in America †   TB/3077
LAWRENCE HENRY GIPSON: The Coming of the Revolution: 1763-1775. † Illus.   TB/3007
LEONARD W. LEVY: Freedom of Speech and Press in Early American History: Legacy of Suppression TB/1109
PERRY MILLER: Errand Into the Wilderness   TB/1139
PERRY MILLER & T. H. JOHNSON, Eds.: The Puritans: A Sourcebook of Their Writings
                        Vol. I TB/1093; Vol. II TB/1094
EDMUND S. MORGAN, Ed.: The Diary of Michael Wigglesworth, 1653-1657: The Conscience of a Puritan
                                                         TB/1228
EDMUND S. MORGAN: The Puritan Family: Religion and Domestic Relations in Seventeenth-Century New England   TB/1227
RICHARD B. MORRIS: Government and Labor in Early America   TB/1244
KENNETH B. MURDOCK: Literature and Theology in Colonial New England   TB/99
WALLACE NOTESTEIN: The English People on the Eve of Colonization: 1603-1630. † Illus.   TB/3006
JOHN P. ROCHE: Origins of American Political Thought: Selected Readings   TB/1301
JOHN SMITH: Captain John Smith's America: Selections from His Writings. Ed. with Intro. by John Lankford
                                                         TB/3078
LOUIS B. WRIGHT: The Cultural Life of the American Colonies: 1607-1763. † Illus.   TB/3005

American Studies: From the Revolution to 1860

JOHN R. ALDEN: The American Revolution: 1775-1783. † Illus.   TB/3011
MAX BELOFF, Ed.: The Debate on the American Revolution, 1761-1783: A Sourcebook △   TB/1225
RAY A. BILLINGTON: The Far Western Frontier: 1830-1860. † Illus.   TB/3012
EDMUND BURKE: On the American Revolution: Selected Speeches and Letters. ‡ Edited by Elliott Robert Barkan   TB/3068
WHITNEY R. CROSS: The Burned-Over District: The Social and Intellectual History of Enthusiastic Religion in Western New York, 1800-1850 △   TB/1242
GEORGE DANGERFIELD: The Awakening of American Nationalism: 1815-1828. † Illus.   TB/3061

---

† The New American Nation Series, edited by Henry Steele Commager and Richard B. Morris.
‡ American Perspectives series, edited by Bernard Wishy and William E. Leuchtenburg.
* The Rise of Modern Europe series, edited by William L. Langer.
** History of Europe series, edited by J. H. Plumb.
¶ Researches in the Social, Cultural and Behavioral Sciences, edited by Benjamin Nelson.
§ The Library of Religion and Culture, edited by Benjamin Nelson.
Σ Harper Modern Science Series, edited by James R. Newman.
º Not for sale in Canada.
△ Not for sale in the U. K.

1

CLEMENT EATON: The Freedom-of-Thought Struggle in the Old South. *Revised and Enlarged. Illus.* TB/1150

CLEMENT EATON: The Growth of Southern Civilization: 1790–1860. † *Illus.* TB/3040

LOUIS FILLER: The Crusade Against Slavery: 1830–1860. † *Illus.* TB/3029

DIXON RYAN FOX: The Decline of Aristocracy in the Politics of New York: 1801–1840. ‡ *Edited by Robert V. Remini* TB/3064

WILLIAM W. FREEHLING, Ed.: The Nullification Era: *A Documentary Record* ‡ TB/3079

FELIX GILBERT: The Beginnings of American Foreign Policy: *To the Farewell Address* TB/1200

FRANCIS GRIERSON: The Valley of Shadows: *The Coming of the Civil War in Lincoln's Midwest: A Contemporary Account* TB/1246

FRANCIS J. GRUND: Aristocracy in America: *Social Class in the Formative Years of the New Nation* TB/1001

ALEXANDER HAMILTON: The Reports of Alexander Hamilton. ‡ *Edited by Jacob E. Cooke* TB/3060

THOMAS JEFFERSON: Notes on the State of Virginia. ‡ *Edited by Thomas P. Abernethy* TB/3052

JAMES MADISON: The Forging of American Federalism: *Selected Writings of James Madison. Edited by Saul K. Padover* TB/1226

BERNARD MAYO: Myths and Men: *Patrick Henry, George Washington, Thomas Jefferson* TB/1108

JOHN C. MILLER: Alexander Hamilton and the Growth of the New Nation TB/3057

RICHARD B. MORRIS, Ed.: The Era of the American Revolution TB/1180

R. B. NYE: The Cultural Life of the New Nation: 1776–1801. † *Illus.* TB/3026

JAMES PARTON: The Presidency of Andrew Jackson. *From Vol. III of the Life of Andrew Jackson.* ‡ *Ed. with an Intro. by Robert V. Remini* TB/3080

FRANCIS S. PHILBRICK: The Rise of the West, 1754–1830. † *Illus.* TB/3067

TIMOTHY L. SMITH: Revivalism and Social Reform: *American Protestantism on the Eve of the Civil War* TB/1229

ALBION W. TOURGÉE: A Fool's Errand. ‡ *Ed. by George Fredrickson* TB/3074

A. F. TYLER: Freedom's Ferment: *Phases of American Social History from the Revolution to the Outbreak of the Civil War. 31 illus.* TB/1074

GLYNDON G. VAN DEUSEN: The Jacksonian Era: 1828–1848. † *Illus.* TB/3028

LOUIS B. WRIGHT: Culture on the Moving Frontier TB/1053

American Studies: The Civil War to 1900

W. R. BROCK: An American Crisis: Congress and Reconstruction, 1865–67 ° △ TB/1283

THOMAS C. COCHRAN & WILLIAM MILLER: The Age of Enterprise: *A Social History of Industrial America* TB/1054

W. A. DUNNING: Essays on the Civil War and Reconstruction. *Introduction by David Donald* TB/1181

W. A. DUNNING: Reconstruction, Political and Economic: 1865–1877 TB/1073

HAROLD U. FAULKNER: Politics, Reform and Expansion: 1890–1900. † *Illus.* TB/3020

HELEN HUNT JACKSON: A Century of Dishonor: *The Early Crusade for Indian Reform.* ‡ *Edited by Andrew F. Rolle* TB/3063

ALBERT D. KIRWAN: Revolt of the Rednecks: *Mississippi Politics, 1876–1925* TB/1199

ROBERT GREEN MC CLOSKEY: American Conservatism in the Age of Enterprise: 1865–1910 TB/1137

ARTHUR MANN: Yankee Reformers in the Urban Age: *Social Reform in Boston, 1880–1900* TB/1247

WHITELAW REID: After the War: *A Tour of the Southern States, 1865–1866.* ‡ *Edited by C. Vann Woodward* TB/3066

CHARLES H. SHINN: Mining Camps: *A Study in American Frontier Government.* ‡ *Edited by Rodman W. Paul* TB/3062

VERNON LANE WHARTON: The Negro in Mississippi: 1865–1890 TB/1178

American Studies: 1900 to the Present

RAY STANNARD BAKER: Following the Color Line: *American Negro Citizenship in Progressive Era.* ‡ *Illus. Edited by Dewey W. Grantham, Jr.* TB/3053

RANDOLPH S. BOURNE: War and the Intellectuals: *Collected Essays, 1915–1919.* ‡ *Edited by Carl Resek* TB/3043

A. RUSSELL BUCHANAN: The United States and World War II. † *Illus.* Vol. I TB/3044; Vol. II TB/3045

ABRAHAM CAHAN: The Rise of David Levinsky: *a documentary novel of social mobility in early twentieth century America. Intro. by John Higham* TB/1028

THOMAS C. COCHRAN: The American Business System: *A Historical Perspective, 1900–1955* TB/1080

FOSTER RHEA DULLES: America's Rise to World Power: 1898–1954. † *Illus.* TB/3021

JOHN D. HICKS: Republican Ascendancy: 1921–1933. † *Illus.* TB/3041

SIDNEY HOOK: Reason, Social Myths, and Democracy TB/1237

ROBERT HUNTER: Poverty: *Social Conscience in the Progressive Era.* ‡ *Edited by Peter d'A. Jones* TB/3065

WILLIAM L. LANGER & S. EVERETT GLEASON: The Challenge to Isolation: *The World Crisis of 1937–1940 and American Foreign Policy* Vol. I TB/3054; Vol. II TB/3055

WILLIAM E. LEUCHTENBURG: Franklin D. Roosevelt and the New Deal: 1932–1940. † *Illus.* TB/3025

ARTHUR S. LINK: Woodrow Wilson and the Progressive Era: 1910–1917. † *Illus.* TB/3023

GEORGE E. MOWRY: The Era of Theodore Roosevelt and the Birth of Modern America: 1900–1912. † *Illus.* TB/3022

RUSSEL B. NYE: Midwestern Progressive Politics: *A Historical Study of Its Origins and Development, 1870–1958* TB/1202

WILLIAM PRESTON, JR.: Aliens and Dissenters: *Federal Suppression of Radicals, 1903–1933* TB/1287

WALTER RAUSCHENBUSCH: Christianity and the Social Crisis. ‡ *Edited by Robert D. Cross* TB/3059

JACOB RIIS: The Making of an American. ‡ *Edited by Roy Lubove* TB/3070

PHILIP SELZNICK: TVA and the Grass Roots: *A Study in the Sociology of Formal Organization* TB/1230

IDA M. TARBELL: The History of the Standard Oil Company: *Briefer Version.* ‡ *Edited by David M. Chalmers* TB/3071

GEORGE B. TINDALL, Ed.: A Populist Reader ‡ TB/3069

TWELVE SOUTHERNERS: I'll Take My Stand: *The South and the Agrarian Tradition. Intro. by Louis D. Rubin, Jr., Biographical Essays by Virginia Rock* TB/1072

Anthropology

JACQUES BARZUN: Race: *A Study in Superstition. Revised Edition* TB/1172

JOSEPH B. CASAGRANDE, Ed.: In the Company of Man: *Twenty Portraits of Anthropological Informants. Illus.* TB/3047

W. E. LE GROS CLARK: The Antecedents of Man: *Intro. to Evolution of the Primates.* ° △ *Illus.* TB/559

CORA DU BOIS: The People of Alor. *New Preface by the author. Illus.* Vol. I TB/1042; Vol. II TB/1043

RAYMOND FIRTH, Ed.: Man and Culture: *An Evaluation of the Work of Bronislaw Malinowski* ¶ ° △ TB/1133

DAVID LANDY: Tropical Childhood: *Cultural Transmission and Learning in a Puerto Rican Village* ¶ TB/1235

L. S. B. LEAKEY: Adam's Ancestors: *The Evolution of Man and His Culture.* △ *Illus.* TB/1019

EDWARD BURNETT TYLOR: Religion in Primitive Culture. *Part II of "Primitive Culture."* § *Intro. by Paul Radin* TB/34

W. LLOYD WARNER: A Black Civilization: *A Study of an Australian Tribe.* ¶ *Illus.* TB/3056

Art and Art History

WALTER LOWRIE: Art in the Early Church. *Revised Edition.* 452 illus. TB/124

EMILE MÂLE: The Gothic Image: *Religious Art in France of the Thirteenth Century.* § *190 illus.* TB/44

MILLARD MEISS: Painting in Florence and Siena after the Black Death: *The Arts, Religion and Society in the Mid-Fourteenth Century.* 169 illus. TB/1148

ERICH NEUMANN: The Archetypal World of Henry Moore. △ 107 illus. TB/2020

DORA & ERWIN PANOFSKY : Pandora's Box: *The Changing Aspects of a Mythical Symbol. Revised Edition. Illus.* TB/2021

ERWIN PANOFSKY: Studies in Iconology: *Humanistic Themes in the Art of the Renaissance.* △ 180 illustrations TB/1077

ALEXANDRE PIANKOFF: The Shrines of Tut-Ankh-Amon. *Edited by N. Rambova. 117 illus.* TB/2011

JEAN SEZNEC: The Survival of the Pagan Gods: *The Mythological Tradition and Its Place in Renaissance Humanism and Art. 108 illustrations* TB/2004

OTTO VON SIMSON: The Gothic Cathedral: *Origins of Gothic Architecture and the Medieval Concept of Order.* △ 58 illus. TB/2018

HEINRICH ZIMMER: Myth and Symbols in Indian Art and Civilization. 70 illustrations TB/2005

Business, Economics & Economic History

REINHARD BENDIX: Work and Authority in Industry: *Ideologies of Management in the Course of Industrialization* TB/3035

GILBERT BURCK & EDITORS OF FORTUNE: The Computer Age: *And Its Potential for Management* TB/1179

THOMAS C. COCHRAN: The American Business System: *A Historical Perspective, 1900-1955* TB/1080

THOMAS C. COCHRAN: The Inner Revolution: *Essays on the Social Sciences in History* △ TB/1140

THOMAS C. COCHRAN & WILLIAM MILLER: The Age of Enterprise: *A Social History of Industrial America* TB/1054

ROBERT DAHL & CHARLES E. LINDBLOM: Politics, Economics, and Welfare: *Planning and Politico-Economic Systems Resolved into Basic Social Processes* TB/3037

PETER F. DRUCKER: The New Society: *The Anatomy of Industrial Order* △ TB/1082

EDITORS OF FORTUNE: America in the Sixties: *The Economy and the Society* TB/1015

ROBERT L. HEILBRONER: The Great Ascent: *The Struggle for Economic Development in Our Time* TB/3030

ROBERT L. HEILBRONER: The Limits of American Capitalism TB/1305

FRANK H. KNIGHT: The Economic Organization TB/1214

FRANK H. KNIGHT: Risk, Uncertainty and Profit TB/1215

ABBA P. LERNER: Everybody's Business: *Current Assumptions in Economics and Public Policy* TB/3051

ROBERT GREEN MC CLOSKEY: American Conservatism in the Age of Enterprise, 1865-1910 △ TB/1137

PAUL MANTOUX: The Industrial Revolution in the Eighteenth Century: *The Beginnings of the Modern Factory System in England* ° △ TB/1079

WILLIAM MILLER, Ed.: Men in Business: *Essays on the Historical Role of the Entrepreneur* TB/1081

RICHARD B. MORRIS: Government and Labor in Early America △ TB/1244

HERBERT SIMON: The Shape of Automation: *For Men and Management* TB/1245

PERRIN STRYKER: The Character of the Executive: *Eleven Studies in Managerial Qualities* TB/1041

Education

JACQUES BARZUN: The House of Intellect △ TB/1051

RICHARD M. JONES, Ed.: Contemporary Educational Psychology: *Selected Readings* TB/1292

CLARK KERR: The Uses of the University TB/1264

JOHN U. NEF: Cultural Foundations of Industrial Civilization △ TB/1024

Historiography & Philosophy of History

JACOB BURCKHARDT: On History and Historians. △ *Introduction by H. R. Trevor-Roper* TB/1216

WILHELM DILTHEY: Pattern and Meaning in History: *Thoughts on History and Society.* ° △ *Edited with an Introduction by H. P. Rickman* TB/1075

J. H. HEXTER: Reappraisals in History: *New Views on History & Society in Early Modern Europe* △ TB/1100

H. STUART HUGHES: History as Art and as Science: *Twin Vistas on the Past* TB/1207

RAYMOND KLIBANSKY & H. J. PATON, Eds.: Philosophy and History: *The Ernst Cassirer Festschrift. Illus.* TB/1115

ARNALDO MOMIGLIANO: Studies in Historiography ° △ TB/1283

GEORGE H. NADEL, Ed.: Studies in the Philosophy of History: *Selected Essays from History and Theory* TB/1208

JOSE ORTEGA Y GASSET: The Modern Theme. *Introduction by Jose Ferrater Mora* TB/1038

KARL R. POPPER: The Open Society and Its Enemies △
Vol. I: The Spell of Plato TB/1101
Vol. II: The High Tide of Prophecy: Hegel, Marx and the Aftermath TB/1102

KARL R. POPPER: The Poverty of Historicism ° △ TB/1126

G. J. RENIER: History: Its Purpose and Method △ TᵛV/1209

W. H. WALSH: Philosophy of History: *An Introduction* △ TB/1020

History: General

WOLFGANG FRANKE: China and the West. *Trans by R. A. Wilson* TB/1326

L. CARRINGTON GOODRICH: A Short History of the Chinese People. △ *Illus.* TB/3015

DAN N. JACOBS & HANS H. BAERWALD: Chinese Communism: *Selected Documents* TB/3031

BERNARD LEWIS: The Arabs in History △ TB/1029

BERNARD LEWIS: The Middle East and the West ° △ TB/1274

History: Ancient

A. ANDREWES: The Greek Tyrants △ TB/1103

ADOLF ERMAN, Ed. The Ancient Egyptians: *A Sourcebook of Their Writings. New material and Introduction by William Kelly Simpson* TB/1233

MICHAEL GRANT: Ancient History ° △ TB/1190

SAMUEL NOAH KRAMER: Sumerian Mythology TB/1055

NAPHTALI LEWIS & MEYER REINHOLD, Eds.: Roman Civilization. *Sourcebook I: The Republic* TB/1231

NAPHTALI LEWIS & MEYER REINHOLD, Eds.: Roman Civilization. *Sourcebook II: The Empire* TB/1232

History: Medieval

P. BOISSONNADE: Life and Work in Medieval Europe: *The Evolution of the Medieval Economy, the 5th to the 15th Century.* ° △ *Preface by Lynn White, Jr.* TB/1141

HELEN CAM: England before Elizabeth △ TB/1026

NORMAN COHN: The Pursuit of the Millennium: *Revolutionary Messianism in Medieval and Reformation Europe* △ TB/1037

3

G. G. COULTON: Medieval Village, Manor, and Monastery
TB/1022

CHRISTOPHER DAWSON, Ed.: Mission to Asia: *Narratives and Letters of the Franciscan Missionaries in Mongolia and China in the 13th and 14th Centuries* △
TB/315

HEINRICH FICHTENAU: The Carolingian Empire: *The Age of Charlemagne* △
TB/1142

GALBERT OF BRUGES: The Murder of Charles the Good. *Trans. with Intro. by James Bruce Ross*
TB/1311

F. L. GANSHOF: Feudalism △
TB/1058

DENO GEANAKOPLOS: Byzantine East and Latin West: *Two Worlds of Christendom in the Middle Ages and Renaissance*
TB/1265

EDWARD GIBBON: The Triumph of Christendom in the Roman Empire *(Chaps. XV-XX of "Decline and Fall," J. B. Bury edition).* § △ *Illus.*
TB/46

W. O. HASSALL, Ed.: Medieval England: *As Viewed by Contemporaries* △
TB/1205

DENYS HAY: Europe: The Emergence of an Idea
TB/1275

DENYS HAY: The Medieval Centuries º △
TB/1192

J. M. HUSSEY: The Byzantine World △
TB/1057

ROBERT LATOUCHE: The Birth of Western Economy: *Economic Aspects of the Dark Ages.* º △ *Intro. by Philip Grierson*
TB/1290

FERDINAND LOT: The End of the Ancient World and the Beginnings of the Middle Ages. *Introduction by Glanville Downey*
TB/1044

ACHILLE LUCHAIRE: Social France at the Time of Philip Augustus. *New Intro. by John W. Baldwin*
TB/1314

MARSILIUS OF PADUA: The Defender of the Peace. *Trans. with Intro. by Alan Gewirth*
TB/1310

G. MOLLAT: The Popes at Avignon: 1305-1378 △
TB/308

CHARLES PETIT-DUTAILLIS: The Feudal Monarchy in France and England: *From the Tenth to the Thirteenth Century* º △
TB/1165

HENRI PIRENNE: Early Democracies in the Low Countries: *Urban Society and Political Conflict in the Middle Ages and the Renaissance. Introduction by John H. Mundy*
TB/1110

STEVEN RUNCIMAN: A History of the Crusades. △
Volume I: *The First Crusade and the Foundation of the Kingdom of Jerusalem. Illus.*
TB/1143
Volume II: *The Kingdom of Jerusalem and the Frankish East, 1100-1187. Illus.*
TB/1243
Volume III: *The Kingdom of Acre and the Later Crusades*
TB/1298

SULPICIUS SEVERUS et al.: The Western Fathers: *Being the Lives of Martin of Tours, Ambrose, Augustine of Hippo, Honoratus of Arles and Germanus of Auxerre.* △ *Edited and trans. by F. O. Hoare*
TB/309

J. M. WALLACE-HADRILL: The Barbarian West: *The Early Middle Ages, A.D. 400-1000* △
TB/1061

History: Renaissance & Reformation

JACOB BURCKHARDT: The Civilization of the Renaissance in Italy. △ *Intro. by Benjamin Nelson & Charles Trinkaus. Illus.* Vol. I TB/40; Vol. II TB/41

JOHN CALVIN & JACOPO SADOLETO: A Reformation Debate. *Edited by John C. Olin*
TB/1239

ERNST CASSIRER: The Individual and the Cosmos in Renaissance Philosophy. △ *Translated with an Introduction by Mario Domandi*
TB/1097

FEDERICO CHABOD: Machiavelli and the Renaissance △
TB/1193

EDWARD P. CHEYNEY: The Dawn of a New Era, 1250-1453. * *Illus.*
TB/3002

G. CONSTANT: The Reformation in England: *The English Schism, Henry VIII, 1509-1547* △
TB/314

R. TREVOR DAVIES: The Golden Century of Spain, 1501-1621 º △
TB/1194

G. R. ELTON: Reformation Europe, 1517-1559 ** º △
TB/1270

DESIDERIUS ERASMUS: Christian Humanism and the Reformation: *Selected Writings. Edited and translated by John C. Olin*
TB/1166

WALLACE K. FERGUSON et al.: Facets of the Renaissance
TB/1098

WALLACE K. FERGUSON et al.: The Renaissance: *Six Essays. Illus.*
TB/1084

JOHN NEVILLE FIGGIS: The Divine Right of Kings. *Introduction by G. R. Elton*
TB/1191

JOHN NEVILLE FIGGIS: Political Thought from Gerson to Grotius: 1414-1625: *Seven Studies. Introduction by Garrett Mattingly*
TB/1032

MYRON P. GILMORE: The World of Humanism, 1453-1517. * *Illus.*
TB/3003

FRANCESCO GUICCIARDINI: Maxims and Reflections of a Renaissance Statesman *(Ricordi). Trans. by Mario Domandi. Intro. by Nicolai Rubinstein*
TB/1160

J. H. HEXTER: More's Utopia: *The Biography of an Idea. New Epilogue by the Author*
TB/1195

HAJO HOLBORN: Ulrich von Hutten and the German Reformation
TB/1238

JOHAN HUIZINGA: Erasmus and the Age of Reformation. △ *Illus.*
TB/19

JOEL HURSTFIELD: The Elizabethan Nation △
TB/1312

JOEL HURSTFIELD, Ed.: The Reformation Crisis △
TB/1267

ULRICH VON HUTTEN et al.: On the Eve of the Reformation: *"Letters of Obscure Men." Introduction by Hajo Holborn*
TB/1124

PAUL O. KRISTELLER: Renaissance Thought: *The Classic, Scholastic, and Humanist Strains*
TB/1048

PAUL O. KRISTELLER: Renaissance Thought II: *Papers on Humanism and the Arts*
TB/1163

NICCOLÒ MACHIAVELLI: History of Florence and of the Affairs of Italy: *from the earliest times to the death of Lorenzo the Magnificent.* △ *Introduction by Felix Gilbert*
TB/1027

ALFRED VON MARTIN: Sociology of the Renaissance. *Introduction by Wallace K. Ferguson*
TB/1099

GARRETT MATTINGLY et al.: Renaissance Profiles. △ *Edited by J. H. Plumb*
TB/1162

MILLARD MEISS: Painting in Florence and Siena after the Black Death: *The Arts, Religion and Society in the Mid-Fourteenth Century.* △ *169 illus.*
TB/1148

J. E. NEALE: The Age of Catherine de Medici º △
TB/1085

ERWIN PANOFSKY: Studies in Iconology: *Humanistic Themes in the Art of the Renaissance.* △ *180 illustrations*
TB/1077

J. H. PARRY: The Establishment of the European Hegemony: 1415-1715: *Trade and Exploration in the Age of the Renaissance* △
TB/1045

BUONACCORSO PITTI & GREGORIO DATI: Two Memoirs of Renaissance Florence: *The Diaries of Buonaccorso Pitti and Gregorio Dati. Ed. with an Intro. by Gene Brucker. Trans. by Julia Martines*
TB/1333

J. H. PLUMB: The Italian Renaissance: *A Concise Survey of Its History and Culture* △
TB/1161

A. F. POLLARD: Henry VIII. º △ *Introduction by A. G. Dickens*
TB/1249

A. F. POLLARD: Wolsey. º △ *Introduction by A. G. Dickens*
TB/1248

CECIL ROTH: The Jews in the Renaissance. *Illus.*
TB/834

A. L. ROWSE: The Expansion of Elizabethan England. º △ *Illus.*
TB/1220

GORDON RUPP: Luther's Progress to the Diet of Worms º △
TB/120

FERDINAND SCHEVILL: The Medici. *Illus.*
TB/1010

FERDINAND SCHEVILL: Medieval and Renaissance Florence. *Illus.* Volume I: *Medieval Florence* TB/1090
Volume II: *The Coming of Humanism and the Age of the Medici*
TB/1091

R. H. TAWNEY: The Agrarian Problem in the Sixteenth Century. *New Intro. by Lawrence Stone*
TB/1315

G. M. TREVELYAN: England in the Age of Wycliffe, 1368-1520 º △
TB/1112

4

VESPASIANO: Renaissance Princes, Popes, and Prelates: *The Vespasiano Memoirs: Lives of Illustrious Men of the XVth Century. Intro. by Myron P. Gilmore* TB/1111

History: Modern European

FREDERICK B. ARTZ: Reaction and Revolution, 1815-1832. * *Illus.* TB/3034
MAX BELOFF: The Age of Absolutism, 1660-1815 △ TB/1062
ROBERT C. BINKLEY: Realism and Nationalism, 1852-1871. * *Illus.* TB/3038
EUGENE C. BLACK, Ed.: European Political History, 1815-1870: *Aspects of Liberalism* TB/1331
ASA BRIGGS: The Making of Modern England, 1784-1867: *The Age of Improvement* º △ TB/1203
CRANE BRINTON: A Decade of Revolution, 1789-1799. * *Illus.* TB/3018
D. W. BROGAN: The Development of Modern France. º △ Volume I: *From the Fall of the Empire to the Dreyfus Affair* TB/1184 Volume II: *The Shadow of War, World War I, Between the Two Wars. New Introduction by the Author* TB/1185
J. BRONOWSKI & BRUCE MAZLISH: The Western Intellectual Tradition: *From Leonardo to Hegel* △ TB/3001
GEOFFREY BRUUN: Europe and the French Imperium, 1799-1814. * *Illus.* TB/3033
ALAN BULLOCK: Hitler, A Study in Tyranny. º △ *Illus.* TB/1123
E. H. CARR: German-Soviet Relations Between the Two World Wars, 1919-1939 TB/1278
E. H. CARR: International Relations Between the Two World Wars, 1919-1939 º △ TB/1279
E. H. CARR: The Twenty Years' Crisis, 1919-1939: *An Introduction to the Study of International Relations* º △ TB/1122
GORDON A. CRAIG: From Bismarck to Adenauer: *Aspects of German Statecraft. Revised Edition* TB/1171
DENIS DIDEROT: The Encyclopedia: *Selections. Ed. and trans. by Stephen Gendzier* TB/1299
WALTER L. DORN: Competition for Empire, 1740-1763. * *Illus.* TB/3032
FRANKLIN L. FORD: Robe and Sword: *The Regrouping of the French Aristocracy after Louis XIV* TB/1217
CARL J. FRIEDRICH: The Age of the Baroque, 1610-1660. * *Illus.* TB/3004
RENÉ FUELOEP-MILLER: The Mind and Face of Bolshevism: *An Examination of Cultural Life in Soviet Russia. New Epilogue by the Author* TB/1188
M. DOROTHY GEORGE: London Life in the Eighteenth Century △ TB/1182
LEO GERSHOY: From Despotism to Revolution, 1763-1789. * *Illus.* TB/3017
C. C. GILLISPIE: Genesis and Geology: *The Decades before Darwin* § TB/51
ALBERT GOODWIN, Ed.: The European Nobility in the Eighteenth Century △ TB/1313
ALBERT GOODWIN: The French Revolution △ TB/1064
ALBERT GUÉRARD: France in the Classical Age: *The Life and Death of an Ideal* △ TB/1183
CARLTON J. H. HAYES: A Generation of Materialism, 1871-1900. * *Illus.* TB/3039
J. H. HEXTER: Reappraisals in History: *New Views on History and Society in Early Modern Europe* △ TB/1100
STANLEY HOFFMANN et al.: In Search of France: *The Economy, Society and Political System in the Twentieth Century* TB/1219
A. R. HUMPHREYS: The Augustan World: *Society, Thought, & Letters in 18th Century England* º △ TB/1105
DAN N. JACOBS, Ed.: The New Communist Manifesto *and Related Documents. Third edition, revised* TB/1078

LIONEL KOCHAN: The Struggle for Germany: *1914-45* TB/1304
HANS KOHN: The Mind of Germany: *The Education of a Nation* △ TB/1204
HANS KOHN, Ed.: The Mind of Modern Russia: *Historical and Political Thought of Russia's Great Age* TB/1065
WALTER LAQUEUR & GEORGE L. MOSSE, Eds.: Education and Social Structure in the 20th Century. º △ *Vol. 6 of the Journal of Contemporary History* TB/1339
WALTER LAQUEUR & GEORGE L. MOSSE, Eds.: International Fascism, 1920-1945. º △ *Volume 1 of Journal of Contemporary History* TB/1276
WALTER LAQUEUR & GEORGE L. MOSSE, Eds.: The Left-Wing Intellectuals between the Wars 1919-1939. º △ *Volume 2 of* Journal of Contemporary History TB/1286
WALTER LAQUEUR & GEORGE L. MOSSE, Eds.: Literature and Politics in the 20th Century. º △ *Vol. 5 of the* Journal of Contemporary History TB/1328
WALTER LAQUEUR & GEORGE L. MOSSE, Eds.: The New History: *Trends in Historical Research and Writing since World War II.* º △ *Vol. 4 of the* Journal of Contemporary History TB/1327
WALTER LAQUEUR & GEORGE L. MOSSE, Eds.: 1914: *The Coming of the First World War.* º △ *Volume 3 of* Journal of Contemporary History TB/1306
FRANK E. MANUEL: The Prophets of Paris: *Turgot, Condorcet, Saint-Simon, Fourier, and Comte* TB/1218
KINGSLEY MARTIN: French Liberal Thought in the Eighteenth Century: *A Study of Political Ideas from Bayle to Condorcet* TB/1114
ROBERT K. MERTON: Science, Technology and Society in Seventeenth Century England ¶ *New Intro. by the Author* TB/1324
L. B. NAMIER: Facing East: *Essays on Germany, the Balkans, and Russia in the 20th Century* △ TB/1280
L. B. NAMIER: Personalities and Powers: *Selected Essays* △ TB/1186
L. B. NAMIER: Vanished Supremacies: *Essays on European History, 1812-1918* º △ TB/1088
NAPOLEON III: Napoleonic Ideas: *Des Idées Napoléoniennes, par le Prince Napoléon-Louis Bonaparte. Ed. by Brison D. Gooch* TB/1336
FRANZ NEUMANN: Behemoth: *The Structure and Practice of National Socialism, 1933-1944* TB/1289
FREDERICK L. NUSSBAUM: The Triumph of Science and Reason, 1660-1685. * *Illus.* TB/3009
DAVID OGG: Europe of the Ancien Régime, 1715-1783 ** º △ TB/1271
JOHN PLAMENATZ: German Marxism and Russian Communism. º △ *New Preface by the Author* TB/1189
RAYMOND W. POSTGATE, Ed.: Revolution from 1789 to 1906: *Selected Documents* TB/1063
PENFIELD ROBERTS: The Quest for Security, 1715-1740. * *Illus.* TB/3016
PRISCILLA ROBERTSON: Revolutions of 1848: *A Social History* TB/1025
GEORGE RUDÉ: Revolutionary Europe, 1783-1815 ** º △ TB/1272
LOUIS, DUC DE SAINT-SIMON: Versailles, The Court, and Louis XIV. º △ *Introductory Note by Peter Gay* TB/1250
HUGH SETON-WATSON: Eastern Europe Between the Wars, 1918-1941 TB/1330
ALBERT SOREL: Europe Under the Old Regime. *Translated by Francis H. Herrick* TB/1121
N. N. SUKHANOV: The Russian Revolution, 1917: *Eyewitness Account.* △ *Edited by Joel Carmichael* Vol. I TB/1066; Vol. II TB/1067
A. J. P. TAYLOR: From Napoleon to Lenin: *Historical Essays* º △ TB/1268
A. J. P. TAYLOR: The Habsburg Monarchy, 1809-1918: *A History of the Austrian Empire and Austria-Hungary* º △ TB/1187
G. M. TREVELYAN: British History in the Nineteenth Century and After: *1782-1919.* º △ *Second Edition* TB/1251

5

C. G. JUNG & C. KERÉNYI: Essays on a Science of Mythology: *The Myths of the Divine Child and the Divine Maiden* TB/2014

DORA & ERWIN PANOFSKY: Pandora's Box: *The Changing Aspects of a Mythical Symbol.* △ *Revised edition. Illus.* TB/2021

ERWIN PANOFSKY: Studies in Iconology: *Humanistic Themes in the Art of the Renaissance.* △ *180 illustrations* TB/1077

JEAN SEZNEC: The Survival of the Pagan Gods: *The Mythological Tradition and its Place in Renaissance Humanism and Art.* △ *108 illustrations* TB/2004

HELLMUT WILHELM: Change: *Eight Lectures on the I Ching* △ TB/2019

HEINRICH ZIMMER: Myths and Symbols in Indian Art and Civilization. △ *70 illustrations* TB/2005

Philosophy

G. E. M. ANSCOMBE: An Introduction to Wittgenstein's Tractatus. ° △ *Second Edition, Revised* TB/1210

HENRI BERGSON: Time and Free Will: *An Essay on the Immediate Data of Consciousness* ° △ TB/1021

H. J. BLACKHAM: Six Existentialist Thinkers: *Kierkegaard, Nietzsche, Jaspers, Marcel, Heidegger, Sartre* ° △ TB/1002

CRANE BRINTON: Nietzsche. *New Preface, Bibliography and Epilogue by the Author* TB/1197

MARTIN BUBER: The Knowledge of Man. △ *Ed. with an Intro. by Maurice Friedman. Trans. by Maurice Friedman and Ronald Gregor Smith* TB/135

ERNST CASSIRER: The Individual and the Cosmos in Renaissance Philosophy. △ *Translated with an Introduction by Mario Domandi* TB/1097

ERNST CASSIRER: Rousseau, Kant and Goethe. *Introduction by Peter Gay* TB/1092

FREDERICK COPLESTON: Medieval Philosophy ° △ TB/376

F. M. CORNFORD: Principium Sapientiae: *A Study of the Origins of Greek Philosophical Thought. Edited by W. K. C. Guthrie* TB/1213

F. M. CORNFORD: From Religion to Philosophy: *A Study in the Origins of Western Speculation* § TB/20

WILFRID DESAN: The Tragic Finale: *An Essay on the Philosophy of Jean-Paul Sartre* TB/1030

A. P. D'ENTRÈVES: Natural Law: *An Historical Survey* △ TB/1223

MARVIN FARBER: The Aims of Phenomenology: *The Motives, Methods, and Impact of Husserl's Thought* TB/1291

MARVIN FARBER: Phenomenology and Existence: *Towards a Philosophy within Nature* TB/1295

HERBERT FINGARETTE: The Self in Transformation: *Psychoanalysis, Philosophy and the Life of the Spirit* ¶ TB/1177

PAUL FRIEDLÄNDER: Plato: *An Introduction* △ TB/2017

J. GLENN GRAY: The Warriors: *Reflections on Men in Battle. Intro. by Hannah Arendt* TB/1294

WILLIAM CHASE GREENE: Moira: *Fate, Good, and Evil in Greek Thought* TB/1104

W. K. C. GUTHRIE: The Greek Philosophers: *From Thales to Aristotle* ° △ TB/1008

G. W. F. HEGEL: The Phenomenology of Mind ° △ TB/1303

F. H. HEINEMANN: Existentialism and the Modern Predicament △ TB/28

ISAAC HUSIK: A History of Medieval Jewish Philosophy JP/3

EDMUND HUSSERL: Phenomenology and the Crisis of Philosophy. *Translated with an Introduction by Quentin Lauer* TB/1170

IMMANUEL KANT: The Doctrine of Virtue, *being Part II of the Metaphysic of Morals. Trans. with Notes & Intro. by Mary J. Gregor. Foreword by H. J. Paton* TB/110

IMMANUEL KANT: Groundwork of the Metaphysic of Morals. *Trans. & analyzed by H. J. Paton* TB/1159

IMMANUEL KANT: Lectures on Ethics. § △ *Introduction by Lewis W. Beck* TB/105

IMMANUEL KANT: Religion Within the Limits of Reason Alone. § *Intro. by T. M. Greene & J. Silber* TB/67

QUENTIN LAUER: Phenomenology: *Its Genesis and Prospect* TB/1169

MAURICE MANDELBAUM: The Problem of Historical Knowledge: *An Answer to Relativism. New Preface by the Author* TB/1338

GABRIEL MARCEL: Being and Having: *An Existential Diary.* △ *Intro. by James Collins* TB/310

GEORGE A. MORGAN: What Nietzsche Means TB/1198

H. J. PATON: The Categorical Imperative: *A Study in Kant's Moral Philosophy* △ TB/1325

PHILO, SAADYA GAON, & JEHUDA HALEVI: Three Jewish Philosophers. *Ed. by Hans Lewy, Alexander Altmann, &Isaak Heinemann* TB/813

MICHAEL POLANYI: Personal Knowledge: *Towards a Post-Critical Philosophy* △ TB/1158

WILLARD VAN ORMAN QUINE: Elementary Logic: *Revised Edition* TB/577

WILLARD VAN ORMAN QUINE: From a Logical Point of View: *Logico-Philosophical Essays* TB/566

BERTRAND RUSSELL et al.: The Philosophy of Bertrand Russell. *Edited by Paul Arthur Schilpp*
Vol. I TB/1095; Vol. II TB/1096

L. S. STEBBING: A Modern Introduction to Logic △ TB/538

ALFRED NORTH WHITEHEAD: Process and Reality: *An Essay in Cosmology* △ TB/1033

PHILIP P. WIENER: Evolution and the Founders of Pragmatism. *Foreword by John Dewey* TB/1212

WILHELM WINDELBAND: A History of Philosophy
Vol. I: *Greek, Roman, Medieval* TB/38
Vol. II: *Renaissance, Enlightenment, Modern* TB/39

LUDWIG WITTGENSTEIN: The Blue and Brown Books ° TB/1211

Political Science & Government

JEREMY BENTHAM: The Handbook of Political Fallacies: *Introduction by Crane Brinton* TB/1069

C. E. BLACK: The Dynamics of Modernization: *A Study in Comparative History* TB/1321

KENNETH E. BOULDING: Conflict and Defense: *A General Theory* TB/3024

CRANE BRINTON: English Political Thought in the Nineteenth Century TB/1071

ROBERT CONQUEST: Power and Policy in the USSR: *The Study of Soviet Dynastics* △ TB/1307

EDWARD S. CORWIN: American Constitutional History: *Essays edited by Alpheus T. Mason and Gerald Garvey* TB/1136

ROBERT DAHL & CHARLES E. LINDBLOM: Politics, Economics, and Welfare: *Planning and Politico-Economic Systems Resolved into Basic Social Processes* TB/3037

JOHN NEVILLE FIGGIS: The Divine Right of Kings. *Introduction by G. R. Elton* TB/1191

JOHN NEVILLE FIGGIS: Political Thought from Gerson to Grotius: 1414-1625: *Seven Studies. Introduction by Garrett Mattingly* TB/1032

F. L. GANSHOF: Feudalism △ TB/1058

G. P. GOOCH: English Democratic Ideas in the Seventeenth Century TB/1006

J. H. HEXTER: More's Utopia: *The Biography of an Idea. New Epilogue by the Author* TB/1195

SIDNEY HOOK: Reason, Social Myths and Democracy △ TB/1237

ROBERT H. JACKSON: The Supreme Court in the American System of Government △ TB/1106

DAN N. JACOBS, Ed.: The New Communist Manifesto *and Related Documents. Third Edition, Revised* TB/1078

DAN N. JACOBS & HANS BAERWALD, Eds.: Chinese Communism: *Selected Documents* TB/3031

7

HANS KOHN: Political Ideologies of the 20th Century
TB/1277
ROY C. MACRIDIS, Ed.: Political Parties: *Contemporary Trends and Ideas* TB/1322
ROBERT GREEN MC CLOSKEY: American Conservatism in the Age of Enterprise, 1865-1910 TB/1137
KINGSLEY MARTIN: French Liberal Thought in the Eighteenth Century: *Political Ideas from Bayle to Condorcet* △ TB/1114
ROBERTO MICHELS: First Lectures in Political Sociology. *Edited by Alfred de Grazia* ¶ ° TB/1224
JOHN STUART MILL: On Bentham and Coleridge. △ *Introduction by F. R. Leavis* TB/1070
BARRINGTON MOORE, JR.: Political Power and Social Theory: *Seven Studies* ¶ TB/1221
BARRINGTON MOORE, JR.: Soviet Politics—The Dilemma of Power: *The Role of Ideas in Social Change* ¶
TB/1222
BARRINGTON MOORE, JR.: Terror and Progress—USSR: *Some Sources of Change and Stability in the Soviet Dictatorship* ¶ TB/1266
JOHN B. MORRALL: Political Thought in Medieval Times △ TB/1076
JOHN PLAMENATZ: German Marxism and Russian Communism. ° △ *New Preface by the Author* TB/1189
KARL R. POPPER: The Open Society and Its Enemies △
Vol. I: *The Spell of Plato* TB/1101
Vol. II: *The High Tide of Prophecy: Hegel, Marx and the Aftermath* TB/1102
JOHN P. ROCHE, Ed.: American Political Thought: *From Jefferson to Progressivism* TB/1332
HENRI DE SAINT-SIMON: Social Organization, The Science of Man, and Other Writings. *Edited and Translated by Felix Markham* TB/1152
CHARLES I. SCHOTTLAND, Ed.: The Welfare State TB/1323
JOSEPH A. SCHUMPETER: Capitalism, Socialism and Democracy △ TB/3008
BENJAMIN I. SCHWARTZ: Chinese Communism and the Rise of Mao TB/1308
CHARLES H. SHINN: Mining Camps: *A Study in American Frontier Government.* ‡ *Edited by Rodman W. Paul*
TB/3062
PETER WOLL, Ed.: Public Administration and Policy: *Selected Essays* TB/1284

Psychology

ALFRED ADLER: The Individual Psychology of Alfred Adler. △ *Edited by Heinz L. and Rowena R. Ansbacher*
TB/1154
ALFRED ADLER: Problems of Neurosis. *Introduction by Heinz L. Ansbacher* TB/1145
ARTHUR BURTON & ROBERT E. HARRIS, Eds.: Clinical Studies of Personality
Vol. I TB/3075; Vol. II TB/3076
HADLEY CANTRIL: The Invasion from Mars: *A Study in the Psychology of Panic* ¶ TB/1282
HERBERT FINGARETTE: The Self in Transformation: *Psychoanalysis, Philosophy and the Life of the Spirit* ¶
TB/1177
SIGMUND FREUD: On Creativity and the Unconscious: *Papers on the Psychology of Art, Literature, Love, Religion.* § △ *Intro. by Benjamin Nelson* TB/45
C. JUDSON HERRICK: The Evolution of Human Nature
TB/545
WILLIAM JAMES: Psychology: *The Briefer Course. Edited with an Intro. by Gordon Allport* TB/1034
C. G. JUNG: Psychological Reflections △ TB/2001
C. G. JUNG: Symbols of Transformation: *An Analysis of the Prelude to a Case of Schizophrenia.* △ *Illus.*
Vol. I TB/2009; Vol. II TB/2010
C. G. JUNG & C. KERÉNYI: Essays on a Science of Mythology: *The Myths of the Divine Child and the Divine Maiden* TB/2014

KARL MENNINGER: Theory of Psychoanalytic Technique
TB/1144
ERICH NEUMANN: Amor and Psyche: *The Psychic Development of the Feminine* △ TB/2012
ERICH NEUMANN: The Archetypal World of Henry Moore. △ *107 illus.* TB/2020
ERICH NEUMANN: The Origins and History of Consciousness △ Vol. I *Illus.* TB/2007; Vol. II TB/2008
RALPH BARTON PERRY: The Thought and Character of William James: *Briefer Version* TB/1156
JOHN H. SCHAAR: Escape from Authority: *The Perspectives of Erich Fromm* TB/1155
MUZAFER SHERIF: The Psychology of Social Norms
TB/3072

Sociology

JACQUES BARZUN: Race: *A Study in Superstition. Revised Edition* TB/1172
BERNARD BERELSON, Ed.: The Behavioral Sciences Today
TB/1127
ABRAHAM CAHAN: The Rise of David Levinsky: *A documentary novel of social mobility in early twentieth century America. Intro. by John Higham* TB/1028
KENNETH B. CLARK: Dark Ghetto: *Dilemmas of Social Power. Foreword by Gunnar Myrdal* TB/1317
LEWIS A. COSER, Ed.: Political Sociology TB/1293
ALLISON DAVIS & JOHN DOLLARD: Children of Bondage: *The Personality Development of Negro Youth in the Urban South* ¶ TB/3049
ST. CLAIR DRAKE & HORACE R. CAYTON: Black Metropolis: *A Study of Negro Life in a Northern City.* △ *Revised and Enlarged. Intro. by Everett C. Hughes*
Vol. I TB/1086; Vol. II TB/1087
EMILE DURKHEIM et al.: Essays on Sociology and Philosophy: *With Analyses of Durkheim's Life and Work.* ¶ *Edited by Kurt H. Wolff* TB/1151
LEON FESTINGER, HENRY W. RIECKEN & STANLEY SCHACHTER: When Prophecy Fails: *A Social and Psychological Account of a Modern Group that Predicted the Destruction of the World* ¶ TB/1132
ALVIN W. GOULDNER: Wildcat Strike: *A Study in Worker-Management Relationships* ¶ TB/1176
CÉSAR GRAÑA: Modernity and Its Discontents: *French Society and the French Man of Letters in the Nineteenth Century* ¶ TB/1318
FRANCIS J. GRUND: Aristocracy in America: *Social Class in the Formative Years of the New Nation* △ TB/1001
KURT LEWIN: Field Theory in Social Science: *Selected Theoretical Papers.* ¶ △ *Edited with a Foreword by Dorwin Cartwright* TB/1135
R. M. MAC IVER: Social Causation TB/1153
ROBERT K. MERTON, LEONARD BROOM, LEONARD S. COTTRELL, JR., Editors: Sociology Today: *Problems and Prospects* ¶ Vol. I TB/1173; Vol. II TB/1174
ROBERTO MICHELS: First Lectures in Political Sociology. *Edited by Alfred de Grazia* ¶ ° TB/1224
BARRINGTON MOORE, JR.: Political Power and Social Theory: *Seven Studies* ¶ TB/1221
BARRINGTON MOORE, JR.: Soviet Politics—The Dilemma of Power: *The Role of Ideas in Social Change* ¶
TB/1222
TALCOTT PARSONS & EDWARD A. SHILS, Editors: Toward a General Theory of Action: *Theoretical Foundations for the Social Sciences* TB/1083
ARNOLD ROSE: The Negro in America: *The Condensed Version of Gunnar Myrdal's An American Dilemma*
TB/3048
GEORGE ROSEN: Madness in Society: *Chapters in the Historical Sociology of Mental Illness.* ¶ *Preface by Benjamin Nelson* TB/1337
KURT SAMUELSSON: Religion and Economic Action: *A Critique of Max Weber's The Protestant Ethic and the Spirit of Capitalism.* ¶ ° *Trans. by E. G. French. Ed. with Intro. by D. C. Coleman* TB/1131

9

GERHART B. LADNER: The Idea of Reform: *Its Impact on Christian Thought and Action in the Age of the Fathers* TB/149

ARTHUR DARBY NOCK: Early Gentile Christianity and Its Hellenistic Background TB/111

ARTHUR DARBY NOCK: St. Paul º △ TB/104

ORIGEN: On First Principles. △ *Edited by G. W. Butterworth. Introduction by Henri de Lubac* TB/311

JAMES PARKES: The Conflict of the Church and the Synagogue: *The Jews and Early Christianity* TB/821

SULPICIUS SEVERUS et al.: The Western Fathers: *Being the Lives of Martin of Tours, Ambrose, Augustine of Hippo, Honoratus of Arles and Germanus of Auxerre*. △ *Edited and translated by F. R. Hoare* TB/309

JOHANNES WEISS: Earliest Christianity: *A History of the Period A.D. 30-150. Introduction and Bibliography by Frederick C. Grant* Volume I TB/53
Volume II TB/54

Christianity: The Middle Ages and The Reformation

ANSELM OF CANTERBURY: Truth, Freedom and Evil: *Three Philosophical Dialogues. Ed., trans., and Intro. by Jasper Hopkins & Herbert Richardson* TB/317

JOHN CALVIN & JACOPO SADOLETO: A Reformation Debate. *Edited by John C. Olin* TB/1239

G. CONSTANT: The Reformation in England: *The English Schism, Henry VIII, 1509-1547* △ TB/314

CHRISTOPHER DAWSON, Ed.: Mission to Asia: *Narratives and Letters of the Franciscan Missionaries in Mongolia and China in the 13th and 14th Centuries* △
TB/315

JOHANNES ECKHART: Meister Eckhart: *A Modern Translation by R. B. Blakney* TB/8

DESIDERIUS ERASMUS: Christian Humanism and the Reformation: *Selected Writings. Edited and translated by John C. Olin* TB/1166

ÉTIENNE GILSON: Dante and Philosophy △ TB/1089

WILLIAM HALLER: The Rise of Puritanism △ TB/22

HAJO HOLBORN: Ulrich von Hutten and the German Reformation TB/1238

JOHAN HUIZINGA: Erasmus and the Age of Reformation. △ *Illus.* TB/19

A. C. MC GIFFERT: Protestant Thought Before Kant △ *Preface by Jaroslav Pelikan* TB/93

JOHN T. MC NEILL: Makers of the Christian Tradition: *From Alfred the Great to Schleiermacher* △ TB/121

G. MOLLAT: The Popes at Avignon, 1305-1378 △ TB/308

GORDON RUPP: Luther's Progress to the Diet of Worms º △ TB/120

Christianity: The Protestant Tradition

KARL BARTH: Church Dogmatics: *A Selection* △ TB/95

KARL BARTH: Dogmatics in Outline △ TB/56

KARL BARTH: The Word of God and the Word of Man
TB/13

RUDOLF BULTMANN et al: Translating Theology into the Modern Age: *Historical, Systematic and Pastoral Reflections on Theology and the Church in the Contemporary Situation. Volume 2 of Journal for Theology and the Church, edited by Robert W. Funk in association with Gerhard Ebeling* TB/252

WHITNEY R. CROSS: The Burned-Over District: *The Social and Intellectual History of Enthusiastic Religion in Western New York, 1800-1850* △ TB/1242

NELS F. S. FERRÉ: Swedish Contributions to Modern Theology. *New Preface by the Author. Additional chapter by William A. Johnson* TB/147

ERNST KÄSEMANN, et al.: Distinctive Protestant and Catholic Themes Reconsidered. *Volume 3 of Journal for Theology and the Church, edited by Robert W. Funk in association with Gerhard Ebeling* TB/253

SOREN KIERKEGAARD: On Authority and Revelation: *The Book on Adler. Translated by Walter Lowrie. Intro. by Frederick Sontag* TB/139

SOREN KIERKEGAARD: Crisis in the Life of an Actress *and Other Essays on Drama.* △ *Trans. with Intro. by Stephen D. Crites* TB/145

SOREN KIERKEGAARD: Edifying Discourses. *Edited with an Introduction by Paul Holmer* TB/32

SOREN KIERKEGAARD: The Journals of Kierkegaard. º △ *Ed. with Intro. by Alexander Dru* TB/52

SOREN KIERKEGAARD : The Point of View for My Work as an Author: *A Report to History.* § *Preface by Benjamin Nelson* TB/88

SOREN KIERKEGAARD: The Present Age. § △ *Translated and edited by Alexander Dru. Introduction by Walter Kaufmann* TB/94

SOREN KIERKEGAARD: Purity of Heart △ TB/4

SOREN KIERKEGAARD: Repetition: *An Essay in Experimental Psychology.* △ *Translated with Introduction & Notes by Walter Lowrie* TB/117

SOREN KIERKEGAARD: Works of Love: *Some Christian Reflections in the Form of Discourses* △ TB/122

WALTER LOWRIE: Kierkegaard: *A Life* Vol. I TB/89
Vol. II TB/90

JOHN MACQUARRIE: The Scope of Demythologizing: *Bultmann and His Critics* △ TB/134

PERRY MILLER & T. H. JOHNSON, Editors: The Puritans: *A Sourcebook of Their Writings* Vol. I TB/1093
Vol. II TB/1094

WOLFHART PANNENBERG, et al.: History and Hermeneutic. *Volume 4 of Journal for Theology and the Church, edited by Robert W. Funk in association with Gerhard Ebeling* TB/254

JAMES M. ROBINSON et al.: The Bultmann School of Biblical Interpretation: New Directions? *Volume 1 of Journal for Theology and the Church, edited by Robert W. Funk in association with Gerhard Ebeling*
TB/251

F. SCHLEIERMACHER: The Christian Faith. △ *Introduction by Richard R. Niebuhr* Vol. I TB/108
Vol. II TB/109

F. SCHLEIERMACHER: On Religion: *Speeches to Its Cultured Despisers. Intro. by Rudolf Otto* TB/36

TIMOTHY L. SMITH: Revivalism and Social Reform: *American Protestantism on the Eve of the Civil War*
TB/1229

PAUL TILLICH: Dynamics of Faith △ TB/42

PAUL TILLICH: Morality and Beyond TB/142

EVELYN UNDERHILL: Worship △ TB/10

Christianity: The Roman and Eastern Traditions

DOM CUTHBERT BUTLER: Western Mysticism: *The Teaching of Augustine, Gregory and Bernard on Contemplation and the Contemplative Life* § º △ TB/312

A. ROBERT CAPONIGRI, Ed.: Modern Catholic Thinkers I: *God and Man* △ TB/306

A. ROBERT CAPONIGRI, Ed.: Modern Catholic Thinkers II: *The Church and the Political Order*△ TB/307

THOMAS CORBISHLEY, S.J.: Roman Catholicism △ TB/112

CHRISTOPHER DAWSON: The Historic Reality of Christian Culture TB/305

G. P. FEDOTOV: The Russian Religious Mind: *Kievan Christianity, the 10th to the 13th centuries* TB/370

ÉTIENNE GILSON: The Spirit of Thomism TB/313

GABRIEL MARCEL: Being and Having: *An Existential Diary.* △ *Introduction by James Collins* TB/310

GABRIEL MARCEL: Homo Viator: *Introduction to a Metaphysic of Hope* TB/397

FRANCIS DE SALES: Introduction to the Devout Life. *Trans. by John K. Ryan* TB/316

GUSTAVE WEIGEL, S. J.: Catholic Theology in Dialogue
TB/301

GIVE ME
ONE SUMMER

Also by Emilie Loring
in Large Print:

Throw Wide the Door
Bright Skies
A Key to Many Doors

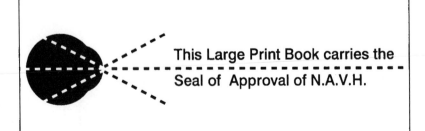

This Large Print Book carries the
Seal of Approval of N.A.V.H.

GIVE ME
ONE SUMMER

Emilie Loring

Thorndike Press • Thorndike, Maine

Copyright © 1936, by Emilie Loring

All rights reserved.

Published in 1998 by arrangement with
Little, Brown and Company, Inc.

Thorndike Large Print ® Candlelight Series.

The tree indicium is a trademark of Thorndike Press.

The text of this Large Print edition is unabridged.
Other aspects of the book may vary from the original edition.

Set in 16 pt. Plantin by Juanita Macdonald.

Printed in the United States on permanent paper.

Library of Congress Cataloging in Publication Data

Loring, Emilie Baker.
    Give me one summer / Emilie Loring.
        p.   cm.
    ISBN 0-7862-1629-8 (lg. print : hc : alk. paper)
    1. Large type books.   I. Title.
    [PS3523.O645G58   1998]
    813′.52—dc21   98-35580

To
IRMA INMAN LORING

AUTHOR'S NOTE

The names of all characters in this story
are fictitious. If the name of any living
person is used it is coincidence.

One! Two! Three!

The girl on the balcony of a house on the crest of a slope, counted the strokes of the village clock. Counted them again as they echoed from a distant ledge. She crossed her arms in their filmy flame-colored sleeves on top of the wrought-iron railing and watched a mist, like spindrift, veil the face of the moon which hung in the sky like a broken silver dollar and laid a path of diamonds on the rippling surface of the harbor. A dark ship floated in with the tide like a great red-eyed bird of evil-omen flying low over the water.

The air was soft as velvet, fragrant with the scent of peonies which rose from the garden and the breath of the pines and balsams which cast purple shadows on the lawns. How still the world was, so still that she could hear the croon of the tide, could hear birch leaves stirring with the sound of lapping water to the accompaniment of the shrill singing of locusts.

She might as well make a night of it here, she decided. She couldn't sleep. "Sometimes I wonder if you ever will sleep again, Lissa Barclay," she said to herself. The strain of the last few months when she had fought to hold her aunt in the world she loved had been heart-breaking. All that was over, the long night-vigils, the even longer days. Today — it was yesterday, now — she had rendered the last tender services she ever could render to Hetty Carson. Looking back it seemed more like ten than three years since she had come to this Maine village to make her home with her father's sister.

What next? she asked herself, as she watched two little fleeces chase a scudding cloud across the star sequined sky like chickens afraid of losing their mother. She answered her own question. The immediate "next" was already planned. Mr. Adams, a trustee of the Carson estate and Hetty Carson's legal adviser, was coming this afternoon to read her will. How could she have had much besides her jewels to bequeath? The income from a large property and Tarry Farm, the Maine estate, had been left to her for life only, all was to go to her husband's nephew, Alexander Carson when she was through. Would he love the beautiful place with its miles of rocky shore, its gardens, cottages and boat houses, or would

8

he give the White Queen's order, "Off with its head!"? It was an expensive estate to run in this tax-logged age. She knew. Hadn't she kept books on it during the last three years?

There would be two persons bitterly disappointed when they learned that the property went to him, Lissa's thoughts trooped on, her stepmother and half-sister. They had arrived at Tarry Farm four days ago. Hetty Carson had refused to see them.

"Buzzards! Buzzards!" she had muttered and closed her eyes.

Were they sleeping tonight or were they lying awake planning how they would spend the fortune they expected to inherit?

A thick cloud obscured the moon. Stars paled. Islands, distant hills, the anchored vessel, dimmed into shapeless shadows. A lighthouse loomed through the haze like a faint gray ghost.

Lissa dropped her head on her arms. The stillness was heavenly. Was that faint sound the dip of oars? It couldn't be. The only person likely to be on the water at this time would be Ozy, and he wouldn't be pulling his lobster-traps this early, neither would he be rowing, his dory would be running under engine power. She was hearing things. Darkness laid its soothing hand on her emotion-strained heart. She slept.

The French window behind her banged. She sprang to her feet. In her sleep she had drunk at some deep, cool spring in her spirit and awoke refreshed. An able-bodied breeze, smelling of salt kelp, was blowing from the harbor. Through a horizontal rift in a cloud, the moon's one eye gazed down upon the sleeping countryside with a knowing squint. Stars twinkled. A flame of scarlet spread in the eastern sky and gilded the upper edge of a fleet of silvery clouds. The lighthouse loomed as transcendently beautiful and unreal as the lamp-conjured palace of Aladdin. A cock crowed.

"I believe I slept," Lissa said and stretched lazily. One arm dropped as if weighted. She brushed fingers across her eyes and stared at the lighthouse. Had a flash, rapier-swift, shot from its great lens into the night, or had her eyes blurred from sleep, played a trick? How like her imagination to seize the bit in its teeth and gallop off on the trail of a mystery. It was a trick of vision, of course.

"You'd better go to bed, my girl, if you are beginning to see, as well as hear, things," she told herself. "That light was discarded by the government three years ago."

10

A half hour later a streamlined cruiser glided smoothly into the harbor. In the pine-paneled main cabin four men bent over a table under a hanging light. The creak of anchor chains came through an open window.

One of the men straightened. A smile lurked in the depths of his gray eyes as they met the intent eyes looking back at him. He said;

"Here we are, my hearties. Two electrical engineers, temporarily; a lawyer, in quest of a vacation and an inheritance, presumably; and a playboy with nothing on his mind but the pursuit of pleasure, apparently."

Gravity routed the cool amusement from his voice and eyes. A muscle in his cheek tensed and relaxed. He tapped the map on the table with his forefinger and reminded in a low voice;

"Somewhere within the area surrounded by those pegs is the person we're after. I'm sure of it. And we are here to get him — understand — we are here to get him."

2

"Now what, Mother Barclay?"

Standing by the mantel in her frock of soft white wool, Lissa Barclay addressed the crisp question to the small woman in black who huddled in a wing chair. As she waited for her stepmother's answer a ray of sunlight brought out the gold and red glints in her auburn hair. Her brown eyes glanced about the library in which she had read and dreamed and rebelled for three years. Now that she was about to leave it she loved the colorful, dignified room with its book-lined walls, its inviting green chairs and couch, its lamp-shaded tables with bowls of yellow roses. Fitful light from a lazy fire flickered on the portrait of a man above the mantel, a man with strong clear-cut features and a quizzical glint in the depths of his gray eyes. It brought out, also, the vivid flame and scarlet of tropical fish swimming in a crystal cylinder in the wrought-iron sconce against the wall. Beyond the long windows which opened on a broad terrace, the afternoon sun sparkled on rippling water, clear and blue as the sky above it; accentuated the red veins in the tawny rocks beyond which a pebbly beach glistened; shone on black and white cattle in a distant emerald green field. Through the wide open French windows came the whir of a mower and the scent of freshly cut lawns.

A girl, curled in the corner of the broad couch, removed a cigarette from her lips;

"Sure that that was old Adams, the lawyer, Lissa, and not a riproaring banshee who tore through laying us all flat with what he called Aunt Hetty's last will and testament?" she drawled. Her eyes were the color of larkspur, her hair spun gold, her mourning frock accentuated the rose-leaf perfection of her skin. Her thin lips curved in a cruel line as she looked at the woman in the chair and demanded;

"Well, Mrs. Barclay, as Lissa observed, 'Now what?' You're the next county to be heard from. We didn't renew the New York apartment lease thinking we'd have this place and a big income from Aunt Hetty with which to pay the bills we left behind us, and she left us nothing. We didn't even have a chance to tell our sob-story, she slipped out on us the very night of our arrival. Bring the wisdom of your years and experience to bear on the situation, Mother."

The blonde woman, whose personality

was as colorless as a sketch done in fade-out ink, twisted a black bordered handkerchief in her plump white fingers. The corners of her mouth drooped as she looked at her stepdaughter who stood straight and curiously remote before the mantel with G-Man, the Irish terrier, squatted on his haunches beside her. His bright eyes had assumed an only-over-my-dead-body-you'll-touch-her expression as they followed the movements of the other two persons in the room.

Mrs. Barclay sniffed and transferred her reproachful glance to her golden-haired daughter on the couch.

"You needn't throw my age and experience in my face, Cleo. I'm still a young woman, only forty-five."

"Sometimes I wonder if you are forty-five, Mother Barclay, you are so casual," Lissa intervened. "I wish you would answer my question. With Aunt Hetty Carson's passing, this great point of land, one mile from a village, a village in itself almost, has gone into other hands. We must get out before the heir — Alexander the Great, Aunt Hetty and I nicknamed him — arrives, and he is likely to appear at any moment."

Mrs. Barclay leaned forward. Her eyes were dry now and angrily bright.

14

"I couldn't believe my ears when that man Adams read the will. Only a thousand dollars a year from a trust fund, Hetty's jewels, her personal property in this house and an island with an old lighthouse for you, Melissa, and that tied up so you can't dispose of a cent of it without the approval of this Alexander Carson. Nothing for Cleo and me. Not even a ring. That divine set of aquamarines and diamonds of Hetty's would have been perfect on Cleo, all the blondes are wearing them this season. Such meanness, toward her brother's family, too. She never said a word of reproach to me for divorcing your father. That couldn't have been the reason she ignored me and my daughter in her will, she was his daughter, too."

"But, Mother Barclay, Mr. Adams explained that that was all Aunt Hetty had to leave. The large income from the property her husband left and this place were hers for life only, and that large income remained large because her husband's will provided that it be kept so by dipping into the principal if necessary. Something tells me that the heir, who is the namesake and nephew of her late husband, and trustee of my legacy — can you imagine a sillier arrangement — will find his inheritance a liability rather

15

than an asset. The three cottages on the place are leased for the summer, but the rents won't pay taxes, interest and upkeep."

Alexander the Great was not the only person who would find his inheritance a liability, Lissa thought. How could she manage taxes and repairs on her island lighthouse and her living, on a thousand a year until she acquired a job?

Cleo narrowed her eyes to slits and inquired;

"Why wasn't the heir here yesterday?"

"Mr. Adams said he couldn't get here."

"Wouldn't take the trouble, probably. Have you met him? How old is he? What's his business? Perhaps he'll fall in love with you, Lissa, perhaps that was Aunt Hetty's scheme to let the Barclays in on the Carson property. I'll promise not to take your beau away this time."

Lissa hoped that her face did not reflect the sickening sense of humiliation which submerged her whenever she remembered that Cleo had lured the man to whom she herself had been engaged away from her, after which she had thrown him over. She declined crisply;

"Thanks for the noble offer, Cleo, but I'm not interested."

Mrs. Barclay brightened and suggested;

16

"Perhaps we ought to stay here at Tarry Farm and welcome the heir. If he has no family —"

"He might be overjoyed to adopt us, Mother means," Cleo interrupted. "What do you know about him, Lissa?"

Lissa remembered Hetty Carson's comment when told that Mother and daughter had arrived at Tarry Farm. Their eyes now had the "buzzard" look.

"Not much," she answered Cleo's question. "Aunt Hetty resented his indifference to her — what she thought was his indifference — and the fact that the property was to go to him, and rarely mentioned him. I know that he is a lawyer, and that he studied for his profession in three universities. Can't you picture a man like that? Stooping, peering through huge bone-rimmed specs. Owlish, if you get what I mean. He lives in Washington."

"Perhaps we'd better stay until Alexander the Great comes, Mother. If he is a one-idea person — and that idea law — we may be of use helping him run this house, at least it would be a friendly gesture to turn the place over to him, it would show we have no hard feelings. I suppose Aunt Hetty gave you presents of money, Lissa? Doubtless you have a sizeable nest-egg tucked away?"

17

Anger sent a wave of color to the soft, uneven line of Lissa's hair. Was Cleo preparing to ask her for money now that Aunt Hetty Carson was no longer alive to help with overdue bills? She felt terribly alone in the world in which from now on she would have to make her way, in which she seemed tragically unimportant. As if he understood, the dog flopped to the floor and laid his black nose on her foot. The feel of him was curiously comforting. It helped her to answer lightly;

"A nest-egg! My savings would liquidate at about $10.95. Suppose I had more, I would have earned it, wouldn't I? When, three years ago, Aunt Hetty wrote that it was the duty of one of us to live with her, you refused to come, Cleo. I came, because I had promised father that if ever his only sister wanted me I would go to her. I've lived in this lonely house, this sea-coast town, for three years, and these last months have been heart-breaking, I felt so powerless to help Aunt Hetty cling to the life, which, ill as she was, she loved."

Lissa turned and stared down at the fire to hide a quick rush of tears. How could she have let herself go before those two hard women?

Cleo shrugged;

"And all the time you were having your clothes from the best places in New York. Stop sniffling, Mother."

The callousness of Cleo's words dried Lissa's eyes.

"Clothes don't make up for freedom. However, why think of that, it's past and I'm on my own. I wonder how often life, real living, I mean, begins with a death as mine has. To return to the will, why are you two making a fuss over the legacy Aunt Hetty left me? You have a comfortable income from the settlement father made on you. You've been living luxuriously."

"Ever know anyone who had enough money?" Cleo's eyes made Lissa think of a cat, always on the watch, always suspicious. "Mother and I are up to our ears in debt. Of course you'll add your thousand to our assets?"

"I will not."

"Look here, Lissa, you've got to. I want to go to England for a year and I'll need every cent I can scrape up. I've been waiting until Aunt Hetty passed out so that you could stay with your mother and help financially."

Lissa laughed. It wasn't a pleasant sound even to her own ears.

"My mother! Your mother, you mean, Cleo. To me she never has been anything

19

but my father's second wife. She never tried to be anything else to the three-year-old, frightened small child she acquired with her marriage. From now on, I live where I please."

Why was she standing here in the library arguing? Lissa asked herself. Beyond the long windows the sea sparkled an invitation. Heavenly day to shoot round the point in the flying outboard she hadn't used for weeks. Now that she was the owner of an island she wanted to land on it, take formal possession, plant a flag. Why not plant the pennant she had won on the last outboard race? What fun! She would take G-Man along as witness.

"Ahem!"

Fenton, the butler, who might have stepped from an English comedy, in his livery and his sideburns, stood in the doorway with a massive silver tray and its tea equipment.

"Good heavens! Fenton! When did you steal in? Your entrances are positively spooky! Put the tray here. I'll pour." Cleo motioned to a table near her.

Except that his long, tapering fingers tightened on the tray, the butler did not move. He said suavely;

"I'm sorry, Miss Barclay, if I surprised

you, in future I'll try to clatter a bit before I enter. Will you pour the tea as usual, Miss Lissa?"

Lissa's lips twitched at his accent on "as usual." She shook her head.

"No Fenton. I'm going on the water. Come along, G-Man."

She left the room by a long window with the dog at her heels, dashed across a brick terrace patterned in gold from the reflected sun and ran down the path to the shore between borders gay with gigantic late tulips, pink and bronze, white and lavender; blushing with huge pink peonies, and splashed with the scarlet of Oriental poppies. The pale green blades of late iris were treasure houses of color which a week of sunny days would release and spill through the border. The air was sweet with the breath of blossoms, spicy with the tang of kelp and the scent of balsam, spruce, pine and arbor-vitae. From a tree-top drifted the throaty call of a plover.

Yellow summer birds flew up from the fern-bordered pool around a fountain and slashed the air with gold as sunlight struck their backs. The dog dashed after them, returned, and with mouth open and tongue hanging, looked up with twinkling brown eyes. Lissa shook her head at him.

21

"You think it's a joke, don't you, to scare those birds? If you don't show more sense, I'll change your name. Don't you know that psychologists use the letter G as the symbol of mental ability? The more G a man has, the more likely he is to be a genius. Some day you'll start after something that won't scare. Then where will you be, Mister?"

The Irish terrier responded with a sharp bark and raced ahead. The slope to the shore was terraced. There were steps between each terrace and a Victorian wrought-iron seat to lure the passerby to linger and enjoy the panorama of garden, white lighthouse, and island-dotted sapphire sea set in a frame of purplish-green hills, their sides slashed by fissures, like scars on the face of a soldier which no plastic surgeon could efface. Sky as blue as the robe of a Madonna canopied the point of land projecting into the sparkling water. A great heron flapped slowly westward, long legs extended like a rudder.

Lissa resisted the temptation to dip into the boulder-enclosed swimming-pool near the shore and ran on to the boathouse. She changed to navy blue shorts, with a top of gay India print, white sandals, and caught up the green and gold pennant.

She stepped carefully into the flying out-

22

board she had named The Scribbler, moored at the float. The dog followed and stretched out on the bow. She adjusted the carburetor and cleaned a sparkplug. A boat chugged alongside, a fisherman's dirty-white dory with a cabin which looked like a shoebox.

"Hey! Lissa! Hold on!"

She tossed back her hair and smiled at Captain Ozias, commonly known as "Ozy," whose forward thrust head gave the effect of a hound on the scent, whose ferret-like eyes seemed always on the trail of a mystery. She shouted to make herself heard above the throb of the engines;

"Howdy, Ozy. What can I do for the sheriff, ace-errand and lobsterman of the county?"

"Got to talk to you." He sniffed and caught the side of her boat. "Say, this is an awful tricky thing you're settin' out in. Shouldn't suppose your folks would let you go alone."

"Alone! I'm not alone with G-Man along as crew. Besides, what could happen to me? I hate to talk about myself, but I'm a fish in the water."

"Always jokin', ain't you? Your eyes are twinklin' with little gold stars. That's an awful deep dimple in your right cheek that comes when you laugh. You've been round here three years now an' I ain't never seen you down in the mouth. I hate to make you feel bad, but folks is gettin' terrible riled 'bout that dog of your'n."

Lissa suspected what was coming. Hadn't G-Man laid two strange bathing suits at her feet this very morning? It wasn't the first time he had brought loot. Apparently he had an irresistible penchant for garments dangling from clotheslines.

"What has he done now, Ozy?"

"You needn't yell, I kin hear you, your voice's clear as a bell. I guess you know without my tellin' what the critter's done. He's been stealing clothes again. You won't hev to go so far as you went before to return 'em. Those he snitched today belong to the folks who've moved into that cottage of your aunt's she calls the Treasure Chest."

"You mean he stole the bathing suits of the Millards, the tenants who came yesterday? They probably think that that is our usual welcome-to-our-cottage stunt. Thanks for telling me. It will save a lot of telephoning."

"Glad to help out, Lissa. Did you know them Millards had a boy? Thought your aunt never let in kids."

"She never has before, but this child is

24

delicate; she decided that he couldn't do any damage to the cottage."

"Damage! By mighty, he looks as if a breath of wind would blow him away. 'Bout eight years old, I'd say."

"He'll gain in this air. How's business?" She waved a hand toward the lobster floats bobbing on the surface of the water near ledges like miniature boats.

"Not too bad. The summer folks eat a lot of lobsters. I got five traps sprinkled round this cove. They ain't doin' so well. Think I'll change an' buoy them on the other side of the island. I s'pose you'll be havin' your big lobster-bake as usual Fair week, an' need a lot? Just stopped in at your other cottage, Red Chimneys, to see if the folks there wanted to engage lobsters."

"Did they?"

"Yep. Say have you met that fella Packard who's hired it? He's a smooth talker. His tongue feeds out words as easy as oil slippin' into a motor engine. I got to be goin'."

"Thanks for telling me where the bathing suits came from. Good-bye, Ozy."

3

Lissa tuned up the engine and cast off. As the outboard shot forward it kicked up a jeweled spray that stung her face. She waved to the man who was watching her.

She called to the terrier;

"G-Man, what was the big idea when you stole those bathing suits? To make a smash-hit with our new tenants? If you don't watch out, you'll be in the dog-jail. Bad boy!"

The terrier gave a short, sharp bark of defiance and tucked his nose between his paws.

The water rippled under a gentle breeze. The rush of wind caused by the flying outboard tugged at Lissa's bronze lashes and blew her short auburn hair in a gollywog effect about her head. She drew the clear air deep into her lungs. She must make the most of it. Soon the ground roar of a big city, the wail of motor horns, the screech of fire sirens, would be in her ears instead of the swish of pebbles on the beach and the faint moan of a distant buoy. What city, she asked herself. She had been at Tarry Farm so long she almost dreaded to make a change. Maybe everyone had to wrench free from the pattern someone else had designed for her, maybe outside that pattern the world would be made up largely of crooked lanes and rough roads, but she had to get outside and take her chance.

She watched a thin drift of cloud wind itself about the top of a purple hill like a sari of rosy marines. Her eyes came back to the harbor. Its strength, its color, its beauty, tightened her throat. A war-vessel lay far out. A ship's bell was striking the quarter hour. The slanting sun set aflame the brass on a streamlined cruiser which rocked idly in a sea powdered with gulls. It was the last word in luxury, must be owned by a plutocrat, she decided. The blue absent pennant was flying at the starboard spreader. The club burgee was like a jewel against the sky. At the stern floated the yacht ensign, red and white and blue. The brilliant colors added the last perfect touch. She would round the point and look the cruiser over before she took formal possession of her island. Her island, but an island only at certain hours of the day when the tide covered the sandy ledge which connected it with the mainland.

The whitewashed walls of the lighthouse and the connecting one-and-a-half story frame building shone like mother-of-pearl against a towering background of balsam, pine and arborvitae. The island was patched with rocks, coarse emerald green grass, low-growing juniper, and groups of gulls.

As she looked at the iron deck above which the great eye of the tower glittered, she thought again of the beam of light. Of course it had been imagination plus. Why should anyone flash a signal? Bootlegging had gone by. Kidnaping was no longer classed among the easy-money rackets.

"My imagination's my fortune, kind sir," she chanted in a low, sweet voice and laughed. "I'd better use it on my plans for the future."

She throttled down the engine. She couldn't think constructively when the boat was shooting through the water. One couldn't live on a thousand dollars a year, plus the small amount she had inherited from her father, and maintain a lighthouse for a summer residence without working, could one?

After the settlement on his second wife and daughter, whom he had left, because, he had confided to Lissa, he couldn't stand their infernal bickering another day, her father had spent most of what remained of his capital traveling about the world with her. She had seen many, many countries but

28

she had not made friends. He had been jealous of her interest in people; the moment she had found someone whom she really liked, he had moved on. Aunt Hetty had been like that, had disapproved of her outboard motorboating, of her devotion to the little church in the village, but she had persisted, they were outlets for her caged emotions.

She thought of her brief engagement to Johnny Grant, whom she had met after the death of her father when she was heartbreakingly lonely; and she thought of her humiliation when he had haltingly told her that he wanted to marry Cleo. She had recovered from her love for him months and months ago — had it been real love would she have recovered?

Never again would she allow herself to care for a man until he had been exposed to her half-sister's fascination. How could she trust one even then? Hadn't Johnny Grant seemed madly in love with her? She was through with men, she'd be one of those career-women whose biographies figure in the pages of magazines. From early childhood she had ached to be a writer and while living with her aunt the chance had come to try. She had devoted hours each day to creative writing. She wanted to write fiction, in spite of the fact that an editor had warned her to think well before she started on the rough and rocky road to authorship, that the woods, to say nothing of the park benches, were full of would-be writers.

She lived over the ecstatic moment when she had drawn a pink cheque from an envelope. Three dollars! It had seemed a fortune. She had sold something! Nothing much but someone had wanted it enough to pay money for it. That was the acid test. Another much traveled manuscript had been in an editorial office six weeks; up to this one its flights had been in the non-stop class. She had had a nervous chill every time she opened the mail-bag for fear she would find it. Other stories had gone out and had done the homing-pigeon act, but not that one. If she did receive a cheque for it, she would deposit it in a travel fund.

Thrilled by the thought of achievement and freedom, she shot the outboard around a rocky point. Her breath stopped. A motorboat was almost upon her. Where had it come from? Had it dropped from the sky? Why hadn't she heard the put-put? Why didn't the dumbbell at the wheel slow down? Was it a villager or a summer resident out on a practice spin? Spin was the word. The top of something that looked like a head was visible. He was making thirty miles an hour, plus. She had the right of way. If she swerved the least bit, the one-man crew wouldn't know what to do.

"Sit tight, G-Man," she warned, as the dog, sensing danger, sprang to his feet.

She regarded the on-coming boat with the fascinated absorption she might bestow on an inch-worm looping its way across a man's collar to his neck. It was shooting straight for her! It couldn't be! It was unbelievable! It was! It would crash —

"Hi! Look out!" she shouted. Kicked off her sandals. Grabbed the pennant. Jumped.

She came to the surface, kept herself afloat with one hand while she drew the pennant about her neck and brushed her dripping hair from her eyes. Something had hit her forehead. Ooch, how it throbbed. Where was G-Man? There he was with his nose above water swimming toward her. Some distance away the motorboat which had crashed into hers, was drifting, it had lost power. Why didn't the man come back to see what damage he had done? Was he blind that he didn't see that her outboard had run amuck? It was buzzing round in dizzy circles. Funniest thing she'd ever seen. She laughed and swallowed an able-bodied wave.

She choked and coughed. She'd better keep her sense of humor battened down until she was out of this mess. Could she reach her boat? She started off in an easy crawl, she mustn't get winded, no knowing when she would catch the runaway. Suppose it charged in her direction? She speeded up, her arms flashed in the late sunshine. She could hear G-Man paddling beside her. The water was icy. She swallowed another mouthful. It made her a little sick. She shivered and her teeth chattered. Why, why didn't that idiot at the wheel of the motorboat come to her aid? She was getting winded. She tried to call but her throat was dry. She couldn't make a sound.

"Hi! Keep away from the outboard! We're coming!"

The words struck against her ear. She raised her head. A man in a launch was shouting through a megaphone. Must have come from the cruiser. Someone on board had seen the crash. G-Man shivered and whimpered as he gallantly kept beside her.

The hum of the boat was louder. A life belt dropped to the water. She clutched it with one hand. Caught the dog's collar with the other. They both went under. Bobbed to the surface. She was drawn along cautiously. A man's voice called;

32

"Steady! Steady! We'll have you safe in a minute."

Someone caught her under the arms. She looked up dazedly into a lean colorless face, into dark, troubled eyes. Hadn't she seen the man before somewhere? He was coatless.

"Women and dogs first," she gasped as she was lifted gently, but firmly, from the water. "Save G-Man, too."

Dizzy from the smart and throb of her forehead, exhausted by the effort to keep afloat in the cold water, she flung herself on the cushioned seat. The dog huddled in a wet dejected heap beside her.

"B—better f—follow that motor b—boat — m—man in it — m—must have f—fainted or someth—thing before he ran me d—down," she advised between chattering teeth.

"Don't worry about him."

"Nice voice," she approved mentally.

"I'll be all right in a min—minute. Soon's I s—stop shivering," she reassured the troubled eyes above her. Something soft and woolly covered her. She snuggled under it and clasped her arms about her shoulders in an attempt to stop their shaking.

"Drink this."

She pushed away the long firm fingers

which held the silver cup of a flask.

"No, th—thanks. I'll be warm in a min—minute, I need nothing but a n—nice cr—crackling fire and dr—dry clothes. See? I've stopped shaking — almost. Don't make an invalid of me because of a silly accident. Accident!"

Memory brought her to her feet. She clutched the blue shirt sleeve of the man who had pulled her from the water. Color from the dripping pennant around her neck ran down her bare legs in little green and gold rivulets.

"What became of the motorboat which cr—crashed into mine?"

He held out the soft camelshair top-coat which had covered her.

"Stop thinking about that boat and put this on."

"Hmp! The ruling class," she told herself, and disciplined an urge to defy the authoritative voice. She dropped the pennant to the seat, slipped her arms into the sleeves and drew the coat close about her. She needed its heavenly warmth now that a strong, ocean breeze had sprung up.

"When we catch a mermaid — to say nothing of her dog — it's up to us to take care of her, isn't it?"

The laughter left his voice. His shocked

gray eyes rested on her forehead.

"What a crack! Lucky it wasn't lower down. Prescott, make for the cruiser! We'll get something that will fix up this bruise."

"Aye, aye, sir!" the white-capped sailor at the wheel responded.

The man drew a fine linen handkerchief from his pocket, folded it and dipped it into the cold water rushing by the boat.

"Shut your teeth, this will smart," he said, and laid the compress on the wound.

The sting of salt on bruised flesh brought a rush of tears to Lissa's eyes, but it served also to clear her mind. The lingering daze vanished with the rapidity of fog in strong sunlight. Her rescuer must be the plutocrat who owned the cruiser. She brushed aside his hand.

"I'll hold it. I'm not going to the cruiser. If you want to help, catch that crazy boat of mine before it crashes into something! Watch it! It's going so fast that the number on the side is a blur."

"Prescott, cut over to the outboard. We'll try and kill the engine by throwing water on it."

"Aye, aye, sir!"

The sailor pulled his cap to a more acute angle and changed the course of the launch. Hands thrust hard into coat pockets, Lissa

35

breathlessly watched her outboard careening in dizzy circles. Something was emerging from the water near it, something dark and glistening like the back of a seal. The tide was ebbing! The outboard straightened out. Made a bee-line for the ledge. Smashed into it with a shower of splinters and spray.

"That seems to be that," she observed with a catch in her voice. She loved that outboard. She was losing everything she cared for. She fought back a torrent of emotion. She mustn't let herself go. She mustn't.

Imagine cracking up over an old boat after what she had lived through these last months. She couldn't be so silly. She swallowed hard before she observed;

"That crash stopped the en—engine."

The man's eyes were dark with concern. Did he fear that he was about to have a sob sister on his hands? She'd show him. She laughed;

"But what's a crash in the life of an outboard? Let it stay there. I'll send for it. Now if you will round that point, I'll tell you where to land me." She drew a long unsteady breath. She had staved off a weepfest that time.

The sailor looked interrogatively at the man who was slipping into a blue coat. His shoeless feet were braced to steady himself.

The boat lurched and kicked up showers of spray as it sped through a sea the change of wind had roughened.

"Round the point, Prescott," he responded to the sailor's unspoken question. "Follow the orders of Miss —" He smiled at the girl and raised questioning eyebrows.

"Barclay," she supplied. She loved the buoyant note in his voice. What would he think if she added: "Lissa — to you." She removed the compress from her forehead. As he protested, she assured;

"It doesn't throb now, really. I'll pull a curl or two over it, see, and then the bruise won't show." She thrust the wet handkerchief into the pocket of her shorts. "It's bad enough to look like a drowned rat without adding a prize-fighter touch; I'll see that your handkerchief is returned spic and span."

Why was he looking at her so curiously? Surprised to find out who she was? As if in answer to her thoughts he directed:

"Make the Tarry Farm landing as quickly as possible, Prescott."

"Of course I'd like to get home, but shouldn't you render first aid to him?" Lissa nodded in the direction of the drifting motorboat. "He hasn't changed his position since I saw him shooting toward me. He

37

may be terribly hurt by the crash."

She thought the sailor chuckled, she was sure that the man now seated opposite her in the stern putting on his shoes said something colorful under his breath before he explained:

"That isn't the head of a man, Miss Barclay, it's a robot at the wheel. It's an automatic steering device which picks up radio waves, transmits their impulse to the wheel and keeps the boat pointed at a 'target' down the bay."

4

"A robot did all that damage?" Lissa demanded incredulously.

"Yes. Two guests on the cruiser are, well, call them engineers. They were experimenting with radio control of the motorboat. It was going like a breeze in a quiet, clear sea, when you shot round that point in your outboard. You know the rest, but, you don't know that terror, for fear I wouldn't reach you in time, took years from my life. When I saw you in the water holding the dog with one hand, and that crazy outboard likely to smash into you at any moment, I —" He ran his fingers under his collar. "I kicked off my shoes, flung off my coat ready to go overboard if you missed the lifebelt."

The memory of the instant when the motorboat had crashed into The Scribbler, sent chills along Lissa's veins.

"Let's forget it," she suggested. "I'm safe. G-Man is safe. Hell-dives are part of the day's work in a flying outboard. If The Scribbler doesn't dash her brains out against that ledge before I can rescue her, I may be able to have her repaired."

"The Scribbler?"

"That's the name of the flying outboard."

"We'll take care of it. Prescott will pick it up. I'd go back for it now but I want to get you home before you take cold. We'll have it repaired. Our robot is responsible for the damage."

"We, sounds like royalty. You'll have to take the question of reparations up with the Carson heir who has just inherited Tarry Farm. Who knows but the late accident may prove the foundation of my spectacular success. Heroine loses boat and acquires black eye. To borrow from the Duchess in Alice, 'the moral of that is,' turn casualty into cash; meaning it would make a grand opening for a story. I could turn the robot into a hero."

"What do you mean by spectacular success? Haven't picked up the motion-picture bug, have you?"

Lissa watched a lavender-winged gull dive into the tumbled, frothy wake of the launch as she answered:

"No, but one quite as deadly. I'm a working girl, did you think me a leisurist? Wonderful word, isn't it?"

She drew a deep breath. "Heavenly afternoon. The sun topping that brownish-green hill makes me think of a huge copper ball

40

being balanced on the snout of a trained seal. It has turned the shore lines to red gold and the lighthouse to a tourmaline pink. How Nature loves jewel glints and tints. Like a woman, isn't she? See that dark ridge between the mainland and the island? As the tide recedes it will leave a road which will be usable for nine hours. I've never seen the mountains more purple nor the winding roads on them look so like silver threads, and man and boy 'I've watched three winters and summers come and go.' " She was working off her turbulence of spirit in chatter, she realized, but that was better than tears.

"I've never heard that last line declaimed better. Have one?" He offered a silver cigarette case.

"No, thanks. I don't smoke."

"Don't smoke! And you headed for screenland?"

"Why so surprised? I've met any number of wonderful girls in my travels who neither smoke nor drink. With some it's a sort of 'I am my brother's Keeper' complex, with others the courage to be different. You're wrong, I'm not headed for screenland. I mean to be a writer."

Was she too friendly? He was the first person, except Aunt Hetty and G-Man —

41

he was a person if ever there were one — to whom she had confided her ambition. After all, one could hardly say "Hail and Farewell" to a man who had saved one's life, could one? One knew the moment one looked at him that he was a man of power. Someone to hold tight to in time of trouble. She liked him. Tremendously. Liked him better than any man she ever had met, and she had seen him for the first time less than half an hour ago! She did need a guardian! The launch rounded the point.

"There's Tarry Farm! Doesn't that half timber and brick English house look as if it had grown against the background of forest? Those streaks of color are the perennial borders of the path from shore to terrace. Aren't the cottages attractive? All leased for the season, too." She blinked back tears, said unevenly:

"I've thought myself a martyr these last three years to have to live here — it has seemed terribly remote in winter. Just as I am leaving it, I realize that I love every inch of the place."

"Why are you leaving?"

She tucked the woolly coat more securely around her bare feet. G-man pressed close against her knees.

"I told you, Alexander Carson has inherited it. Apparently you haven't listened to my chatter."

"I can tell you every word you've said. So, this is Lex Carson's property?"

"Is he called Lex for short? Nice name. Do you know him?"

"Very well. He came in on that cruiser to — to take over his inheritance. He has spoken of you, but until you said you'd lived at Tarry Farm three years, I didn't know which one of the, quote, beautiful Barclay sisters — unquote, you were. I hoped that you were Lissa — or is it Melissa?" He was even better looking when he smiled, she decided, his teeth were so white and his gray eyes turned so dark and shining, and he didn't need to be any better looking than he was with his face in repose.

"Melissa for my grandmother but only one person in the world calls me that. I'm Lissa to my friends. Evidently you've heard all about my family from Alexander Carson?"

"I wouldn't say 'all.' I still have a lot to learn about you. Already I know that you are a writer."

"Intend to be a writer. They tell me it's a long slow road, that only about nine percent of those who start out carry through the first year. Even after that winnowing, the fatalities are staggering."

"Remember the old proverb, 'Leg over leg the dog went to Dover.' You'll arrive if you keep everlastingly at it."

"What else have you learned about me?"

"You mean this afternoon? That you have two freckles like tiny flakes of gold on the bridge of your nose — don't try to brush them off, you can't — that you're a grand sport, that your amazing eyes are pools of beauty."

"It listens lovely." Almost Lissa was tempted to believe him. Silly. Hadn't Johnny Grant said practically the same thing about her eyes? Only he had said they were "tops."

Cigarette between his lips he bent his head to the light cupped in his hands before he asked:

"Your half-sister Cleo was engaged to Johnny Grant, wasn't she? I hear she's a knockout."

Anger flamed through Lissa.

"Better take a leaf from the book of Ulysses, put wax in your ears before you meet her, then you won't hear the voice of the siren. It's fatal."

She was aware of his quick glance. Was he setting her down as a jealous cat? The launch was almost at the float. She wouldn't have much more chance to reveal her disagreeable nature.

He tossed the cigarette overboard and stood up. Feet planted squarely apart to steady himself, he smiled at her.

"I don't need to take a leaf from the book of Ulysses, I'm immune to sirens."

"Sez who?" she mocked.

"Sez I," he mimicked. "Hope I haven't hurt you."

"Hurt me? How?"

"By referring to the engagement of your half-sister to the man to whom you were engaged."

She jumped to her feet and clutched the camelshair coat about her. Her eyes blazed.

"You have learned a lot about me, haven't you? How dare you refer to that — that maddening experience? I'm sunk in humiliation when I think of it."

His eyes steady and direct met hers.

"Then you still love him?"

"Love him! My love for Johnny Grant was as rootless as a mushroom."

"Thanks. It has suddenly become enormously important that I know."

"Why?"

The boat slid alongside the float. He stepped to the landing without answering her question and held out his hand.

45

"Come on! Why take along that messy pennant? What were you doing with it?"

Lissa looked at the wet stuff she was gripping which resembled nothing so much as a bunch of over-cooked spinach.

"I had gone very Admiral Byrd. I was about to plant it on my recently acquired possession, my island."

"Your island. The island with the light?"

"Yes."

He turned to look at the white tower.

"Sold by the Government, wasn't it?"

"Yes. Aunt Hetty bought it. She willed it to me." She confided in a hushed voice, "At dawn this morning I thought I saw the light flash."

"Isn't the tower kept locked?"

His face hadn't changed, but she had the curious feeling that he was taut as he waited for her answer.

"Yes. Of course it was a trick of vision. My eyes were tired."

"Of course, how could a person get in and why should he want to? Did you plant the pennant?"

"No. The outboard crashed before I could land."

"That disappointed-little-girl look in your eyes hurts me. I'll get another pennant and we'll plant it together. Shall we?"

46

"Don't talk to me as if I were four years old and had broken my doll. I'm a big girl now."

"Think I don't realize that?" He spoke to the sailor in the launch. "Prescott, pick up the outboard. Bring it in and wait for me here." He looked at her bare feet with their gemlike pink nails, then at the path that loped leisurely upward to the terrace of the big house. "You can't walk on those rough stepping stones without shoes. Where are they?"

"Kicked my sandals off before I dove. I have another pair in the boathouse. I have a frock there too. It won't take me a moment to get into it. Take your coat. Thanks for everything. Run along home, G-Man."

She threw the dripping pennant over one shoulder and lingered to watch the dog. He ran part way up the path, stopped and looked back.

"Go on!" she called, "and don't go near a clothesline!"

She ran ahead to the boathouse. She stared unbelievingly at the man who jumped the rail of the veranda and came toward her with outstretched hands.

"Lissa!"

"Johnny Grant! Is it really you?" For some unaccountable reason the sight of him set her a-shiver again. Had his eyes always been so colorless, his hair platinum blonde? Had he always swaggered a little?

"Sure, it's I, sweet thing. Don't look at me as if you'd been bumped awake. I'm stopping at the Inn in the village. Made a bee-line for you as soon as I heard that your late, if not lamented, Aunt Hetty had passed out and that you were free, Princess released from the dark tower stuff, what? That was only a brainstorm I had over Cleo — I'm crazy about you —"

He looked beyond her and called:

"Look who's here! Where did you drop from, Lex Carson?"

5

Lissa glanced at the man who had rescued her. There was a quality of strength and self control about him in sharp contrast to Johnny Grant's puffy outlines. His mouth was stern as if trained to command, yet, boyishly tender when he smiled. His eyes were dark, intent, with quizzical lights in their depths. The picture of Alexander Carson as she had imagined him, stooping, peering owlishly through bone-rimmed specs, had been so deeply etched on her mind, that she doubted even now if she had heard Johnny's hail correctly.

"Are you really Alexander Carson?" she asked.

"If you don't know who he is, Lissa, perhaps you'll tell me why you've been sporting round with him in a launch, in those shorts? You look as if you'd been trying to qualify for Miss State of Maine with that striped thing over your shoulder. How did you get that vicious bump on your forehead?"

"I don't like that word 'sporting,' Johnny, and I don't care for the 'Hands up!' tone in which you ask questions."

"Nothing to get excited about, Grant. Miss Barclay's flying outboard ran amuck — she got a nasty crack on the head — and I pulled her out of the water. At a time like that, one doesn't insist upon introductions. I am Alexander Carson, Miss Barclay. Lex to you, I hope."

"Lissa! Are you so glad to see me that you've gone dumb?" Grant inquired with a pleased grin.

Lissa regarded him coolly:

"Pity you have such an inferiority complex, Johnny. That's sarcasm, in case you care. Been to the house to see Cleo?"

"I have not. It would be too soon if I never saw her again. I came to see you. The butler — that man is too English to be genuine — told me that you were on the water. He showed me how to get here in my car. I waited knowing you'd have to come this way. Jump into your clothes. I'm taking you out to supper."

From the corners of her eyes Lissa glanced at the man who stood straight and tall beside her. Was he thinking, as evidently Johnny Grant thought, that her one-time fiancé had but to whistle and she would drop into his arms? She declined crisply:

"Thanks, but I'm not going with you, Johnny."

"Sure, you're coming. You wouldn't break my heart, would you?"

"Your heart break, Johnny? It couldn't. Your heart is a graveyard of buried loves."

Grant grinned engagingly.

"That's a swell line. You're good, Lissa. Come on. Remember what corking times we've had hunting up new places to eat? We'll find tops tonight."

Lissa felt her color rise. Would he see it and flatter himself that she still cared? She grew redder at the thought.

"Not interested, Johnny. Please go."

"Better get going, Grant," Carson suggested pleasantly but uncompromisingly. "Miss Barclay is shivering again. The water was icy. Get into your dry clothes — Lissa."

As she took a step forward, Grant blocked her way.

"You're not going until you hear what I —"

"Your mistake. She is going at once." Carson's voice and eyes were dangerously cool.

"Who are you to say who will come and go here, Lex Carson?" Grant demanded.

Eager as she was to escape, Lissa lingered. Johnny's face was an angry red. Alexander

51

Carson's had whitened. They looked ready to fly at one another's throats. She must stand by and stop it. Carson said quietly:

"I happen to be the owner."

Lissa had heard the expression, "his jaw dropped" and had thought it a phrase sacred to the use of writers. Now she knew it to be true. Johnny Grant's jaw not only dropped, it waggled.

"So you're the heir. Somehow I never connected the Lex Carson I met last winter in Washington — to whom in an incandescent glow, I confided the flop of my engagements — with Lissa's Aunt Hetty. What an inheritance! In spite of your high-hatting, I'll be noble and hand you a tip. Watch out for Mamma Barclay. She'll tell you what to do till you're ready to bash her over the head. What this country needs most is an advice exterminator. She'll have you roped and laid at the feet of the lovely Cleo before you know where you're at. It's already in the bag. You won't have a chance You're a richer haul than I was, Gunga Din. Don't glare. I'm going. I'll be back, Lissa. I understand that you want to introduce the heir to his new relatives, so I'll step aside this time, but never again. No hard feelings, Lex, I'm too sorry for you. I'll be seeing you."

Lissa clutched Carson's sleeve.

52

"Don't follow him, please. He didn't mean anything — by that 'never again' — I mean."

"He meant enough to make you shiver with fear."

She laughed, an unsteady laugh, but it served to relax the muscles in the arm under her hand. She watched Grant's red roadster flame up the road before she removed her fingers.

"That wasn't fear. I never was afraid in my life. When you know me better, you'll discover that I always shiver at the strategic moment. Better than fainting, isn't it? The old time heroine belonged to that school of thought."

His laugh brought the color back under his bronzed skin.

"The fiction viewpoint sticks out in everything you say, doesn't it? Would a man dare love you, or would he suspect that his reaction to your charm would be merely good copy to you? Don't answer. That was a foolish question. Get into your clothes. I'll wait. I'm going to the house with you."

When Lissa rejoined him he was standing at the foot of the garden path, which was gay as an Oriental runner, with red and yellow, pink and blue blossoms of creeping plants set between the stepping stones. Hands in his coat pockets, he looked up at the house on the crest of the slope.

"Display seems to have been the architect's idea when he planned this place. The buildings are so much bigger than a person wants — these days. The upkeep must require an able-bodied fortune and employees by the regiment."

"It does. You haven't seen the half. Beyond the house are cattle barns, poultry houses, fields of grain, and fat silos. Your uncle and then his widow went in for model farming on a large scale, with Simonds, a dour Scot, as foreman. He and Fenton, the butler, are Czars in their departments." And because she knew what a staggering amount of money the upkeep required, Lissa could think of nothing cheering to add. She conquered an absurd urge to smooth out the two little lines between his brows and drew a deep breath:

"Isn't the air sweet?" She picked a bunch of rich blue bachelor buttons. "The first of the season. When the autumn flowers come, I think they are the loveliest and now that June is going, I'm all for tulips and columbines, peonies and iris. There's fickleness for you. Here's a boutonniere."

"Put it in, will you?"

She pulled the stems through the lapel of his coat.

"Aren't they a gorgeous color? The blue of the sea when it's deep and secretive and still. That doesn't mean that you are to stand there and admire them. You really should go to the house and be presented as the heir."

He strolled on beside her evidently in no haste to take possession of his inheritance.

"Plenty of time. Know what I was thinking when I watched you put the flowers in my coat? I was wondering if you were jotting it down as good fiction-copy."

"Jot that down! Old stuff like that? You're not supposing that I never have put flowers in a man's coat before, are you? Am I that unattractive?"

"Fishing, aren't you?"

The laughter in his eyes was reflected in hers.

"I'm not fishing. I'm expanding. For three years I have been one of America's 53,000,000 rural inhabitants, and now the curtain is rising on a brand new life. Aunt Hetty was jealous if I appeared interested in anyone. Before that, I traveled with my father, who didn't care to have me make acquaintances. You've heard a lot about the richest girl in the world. I'm the poorest girl in the world when it comes to real friends. However, that's behind me. All my yesterdays have been dropped overboard. I intend to be madly, extravagantly, gorgeously gay — if one of my aversion to drinking parties and all that goes with them — can be. I'm a new person even before I'm in a new environment. Reorienting myself, I suppose you'd call it. Do you wonder that I'm excited and trying out a line I haven't had a chance to use?"

"I don't. Go to it. I'll stick around so that you may have me to practice on. All right with you?"

She ignored the question, which was more of a demand, in his smiling eyes.

"Do you know, Mr. Carson —"

"Lex. We are cousins-in-law, aren't we? Why be formal?"

"Lex, it is. I had a feeling when you pulled me into the boat, that you'd be like this."

"Like what?"

"Oh, understanding and good fun and hard as steel if you were crossed. By all the rules of fiction, I ought to hate you violently."

"Why? Because I have inherited this place? That's the reason I didn't tell you at once who I was. I thought you might be bitter because the property came to me. I wanted to make friends with you before you found out."

"Of course I'm not bitter. Why shouldn't your uncle's property go to you?"

"That takes a load from my mind. To return to your fiction complex, you might put Johnny Grant and me in a story and work it out. Do you believe in love at first sight — in fiction — of course?"

"I do, in fiction and in real life. It's the Shakespeare in me. Remember that once there was a boy named Romeo and a girl named Juliet?"

"Yes, I believe in it, too. Take this path slowly. There are a number of questions I want to ask. Your Aunt Hetty wrote that you knew this place from A to Z, were capable of running it, if I needed a manager."

Aunt Hetty had written that? Had she told him also that she had made him trustee of the legacy? No. Had he known it, he would have referred to it.

"Your Aunt and I patched up our differences via airmail and became rather fratty on paper," he went on. "She invited me to spend the summer with her."

"Here! At Tarry Farm? Strange she didn't tell me. Were you coming?"

"I was. I was winding up some business so that I could take a vacation for the first time in years, had interested Tod Kent in the location as a summer port for his cruiser, The

57

Sphinx, when the wire came that she had slipped away. Then, I stayed and finished up, and here I am."

"And the whole darn Barclay family, too. We'll be out of your way as soon as possible. Tomorrow I'll turn my books over to you and —"

"What's the rush? The cottages are leased?"

"All three."

"Are they much care?"

"Not if we have plenty of rain. Wells supply the water. Tenants come from the city where water is inexhaustible and drain them usually the first month. If we have a dry summer, I have an attack of water on the brain. Stand here with your back to Tarry Farm, and you can see the cottages on the shore. The Treasure Chest is the brown shingled house at your right. At your left is Red Chimneys — that's my favorite — and beyond on a point near the island, Pirates' Den. Observe that each house has a motorboat moored in the offing. That is included in the rent. The cottages were Aunt Hetty's pride and she furnished them luxuriously even to books and boats. The tenants arrived at Red Chimneys a week ago."

"Are they husband and wife?"

"No, brother and sister, Ralph and

Sidonie Packard. Romantic name that last, isn't it? Their references — Aunt Hetty was a stickler for references, informed us that Mr. Packard wanted a place in which he could be quiet and work. The inference was that he was a writer. Wouldn't it be grand if he would give me points?"

"If your eyes shine much more at the possibility, they'll explode the way the stars do. I recommended the place to the Millards who have taken one of the cottages. They are my friends. They have a delicate boy and I remembered what Maine air did for me when, as a kid, I came to visit Uncle Alexander after scarlet fever, his first wife was alive then. They lost two little girls, but you'd never know it from Madge, the mother, who is, I think, the bravest woman in the world. Jack, her husband, is a forester — when he works at it. He has a bit too much money to make his mark in his profession. If ever you've been cynical about marriage, you'll find your faith restored when you see them together. Let me take you there to call, will you?"

"I will. G-Man stole their bathing suits this morning. I would like your moral support when I make my apologies."

"Mr. Adams is coming here tomorrow with the trustees' final accounting. What

59

you have told me about the cottages will help me appear intelligent. Yearly reports on the estate have been submitted to me so I know how the principal has dwindled."

"Have you seen Aunt Hetty's will?"

"No. That doesn't affect me."

"Doesn't it? Wait till you hear it, you'll be surprised."

"All right, let's skip that, I'll be surprised. Tell me about the other tenants. When do they come?"

"Your friends, the Millards, who have hired the Treasure Chest, came yesterday, and Major Fane takes possession of Pirates' Den on Saturday."

"What sort of Major?"

"An army officer on sick leave with two men servants. From what Aunt Hetty told me, I judge he is about fifty."

"Did she hobnob with the tenants?"

"Aunt Hetty hobnob! I forgot, you didn't know her, did you? She called upon them after their arrival, invited them to a lobster-bake during Fair week and let it go at that."

"Lobsters! The mere word makes me ravenous. Are there many about here?"

"Those lobster-trap floats bobbing in the cove are the answer."

"Do they belong to Tarry Farm?"

"No. To Captain Ozias — commonly

called Ozy — who is fisherman extraordinary, as well as errand man and sheriff, to the community. Who is that crossing the terrace? He's waving his hand."

Lex Carson waved in return. Explained to Lissa:

"That's Tod Kent. As I told you, I came in on his cruiser. He is my best friend. He has more money than he can spend, added to which he has a public service complex. At present, he's engaged in research — for the Government. That explains the radio-control of a motorboat experiment."

"Research! For the Government in our harbor! How exciting. Tarry Farm has been a sort of Sleepy Hollow. Now it has suddenly come wide awake."

Eagerly Lissa appraised the man as he drew near. He was short, heavy, ruddy. His eyes were greenish hazel, his hair was red and laid close to his scalp in tight curls. His nose was retrousse to a degree, a comic-strip nose. Carson laid a hand on his shoulder:

"Miss Barclay, my friend, Tod Kent."

Kent's smile was of the ear-to-ear variety. Generous, heartwarming.

"Where did you find Lex, Miss Barclay? He was to meet me at the house above at four-thirty. I've been boring two ladies in its

61

living-room ever since. Who hit you?"

His shocked question sent Lissa's fingers to the bruise on her forehead. She flinched. She smiled at the ruddy-faced man. She liked him, liked him immensely. This seemed to be her day for taking instant likes. Was it because she was on the threshold of a brand new life, looking for adventure? She shook her head and laughed:

"Don't look so accusingly at your friend, Mr. Kent, he didn't hit me. My outboard cracked up. Now that you have met my stepmother and sister, won't you present Lex to them?"

"Where are you going?" Carson demanded.

"To Red Chimneys to welcome the tenants and inquire if everything is satisfactory. I sent Fenton the day they arrived. I couldn't leave my aunt. Won't you both dine with us? You needn't change."

"Oh, I say, don't leave us," Tod Kent implored boyishly.

"We'll wait for her here. She can't shake us like that. Don't be long, Lissa, or we'll come after you," Lex Carson warned.

The two men watched her as she ran through cool green shadows under the trees. She turned and waved to them before she disappeared from their sight. Tod Kent drew a long breath.

"That girl has a warmth and fire and sparkle that warmed my old bones to the marrow. The French call it *joie de vivre*, don't they? Did you inherit her with the property, Lex?"

"No."

Carson's reply was curt. Hands in his pockets he looked up at the house on the crest of the slope, let his eyes travel along the shore.

"I'm staggered at the extent of this place, Tod. Feel as if the Empire State Building had toppled over on my shoulders."

"It is big. Does that island go with it?"

"No. Mrs. Hetty Carson bought it when the Government sold it and willed it to her niece." He lowered his voice. "Lissa told me that early this morning she thought she saw a flash from the lighthouse."

"Is the lamp working?" There was a hint of excitement in the question.

"No. Hasn't been for three years, but, a small electric torch inserted in that lens would throw a good-sized beam."

Kent's eyes bulged.

"Jiminy, we haven't picked up a loose-end here miles from where we expected to find one, have we? There must be a catch in it somewhere."

"Sure there's a catch. Lissa had been asleep and doubtless imagined she saw the flash. Loose-ends are not picked up so easily." Carson's brows drew together as he looked at the island. "Just the same, fella, we'll keep an eye on that light."

6

Whip-poor-will! Whip-poor-will! Whip-poor-will!

The bird's call drifted from among the trees. Lissa loved it, it never depressed her. Some of the villagers thought it unlucky, had she heard it before she went on the water, they would have shaken their heads and insisted that it had foreshadowed the crack-up of the flying outboard. Of course it hadn't. There would be just as much sense in thinking it meant good fortune. That it had foreshadowed meeting Lex Carson.

She stopped running and walked as she visualized the events of the afternoon. Old Adams as he had read the will; the crash of the two boats; Alexander Carson's face as he had lifted her from the water; Johnny Grant vaulting the boathouse rail. Her heart had pounded in her throat when he appeared so suddenly. Was it possible that she was such a poor-spirited creature that she still loved him after his faithlessness?

She reached the question and Red Chimneys at the same moment. Admiration for the house which was a smaller model of the mansion above wiped Johnny Grant from her mind as effectively as a wet sponge erased chalk marks from a blackboard. Its two chimneys were the exact shade of the scarlet geraniums in the window-boxes. Lawns like green velvet surrounded it, a pine, twisted in the best Japanese manner, hung over the boulders which buttressed a sandy shore, a glassed-in porch extended almost to a pier which jutted into the water.

What were the tenants like, she wondered, as she had wondered each time her aunt had signed a new lease. Season after season they had come and gone in the three cottages without leaving the slightest impress on the lives of the occupants of the big house above them. Each year she had hoped that someone really interesting would come, someone who would provide a plot for a story.

She pressed the bell beside the wide open door.

"Help! Help!"

A woman's voice! "It can't be real! It's my plot fixation," Lissa thought, and dashed into the house.

"I'm awake," she told herself, in the instant she paused on the threshold of the chintz-hung living room. The flames licking the muslins at the window were real; the

66

man beating at them with his hands was real, so was the woman shrinking against the book shelves.

"Why don't you help, idiot?" Lissa fumed mentally in the split second it took her to cross the room.

"Stand back!" she warned the man who was still beating at the burning muslins. "You can't put it out that way. Grab that small rug!"

She yanked at an untouched side of the curtain. It came down rod and all, a blazing mass on the floor. She snatched the rug from the man's hand and covered it.

"Now, if you'll stop being jittery, Miss Packard, and bring those two hand grenades from the hall, all danger will be over," she said to the woman.

"Stay where you are, I'll get them, Sidonie," the man ordered. Even in the excitement, Lissa noted his voice, remembered that Ozy had compared it to oil in smoothness.

"Hundred percent helpmate, aren't you, my girl?" she thought as the woman collapsed in a big chair and covered her face with her hands. She snatched the grenade from the man who seemed not to know what to do with it and flung it on the smoking mass. She administered another and watched the result.

"That settles that. You'll find those grenades at strategic points all over the house, Mr. Packard," she explained, the woman was too stupid to bother with. "Next time, get busy with those first, and save your hands. I'm the — the representative of your landla— lord."

Her smile stiffened as she met his eyes. She had seen the expression once before in the eyes of a suffering dog. Her glance dropped to his short, thickset hands. She shut her teeth on her lips to steady them. She spoke to the woman huddled in the chair.

"Get some oil, olive oil if you haven't anything else, and some gauze, and take care of your brother's fingers."

The huddled figure shuddered.

"I can't, it will make me faint to look at them."

"Then bring me the first aid kit in the large dressing room. Quick!"

Lissa waited until the woman had left the room before she suggested:

"You'd better sit down, Mr. Packard. First though, let's get that coat off. Hold out your arm."

Carefully she slipped a sleeve over one burned hand, then the other. She appraised

the tailored clothes and the elaborate monogram on the blue shirt sleeve. Evidently this
author earned enough to have plenty of jam
with his bread and butter, no park bench for
him. His teeth were set hard in his lips. He
shut his eyes as he sank into a chair. Lissa
filled a glass with water from a carafe in the
dining room, came back, knelt beside him
and held it to his lips.

"Drink this. No? Don't you like water?
Hold your hands up, they won't smart quite
so much. Ooch! It got every finger didn't it?
You'll have to let someone else do your
typing, or perhaps you are one of those ge-
niuses who talks his stories into a dicta-
phone?" she suggested, in the hope that the
mention of his work might take his mind
from his smarting fingers.

He opened his eyes, dark with suffering.
There was something else in them too,
something that flickered.

"My stories?"

"Yes. Aunt Hetty and I imagined you
were a writer because you wanted quiet and
privacy. Perhaps you're not. Perhaps —"

"But — I am a writer. You have been so
kind — why —" he gritted his teeth, as if
shutting back a groan, closed and opened
his eyes before he added — "shouldn't you
know? I'll be glad if you won't broadcast the

69

fact — you've no idea how I'm bothered with autograph hunters. I hope to bury myself here and escape them."

Whip-poor-will! Whip-poor-will! Whip-poor-will! The sound drifted through the open window. Ralph Packard swore under his breath.

"There's that infernal bird again. It's been round here every night since we came. I counted twenty-five calls the last time. How my fingers burn!" He dropped his head back and clenched his teeth.

His sister entered the room followed by a houseman in a white coat. He was striking-looking in a dark Italian-bandit way, his eyes were close-set, one cheek was scarred. She was calmer, she even smiled.

"I'm sorry I lost my head, Miss Barclay. Fire always terrifies me. We'll take care of him now. Nino is an expert in accidents."

"He needs to be if he is traveling round with you," Lissa thought as she rose from her knees.

"Then I'll go." She smiled at Ralph Packard who was looking up with that curious blend of pain and something else in his eyes. Could it be mockery? "Don't trust those hands to home talent, Mr. Packard. Better have a physician look at them. There is an excellent one in the village. Please don't rise. I'm going. If I can help in any way, phone me, Miss Packard. Good-afternoon."

As she walked slowly through the orchard and up the flower-bordered path which climbed toward the house, she visualized the room she had left. At the time she had been too excited to notice details but now the slim figure of the woman in a colorful printed chiffon gown standing against a background of books came back to her. Not too young, late twenties, perhaps. Pretty, strikingly pretty. Her beautiful coifed hair was so blonde that it was silvery; her eyes were deep blue, her hands which had been constantly in motion, flashed with jewels. Her brother's hair was darker, she couldn't tell much about his face, except that his eyes were enormous and black as midnight.

He had seemed surprised when she had mentioned his stories. Had she not been interested in creative writing herself, she wouldn't have divined from the letter of application for the cottage, that an author was seeking a place in which to work. He must be well-known to have autograph hunters on his trail. Packard. The name didn't click in connection with fiction, biography or science. Perhaps he had assumed it as a disguise or perhaps he used it as a *nom de*

71

plume. No. The cheque for payment of rent in advance had been signed Ralph Packard. It must be his real name. He might be publishing under another. He was extremely good looking perhaps in the early forties. She visualized again the living room at Red Chimneys, the Italian servant with the close-set eyes and scar across one cheek. She said aloud;

"I'd hate to meet you in the dark, Nino. I'll bet you'd cheat yourself at solitaire, if a houseman plays solitaire."

Quite suddenly her knees threatened to fold up. Her nerves shivered. Coming on top of the boat crash, the burning curtains had been a shock. She sat down quickly on one of the wrought-iron seats.

Time had galloped since she left the house for what had proved to be a spill in the flying outboard. From behind a dusky hill the sun was flinging up streamers of gorgeous lemon, pink and lavender. The sky was pale apple green where yellow blended with the blue. Fluffs of cloud were fringed with Roman gold. The color magician had transmuted the islands in the harbor to chunks of amethyst, and set them in a sapphire sea. Against one of them the brass trimmings of the cruiser gleamed blood-red. The lighthouse was rosy pink, its great glass eye shimmered like a plaque of burnished copper. The ocean breeze was crisp with brine from the choppy water of the bay. What a glorious world.

"I was about to organize a search-party for you," said Alexander Carson behind her. "What's happened? You're white."

Color and calm returned together. Lissa rose.

"I was waiting to get my balance after another hectic adventure. This is proving to be just one of those days, that's all. G-Man started the ball rolling merrily by stealing bathing-suits; the cat Blessed Evented — there were four kittens — in the cook's best hat and she says she'll be blowed if she'll stay in such a house; Mr. Adams read Aunt Hetty's will — its contents set my stepmother and sister in a rage. You saw the spill in the outboard, and to add the last perfect dramatic touch, there's been an accident at Red Chimneys. Where did you come from? Haven't you been to the house?"

"I told you we would wait for you. I've been smoking and thinking under the trees. Tod Kent has gone to the cruiser, he'll be back. We've accepted your invitation to dinner. What kept you so long? What did you mean by another hectic adventure? What was the accident?"

I would hate to be on the witness-stand being cross-examined by you, Lissa thought, as she met his intent eyes. She told him what had happened at Red Chimneys.

"You touched those blazing curtains! You need a guardian."

"I have one — I forgot. You don't know yet, do you?"

"To what are you referring? Do you always speak in conundrums?"

"No, I speak in facts. To return to the blazing curtains. What else could I do? The man was beating at them, you should have seen his hands — his finger-prints are changed for all time, and his fool sister — pretty but stooge variety — was shrieking her head off without trying to help. I've seen burning muslins before and I knew that the curtain rod came down easily."

"Let me look!" He caught her hands gently and turned them palms up. "No burns? Are you sure?"

"Sure. Total casualty for me, a few scorched spots on my frock. I'll have time to change before dinner. It will save cross-examination from the family. The less said about the affair at Red Chimneys the better."

"Agreed. I'll drop in there on my way to the boat this evening and inquire if I can help. The man beat at the curtains? Hadn't much thought for his hands, had he? What did you say the name was?"

"Packard, Mr. and Miss Packard. They are from the middle west. Apparently the whip-poor-will is unknown there. Mr. Packard's nerves were upset by his accident and the whip-poor-will's call shot them to pieces."

"Packard. I know some people by that name. Whom did they give as references?"

"I can't tell without looking up the correspondence. They are on the crest of the social wave if one is to believe Fenton. He approved of them, had a friend who worked for them."

"Admire that butler a lot, don't you?"

"As a servant, he's perfect, as a man I don't like him. I can't explain why. Except for a week-end off every month he has remained on his job during the three years he has been here. Sometimes I've wondered if he were the younger son of a titled English family, working where he was unknown, to pile up a little fortune. His wages have been spectacularly high. Aunt Hetty liked him, he would talk with her about world affairs. I suspect he's something of a student. These last few months I was up a great deal with my aunt at night. I could see his lighted

75

window in the ell from her balcony. Evidently he reads until very late. After he decided to stay, he told Aunt Hetty that he would like to send for his books and asked if he might have some cheap shelves built into his room. She was so glad to have him contented, she would have built a cottage for him had he asked for it."

"Let's hope the model Fenton approves of me. I'll be needing him."

He followed her across the brick terrace, through the open French window to the library.

"Mother Barclay, Cleo, this is Alexander Carson."

In the instant of surprised silence, which followed her announcement, Lissa glanced at the portrait above the mantel. No wonder she had thought she had seen Alexander Carson before. He was a young edition of his uncle.

Mrs. Barclay fluttered forward and welcomed him effusively. She presented her daughter.

Lissa burned with resentment as Cleo laid her hand in his and looked up at him. Sure of her charm, wasn't she? It didn't help that the bruise on her own forehead throbbed intolerably and reminded her that she must look as if she had been in a brawl.

76

"We've been waiting to turn this charming place over to you, Cousin Alexander," Mrs. Barclay purred, "and to tell you of a few things that must be done. We are packed and ready to go."

"But you mustn't think of leaving," Carson protested. "I'm counting upon you all to stay a month at least. I shall need you to show me the ropes."

Lissa resisted an almost irresistible urge to protest. He had invited them to stay a month! He'd been bowled over by his first look at Cleo, had he? He could have her. As for herself, she would rush through the inventory of the things in the house her aunt had bequeathed to her, and be off on her own adventure in living.

Carson stopped her as she reached the door.

"Don't forget our date," he reminded in a low voice.

"What date?" she asked in honest surprise.

"Have you forgotten so soon that you and I are to take formal possession of your island and the lighthouse? Take care of that bruise," he advised before he turned back into the room.

7

Seated on a corner of the flat desk in the oak paneled room which passed as the residence office at Tarry Farm, Alexander Carson frowned thoughtfully. Sunlight, which filtered through the slits of a Venetian blind, barred his tan slacks with gold, and striped the old-fashioned black frock coat of the thin bald-headed man with bushy gray mustache, who sat stiff and erect in a chair opposite. Carson tapped the paper in his hand.

"If this statement is correct, Mr. Adams, and of course it is, something tells me I'm in for a trimming!"

Adams fitted his fingertips together and nodded sombrely.

"I tried to make you understand the situation, Alexander."

"I'm not blaming you, sir. You suggested times enough that I come here and make friends with my uncle's widow but it seemed like snooping round the property which, eventually, was to come to me. If my uncle had wanted me to know about the estate, he would have made me a trustee, wouldn't he?"

"You were too young for that at the time he died. Who would have thought when he made his will, that many of his gilt-edge investments would be wiped off the slate and that the income from others would be halved and halved again? We lawyers have learned something. We draw wills in terms of percentages now. We could have kept the head of the estate above water had it not been for the provision in the will that the income paid to the widow was to be kept up to a certain amount even if part of the principal was used."

"Did you speak to Mrs. Hetty Carson about it? With her consent you could have appealed to the Court to have her income reduced sufficiently to save mortgaging the cottages and city real estate."

"When we raised those loans, we thought things would come back. Instead firms folded up and left us holding leases and empty offices, and now the banks are getting restless. Perhaps you know what that means?"

"Know! I'll say I know! Didn't my father lose everything? He warned me before he died;

" 'Keep out of debt, Lex. Debt wrecks more homes than infidelity. Don't borrow. You won't need to in your profession, business is different. If you haven't money to pay for what you want, don't buy it.' I have remembered his warning and now it looks as if I'd be buried under debts not of my incurring."

"Who's rapping?" Adams asked impatiently.

Carson opened the door. A man stepped forward. A gaunt, gangling man, whose eyebrows, arched like the back of an angry cat, above eyes like those in a faded daguerreotype, contributed an expression of perpetual surprise to a face set between big ears which were full of spirals of black hair. He twirled a pencil on the end of a cable of gold chain, as he explained;

"I'm Simonds, the foreman. My wife and I came to welcome you to Tarry Farm, Mr. Carson."

His tone was aggressive, he spoke with a strong Scotch burr. One ugly-looking hand gripped the shoulder of a wisp of a woman in a blue and white print dress, and drew her forward. She tipped her head at a birdlike angle and looked up with eyes as black as her hair.

"Lem and I hope you'll be very happy in this beautiful home, sir," she said.

"Thank you, Mrs. Simonds," Carson responded cordially. "I'm new to everything here, and I shall rely upon you and your husband to show me the ropes."

She opened her lips to answer but Simonds forestalled her.

"There's nothing on this place I don't know all about," he assured pompously. "I run the stock and the fields and boss the men in all departments. Come along, Marty. Mr. Adams is here on business. We mustn't interrupt." He scowled in the direction of the trustee. "Run down to my office whenever you want information, Mr. Carson. You may find me and you may not. I'm a very busy man. Good morning."

He pushed his wife ahead of him into the hall and closed the door behind him. Carson looked at the door and then at Adams.

"He asked me to 'run down' to his office. Slightly swelled about the head, isn't he? He didn't look at you as if he loved you, sir."

"He doesn't. Hates me like poison. I tried to get Hetty Carson to cut his pay — it's ridiculously high — and of course she told him. He's picked up the share-the-wealth bug. He's Scotch and I'll bet he has the first dollar he ever earned. He's a crack-a-jack foreman, though."

"I liked his wife."

"Marty Simonds is an angel from heaven, a peppery angel, I guess some of them come

81

that way. She must lead a drab life with him. One of the great unsolved mysteries of the world is, why some women marry some men and vice versa.

"Let's get back to business. Simonds, like the poor, will be with you always. I want to return to Boston as soon as possible. The financial condition of the estate is a tough break for you, boy. I talked with Hetty Carson two years ago, then again last year, stated conditions in the hope that she would agree to a reduction of her income, but, nothing doing. Why should she give up a cent to be saved for the man who was to inherit after her, she argued. She kept on buying blooded stock at high and selling at new lows. I felt that Fenton, the butler, egged her on. She wanted — and needed at the rate she lived — every dollar the will awarded her."

"And she got it." Carson ran his eyes down the column of figures. "It was some income. She closed her town house and lived here for the last three years. I realize that Tarry Farm is an expensive place to run but she couldn't have spent all that money on it."

"She didn't, not quite all. She put some of it into a trust fund for her brother's daughter, Melissa Barclay, not an ironbound trust fund, there is a provision that the girl may draw from it if the trustee agrees and who do you think was named trustee?"

"You, I hope."

"No, you."

"I! I? But, Hetty Carson didn't know me!"

"She thought she did. She told me that she had invited you here for the summer, said she wanted to see the man who would control her husband's fortune. She told me also that from your letters she judged you would be hard-boiled enough to combat Lissa's stepmother and half-sister, who, she was sure, would begin to chisel at the girl's income to say nothing of the jewels — she can't sell or give them away without your consent — as soon as they were hers. She knew, because they were everlastingly appealing to her for money with which to pay overdue bills."

"I shan't accept the trusteeship."

"Think it over. The money left to Lissa was taken out of the property, if you refuse to serve she may think you begrudge it to her. She earned it. She lived here for three years, managed the cottages, ran this great house, the servants like her. Hetty Carson was not a comfortable person with whom to live. She kicked up a row if Lissa made

83

friends, and I guess it was simpler for her not to make them, though she did insist upon outdoor exercise and playing the organ at the little church in the village, but she never invited young people here."

"What a tough life for a girl like that."

"She could take it if anyone could. She has so many resources within herself. Life never can lick her. These last few months have been a terrific strain on her affection and emotions. In spite of weakness and suffering, Hetty Carson clung to life and to her niece. Lissa had all the last arrangements to make. I wouldn't be surprised if she went to pieces from reaction."

Carson looked at the papers in his hand but he was seeing a girl in a boat valiantly fighting back tears. Only sheer grit had kept her from going to pieces then. He said quickly;

"Of course I don't begrudge the money. How much is the legacy?"

"It will give her a little over one thousand dollars a year. Do you realize how much principal you have to get together nowadays to be sure of that income?"

"I do. I realize also that the income that comes to me from the estate won't carry the business property and this place. Well, I can sell it."

Adams' sombre eyes retreated into their caverns till they looked like the eyes of a prairie-dog peering from his hole.

"I hope you can, my boy, I hope you can. Real estate is coming back, but people aren't buying places the size of Tarry Farm, they cost too much to carry. In years to come this will be looked back upon as the tax-age."

"What can I do with it? I have a good income from my practice and a small one from a trust fund left by my grandfather. Can't touch the principal for five years, till I'm forty. There's no mortgage on this house. If I can't sell it, I'll scrap it. I will not break my back carrying a burden of debt. Lucky I had planned to take this summer off for a vacation, the first of any length since I opened my office. Vacation! Sounds like a joke. How soon will I have a free hand in managing the estate? I'm not familiar with Maine law."

"I'm filing the necessary papers now. The property comes at once to you. You can get busy looking things over and cutting expenses. I've asked Lissa to make an inventory of the personal property left to her. When she has it ready, we'll have an appraisal. She'll have a big tax to pay on the jewels."

85

"Where are they?"

"In a bank in Boston. I advise you to get rid of the blooded stock. That will cut down outside. This house swarms with servants. You can save there as soon as Mrs. Barclay and her daughters go."

Carson put his hands hard into his pockets.

"But, they are not going. In a lavish 'I'm the heir' gesture, I invited them to be my guests for a month."

"For the love of heaven, why? You don't like that whiny woman and her yellow-haired daughter, do you?"

"Not especially — but I like her step-daughter; that doesn't mean that I shall accept the trusteeship. I couldn't keep one here without the others, could I?"

Adams hunched his thin shoulders in relief.

"You like Lissa? That's good news. You'll feel differently about the trusteeship when you know her better. She knew I was troubled about expenses here. I told her that these were uncertain times — as if that bright girl didn't know — and that perhaps she could persuade her aunt to go a little slow in spending."

"What effect did that have?"

"None, except that Hetty Carson immediately had living room and dining-room at the Treasure Chest done over, Wedgewood, I believe she called it, and paid an exorbitant price for a Holstein cow. She went in for Holsteins after her husband died because their black and white was in keeping with her mourning clothes. The expenses of running this place outside the house didn't come out of her personal income — the will provided that it was to be kept up as she wished it to be. The trustees had no power to hold her down."

"What a cockeyed will. Why appoint trustees? Why didn't her husband leave everything to her?"

"We've been useful in handling investments. I don't wonder you're bitter, Alexander. You're the son of my old friend and many a night I've walked the floor thinking of the raw deal that would be handed you."

Carson laid his arm about the thin shoulders.

"I'll do the walking now. I can take it. As you know, my mother died when I was a boy and I began young to accept responsibilities, to face problems and work out decisions. Better go off on vacation as soon as you get the papers through. Where are you staying?"

"At the Inn in the County Seat to be near

the Court House. I'll be going. Sorry you've had so many problems dropped on your shoulders, Alexander. Phone me if you have questions to ask, though Lissa Barclay can give you more details about running the place than I can."

"I asked her to come here. She'll be along any minute now. Is your car in the drive? I'll come out with you."

He stood on the steps until Adams' sedan passed between the ornate iron gates which opened on the highway. Suppose he had told the old man that business problems were not the only ones that had been dropped on his shoulders, that he had been drafted by the Treasury Department to find and deliver a public enemy, who, it was suspected, was operating somewhere in the state? He had specialized in the legal science of criminology, but he'd never practiced the science of detection. The head of the Department knew that and had assigned him to the job. It was up to him to make good. He didn't like a man-hunt. But, the Government had organized a war against crime and one didn't refuse to serve one's country in time of war.

Grand day, it made anything seem possible of achievement, he thought, as he looked at the gold-edged hills, mere purple

88

cut-outs, as they were reflected in a sparkling ultramarine sea. He had forgotten that the sky could be so luminous. The atmosphere shimmered.

As he returned slowly to the room he had left, he thought of his inheritance, and he thought of the burden it might prove to carry. He straightened his shoulders. If it did prove a burden, he would sell it, if he couldn't sell it he could pull down every building on this place — that wasn't mortgaged — and save taxes. It was being done — meanwhile there was a small army of employees to be paid.

Lissa turned from the window as he entered the room. He closed the door and stood for an instant watching her.

Yesterday when her hair was wet, I didn't realize that it had so much gold in it, nor that it was so satin soft, nor that she walked straight into my heart when she looked up at me from the water, he thought. Perhaps it was her eyelashes, they're so long and curling at the tips and they sweep up so when she laughs, perhaps it was her mouth, it's such a gallant mouth, its lips are so naturally red and tipped-up at the corners and that dimple — oh well, what's the use in trying to explain myself to myself? "Fire and warmth." You said it, Tod. She had been lovely in white but there was something about the lilac cotton frock she was wearing that deepened the velvety brown of her eyes and accentuated the creamy delicacy of her skin. He asked;

"How is the poorest girl in the world after her ducking?"

"Not so poor, thank you. I'm sorry you remembered my sob-sisterish remark."

"Something tells me that I shall remember all your remarks. Why didn't you come to the library after dinner last night? I sent Fenton up twice with messages."

"He delivered them. I devoted my evening to denaturing the color of that." She pushed back her hair and revealed the bruise on her forehead. "It isn't quite such a lively purple as it was. I'll get by without the family knowing of my spill, unless you told them about it."

"Just a minute! Do I look like a person who goes about telling everything he knows?"

He loved her laugh. It was low with a trill running through it.

"On the contrary, you look like a person who would stand up under several third degrees without telling All."

She crossed to a filing cabinet, removed papers and laid them on the desk.

"Here are the leases and references for the tenants of the three cottages. Before you look them over, I want you to understand that I did not know that Aunt Hetty was gouging from your estate to leave that trust fund for me, nor that she was loading the care of the legacy on your shoulders. I knew she refused to take a cut in income — but I didn't know why. You, a lawyer, must know how to sidestep that trusteeship. Now you understand why I said that according to all fiction rules, I should hate you violently. In novels wards always fight with guardians."

"Sometimes they love them."

"I'm beginning to think you have a love complex. Seriously, if you need that money to help carry the property, you are to take it — understand?"

"I'm surprised, Miss Barclay, that you would make the unethical suggestion that a trustee use a ward's property."

"Don't laugh, it isn't a joking matter. But you won't be my trustee!"

"Oh, yes I will." When had he decided that, he asked himself?

"I don't need you. I've handled the small property my father left me. I'm twenty-five years old!"

"I've known women over that advanced age who have invested principal in Treasure

Hunts and mines that existed only on paper. I'll stick. I won't interfere with you — unless you want to do something crazy. Do you need money?"

"No, and please don't give me any until after I leave here. You could say, couldn't you, that you would make no payments to me until the estate is settled? Why are you frowning? Is that another unethical suggestion?"

Carson drew his hand across his forehead. He had been wondering if she thought her stepmother and sister would begin to draw upon her to help pay overdue bills. Aloud he said;

"Have I smoothed out the frown? Don't worry. I'll hold the money. Let's skip the trusteeship. Tell me about the tenants."

"I've told you of the Packards. You know the Millards, so that leaves Major Fane who moves into Pirates' Den Saturday. The advance of half the season's rents has been paid. We got better prices than for several years. I read somewhere that it was getting to be a landlord's market instead of a renter's."

"Sit down, please, while I look over the leases."

He seated himself at the desk opposite her. Sounds from the outside world broke the stillness of the room; the monotonous drilling of a woodpecker on a nearby tree, the faint, far moan of a bell-buoy, the wail of a distant motor horn. A gay little peony-scented breeze danced in through the open window and was gone. Paper crackled as he examined leases. He frowned at a sheet of figures.

"The cottages are not paying for themselves."

Lissa leaned forward and crossed her arms on the desk.

"Paying! They are eating themselves up. Between taxes and repairs, interest, improvements upon which prospective tenants insist and their financial sob-story about what they can't afford for rent, those three houses are fast getting to be a liability. The Packards are the first applicants in three years who didn't ask for a reduction in rent."

"Did they come across with the advance promptly?"

"Yes. That reminds me. Did you call at Red Chimneys last night?"

"Tod and I stopped on our way to the boat. The Italian servant said that the doctor had been there and had given 'the boss' something to quiet him and that Miss Packard, much upset from the shock, had gone to bed."

"It's just too bad about that woman. She's really a girl, I suppose, though to me she seemed as if she had known the world and its ways for years. I'll wager she's concerned only in the spoils of her brother's work, not in the work itself."

"Why are you so interested in those two, Lissa? You didn't fall in love with the man, did you? You said you believed in love at first sight."

Her big, brown eyes were turbulent pools as she denied;

"Fall in love! I'm off falling in love forever. I'm now one of those persons who has to trust a lot to love a little. I told you yesterday that I suspected he was a writer. I thought if I were a perfect lady and laid offerings of fresh eggs and flowers at his sister's feet, he might answer a few How-to-be-an-author questions."

"Not above bribery, are you?"

"You would make a joke of it. Now I shan't need him."

"Why won't you need him?"

"Because I'm checking out at the end of the week."

8

Carson sprang to his feet and as suddenly returned to his seat.

"Why the Jack-in-the-box act?" Lissa inquired flippantly.

"Surprise, just surprise that you should think of deserting the ship. You can't leave Tarry Farm. I need you."

"Need me! You have invited my stepmother and sister to stay, haven't you? You don't know them or you wouldn't think you needed anyone else."

"They know nothing of the management of the estate. You do. You can help me. Give me this summer. One summer. Is that much to ask? If you are thinking of money —"

"I am. Know anyone who isn't these days? I'm thinking of other things, too. I have my living to earn while I am learning to write. Aunt Hetty paid me a small salary —"

"I'll double it."

"Double it! What would you want me to do to earn that money?"

"Just what you have been doing. Look after the cottages and the tenants, manage

95

this house besides showing me where to cut expenses. If you will do that, I can concentrate on the business property. The fortune left by my uncle has been run ragged. I mean to devote what income there is to paying off the mortgages on the real estate."

"Same old battle-cry, Balance the budget. And you talk of doubling my salary! I'll stay on two conditions. First, the same salary Aunt Hetty paid, second, your promise that if you need it to carry the estate, you will use some of the money she left me."

"I will not."

"Then I'll not stay after this week."

"Lissa, don't be stubborn."

"Stubborn? I'm surprised that you are so out-of-date. The modern term is, 'rugged individualism.' Aunt Hetty takes money from you and hands it to me. I give it back when you need it. That seems logical to me."

"But I won't need it."

"Wait till you've lived here a week, you won't be so sure. Do I stay?"

"What a bargainer! Sort of a female Shylock, aren't you? I will not use it. You can't go," he announced triumphantly. "You'll have to stay until the property your aunt left you has been appraised. You and I must go to Boston to check up on the jewels at the bank —"

"They're not in the bank," Lissa whispered.

"Not in the bank! Where are they?" His voice was low as hers.

She looked at doors and windows before she glanced at the ceiling.

"Upstairs?" he demanded incredulously. "All of them?" She nodded. "How long have they been there?"

"Two weeks. Aunt Hetty wanted the thrill of handling them, and had them sent here."

"What an insane thing to do! Are they in your aunt's room?"

"No. In mine."

"Girl, you're crazy! I'll move my traps from the cruiser to this house this afternoon. As soon as the coast is clear after I arrive, give me the jewels. It isn't safe for you to have them. Does anyone know they are in the house?"

"No, unless Fenton suspected when an armed expressman brought them in."

"Nicely advertised, I'd say. The jewels are another reason why you must stand by. We've got to guard them until I can get away from here. You'll stay, won't you?"

"If I can really help."

"Lissa, you're adorable."

"That's what Johnny Grant says. Where were we when you went off at a tangent about the jewels?"

"We were about to cut expenses," Carson answered drily. "Does Johnny converse with you about that, too?"

"You're positively motion-picturish when you scowl." She nodded toward the paper he held. "First question?"

"This lists fifteen men outside the house on the pay roll. Do we need so many?"

"Yes, if the place is to be kept up as it is at present. The men are not only farmers, there are painters and carpenters among them, two take care of the boats and boathouses. You've no idea how much care Tarry Farm requires."

"Light is beginning to seep through. I'll look over things carefully before I begin to cut. That's where you can be a tremendous help. I suppose you know all the families, how many dependents the workers have and where the cuts will hurt least?"

"I do and what I don't know Marty Simonds will tell me. She is the wife of the foreman. She's a dear!"

"I agree with you. Wish I could say as much for her husband. They dropped in on me this morning."

"You didn't like Lem?"

98

"That's expressing it too mildly. I had an almost uncontrollable urge to punch his head. Make a list of the employees, will you? Use this room as usual for your office. I'll make my headquarters in the sports room, that door leads to it, doesn't it? When you are writing, hang out a sign SILENCE the way they do in the libraries and I'll never intrude. I happen to know an editor, or two —"

There was suggestion in his laughing pause.

"Who is bribing now?" Lissa accused. "I don't write here. I've had a desk in the lighthouse for the last year."

"Don't work there alone. It isn't safe —"

A whistle low and clear drifted in through the open window on a blossom scented breeze. A fragment of a gay little tune, twice repeated.

"Who is that?" Carson demanded, though he had known the moment his eyes met hers, big and brown and startled.

"It's Johnny."

"Johnny again! For whom is he whistling?"

She looked up from beneath long lashes and laughed.

"Something tells me it's for me."

A red-hot wave of anger swept him.

"Tell that playboy to keep away from my secretary or there'll be a dead body round here." He laughed to offset the husky break in his voice — "Guess whose?"

"But even a secretary should have some hours off."

"Sure. How about taking possession of the island — don't listen to that whistle — this afternoon?"

"Perfect! At sundown? It will seem so much more romantic then. But what will we do for a flag? The pennant is ruined."

"I'll get one in the village. Let's take a picnic supper and watch the moon rise."

"We'd have to stay until nearly midnight for that. Yesterday morning the man in the moon had but one eye."

"What were you doing up so late?"

"Up so early, you mean. I couldn't sleep so I snuggled into a chair on my balcony and tried to think things out."

"Was that when you saw the light flash?"

"When I imagined I saw it flash. We'll go to the island by water. The bar road will be clear but I love a boat. I'll be at the pier at six with the supper and —"

"What do you mean — and?"

"You really should cure yourself of that habit of pouncing."

"I'm sorry. I thought you might be planning to bring a third party and I would hate that like the dickens. Don't forget that you are to be in the offing when I arrive bag and baggage this afternoon. After I've taken care of the jewels, let's stop at the Millards and say 'Welcome to our city,' will you?"

"I'd love it. I'll meet you there. I'm not likely to have a follower. Watch your step, or you'll have one. I know, I'm psychic," Lissa warned theatrically before she left the room in answer to the imperative summons of an automobile horn.

Lissa had been right, Carson thought in the late afternoon as he stood in the living room at the Treasure Chest. Mrs. Barclay and Cleo had been tireless in their attention. He had had barely time to secrete the jewels before Fenton had rapped on the door to say that madam and her daughter — would like him to join them for tea in the library. He had felt like a sneak as later he gumshoed down the service drive to the Millards' cottage.

He glanced around the room. If some of the loans raised on the city property had gone into decorating it, he'd admit that the money had been artistically squandered. The walls were Wedgewood blue, in a niche over the white mantel was a blue and white Wedgewood urn. Lamps were blue and

101

white and the chairs were Adam upholstered in blue linen like the hangings at the windows.

His troubled eyes lingered on the fair-haired little boy on the couch. His throat tightened. That child must get well. As if he felt his intense regard, the boy raised heavy lashes and looked at him with translucent hazel eyes which seemed enormous in his white face.

"What's the matter, Lex, you're scowling."

Carson crossed the room and stood looking down at him.

"Am I, Andy? I was wondering how soon I can get you out in a boat fishing. How soon do you think that will be, Madge?" he asked the beautiful dark-haired, dark-eyed woman in the pink frock who entered from the glass-enclosed porch. She was followed by Lissa Barclay and a tall blond man with a lean, studious face, lighted by clear, friendly blue eyes.

Madge Millard sat on the end of the couch and smiled at the boy.

"How soon will it be, Andy?" Her voice was low, warm, with a hint of sadness.

"Mother! Mother dear, if only you wouldn't tease me to eat and would let me go to sleep and never, never wake up, I'm so

102

tired," the child pleaded. Two big tears started from under his lids.

"Oh! Andy! No darling!"

Jack Millard caught his wife by the shoulders and drew her to her feet.

"Steady, dearest." He tightened his arm warningly. "What's that curious sound outside? A dog crying?"

Carson could see the tears in Lissa's brown eyes, felt the effort she made to keep her voice light as she said;

"That's my dog, G-Man. Shall I invite him in and let him apologize for stealing your father's and mother's bathing suits, Andy?"

The boy's lashes flew up. A faint color came into his cheeks.

"A dog! A real dog! Mother said the lady who owned the house wouldn't let me have a dog!"

"That lady has gone away on a long, long journey."

She opened the door. G-Man dashed in. For an instant he stood with black and tan body rigid, his wiry coat bristling, his V-shaped ears close to his cheek. Then with a bound he was on the couch. He stretched his long head on the boy's knees and licked his thin little fingers with a rough tongue.

"Oh, be careful!" Madge Millard warned.

103

Her husband held her as she started forward. "Let them alone, watch Andy."

The boy laid a clawlike hand on the dog's flat skull. G-Man looked up at him, mouth open, red tongue dangling, eyes sparkling like brown beads.

"Mother! Daddy! Look! He's laughing. He makes me laugh, too." It was a pathetic little laugh, but it was a laugh. Madge Millard turned her face against her husband's shoulder. He rested his cheek against her dark hair and whispered. She lifted her head.

"I know, Jack, I know, but — but he laughed! He hasn't laughed before —"

She was smiling when she knelt beside the couch.

"G-Man, funny name for a dog isn't it, Andy?"

Lissa knelt on the other side as she explained;

"That name is supposed to mean that he has a fine mind, but I think it shows mighty little intelligence to go about stealing clothes, don't you, Andy? Say, 'I'm sorry,' G-Man."

At the imminent danger of sliding off, the dog sat up on his haunches, barked once and offered his paw. The boy raised himself from the pillows and caught it eagerly.

"You're excused, Mister G-Man. You're the bestest dog I ever saw." He dropped back and closed his eyes.

Lissa stood up. "I'm glad you like him, Andy. You'll have a fine time with him on the shore, he'll wear you out begging you to throw sticks into the water. Eat everything Mother wants you to, dear. There's so much fun ahead. Swimming and motoring and then the County Fair. You'll love that." The boy opened his eyes;

"Will there be a merry-go-round?"

"A grand one. So, rest and eat, won't you? You were sweet about the bathing suits, Mrs. Millard. If there is anything at Tarry Farm that will make Andy more comfortable, let me know and I will send it — I forgot. I'm no longer representing the landlady. It all belongs to Lex, now."

"Whatever belongs to me is yours when you and Jack need it, Madge," Carson assured. "Come on, Lissa. We have serious business on hand before sundown."

At the door she stopped to whistle. G-Man raised his head. Looked hard at her as if with all his might he were trying to talk, and laid his nose on the boy's thin hand.

Andy pulled himself up from his pillow, his eyes were like stars, his face was flushed. He said eagerly;

"He wants to stay with me! Please let him stay, Miss Barclay?"

"Of course he may stay, Andy dear. When you are tired of him, turn him out."

"I'll never get tired of him, never!" The boy put his arm around the dog's neck and cuddled his cheek against it. "I'll never get tired of you — dearest."

"He said 'dearest' in the exact tone in which his father speaks to his mother," Lex Carson remarked as he and Lissa walked along the path to the pier. "He's named for me, Alexander Carson Millard," he added gruffly.

"He's a darling. When he laughed the expression on his mother's face twisted my heart unbearably. Perhaps I don't know enough about it to judge — but it seems to me she's smothering the boy in a fog of fear."

"You can't blame her for being afraid of losing him. If only he will get well."

"I don't blame her for anything. Were I in her place, I wouldn't have half her courage. I go panicky if G-Man has the sniffles, I'd probably be shot to pieces if anything happened to a child of mine. Of course that boy will get well." She drew a deep breath. "Can anyone help getting well in this air? He'll be swimming and racing and eating before this summer is ended."

"Lissa, you're adorable!"

"That's been said before, begins to sound like a refrain. If we don't hurry, we won't get the flag planted, and that's our reason for coming, isn't it?"

"I wouldn't say it was the only reason," Carson qualified. "Here's the boat. Jump in!"

9

Standing beside Lissa on the deck of the lighthouse, Lex Carson looked across at the Treasure Chest, a brown shingled cottage, snuggled against a dark green background of pine and arborvitae. Was Lissa right? Was Madge, in her terror of losing the boy, smothering him with fear? Would the realization of her apprehension keep Andy's mind focussed on his weakness?

"I think you've got the right idea," he said aloud.

Lissa, with arms crossed on the iron rail, responded lazily;

"Thanks for those kind words, but which one of my world-beating ideas were you approving? I have a lot of them."

"I mean about Madge being too anxious about the boy. They have a competent nurse but his mother rarely leaves Andy."

Lissa's eyes were on the Treasure Chest.

"Watch the lavender smoke from that chimney. It rises straight until it gets above the tree tops then spreads like the hair of a mermaid under water and drifts to the east. That means a gentle western breeze. It seems hardly fair to her husband. You look dazed. My nimble mind has leaped back to Mrs. Millard's devotion to her son."

"Jack doesn't mind."

"Doesn't he? I wonder. If you loved your wife very much, would you like to be pushed aside for your son, no matter how much you loved him?"

"But the boy is sick."

"So is the man, sick at heart, as he looks on at her suffering and is powerless to help."

"How do you know so much about a man's heart?"

"I don't know, but I'm always imagining myself in the other person's place and I think your friend Jack Millard could do with a little coddling. Almost any man needs a woman who has time to make him believe he is her dream prince. Unless I miss my guess, there are two blonde sirens in the neighborhood who are not extremely busy at the moment, who'll be tempted to try their practiced hands on him."

"Don't be so cynical. Do you think that a man who loved beautiful Madge Millard would look at another woman?"

Her eyes flashed up to his, a soft color rose to her hair. "Now I understand what you meant," she said.

"What do you mean by 'now I understand

what you meant'?" he demanded sharply, in an effort to rid himself of the uneasiness her reference to two blonde sirens had set pricking in his mind. Of course she referred to Sidonie Packard whom he had not met, and Cleo whom he wouldn't trust as far away as he could see her. Equally, of course, Jack wasn't in the least danger, but, it would do no harm to suggest to Madge that she go out with her husband more, he could argue that she would come home fresher and with more strength to give to the boy. Lissa's voice interrupted his troubled thoughts. It took him a second to realize that she was answering his question.

"I'm sorry. I was speaking in what you call conundrums. Do you know, I didn't believe you'd make it."

"Make what? You hop from subject to subject so fast I can't follow you."

"My nimble mind again. I referred to your arrival at the Treasure Chest unaccompanied. You did it! I hope you had enough to eat. The cook is unused to preparing picnic suppers for men."

"She's a grand cook and it was a grand supper and I liked having it on the rocks so near where we took possession of your island. The Stars and Stripes look great, don't they?" he indicated a small flag fluttering below them.

"Perfect. They are beautiful anywhere but never more throat-tightening than when floating between sea and sky. How salty the air is. I feel as if I owned the world and a little bit of heaven when I'm up here on the deck of the lighthouse."

"You look like part of the sea and sky in that turquoise blue jumper, Lissa, your amethyst scarf and skirt tie you to earth, though. There's a touch of drama in the way you wear your clothes. You have an instinct for the right colors for your gorgeous hair, haven't you?"

"You're rather snappy, yourself. I like that coarse-weave blue shirt and the tannish-yellow pull-over the color of your flannel slacks. The perfect costume for the well-dressed man on a picnic."

"I strive to please." Gravity routed laughter from his voice. "I wonder why this light was given up. When Tod Kent planned to bring The Sphinx here, he studied charts. This harbor is of easy access night and day and affords anchorage for the largest vessels. It's frequented by many small craft too, isn't it?"

"It is, but the powers that be decided that the site was too low for the light and that the sound of the fog bell was masked in some directions by neighboring hills. Isn't Tarry Farm beautiful from here? How plainly we can see Red Chimneys. There goes the sun! It has left a flamingo sky. See the thin clouds scurrying! They look like long-legged crimson birds with wings outspread. How the brass on the cruiser glistens. All the little islands in the bay have turned dusky purple. The blue of sea and sky is darkening. I love it! Don't you?"

"I do. Let's sit on the outermost rock of the point till the glow fades. It will seem like setting out to sea."

"That's a thought. I want you to stop a minute in my workroom first, though. You didn't really see it when we came in. It was the service room of the lighthouse and I still call it that."

She lingered at the head of the winding iron stairs. Asked, over her shoulder:

"What did you pick up in the lamp-room?"

"Have you eyes in the back of your head? My sandal buckle was loose."

The truth, but not all the truth, Carson admitted to himself as he followed her down. Why tell her that he had picked up a cigarette stub? She had said that she had imagined a flash from this long unused light yesterday morning. He pressed the stub in

112

his pocket between his fingers. It might have been a flash, not imagination.

He looked with interest at what had once been the service room of the lighthouse. There were wicker chairs cushioned in red and pink hollyhock chintz; shelves of books, an old gilt-framed mirror, a filing cabinet, a typewriter on a table desk beside a window, a gay knitting-bag on a hook. Oil cans, dust pans, funnels, lamps, shone like gold.

"Who keeps this brass polished?" he asked.

"One of the men on the place. It was part of the equipment of the lighthouse. Fenton came over when my aunt bought the island and gave it the first rub-up. Everything had to shine like that when the Government operated the light. Aunt Hetty and I selected the furnishing for the rooms. I didn't know then that she intended to will it to me."

Carson crossed to the fireplace, looked at the map above the mantel, then down at the birch logs piled on the andirons.

"What item did you clip?" He indicated a corner of a newspaper sticking from between the logs. A diamond-shaped piece had been torn from it.

"I didn't tear that out. When I want an item for my files, I cut it. Probably the man who brought old newspapers from Tarry

113

Farm and laid the fire saw an ad he wanted to answer."

The hole in the paper pricked at Carson's mind. Suppose the person who had dropped the cigarette in the lamp-room had torn out an item which interested him? Suppose the two were in some way connected? A crazy idea, but when one was on a quest like his, one didn't pass up even a crazy idea. He said aloud;

"I can't hand much to the man who laid this fire, Lissa, I'll take it apart and lay it so that it will burn the instant you touch a match to it. Meanwhile, get me a drink of water, will you? Those eggs stuffed with anchovy were grand, but they've left me with a terrible thirst."

"I never saw a man yet who didn't itch to re-build a fire someone else had laid. I suppose it's the Boy Scout influence working in them," she flouted gaily.

As she left the room, he removed the birch logs, pulled out the newspaper. He tore off the corner from which the piece had been removed and the date at the top of the page.

"Last February," he said to himself. "Last February."

As the sound of pumping stopped in the kitchen, he thrust the scraps into a pocket of his slacks. When Lissa entered with a glass of crystal clear water, he was replacing the birch logs. He stood up.

"You won't have trouble starting that fire, Lissa. This is wonderful water. Do you compose your masterpieces at that desk by the window?"

"You're laughing at me. I'll never write masterpieces. I'll leave the miseries, ironies, vain hopes, and frustrated dreams to more experienced writers. I want to write the kind of story — it will be just as much a part of the real world — that will cause persons who see 'Melissa Barclay' on a cover to plump down their problems — and incidentally the price — and seize the book. If, when they reach 'the end' they forget to go back for their problems and march blithely toward the day's work pepped up and refreshed, refreshed — it's a great word, isn't it — I shall feel that I have achieved something. Wasn't it Emily Dickinson who said; 'If I can stop one heart from breaking, I shall not have lived in vain'? That's the way I feel about my writing."

"You're too young, too gay in spirit, Lissa, to know so much about breaking hearts and problems."

"But I've had such a lot of time in which to observe and think. One can learn much in

115

twenty-five years, most of them motherless, many of them spent traveling about the world with a temperamental father and three with a woman like Aunt Hetty Carson. Even after that discipline, I still believe that the beautiful things of life are as real as the ugly things of life; that gay courage may turn threatened defeat into victory; that hitching one's wagon to the star of achievement lifts one high above the quicksands of discouragement. In short, that it's a great world to the valiant."

"Optimist, aren't you?"

"I hate that word, because so many of the people who use it put a sting in it. Be honest, have you ever known gloom or depression to solve a problem? Problems aren't solved that way. Instead it settles over one's spirit like a fog and that fog attracts more fog and there you are in the middle of it groping for a way out, but if, instead, you keep in the sunlight of courage, even if a gale of misfortune blows you off your feet and whirls you along, at least you will have the thrill of seeing where you are going while you ride it."

"What cult taught you that?"

"It's not the philosophy of a cult or ism, it's just plain commonsense. Why do I tell you my innermost thoughts, I wonder? I never talk to anyone else except G-Man — about myself."

"I hope you'll always tell me your innermost thoughts, Lissa," he declared on a sudden note of tenderness. "We'd better go, or we'll lose the rest of the sunset."

"Lock up, will you?"

Hand in hand they climbed over boulders. They stopped to poke a backing crab out of a tide pool in which it had been marooned. Seated on the top of a great rock that dropped precipitously to the water which fringed it in white, they looked off to sea. Lissa sighed rapturously;

"Isn't it heavenly?"

"It is at present, the sea is as bland and smooth as a campaigning woman politician, but she's a fickle jade. When she's in a temper the waves must lash at the light tower till it shudders under their fury."

"They do and in the migrating season ducks dash themselves against the lantern and drop on the rocks and provide game dinners for the keeper. Can't you imagine sailors in years past, peering through fog or storm for this light? I'm glad I own it. There goes Ozy in his dirty old dory to pull his lobster traps. I go out with him whenever he'll take me, in spite of the fact that his boat smells horribly of oil and the dead fish he uses for bait."

"Does he get many lobsters?"

"Yes. He has the sole right to set traps in this cove. Perhaps it isn't a legal right, but the villagers never trespass. How large The Sphinx looks from here. How long is she?"

"She's a 63 footer."

"The owner's burgee is being run up. Mr. Kent must be going on board. I like that man. Wasn't he amusing at dinner last night? In spite of his way of turning everything into a joke and his lazy manner, I have a feeling that I wouldn't care to have him on my trail were I defying the law."

Carson looked at her quickly. Suppose he were to tell her the truth? That The Sphinx was anchored in the harbor that its owner might be on hand to assist him in his manhunt? She might help. She was used to working out plots, and there were plots a-plenty tangled up in Tod Kent's reason for bringing his cruiser to this harbor. It was worth considering. He attested;

"Tod may appear lazy, but he has an enormous capacity for work and infinite resource and sagacity. I'm glad you like my friend, but don't like him too much, will you?"

"Never, never again will I like a man 'too much,' " Lissa rejoined passionately. She

118

added in a lighter voice;

"The vivid color is fading, sky and sea are darkening, Venus glows like a lantern lowered from Heaven. Listen! The music must be coming from the cruiser's radio."

From across the water drifted a man's voice singing;

" 'Somewhere a voice is calling

" 'O'er land and sea

" 'Somewhere a voice is calling, calling for me.' "

Lissa fought a surge of emotion. She rested her elbow on her knee, and held her chin tight with one hand. It mustn't quiver, it must not. Why should that song make her wonder if life were worth living? Make her think of Lex Carson's face as he had said; "Do you think that a man who loved beautiful Madge Millard would look at another woman?" That was what he had meant yesterday when he had boasted that he was immune to sirens. He loved her. It didn't make sense. It was just that her nerves were a-shiver after the strain of the last few months.

" 'Night and the stars are gleaming, tender and true,' " the rich passionate voice sang on;

" 'Dearest, my heart is dreaming,

" 'Dreaming of you.' "

119

Lissa covered her eyes with her hands and the storm broke. Her body shook with sobs.

With an exclamation of concern, Carson flung his arm about her and drew her close. His warm protecting tenderness swept away the last crumbling dam of self control. She turned her face against his shoulder, clutched his pullover and cried her heart out to the sound of a man's voice singing and the ebb and flow of the tide.

She struggled to control her sobs, drew long, ragged breaths. It was wonderful to lean against someone, she had lifted and braced others so long. She felt his cheek against her hair, heard his husky voice;

"Cry it out, beautiful. You had it coming to you."

She made a desperate effort for composure, flamed with self-contempt when she realized that she had been clinging to a man who loved another woman.

Hadn't she become engaged to Johnny Grant when she was lonely. Hadn't that affair been a farcical flop? Here she was feeling sorry for herself again and quite ready to drop like a ripe apple into the arms of a man with disturbing eyes and a boyish smile. If only she had known that he loved Madge Millard before she had promised to stay at Tarry Farm. Impatiently, she drew away.

120

"Don't move till the storm is over," Carson commanded and pressed her head back against his shoulder. He gently dried her long bronze lashes with his handkerchief and tucked it under her hand.

"Better use this."

She freed herself from his arm. In between raggedly drawn breaths, and dabs at her nose and eyes, she explained;

"I — I don't k—know why I w—went to pieces l—like that. I never d—did it before. I — I can't remember c—crying like that in all my — my life. It just sneaked up on m—me."

"There's a first time for everything. Give me the handkerchief. I see a tear you've missed."

He touched her cheek tenderly. Lissa's breath caught.

"Don't — don't be nice to me. I — I should be shaken and scolded."

"Okay, I can do that, too. Come on, it's getting dark. Let's go."

It was high time they were going, Carson told himself, if she looked at him again with those eyes like great velvety wet pansies, he would kiss her and then where would he be? Even in this age of easy kisses, she was not a girl who would welcome a kiss from a man whom she had known only twenty-four

121

hours, not while her heart and pride were still raw from Johnny Grant's defection.

"As you suggested, we'd better go," Lissa reminded in a voice still roughened by tears. "Come on!"

He held out his hand to help her but with a shake of her head, she thrust hers into the pocket of her turquoise blue jumper. Side by side they climbed the rocks, still pink in the lingering afterglow, skirted the lighthouse and clumps of junipers. Stars were pricking through the darkening sky, boats blossomed with riding lights, a million little flying, creeping, hopping things swarmed a rhythmic accompaniment to the soft swish of the tide.

"You haven't spoken for five minutes. You're not going to sleep on your feet, are you?" Lissa inquired with exaggerated concern. She looked up with a smile that was like sunshine after showers. Her voice still caught between words, "Don't, because we're on the runway to the float and you might walk off into the water. It would be such cold water, I should have to plunge in after you." She shivered delicately. He untied the painter of the motorboat.

"I wasn't asleep, I was thinking that a little more than twenty-four hours has passed since your outboard went crazy. I feel as if we had been friends for years — we are friends, aren't we, Lissa?"

"It's rather too soon to know. I —"

"Hi, Lissa!" Johnny Grant hailed her from the red roadster which stopped with a grinding of brakes in the road beside the pier.

"Cleo told me you were here. I came over the bar road to take you home." His blonde hair shone like pale gold above his white polo shirt. Lissa looked up at him, called:

"I'll go with you, Johnny. Lex must be bored to death —"

Carson caught her as she took a step forward. Swung her into the motorboat and jumped in.

"When I start out on a party with a girl, I take her home," he announced and threw on the self-starter.

"Hasn't the girl anything to say about it? I'm going with Johnny," Lissa defied and kicked off her sandals.

Carson seized her as she stepped up on the seat. He pulled her down, kept an arm tight about her shoulders as with one hand on the wheel he steered the boat.

"Planning to swim to your Johnny, were you? Nothing doing."

"Let me go! You're holding me!"

"That's the underlying idea."

"I won't be told what I can do!"

"Your mistake! You're being told what you can't do. Stop twisting!" The motor-boat bucked a wave which drenched them with spray. "Now see what you did! I don't know this harbor and I may smash into a ledge. We'd look pretty funny, wouldn't we, perched on a ledge all night?"

He glanced over his shoulder at the pier. Laughed and removed his arm.

"If you go overboard now you'll have to call for help, and you'd be too proud to do that, wouldn't you? Sit here beside me, Lissa, and give me steering orders. As has been said before, I don't know this harbor."

"You seem to be getting on without help. Do you know, you don't belong in this country. You ought to be across the water with the other dictators." She retreated to the stern.

"Oh, but I'm needed here. Didn't your aunt leave you to me to take care of?" The laughter left his eyes. "And from what I have recently observed, you'll need some care, lady."

He didn't speak again until they reached the Tarry Farm float. Then he announced curtly;

"Your friend in the red roadster is break-ing all speed records across the bar. Now, you are quite free to go with him. Good-night."

He jumped back into the motorboat and steered for the cruiser.

10

Sunshine poured into the breakfast room at Tarry Farm. The French windows, which formed one side, had been folded back to leave it open to the terrace. Beyond the terrace, stretched a panorama of loping, mist-girdled hills; sky, turquoise and pearl, pierced by an ivory tower; sea, sapphire and malachite; islands, emerald and amethyst and faint topaz. Gold flickered on the soft green walls and ceiling. A breeze, fragrant as balsam boughs, cool as dew, soft as the breast of a dove, stirred the mauve linen hangings and fanned the flames under the old-fashioned silver chafing dishes on the maple buffet till they danced like tiny scarlet and vermillion dervishes.

Lissa at the table, in a pale yellow linen frock, absentmindedly dropped a lump of sugar into her coffee. Three weeks had passed since she had told Lex Carson she would stand by while he needed her, three weeks since she had collapsed in his arms and cried her heart out, and he in love with Madge Millard! It was also three weeks since he had held her in the motorboat. She

126

must have had a brainstorm when she started to swim back to Johnny Grant. She had been determined to break the charm of Lex Carson's eyes and smile. Lot of good the attempt had done her. She could feel the warmth and hardness of his arm about her shoulders now.

"Did you speak, Miss?" Fenton hovered beside her. "I thought you said 'ouch!' Miss. Perhaps the coffee was too hot?"

"Perhaps it was, Fenton. Are the others coming to breakfast?"

"Yes, Miss. Mrs. Barclay and Miss Cleo sent word to the pantry that they would not have trays in their rooms as usual. The morning was so beautiful they would breakfast here. Mr. Carson returned last night, Miss."

Lissa looked quickly at the butler who was filling a glass. Had he intended that last sentence to be as significant as it sounded?

"Oh, I see. Is he coming to breakfast?"

"He is, Miss. Before the ladies and he arrive, I'd like to say a word to you, Miss."

Had he more complaints from the house-staff to report, Lissa wondered. These last three weeks had been a battleground. Mrs. Barclay was determined to take over the management of the house. Now that Lex was at home, he could settle the question this very day, choose her stepmother or herself to take charge. She had had several phone calls and one letter from him about her legacy. They had been crisp and businesslike, not even a friendly inquiry as to how she was getting on. Why should he care? She had been snippy and disagreeable to him on the motorboat. Besides, hadn't she gone cry-baby on the rocks? Men hated tears. Mrs. Barclay had stirred up so much trouble that it had taken hours that she herself wanted to devote to writing to placate the maids.

"What is it, Fenton?"

The butler glanced over his shoulder at the sun-flecked terrace, toward the door before he confided;

"It's about the jewels, Miss. They're not safe here."

Lissa did a bit of rapid-fire thinking. Her voice was as amazed as her eyes as she demanded;

"What jewels, Fenton?"

"I see that you don't wish me to remember that the late Madam had her jewels brought here, Miss." His face was as bland as his voice. "I spoke only in the interest of the estate. There's a lot of breaking and entering of summer houses, I hear, Miss."

"See our little early bird, Mother," Cleo

128

exclaimed, as in a frock as blue as her eyes, she posed on the threshold. Mrs. Barclay in a dusty-pink gown stood beside her. They had discarded mourning shortly after the reading of Hetty Carson's will, Lissa remembered.

"What worm are you out for, Lissa, my girl?"

"Not the one you're stalking," Lissa snapped and was promptly ashamed of herself. Would she never become callous to her sister's digs?

"And what worm am I stalking, Miss Barclay?" Cleo's voice was as sweetly puckery as the core of a persimmon. She lifted a silver cover and peered into the chafing dish. "Scrambled eggs again! I wish someone would make the cook variety-conscious."

Mrs. Barclay at the table lifted plump, white hands and dropped them to denote futility.

"I've tried, Cleo, you know I've tried, but what can I do when Melissa — Oh, here you are, Alexander. I hope you've come to stay! Sit here beside me, dear boy. Fenton, serve —"

"I'll serve myself, thanks. Good morning, Cleo. Hello, Lissa."

Lissa nodded curtly in response to the

129

buoyant greeting. What business had he to look so carefree when the whole darn load of managing Tarry Farm was on her shoulders? She glanced at him from under the fringe of her lashes, as he lifted silver covers at the buffet. He was in white from collar to shoes. Did that mean that he had come to stay?

As if he had divined her question, he drew out the chair beside her and deposited a plate in front of him.

"Home is the sailor, home from the sea," he announced blithely — "home for twenty-four hours at least."

"Are you really, Lex?" Cleo, in a chair across the table, tucked her sandalled feet under her and beseeched with eyes as well as voice — "Let's do something to celebrate."

"After I've — what's the commotion in the pantry, Fenton?"

The butler put his fingers to his lips.

"Ahem! It's the cook, sir. She insists upon seeing you, sir."

"Seeing me! I haven't anything to say about — the cook." There was a hint of panic in his voice. He looked helplessly at Lissa who kept her eyes stubbornly on her plate.

"Of course, you shouldn't be bothered,

130

dear boy," Mrs. Barclay twittered into the breach caused by her step-daughter's silence. "I would have spared you this, but Melissa insists upon —"

"Let the woman come in, Fenton," Carson snapped with a suddenness that caught Mrs. Barclay with both voice and lower jaw suspended.

"Yes, sir! Mrs. Loosch will be glad to speak to you, sir."

The butler opened the door to the pantry and admitted a huge woman dressed in white.

Carson dropped his napkin on the table and stood up. Did he think he could take what was coming better on his feet, Lissa wondered and disciplined a chuckle. He didn't know the half yet, Mrs. Loosch was good when she got started.

The woman's eyes were mere slits of brightness above her apple-red cheeks. She crossed arms bare to the elbow on her breast and braced her feet for battle.

"Fenton says you wish to speak to me, Mrs. Loosch?"

Carson's smile and courteous inquiry perceptibly reduced the cook's temperature. She changed weight from one foot to the other before she answered;

"I do, sir. I want to know from whom I'm

131

to take orders. Miss Lissa makes out the menus for the day — I never before worked under a person so pleasant and so efficient — then Mrs. Barclay or her daughter comes to the kitchen and gives different orders. Not that I take them, sir. I'll be blowed if I will, but it's very upsetting, sir, not to know who's managing this house." Her fat-encased heart pumped her breath to the tune of excitement.

Lissa glanced at the faces in the room. Fenton's lips were touched by a secretive smile. Mrs. Barclay's eyes were sparking blue fire. Cleo was looking at her brilliant-nailed fingers as they rolled a crumb on the satin surface of the maple table. Lex Carson stood straight and tall before the fireplace. Two sharp little lines cut between his brows, color stole to his hair as he announced in a voice which made Lissa think of tempered steel;

"You're to take orders from Miss Barclay, Mrs. Loosch. When I came here I asked her to continue to manage the house and grounds as she had done while living with her aunt. She consented. Mrs. Barclay in her desire to help me, didn't understand. I hope this will satisfy you, Mrs. Loosch. You're a grand cook and I'd hate to lose you."

Mrs. Loosch's grievance went limp as a deflated parachute in response to his boyish smile and praise.

"I'll try to please you, sir. I know a gentleman when I see one — and a lady too." If a glance could burn, Mrs. Barclay would have shriveled like a gelatin film exposed to flame. She backed toward the pantry door.

"Just a minute, cook. I'd like to have the tenants in for dinner this evening. Could you manage five courses in your top style, than which I'll bet there's nothing finer?"

Mrs. Loosch simpered.

"Sure, I can, sir. If Miss Lissa will plan the menu, I'll see that it's cooked to the queen's taste. It'll be grand to cook for men again. I never did like catering to women. They don't eat. They pick."

She flung a flaming glance at mother and daughter and departed kitchenward.

Mrs. Barclay sniffed into her handkerchief.

"Terrible woman. I wonder if she's a safe person to have in the house. I didn't mean to make trouble, Alexander. I wanted to help. Melissa is away so much. She spends hours and hours on that island —"

"And running round the country in a red roadster with her ex-fiance," Cleo interrupted smoothly.

"I —" Lissa on her feet, snapped her teeth on a furious denial. What did Lex Carson care whether or not she was running round with Johnny Grant? She asked;

"Has the mail come, Fenton?"

"Yes, Miss. It's on your desk in the residence office, Miss."

"Have you also given Lissa sole authority over the distribution of the mail in this house, Lex?" Cleo demanded. "Everything that comes is sifted in her 'office' before it reaches us. Sometimes I suspect she's carrying on a clandestine correspondence with a man who is not an ex-fiance, someone whom she picked up when she was wandering about the world, someone of whom she's ashamed."

The anger which Cleo's insinuation roused was transmuted into a nervous desire to laugh as Lissa thought of the reason the mail was "sifted" in her office. She didn't intend that either her stepmother or her sister should know how often manuscript-filled Manila envelopes winged home to their nest. She could endure their digs on other subjects, but sneers at her determination to be a writer would jab at her very soul.

"If you wish to keep your mail separate better have a bag of your own, Lissa," Carson suggested in a cool, clipped voice.

"That's a thought," Lissa agreed. "Come along, Fenton, and I'll give you the family mail to distribute."

She heard Cleo and her stepmother talking in unison as she left the room. Heard Mrs. Barclay inquire;

"Do you think it quite proper to have a dinner party so soon after dear Hetty's passing, Alexander?"

"But this isn't a party," Carson disclaimed impatiently.

Would they give Lex a chance to finish his breakfast? He wouldn't repeat the experiment of a day in his happy home after this morning's blowup. Not a chance.

In the room which she and her aunt had jocularly named the residence office — they had picked up the term from the description of the home of a motion-picture star — Lissa sorted the mail. She handed a bunch of letters to the butler. What was he thinking? She'd like to take a sight-seeing bus through his mind. She had the feeling that there might be secret passages and shuttered memory cells it would be exciting to explore.

"Thank you, Miss. If you will allow me to say so, I think Mr. Carson's suggestion a good one. If you say the word, I'll have the postmaster lock your mail in the Tarry

Farm bag, and leave the rest outside, Miss."

He glanced at two large Manila envelopes on the desk.

"I think I know what you're doing, Miss, and I wish you success. I'm sure you'll make a great writer — in time, Miss."

Lissa frowned at the door he closed softly behind him. Fenton the omniscient. He knew that she was writing, that the jewels were in the house — how could he know about them?

She slid the Manila envelopes under the blotter before she answered a light tap.

"Come in!"

"The plump Mrs. Loosch certainly gave you an A1 reference," Lex Carson approved as he entered. He closed the door and crossed to the table-desk. Perched on one corner he demanded;

"Look here, you think it's all right to have the tenants in to dinner tonight, don't you? It isn't a party and even if it were, I wouldn't be showing disrespect to Mrs. Carson's memory. I never knew her."

"It's quite all right. Aunt Hetty was violently opposed to any sort of mourning. Perhaps you have noticed that I have not worn black. She felt that it was a depressing factor in the world."

"Then that's all right. I've asked Mrs.

Barclay to phone the guests — I thought an invitation to dinner would come better from her — got to kowtow to the conventions once in a while."

Lissa picked up pad and pencil.

"Whom are you inviting?"

"The Millards, Packards, Major Fane and Tod Kent. That will make an even number. To date I've had no chance to get acquainted with my tenants and I want to know them. Forgiven me yet for keeping you from going home with Grant, the night we were at the island, Lissa?" As she turned to lower a Venetian blind, he went on, "You needn't answer, I understand. Have Cleo and Mrs. Barclay been bothering you a lot about the housekeeping? Think you can stick it out?"

"I'll stick it out. I like to finish a job I begin."

"Don't be so grim about it, beautiful. Makes me feel as if I'd chained you to a treadmill. I told Fenton —"

"Fenton! That reminds me!" Lissa came close. "Fenton knows that Aunt Hetty's jewels are in the house."

"How the dickens can he know?"

"I told you, an armed expressman delivered them."

"I see. He put two and two together." He

drew his finger across her brow. "Smooth it out. No occasion for worry. The jewels are back in the vault."

"Really, Lex?"

"Really, Lissa. Have you a list of them?"

"Yes. I made one for Aunt Hetty when she looked them over."

"I'm asking because some of the jewels must be sold to pay the inheritance tax. Go over the list and check the pieces you can best get along without, and I'll attend to selling them for you."

"Get along without! That's the funniest thing I ever heard. I've done very well for twenty-five years without owning one jewel."

"Don't you like rings?"

"Mad about them. I'll keep Aunt Hetty's and the set of emeralds and diamonds, they're being worn with red hair this year, I understand. We'll sell some of the pieces that would make me feel as if I were wearing diamond plasters if I put them on. How soon do you want the list?"

"Give it to me this evening after the guests have gone. I'm off again in the morning. Play with me today, will you?"

Lissa opened her lips to say, "I'd love it." Closed them. Apparently she was putty, just putty when he smiled at her. Didn't he love Madge Millard?

She declined hastily.

"Can't. I've got to work. No one has to tell me that no matter how one's mind sparks with ideas, unless one writes, nothing gets written. I've learned that still living truth. I'm writing a novel. Don't laugh."

"Why should I laugh? I presume that even the most successful novelist wrote a first one. I understand why you have the mail delivered to you first so you may let out what you call homing pigeons, isn't it? I know you're not carrying on a clandestine correspondence. I wish I felt as easy about that red roadster. I — Come in!"

"Long distance phone for you, Mr. Carson," Fenton announced from the threshold.

"All right. How are you going to the island, Lissa?"

"I'll walk across the bar. Need the exercise."

"I'll come for you. My roadster isn't red. It's dark green with lighter green cushions, they're being used with red hair this year, I understand. It's a snappy number. You'll like it," he prophesied and went into the hall.

11

Humming in a sweet, husky undertone, Lissa ran down the path between borders filled with a wealth of canterbury bells dangling from their stalks like huge pink tourmalines; spikes of anchusa, blue as the sky; Madonna lilies by the pearly, fragrant score and stately towers of delphiniums, amethyst, azure and indigo purple. Roses, there were, clumps of them; pink and yellow, crimson and white, they scented the air. Shrubs in the background threw grotesque shadows.

Lex Carson's defense of her, in the face of her family's complaints, was what had set her spirits ballooning, she decided. Why had he invited the tenants to dinner? As she had listened to his plan, she'd had a curious feeling that there was more behind it than a desire to become acquainted with them. Two were his friends. Why shouldn't he want to entertain in the house he had acquired so recently? How like her to imagine an ulterior motive. She'd better put Lex Carson out of her mind and concentrate on her novel, it needed thinking about and then some.

Too hot to think. She pulled off the green kerchief tied gypsy fashion over her hair. Gorgeous day but too hot to run. The air shimmered with heat. A cicada shrilled and from a distance another answered.

As she crossed the bar which connected mainland and island, she felt like an atom crawling in infinite space. Innumerable shades of blue in sea and sky in ever-changing values encompassed her. A blue heron, fishing for his breakfast, balanced on one slender leg in sun-kissed shallows. Against a dark bank on the horizon, the white sail of a fishing boat flashed as it caught the sun.

The sight of the dark bank plunged her back to reality. If three summers in Maine had taught her anything, they had taught her that the bank on the horizon meant fog. Would she have time to get in a few hours' work at her desk at the lighthouse before it crept up? Why worry? The wind might change and blow that dark bank out to sea. If Lex came for her —

Resolutely she forced him and the memory of the morning friction at Tarry Farm into retreat and brought forward the plan of her novel. Long ago she had discovered that the power to close the door on problems was one of the perquisites of creative writing. One dwelt in another world

141

when one was at work on a story.

The service room of the lighthouse was like an oven when she entered. She left the door wide. Opened the window beside the typewriter desk and let in the smell of the sea and the monotonous moan of the buoy. It was too hot to work. She sharpened a bunch of pencils. Went to the kitchen and pumped clear, sparkling water into a glass. Drank it. Back in the service room, she re-arranged pink and white Shirley poppies in a green bowl. That accomplished, she glanced around for something else to do and met her own eyes in the mirror.

She made a little face at the flushed, auburn-haired girl, who grimaced at her in return. She accused;

"Stalling, just stalling, aren't you? Your story stuck yesterday and you dread to tackle it because you don't know how to push it ahead. Go to it, my dear, go to it."

She sat down before the typewriter and resolutely kept her eyes from the window, that alluring window, beyond which the sea sparkled and beckoned, and outboards, scooting round the harbor like a flock of prehistoric waterfowl tempted her to join them. She opened her manuscript at the page where the story had stuck, read it, went back three chapters and read up to it again.

The characters just wouldn't carry on.

Sheer terror stopped her heart. "Am I all through?" she asked herself. "Has my imagination petered out? Can't I write any more — ever?"

"You're the world's worst quitter if you get panicky over a thing like that," she scolded herself. "The story started off too easily. You've barely scratched the surface of your mind. Dig in, gal, dig in."

Hands clasped behind her head, eyes on a dog-shaped stain on the wall, she thought of how the male lead had dashed up a flight of stairs in pursuit of the clue to a mystery which threatened his love interest and how on the top stair he had stopped, one foot extended, like a mechanical toy which had run down. She couldn't budge him. Suppose she had sent her hero down in the first place, instead of up? She'd try it.

She slipped a sheet of cheap yellow paper into the machine. She sent the man to the street and "click" the story was off again. Her cheeks burned, her fingers flew as they kept pace with the thoughts that flooded her mind. The keys changed tempo with the mood of her story. Once she held her breath as she touched them as softly as if she heard cautious footsteps. Once she laughed. She stopped to brush fingers across her wet lashes. Once she frowned.

She rested her hands and looked at the world outside. The hills were girdled by a crawling, gray mist. The sky was gray. The islands had turned to gun-metal. The buoy sounded muffled. She pulled down the window to shut out the smell of fog, and the depressing moan. Closed the door, lighted the fire, the fire Lex had laid, she remembered. She glanced at the clock. The bar would be passable for two hours more. She must finish the chapter while her mind was tingling from the impetus of the story.

She typed on and on until tired, but triumphant, she curled up in the wicker chair and read aloud what she had written. She nodded satisfaction and exulted;

"Sending our hero down instead of up did the trick. It started the story off again with a bang. I'll thumb-tack a reminder on the wall;

"WHEN STUCK GO INTO REVERSE."

She slipped the manuscript into a drawer and hooded her typewriter while she planned the next chapter of her story. It should have a surprise ending. O Henry was the master of surprise endings. It would help to study his method. There was a set of his stories at Red Chimneys. She'd borrow the books and reread them.

Someone outside! The sound snapped Lissa out of the world of imagination into the world of fact. Had Lex come for her? She opened the door.

"You hav a vera nice place here, signorina," approved an oily foreign voice.

Against the casing leaned Nino, the Packards' houseman! In one hand he held a lighted cigarette. Behind him fog twisted and billowed in thick coils. Its cold grayness accentuated the sinister effect of his close-set dark eyes, and the deep scar on his cheek.

"What do you want?" Lissa demanded.

"Vera sorry to trouble you, signorina, but the water at our house no longer run. Signorina Packard must washa the hair. I phone beeg house to tell you. They say you here, so I come."

"Did you look at the engine?"

"No, signorina. I no engineer. I houseman. I hear the pump going."

"Probably the belt has slipped. Go back and look at it. If it has, pull the switch and stop the engine. Then slip the belt onto the wheel. It doesn't take an engineer to do that. Start the engine, then if the water doesn't run, phone the village electrician.

145

You'll find the number tacked up in the pump-house."

"I go, signorina. May I first go up the stairs and see the great lamp?"

Through Lissa's mind flashed her appraisal of the man the first time she had seen him;

"I'd hate to meet you in the dark, Nino."

This wasn't the dark but it might as well be. Fog filled the world.

"No. No one is allowed in the lamp-room. You'd better hurry back and attend to that engine."

She banged the door. Turned the key on the inside. She leaned against the casing. Listened. Not a sound outside but the hollow warning of the buoy.

"Just what have you gained by locking him out and yourself in?" she inquired aloud.

The sound of her voice helped dispel the spooky effect of the fog-whitened windows. The room vibrated with curious little sounds, a vine tapping outside, the wicker chair creaking as if stretching after being relieved of her weight; a beam cracking; the tick-tock of the brass clock; soft whispers among the scarlet and orange embers on the hearth.

She tried to pick up the plan of her story,

but the advent of the scar-faced Nino had blown it to smithereens. She'd better start for home before the fog became more dense. In front of the mirror she tied the green kerchief over her hair. A golden glow flickered on the wall. Headlights! An automobile horn wailed like a lost spirit with a cold in its head. A fist pounded on the door. A voice called;

"Lissa! Lissa! Are you here?"

She turned the key and flung open the door. Hatless, in a yellow slicker glistening with moisture, and with another over his arm, Lex Carson frowned at her.

"I've been blowing the horn like mad. Why didn't you answer? I almost turned back, thought perhaps when you saw the fog coming, you beat it home. You're shivering. Put this on. Why were you locked in?"

She slipped her arms into the slicker he held. "I wasn't locked in. Someone was locked out."

"Who?"

The question cracked like a boy's mammoth torpedo flung against a wall. Should she tell him, Lissa asked herself, and answered on the same thought-wave;

"The Packards' houseman, Nino."

"What did he want?"

"He came to report that the water had

147

stopped running at Red Chimneys."

"Suppose it had? What could you do about it?"

"Tell him what he could do about it. After that he asked to go up and see the 'great lamp.' "

"Did you let him?"

"Let him! You do ask a lot of foolish questions, don't you? Of course I didn't let him. Listen! Isn't that the put-put of a motorboat leaving the island pier? He's gone. Let's get away from here. The fog is rolling in thicker and thicker. It will be tricky crossing the bar road."

"Pity you didn't think of that two hours ago," Carson reminded as he locked the door.

"But it came so quickly. One moment it was a dark bank on the horizon, and the next, the world was blotted out. I wish that Italian houseman would drop his stub at home. It isn't an addition to my doorstep." She pushed the fragment of a cigarette with her foot.

"Hold on. I'll take it along and fling it into a bush as we pass. Pretty fussy about your doorstep, aren't you, Miss Barclay," Carson teased. "Hop into the car."

The lights of the roadster glowed feebly, the eaves of the building, the foliage on nearby shrubs dripped, dripped, dripped.

Seated beside Lex Carson in a weird unreal world, Lissa glanced at his strong hands on the wheel, at his profile, as head bent slightly forward, he peered into the mist. His usually brown skin looked chalky in the ghostly light. Beads of moisture tipped the short hair at his temples.

"Keep your eyes on the road, will you, Lissa? That last fog-shrouded shrub we passed almost gave me heart-failure. Thought it was a man stepping in front of the machine. Two pairs of eyes are better than one in this thick whiteness, especially when one pair is familiar with the road."

Had he felt that she was looking at him? Lissa teased gaily;

"Eyes front, it will be, your Honor. If you don't watch out, some day you'll be a judge and wear a black gown. Already you have acquired the stern judicial manner. Here we are on the bar road. We haven't come a moment too soon. Hear the oily lash of the tide."

"How the darned fog rolls and twists. Makes me think of the evil genie which was everlastingly rising from the sea in the old fairy stories. Speaking of stories, did genius burn this morning?"

"It took a lot of work to get the fire

started. My hero went dead on me. I tried blood transfusion, artificial respiration. He wouldn't breathe. Then I seized him by the shoulders and faced him the other way. After that, he went so fast I couldn't keep up with him."

She peered around the side of the windshield into the cold whiteness ahead.

"We're almost across. Then the wood road and we're at home. Can't get there too quickly to suit me. The monotonous swing of those two windshield wipers makes me dizzy. I feel smothered, oppressed, as if something were closing in on me, as if I must scream."

"Don't." He gave her an oblique smiling glance. "I need both hands on the wheel."

She remembered how he had held her in the motorboat and shrank as far away as the green leather seat permitted.

"I shan't scream. That was a figure of speech. We're across the bar road. Doesn't the moisture dripping from those ghostly pines sound like rain? There's something moving ahead! It's a person! Hear the call? He's lost! No, it's a woman's voice!"

Carson pressed the accelerator. Stared incredulously at the slender figure that ran forward. Stopped the roadster. Jumped out.

"Madge!" he exclaimed. "Madge!"

"Oh, Lex! Lex, dear! I'm so — so glad to see you, I was lost!" Madge Millard half laughed, half sobbed.

That fervent "dear" was like a steel hand twisting Lissa's heart. Did Madge Millard love Lex? Next time she felt herself go all soft and quivery inside when he smiled at her, she'd put that word into her memory phonograph and give it a whirl. Meanwhile, she was sitting like a bump on a log. With one foot on the running board she suggested;

"Take Madge home, Lex. I'll walk. I want to stop at Red Chimneys and make sure the engine is running. I could find my way from here in the dark."

"Of course you won't walk, Lissa. Don't make me feel more like a sob-sister than I feel at present," Madge Millard protested. "When I started from the Treasure Chest — I go to the farmhouse every day for eggs — there was only a faint mist. Then suddenly everything became blurred, unreal, weird. I was confused and lost my way."

"I don't wonder," Lissa sympathized, "but now that you're safe, charge the adventure up to education. You wouldn't have seen a typical summer here unless you had experienced one fog. I'll see you at dinner tonight."

It seemed but an instant to the man and

woman looking after her before she disappeared in the mist.

"You'd better follow her, Lex," Madge Millard suggested anxiously. "She'll lose her way."

"No. She knows these woods and trails better than I do. Get in and I'll take you home."

He drove on through the mist with the eyes of his mind following Lissa, with Madge saying how much she liked the Treasure Chest and how wonderful Lissa had been to Andy and didn't he think she was about as charming a girl as he'd ever met?

"The most charming," he attested crisply.

"Care for her a lot, Lex?"

"Mad about her."

"Thank heaven you're in love at last. Jack and I have worried about you. We've suspected that you'd had a disappointment which made you cynical about women."

He smiled. "You're right about the disappointment but not about its lasting effect. I can laugh now, but it was a tragedy when it happened. I invited the girl with whom I was terribly in love to my Class Day. She fell for my roommate. I was a cynic about girls for months. Then, I took up law, got tremendously interested in my work and kept women outside my life. I haven't met a girl I wanted to marry until I pulled Lissa Barclay out of the water."

"Then — then why let her spend so much time running round with that light-weight, Johnny Grant? The Packard man also is too devoted."

"I'll have to take my chance, Madge. I can't stay here for the present — I've got to get the mess of my uncle's estate cleared up. After that —" he abruptly switched the subject. "How's Andy?"

"He has made a wonderful gain. Everyone is so good to him, even your butler, Fenton, comes to inquire for him, brings him something the cook has prepared especially to tempt his appetite. Andy has taken the greatest fancy to him. I — I — can hardly believe it, his improvement, I mean." She steadied her voice. "It seems like a miracle."

"I knew this place would fix him up." His color rose as he suggested;

"Now that the boy is better, why not play round more with Jack? I think he's lonely. He — he, well — you know he's friendly and likes people and —"

He was bungling what had started out to be a simple suggestion that she devote more time to her husband.

Her hand gripped his arm, her face was white, her eyes were terrified.

"Are you trying to tell me something, Lex? Something about a woman and — and Jack?"

"No! No! It's only that Jack seems sort of low in his mind — he loves the boy as much as you do — and I thought — well, you know how I feel about Jack — you and he are my dearest friends — and I can't bear to see him hurt. Here we are at the Treasure Chest."

He caught her hand as she stepped from the roadster.

"You do understand what I meant about Jack, don't you, Madge?"

"Better than you think, Lex," she answered and went into the house.

In the residence office at Tarry Farm, Lissa frowned at the pad on which all phone calls for her were listed. No record of a call from Red Chimneys. She had stopped there on her way home. The servants in the kitchen had been surprised when she inquired if the water was running. Sure, they said, did she think it had stopped?

She visualized the Italian houseman in the doorway of the lighthouse. Why had he come there? Why had he wanted to see the lamp-room? She laughed! Already her imagination was hot-footing on the trail of scar-faced Nino.

154

12

Fenton was serving coffee on the terrace. In mid-afternoon the fog had blown out to sea. The sun had blazed down on a steaming world long enough to dry it. Now the glassy surface of the harbor mirrored a three-quarter moon and a scatter of shimmering stars. The still air was sweet with the breath of lilies. Silver tinkled against china to the accompaniment of low voices and soft laughter.

Lissa, in a fan-back chair, looked up at Tod Kent perched on the brick wall of the terrace. Moonlight turned his white dinner jacket to silver and silver-plated his red hair, it even threw a kindly shadow on his retrousse nose. He responded with an understanding grin.

"Admiring me, are you? Just one more victim to my deadly charm?"

"Too bad you haven't more self-confidence, Tod. Why not consult a psychoanalyst? He might help."

"That-a-girl! Glad to hear you laugh. You were so serious during dinner I thought of suggesting that you sob out your sorrow on my shoulder. It's being done. Now, what is

155

there about that mild ribbing to turn your face as red as one of those roses in the garden?"

"Your eyes are playing tricks. My face didn't turn red. It's sunburn being shown up by the moonstone blue of this frock."

"Is that so! The customer is always right. How come that you're alone for a minute? Packard didn't talk or look at anyone but you during dinner. With Lex devoting himself to the fair Sidonie, those two were on the crest of the social wave and" — he lowered his voice — "if you ask me, that's what they're out for."

"Sidonie is lovely and that glittering gold frock of hers is the answer to a maiden's prayer."

"It may be, but it isn't a patch on the blue and silver rag you're wearing. It does things to your eyes and your gorgeous hair — added to beauty you have brains, which, boys and girls of the radio audience, puts the pep into beauty. I've met 'em beautiful and dumb before, but Sidonie is the dumbest yet. I have a hunch she's afraid to talk. Look at her now with her brother. I'll bet she's scared stiff of him."

Lissa's eyes rested on the girl to whom Ralph Packard was talking. She remembered her hysterical incompetence at Red

Chimneys when the curtains were burning. A person of that type would be dominated by a stronger nature and there was no doubt that the brother was the stronger of the two. That didn't necessarily mean that she was afraid of him. She protested;

"If you see signs of fear in Sidonie Packard's manner with her brother, you've a keener imagination than I have, Tod. They're all going in. Cards, of course. It is the first time I've seen our tenants together. Varied, aren't they?"

She rose and leaned against the terrace wall as she appraised the guests. Cleo and Jack Millard were standing in the shadow of a palm. The glow of a cigarette lighted his fine eyes, they were too fine to be wasting a glance on the girl beside him. Moonlight reduced Mrs. Barclay's age by a decade, as she listened with flattering attention to Major Fane. Without doubt he was treating her to a detailed account of his late operation, she, herself, had heard it twice. His white dinner clothes made him appear short and stocky. His shiny bald head — which wind and weather had burned a fiery red — with its fringe of iron-gray hair, made Lissa think of the sun, with a ring around it. Her eyes moved on to Lex Carson talking to Madge Millard. She winced. Even from the distance, she could see the tenderness of his expression.

"I'd like to know the stories woven through the life of each one of the tenants, wouldn't you, Tod?" she asked. "They look smooth enough on the surface, but I have a feeling that beneath some of them there may be seething retorts of emotion ready to blow-up at a spark, undercurrents sweeping them along. Curious that I should feel so about this group. Previous tenants have come and gone without stirring my imagination."

She was aware of Kent's quick look at her.

"You have me scared, Lissa. If I stay here a moment longer, you'll ferret out the dark secret of my young life and shove it under your microscope. I'm going. I'll grab Madge for a partner before Lex gets her. Those two play contract like nobody's business."

Lissa's thoughts followed him. He knew of undercurrents in the lives of some of the guests here tonight, she was sure of it. He had betrayed the knowledge by his quick look at her. Which ones? Did he know Lex loved Madge?

"Do you and I have to go inside this perfect night?"

Ralph Packard's smooth query brought Lissa's thoughts rightabout face. She looked

158

up at the man whose dark eyes made her think of smoldering coals. He extended his hands with their square, reddened fingertips.

"It is really painful for me to hold cards."

"O-o-o!" Lissa crooned compassion. "You must be careful of your hands. We are not needed at the card-table. There are enough without us. I agree with you, it is too fine an evening to go in. What shall we do?"

"Look at the harbor from one of the upper balconies of this house. Ever since we arrived, I have wanted to see the world — this fragment of it — from one of these windows. Red Chimneys is all right, but I like to look off from high places. May I?"

"You may. We'll go to the balcony of the conservatory at the head of the stairs."

Lex Carson stepped out of the French window of the living room. He loomed superbly tall against the lighted background.

"You're the one in a hundred who can wear a white dinner jacket without looking like a deck steward," she thought as he approached her.

"I missed you, Lissa. Be my partner, will you?"

"Too late, Carson. I've engaged Miss Barclay to personally conduct me to the up-

159

stairs balcony from which we are to view the moon."

Ralph Packard's velvet voice was not quite so smooth. The pile had been rubbed the wrong way. He produced a flashy cigarette case, all red enamel, and gold. A monogram in diamonds glinted on the top as he snapped it open and offered it to his host.

Lex Carson looked down at the case. Why was he hesitating, Lissa wondered? She saw a faint color come into his face before he helped himself to a cigarette. Packard snapped a jeweled lighter.

"Thanks. Sorry I'm too late, Lissa," Carson regretted. "Perhaps you'll play later. I like this cigarette, Packard. I'll bet a hat it didn't come from this part of the country."

"No. I import them. Have them made especially for me."

"I judged so from the monogram. By the way, I don't know why this cigarette should remind me of it — I hope the water is running without a hitch at Red Chimneys?"

"Running! As far as I know it is. Why did you ask?"

"Your man reported that the engine was running wild. Probably didn't want to disturb you about it, so phoned to us. If you

160

gaze at the moon too long, Lissa, I shall come after you. Remember, you are my responsibility." He stood aside for her to enter the house.

"What did Carson mean, when he said you were his responsibility?" Packard demanded of Lissa as later he leaned against the rail of the conservatory balcony.

His head was dark against the moon-lighted sky. The tip of his cigarette and the shine of his eyes were sharp accents in the face she couldn't see clearly.

Below, the garden lay fragrant and still. The spray of the fountain turned to silver mist before it tinkled back into a molten pool. Tree tops and shrubs were tipped in silver, and across the harbor the lighthouse was a silver shaft. Lissa leaned her elbows on the railing.

"An enchanted world, isn't it? The moon gives a lovely light."

"You haven't answered my question about Carson. Why are you his responsibility?"

Eyes on the distant island she answered;

"Am I to believe that you have been at Red Chimneys over three weeks and do not know that my aunt left a trust fund for me to be administered by Lex Carson? If you don't, you're the only person within a radius

161

of three counties, who doesn't."

"I remember now. Sidonie was quite excited when she heard about it. Told me that not only was there a trust fund but a legacy of fabulous jewels. Why aren't you wearing some of them? I'm not jewel-wise but I know enough to know that those three broad bracelets are genuine — rhinestones. Afraid to keep the real jewels here?"

Lissa held up her left arm and moved it till a million facets caught the light and shot forth a million iridescent sparks. Why should he be interested to know where the jewels were kept?

"I hope you don't mind my question, Miss Barclay," Packard went on. "It was my story-hound scenting the trail of plot material. I presume when you leave Tarry Farm you'll be swept into a whirl of dinners and gayety in your social circle?"

Curious, the earnestness with which he asked the trivial question, Lissa thought before she answered;

"Not I. Socially, I'm the poorest girl in the world. I have traveled so much that I have no 'circle' of any kind. Cleo is the socialite. She has scores of friends, the kind who have several country places, yachts and polo ponies and chateaus in France and Italy, she belongs to what the fashion journals call the International set. When I return to the city I shall get a job and probably be able to afford one small room — until — gorgeous thought — I begin to sell stories. And speaking of writing, is genius burning? Can you write at Red Chimneys?"

"I tried typing but my fingers are still too tender. I had the grandest idea for a story, tried dictating it to Sidonie. She took it in longhand, and pretty bored she was about doing it, too."

"Let me type it for you from her copy," Lissa offered eagerly. "Think what a lot I would learn. You've been so modest, never telling me the name of one book or article of yours. I know you must write well, you talk so well. I won't let anyone know what I am doing. Not afraid I'll steal your ideas, are you?"

"Of course not. I'd prefer to read Sidonie's copy to you. It's crude. Between you and me, that sister of mine hasn't a language cell in her brain."

Or any other, according to Tod, Lissa thought. She said hurriedly;

"I have a typewriter in my work room on the island. I'll stop for you on my way over tomorrow. Together, it won't take us long to make a copy."

"I shall be eternally grateful for your help.

163

How the lighthouse shows up from here. It has been discarded by the Government, hasn't it?"

"Yes, but —" Lissa caught back the incident of the flash she had been about to confide. That was her story. She intended to use it in her novel.

"Why did you break that sentence?"

She met his eyes. She had seen the same flicker in them the afternoon he had been burned. She had thought it mockery. Was he secretly amused at her attempt to be a writer? Some successful authors were like that, contemptuous of beginners. She'd met them.

"An idea for a story derailed it. Don't they ever come to you like that? Let's go down. After all, I'm a hostess of sorts here."

Sidonie Packard was standing at the foot of the curving stairway as they descended. Lex Carson was holding her shoulder cape of green maribou.

"Ralph, I have a horrid headache. Won't you take me home?" she pleaded.

Her eyes were as glittering as her frock. Two spots that were not rouge, burned in her cheeks.

"We'll go at once, Sidonie." Packard took the cape from Carson and placed it over her shoulders. "Say good-night to the others for me, will you? I must get my sister home. She's apt to go to pieces when her head aches. I'll be waiting for you tomorrow, Miss Barclay."

Lissa and Carson stood side by side until the tap of heels across the terrace died away. He slipped his hand through her arm;

"Come with me."

In the sports room with its motley collection of stuffed fish, moose heads, guns, golf clubs and tennis rackets, he closed the door and drew a chair to the desk.

"Sit down, Lissa. I want to talk to you."

"I'd rather stand." She backed to the mantel as he approached. Why was he so colorless? His eyes probed hers as he demanded;

"Where are you meeting Packard tomorrow?"

Why should his question start her pulses racing? She brought up her shock troops of defense.

"I shan't tell you. You may have authority over my money, but not over me."

"Granted, but, won't you tell me if I say, 'please,' beautiful?"

She steeled herself against the smile in his eyes, the caress in his voice. She thought, "that's the way he looks at Madge."

"No. My friends, if not my money, are

mine to enjoy as I please. I refuse to have my dates checked up."

He came a step nearer. His color was high now, his gray eyes black with anger.

"Making a lot of dates with Johnny Grant too, aren't you? Perhaps you're thinking of getting engaged to him again?"

Lissa flung back her head.

"Perhaps I am. What can you do about it?"

"I'll show you what I can do about it! Come here."

His hand on hers seemed an irresistible magnet drawing her. Ecstasy in the feel of it, torment as she remembered Madge Millard. She gripped the edge of the mantel, clung to it.

"No. I —"

A tap on the door.

"Reprieved!" he said with a note in his voice and a look in his eyes which caught at her breath.

She opened the door, smiled radiantly at the man on the threshold.

"Come in, Tod, dear. I'm just going." She turned and flung a folded paper on the desk. "There's the list of the jewels, L—Lex. Good-night."

Kent frowned at the closed door, then at Carson unfolding the paper.

166

"Have I gone haywire or did she call me dear?" he looked askance at his friend before he reminded;

"You told me to come here as soon as the card-party folded up, Lex. I came but I have a feeling that my arrival was — to put it mildly — inopportune."

"It's all right."

Carson thrust the paper into his coat pocket. Kent watched him, as he turned the combination of a safe and withdrew a tin box. He placed it on the desk, opened it.

"I've got something," he said. "It may have nothing to do with what we're after, but something queer is going on round here."

He opened a roll of tissue paper and displayed portions of three cigarettes. With long, delicate tweezers, he picked up the shortest stub and laid it on the desk.

"Exhibit A. Found in the lamp-room of the lighthouse the day after Lissa saw the flash."

He placed another stub beside it.

"Exhibit B. Nino, the Packards' houseman, dropped this on the doorstep of the light this morning."

He held up the third piece.

"Exhibit C. I took this from Packard's case this evening." He laid it beside the others. Kent looked at them.

"What's it all about?" He turned the cigarettes over with the tweezers. Looked up with incredulous eyes.

"Jiminy, Lex! They're monogrammed R. P."

"They are. From now on, watch the light on the island from midnight to dawn — every night — don't trust it to anyone else. Understand, Tod?"

Kent's voice was rough with excitement as he answered;

"You bet I understand."

13

At the open French window in the sports room at Tarry Farm, Alexander Carson watched a ruby-throated hummingbird still fluttering wings above a mass of pink petunias in a huge vase on the terrace, saw it thrust, and dart away. He crossed to the desk and looked at the calendar. The middle of August. The days seemed speed-mad.

Besides working on the problem which had been apportioned to him by a Department confident in his ability to solve it, he had sunk his intelligence teeth into the job of straightening out the estate he had inherited. He squared his shoulders, he wouldn't allow discouragement to shake him off. He knew what he should do and he intended to do it. It would take longer than he had thought to put things on a paying basis, but it was up to him alone to keep the property which should be an asset, from sucking him into financial quicksands.

He had had so little time to devote to Lissa. During the week-ends he had spent at Tarry Farm she had avoided him. He had had only a few words with her since the

169

night she had intimated that she might again become engaged to Johnny Grant. Had she meant it?

He'd better stop thinking of her, if he could; she was in his mind, in his heart, in his very soul. Resolutely he switched his thoughts to the estate, which was proving a maze of new responsibilities. Mrs. Carson's will had been probated and he had been appointed trustee of her niece's legacy; he had sold enough of the jewels to pay the inheritance tax when it was due; his uncle's estate had been turned over to him.

Yesterday he had announced a cut in wages to all on the place to take effect next week. He had to cut even though he might keep the house open but a few weeks longer. The outside expenses would go on and he couldn't afford them as they were at present. He had told Fenton, the butler, to inform the house-staff. He had called in the men who worked outside and had been listened to in grim silence. When he had finished, they had walked out without a response. He didn't need a psychologist to tell him that they resented the cut. There had been a look in the eyes of the hairy Simonds, he hadn't liked. If they but knew it, they were lucky that it was only a cut, not dismissal. He answered a knock on the door.

"Come in. Good morning, Mrs. Barclay."

The small woman in a pale gray linen frock had lost the faded look he had noticed the first time he saw her. She was really pretty and young looking. If she hadn't an advice complex and that infernal twittery way of talking, she might be fairly attractive.

"Good morning, Alexander. No, thanks, I won't sit down." She declined the chair he pushed forward. "I know that I'm intruding on your business time but do you realize that you invited Cleo and me to stay with you a month and that we have been here longer than that now?"

Carson did some rapid-fire thinking. He had come to intensely dislike the woman and her daughter, but he was away so much that he didn't have to see them often. If they went he would lose Lissa — she couldn't stay at Tarry Farm without her stepmother — if he hadn't lost her already.

"Not getting bored here, are you, Mrs. Barclay?"

"Bored? My dear boy! This is the most enchanting place. The summer residents for miles round have made us welcome, Cleo knows so many people, and last evening we dined with the tenants at Red Chimneys. Mr. Packard seems fascinated by my lovely girl. I shall depend upon you, Alexander, to

171

look up his financial standing, should his attentions to her become serious. With Tod Kent and his cruiser at our disposal, how could we be bored?"

"Then don't think of going at present. If you can bear it, stay on until after Labor Day — by that time —"

"You are not thinking of closing this divine house then, are you? Maine is so gorgeous in the autumn. You mustn't do it, Alexander. You really should stay through October."

The sharpness of her eyes offset the softness of her voice. He evaded;

"It is too soon to decide what I will do. I shall keep the place open the rest of the summer anyway." He opened the door to the hall. "Sorry to hurry you but I have an important appointment. It's settled, isn't it? I may count upon you to stay a while longer?"

"Dear boy!" She patted his sleeve. "Of course you may, just as long as you need me. I'm glad to be of use to someone. My girl is so independent that sometimes I feel like a fifth wheel and Melissa is such an unstable person. By the way, while on the subject of my stepdaughter, I hope she is getting the little income dear Hetty left her? She is so reticent that I can't learn from her if it is being paid."

She was sounding him to find out if her stepdaughter had anything she could borrow, Carson suspected. His voice was confidential as he answered;

"It's unfortunate, but the estate is in such a mess that it will be months before Lissa will receive her little income regularly. In the meantime, if you could help her out —"

She gasped as if water had been dashed in her face. "I'll see what I can do. I'll talk with you later."

As the door closed behind her, Tod Kent appeared at the open window.

"Coast clear?" he inquired in a sepulchral whisper.

"Yes. Come in."

Carson crossed to the mantel and stood back to the fireplace. Mrs. Barclay's estimate of Lissa stuck in his mind like a thorn. Was she unstable? She was stepping out a lot with Johnny Grant. Why in thunder did he mind what that woman said? She was a nettle. She left a prickly spine in him each time she came near.

Kent, perched on a corner of the flat desk, glanced up over the lighter he was applying to a cigarette.

"You look as if you'd been given a shot of poison, Lex, or a dose of advice. Mrs. Barclay has that effect on me too. She should head an advice clinic. How does a woman get that way, everlastingly telling everybody what he should do? She and the lovely Cleo dined with the Packards last evening."

"So I hear. Was Lissa there?"

"No. She's been seeing a lot of Packard, though. They have something up their sleeves which interests them both. They make sort of a mystery of it. Mother Barclay is not taking 'Melissa' out in company with her golden-haired daughter, believe it or not."

"I believe it. How do you know Lissa wasn't at Red Chimneys last night?"

"Because I was. The Millards also were guests. Unless I miss my guess, the fair Cleo is out to annex Jack, if I know her type, and I do. Sidonie, the beautiful but dumb, was a nervous hostess. Kept looking at her brother. He was as smooth as cream, but all the time I had the feeling that if one scratched his civility too deep, one would find a tough guy."

"Something tells me you're right. Let's skip him. I got word today that some of the stuff we're following up has cropped up hundreds of miles from here."

"Got by us! What do you know about that! I've watched that lighthouse every night as you ordered. Not so much as a glimmer from it. That proves that the flash and the cigarette exhibits have nothing to do with our hunt."

"Soft pedal. Someone's at the door. Come in," Carson called. "Glad to see you, Ozy."

Captain Ozias' ferret-like eyes snapped as he entered the room. His thrust forward head waggled as he held out a large, over-stuffed, legal looking envelope.

"Special Delivery. Say, Lex, you ought to tell folks that there ain't no such animal in this village for the rusticators. The summer houses is all too fur away from the post-office."

Carson glanced at the postmark and laid the letter on the desk.

"Nothing of importance. Sit down, Ozy. You look hot and bothered. I'll have Fenton mix you a drink."

Fright distorted the face of Captain Ozias.

"No! No thanks. I ain't never going to drink nothing again."

Kent slid from the desk and joined Carson in front of the mantel.

"What's the matter, Ozy? Been seeing sea-serpents? Nice, slimy, wiggly sea-serpents?"

175

"No, 'twasn't nothin' like that, Tod."

The captain peered furtively over his shoulder before he approached the two men and confided in a whisper which carried to the remote corners of the room;

"I ain't a reg'lar beer-drinker, boys, but one evenin' long 'bout the last of June, I was kind of tuckered, I'd had so many errands to do, so I went into the open-all-night eatin' place in the village and got my supper. The first glass of beer tasted good, an' I had a second. 'Twas terrible late, most midnight, but I felt fine an' come round to the island in my dory to pull my lobster traps, 'cause I knew I wouldn't hev a chance next day an' if you leave the critters trapped too long they're likely to eat off each other's claws. Kinder playful that way at times."

"You didn't fall overboard, I hope?"

"Course I didn't fall overboard, what d'you take me for, Lex? Trouble wasn't in my legs, 'twas in my eyes. When I got out to the lobster floats each one was twins. I checked up on 'em all. Where I'd buoyed one trap, there was two."

"Nothing in that to frighten you. Someone else is poaching on your fishing ground. That wasn't beer in your eyes, Ozy."

"Mebbe 'twasn't, mebbe 'twasn't, Lex, but, I was so upset to think that two mugs of

176

beer had made me fuzzy that I went home without pullin' the traps. Reckoned I'd get a few hours' sleep before I touched 'em. I went out 'fore sunup next mornin'. 'Twas kinder misty — an' how many do you think was there?"

"Look not upon the beer when it is foamy, Ozy. How many did you find?" Tod Kent chuckled.

"Jest five floats, one in each place where I'd let down a trap. No twins. Do you wonder I'm off drinks from now on? I'd seen double. I got to get goin'. Beats all the number of errands you summer folks have. Anything I kin do fer you boys?"

"Nothing, thanks. Sure you won't have an orangeade? There would be no extra floats in it, I promise."

Captain Ozias shook his head. "You think it's a joke, Lex Carson. I'll tell you it ain't a joke to see double. Tell Lissa she can count on all the lobsters she wants for the bake next week, an' tell her I'll be on hand to open 'em as usual."

Kent waited for the door to close before he laughed.

"Poor old codger, he'll never touch beer again. Someone is poaching on his ledges, of course."

"It must be someone from away then,

Lissa says that no villager would trespass."

"Good morning, Lex."

Framed in the opening of the French window stood Madge Millard.

"Come in," Carson welcomed.

"You here, Tod?" she exclaimed as she entered. "The sun is so strong outside. I didn't see you in the shadowy room. If you two boys are in conference — I'm posted on business terms, please take notice — I'll come some other time. I was on my way to the farmhouse for eggs and thought I'd take a chance on finding Lex. He's so absorbed in estate matters that he hasn't been to see us."

Her nervous chatter was so unlike her that Carson glanced at Kent. He gave an imperceptible nod of understanding before he assured;

"Lex and I had finished conferring, if one can call listening to Ozy, the sheriff, a conference. I'll be seeing you. Bye-bye."

As the sound of his footsteps on the terrace died away, Carson said gravely;

"Come into the room, Madge. Don't stand there by the window as if you were afraid of me."

"Afraid of you, Lex! You're the last person in the world of whom I'd be afraid. You've been so wonderful to Andy and Jack

178

and me. You've been like a rock to cling to when it seemed as if I couldn't bear anxiety a moment longer."

Her yellow frock was like a patch of sunshine against the dark wood of the mantel. She was pale. Her voice had broken on the last word.

"Andy's not worse, is he?"

"No. Better, amazingly better. I never can be grateful enough to Lissa Barclay and her dog. That girl is the sweetest thing, I don't wonder you love her, Lex. She has taken Andy out in her yellow roadster every day with G-Man sitting like a sentinel between them. He adores her. He said to me only yesterday;

" 'Lissa isn't afraid for me, Mother, she makes me feel that I'll be strong and well and rough like other boys some day. Gee, I'd like to feel rough.' "

"Is Andy's admiration of Lissa what is troubling you, Madge? Are you jealous of her?"

"No! No, Lex, how could you think that? It's — it's Jack. Remember that you warned me that — that he might be lonely?"

She rested one arm on the mantel. Head averted, she said;

"Don't think I blame Jack. You were right, I haven't been very companionable."

"I ought to be shot for putting such a fool idea into your head. Who's the woman?"

"Cleo Barclay. You would have known if you hadn't been away. She is always dropping in for tea and taking Jack off in her car to tell her about some unusual tree she has discovered. She says she's writing a book about trees and needs his expert advice."

Carson checked a laugh as he saw the expression of her eyes.

"Cleo writing a book! That's the funniest thing I ever heard. You know that Jack adores the very ground you walk on. Cleo Barclay is a blonde, and an artificial one at that. Ever know him to fall for a blonde? He likes 'em dark. You ought to know that."

She raised her head and smiled through a mist of tears.

"I do! I do! I got panicky, and went all to pieces. Now that anxiety about Andy isn't pressing on me like a leaden weight, I've lost my bearings. Lex, you're a dear! You know how I love Jack. It cut to the quick when that girl —"

She hid her face against his shoulder and broke into a passion of tears. He put his arm about her tenderly.

"Cry it out, Madge! You've had a good cry coming to you for months." He had said that to Lissa, he remembered. "You —"

180

"Look at me, Lex! Look! I walked here!" called a high boyish voice.

Madge Millard raised her head. Lex Carson's eyes flashed to the open window. Lissa Barclay and Andy stood there looking in.

14

Swiftly the boy's mother crossed the room, dropped to her knees beside him, encircled him with her arms. Her face was radiant.

"You walked! All the way from the Treasure Chest, Andy? How marvelous! Tired, dear?"

He straightened his thin shoulders. His eyes reflected the blue of his linen blouse and shorts as he disclaimed;

"Tired! Course not, but, your roadster's outside so I guess I'll ride home." He spoke to the dog, who with head on one side, was watching him. "Coming, G-Man?"

The Irish terrier looked at Lissa. She nodded.

"Run along, G-Man. Send him home when you take your nap, Andy."

"I will. There's Fenton! Hi, Fenton!" the boy hailed. The butler who was passing on the terrace stopped.

"How are you today, Master Andy?"

"I'm fine. I walked here. I'm getting strong, Fenton. Gee, feel my muscle!" He held out a thin, tanned arm. The butler closed his hand about it and nodded approval.

"It's coming along, Master Andy. It's surely coming along."

"I guess there'll be no trouble with my holding on with that arm when I ride in the merry-go-round at the Fair, will there, Fenton?" he asked anxiously.

"Not the slightest in the world, Master Andy. And if Madam, your mother, is willing, I'll ride beside you and show you how to sit your horse."

"May he, mother? May Fenton take me on the merry-go-round?"

"Of course dear, it's kind of Fenton to think of it. Come home now and get your rest."

With her arm about the boy's shoulders, she lingered in the embrasure of the window.

"Thank you, Lex, for — for everything. I can't begin to thank you, Lissa, you've been so wonderful —" Tears choked her voice.

"Don't thank me. I love being with Andy. For three years I lived with Aunt Hetty who had forgotten how to be young. Playing round with him makes a fair average."

Lissa's voice died away as she and the mother and boy crossed the terrace.

She had gone without a word to him. Lex Carson paced the floor. He visualized her startled eyes as they had met his above

Madge's head against his shoulder. Of course she would misconstrue the situation, equally of course, she couldn't understand that Madge had had to cry, had needed terribly a shoulder against which to sob out the pent emotion of months. Unfortunate, darned unfortunate, that it had happened to be his and not her husband's.

Could there be any truth in what Madge had told him about Cleo Barclay? He wouldn't put it past her to try to fascinate Jack. She was the family-breaker type, and he was attractive enough and rich enough to be fair game for her. What a crazy suspicion. He wouldn't fall for a girl like that. He couldn't believe it. Not of Jack. He'd better forget it — quick.

Impatiently he picked up the special delivery letter, ripped it open and pulled out a newspaper. His eyes flashed to the date.

"February! It's come! About time," he said under his breath.

He spread the paper on the desk. Took from the safe the two scraps he had torn from the newspaper in the lighthouse. He compared the dates. The same. He tried to fit the torn-off corner on the newspaper. It didn't match. He compared dates again. Okay. It might be a later edition which had omitted the item he was after. Only one more page. He had it! He had it! The printed lines ran parallel!

He read the item framed within the diamond-shaped opening in the scrap he had brought from the lighthouse. It didn't make sense. He picked up the long envelope in which the newspaper had been mailed. Waste of money to have sent it special delivery, waste of Ozy's time —

Ozy! A light blazed through his mind. Ozy! Ozy had said "one evenin' long 'bout the last of June —"

He seized the paper and reread the item which stood out as if boxed within the diamond-shaped opening.

"I'll be darned!" he said under his breath. "I'll be — darned."

Someone knocking. He caught up the papers and thrust them into the safe. His pulses raced. He had to steady his voice before he called;

"Come in."

Simonds, the foreman, entered. His gaunt, gangling figure was attired in good looking clothes which proclaimed him dressed for an occasion, not work. The man had come to make trouble, Carson was sure of it. He motioned to a chair.

"Sit down, Simonds, and tell me what's on your mind."

185

"No. I'll stand." The foreman twirled the pencil at the end of his gold chain. "It won't take me long to say my say. The men won't accept a cut in wages."

"What does that mean? Don't beat about the bush. Give it to me straight."

Simonds thumped one hairy fist on the top of a crimson leather chairback.

"It means this. We listened to your talk of cutting wages. You've come into one of the biggest fortunes ever willed in this state — I hear you're rich in your own right, too. They say you're a smart lawyer. Well, let me tell you, there isn't a lawyer in this country smart enough to cut the wages of the bunch of men working on this place. What've you got to say to that?"

"What I said yesterday. The wages will be cut."

"Oh, no they won't. Because we won't take them. We'll give you time to think it over, if you still say 'cut,' at the end of the week, we'll walk out."

"If you walk out, not one of you ever will walk back. There are fifteen of you, fifteen families will be without a weekly pay-cheque. Better think it over."

The big Adam's apple in Simond's throat bulged and contracted.

"I guess you're the one to think it over.

About sundown when the prize cows haven't been milked nor fed, and the poultry is clucking its head off for food, you'll think us men worth the wages we were paid. Good morning. You know where to find me when you want me."

"Yes, I know where to find you. At your 'office.' And, Simonds, be sure that the men understand that if they walk out, they walk out for good."

He opened the door to the residence office in response to a quick tattoo on its panels. Lissa stood there. Her eyes were like stars. She waved an envelope.

"It's come, Lex. An acceptance of my story, after, I'll confess now — the twenty-fifth trip. I believed in that story. I don't dare open it myself. Will you —"

The radiance faded from her face as she saw the foreman. He spoke quickly;

"You'd better make the new boss listen to reason, Miss."

Lissa's eyes followed him as he strode into the hall and banged the door behind him. They came back to Carson still standing before the mantel.

"What did Simonds mean?"

For an instant his voice failed him, a pulse drummed in his throat. The expression of her eyes when she had turned away with

Madge and the boy had been like a steel clamp about his heart, squeezing it intolerably. The relief, the incredible relief, that she had come to him in her happiness! He said, with an effort to keep his voice light;

"Simonds and the men threaten a walk-out if I persist in the pay-cut."

"Will you?"

"I must. I can't afford to pay what I offered, which is more than they would get if they were working for the county, but I couldn't let them down too much."

"I wonder if Marty Simonds knows of the planned walkout?"

"Let's skip them, Lissa. Let's talk about you and the short story."

"The short story." Her eyes blazed with excitement. "Imagine my forgetting it for anyone. I came to you directly I found this in my mail. Remember I told you that you were the only person to whom I talked about my work — that is, before I met Mr. Packard?" She held out an envelope. "Open it, will you? That story has been in the editor's hands over three months. I'm too shivery. Know what I've planned to do with the cheque? Start a travel fund."

"Lissa, don't take it so seriously. Suppose it shouldn't be an acceptance?"

"If it isn't, I can take it. But, what else can

188

it be after all this time? The manuscript hasn't come back. Open it!"

Carson slit the envelope and drew out a sheet of paper. His eyes followed the typed lines.

"Hurry up! Read it!" the girl prodded. "It is an acceptance, isn't it?"

"An acceptance — of sorts." He read aloud —

"Dear Miss Barclay;
We like your story, HIGH HARVEST. You have a great theme. The denouement is a bit too obvious but with your permission we will change that. As we are not at present paying cash for contributions, we are giving you four yearly subscriptions to our magazine. Trusting that this will be satisfactory, we are,
Very truly yours,
The Editors."

Lissa's face was blankly incredulous, then it crinkled into laughter, though Carson could see the glitter of tears in her eyes.

"Four subscriptions! For my grand story HIGH HARVEST! It's too — too funny! Suppose I can sell them for my travel fund? Perhaps you'll buy one?" The sentence rippled into a shaky laugh.

"Steady, Lissa. You'll have hysterics if you don't watch out."

"I? Never. Writers who get there don't have hysterics. I've always claimed that success in writing — provided of course one had what it takes to make a writer — is like success in marriage, largely a question of good sportsmanship, of keeping on keeping on, of giving one's best and trying, everlastingly trying to make that best, better. The offer struck me as funny, that's all."

"Will you let it go for four subscriptions to their dinky magazine? Will you let them change the ending?"

"No, to that last question. It isn't a dinky magazine. It has good backing but I think too much of my ch—child —" her voice caught, "to let it go for that."

"Apparently you've made a smash hit with the theme. What is it? Mind telling?"

"No. The idea came from a sort of back-to-the-family article I read. It may be because my own family life was such a hodge-podge that it seems to me that there is no more important, no more up-to-the-minute need, no higher career for a woman than that of wifehood and home-maker, to answer 'Here!' when a child comes home and calls, 'Where's Mother?' It takes in everything, economics, business and government laws, a communal viewpoint, and comradeship, courage, sacrifice, and last, but not least, a sense of humor. It calls for a sporting instinct if anything does."

"What's the matter with that theme? It's vital."

"Speaking with the Voice of Rejection Slips, it has a 'Woman's-place-is-in-the-home' taint which is out-of-date at present, and my story is worth four magazine subscriptions, nothing more."

"Lissa, don't feel so hurt. I — I can't bear it, darling."

"Don't call me that! First, Madge, then me. When I saw this letter I was so excited I forgot the tender scene I interrupted a few moments ago."

"Lissa! You're wrong. I'm too old-fashioned to go in for wife-snitching. You're not consistent. You said you believe that the beautiful things of life are as real as the ugly things of life, yet you won't believe that a man's love for you may be true and steadfast."

"I believe my eyes, too. I was silly enough to have put you on a pedestal. Now you've fallen off and — and — crashed and there isn't a piece of the person I thought you were, big enough to pick up."

She had put him on a pedestal! She had liked him that much! She wasn't in love with Johnny Grant, she couldn't be. He could explain. He'd make her love him. He'd wait until her anger had cooled, meanwhile he'd try diplomacy.

"I'm sorry you feel like that, Lissa, because I'm in a jam. Tod and I need your help."

"My help! Is Tod in love with Madge, too?"

"Forget that — please. I'll take up the matter of whom I love, later. What I am about to tell you is strictly confidential. Can I trust you?"

She crossed her throat with a pink-tipped finger.

"I promise."

He glanced into the hall. Closed the door. Returned to the desk. A soft breeze sifted through the Venetian blinds and stirred a lock of the girl's auburn hair. A sparrow chirped outside.

"I am a lawyer, Lissa, but because I've specialized in criminal law I've been drafted by the Treasury to work on a case."

"Are you a — a G-Man, Lex?" Her brown eyes were wide and startled.

"Nothing so dramatic. Do you remember that in a world-famous case ransom money was traced by a map?"

He unlocked a flat drawer in the end of the desk. Lissa, beside him, looked down. Her eyes flew to his.

"Why — why — it's a map of this state and New Hampshire!"

He nodded and indicated colored pegs which outlined a large area near the coast.

"What do the pegs mean, Lex?"

He closed the drawer. Locked it and dropped the key into his pocket.

"Stand beside me." His voice was low. "Face doors and windows. Keep watch for shadows outside, while I tell you that somewhere within that pegged-in area is a man or men whom the Government wants."

"I'm a-shiver with excitement. What are they? Bootleggers? Kidnappers?"

"Neither. Nothing so rough. White-collar workers. Counterfeiters."

15

"Counterfeiters!" Lissa echoed incredulously.

"Yes. Did you have time to notice that the pegged-in area covers several counties on the coast? A year ago, it was discovered that counterfeit coins and bills were seeping through the two states. The map was set up. Whenever a piece of bad money was reported, the town from which it came would be pegged. Two hundred thousand bogus dollars and unlimited small coin has been rounded up. So far the gang — my mistake, organization is the word now — hasn't tried to pass anything but small stuff, but undoubtedly there are bigger bills ready to float."

"Has no one been caught trying to pass the bad money?"

"There are ten persons serving time now, but they say they don't know where it came from, though they confess they bought it, sometimes one hundred dollars' worth of bogus bills and coins for ten dollars in good money. We're after the man who, we are sure, is the brains of the organization. One of his aliases — he has a number, is 'The Ace.' He was arrested about four years ago, and fingerprinted, but was not convicted."

"Then you're a detective?"

"No. I'm a lawyer — with a few cells in my brain which start pricking when there's a mystery in the air. The Treasury Department heard of one case I solved and drafted me on this. Not being a professional, it figured I could get at things better than one of its men. The fact that I was the residuary legatee of Tarry Farm gave an excellent reason for my vacation in the very middle of the pegged-in area."

"Are Tod Kent and the electrical engineers here on that business?"

"Yes. The harbor was the best port for the cruiser. We can spread out in all directions from here. Tod helped me once before and the two men who pass for engineers are really criminologists. Somewhere within that pegged-in area are the plates of a complete counterfeiting outfit, I'm sure of it. One whisper of our errand and all our work to date would go blooey. You realize that, don't you?"

Lissa's eyes were brilliant and eager and friendly.

"I do. I realize also that this county is in the middle of the area. You wouldn't have told me this unless you thought I could help, would you? Of course I will, I promise. I hope I shan't feel like Mata Hari doing it. I — that's Fenton's discreet knock. What does he want? Sure you locked that drawer?"

"I did, don't look at it. Not that Fenton would know what it meant if you did. I told him yesterday what I would pay the house-staff and asked him to lay the cut before them. He's probably here to report another walk-out. Come in!"

Fenton closed the door behind him. He looked at Lissa and then interrogatively at Carson, who responded to his unspoken question;

"It's all right, Fenton. Miss Barclay knows that I asked you to interview the house servants. Shoot. What's the verdict?"

"We accept the cut, sir. The maids realize what a power for good in the community the late Madam was, sir, and that they have been highly paid and we're all glad if we can help you get your business affairs straightened out, sir."

It was an instant before Carson could swallow the lump the unexpected decision brought to his throat.

"Tell them I appreciate their co-operation, Fenton."

"Yes, sir, they'll be glad to hear that you are pleased, sir. As I told them, 'Man may not live by bread alone.' There's something in the world besides money. Anything else, sir?"

"Only that the men outside have threatened to walk out."

"Is that so, sir? If you will excuse me for asking about something that is outside my department, what will you do about the cows, if they do, sir?"

"Cows?"

"Yes, milking them, sir. We are exhibiting at the County Fair shortly and we'd lose a ribbon or two if they get out of condition. I helped select some of them. My father had the care of the prize cattle on Lord Byram's estate in England. I got to know a lot about them. I'm — I'm very fond of cows, sir, in short, I have a sort of passion for them. I'll do the milking — if necessary. The late Madam wouldn't allow mechanical milkers to be used."

Carson was aware of the flash of laughter in Lissa's eyes. Had she visualized as he had the butler's immobile face and sideburns bent over a milk pail?

"Thank you, Fenton, if the men do walk out and things get screwy, it will help to know that you're standing by. But, I can't

197

believe they will. They have too much to lose."

"I wouldn't be so sure, sir. One specked apple in a barrel can do a lot of damage to the other apples, and if you'll excuse me for saying it, sir, Simonds, the foreman, is badly specked. I presume that the party at the pool and the lobster-bake will come off next week as planned, Miss?"

Lissa looked at Carson. He assented;

"Of course, that is unless we are boycotted and can't get the goods for it."

"The barrels have already been delivered, sir. Captain Ozias will bring the lobsters and clams, there's no danger of him striking. If you will excuse my saying so, I have seen this walk-out coming. I know human nature, sir. If that's all, I'll get back to my work. Thank you, sir." The door closed behind him.

"Fenton's a trump. How long has he been here, Lissa?" Carson asked.

"Three years. During that time the others on the housestaff, except the cook, have been from about here. When Aunt Hetty decided to make her all-year home at Tarry Farm, she decided also, that in so far as possible, the money to carry on the place should be spent in this county. It was her idea of community service. The village girls have come here, been perfectly trained as waitresses, parlor, personal, upstairs maids and laundresses, have even been taught to cook; have departed to give place to others. Their wages were high, but — perfect service was demanded in return. Aunt Hetty believed that the mental discipline and efficiency acquired by such rigorous training would be invaluable when they took up other work and that the how-it's-done knowledge would cost them nothing to carry around."

"I call that community service — plus. Didn't Fenton protest at the program? It must have made extra work for him."

"It did, but he appeared to be as proud of results as Aunt Hetty was. I trained the upstairs and he the downstairs maids. He was a stiff disciplinarian, but the girls liked him. His salary has been spectacularly high, but you have cut it and he stays on. I feel as if I should go down on my knees and apologize to him. As I told you before, I've never really liked him."

"Why?"

"I don't know why. I couldn't state a single incident upon which my aversion was founded. He did all the buying for the place — Aunt Hetty would give him cheques and he would pay cash. She wouldn't allow us to have a bill. Why do you look at me like that?"

"Like what?"

"As if you were staring through my head at something that startled you. Your face went white."

"Thought someone moved outside the door. It was a risk to tell you what I'm after where we might be overheard. Do you wonder I'm suspicious of every sound? If anyone is outside, keep your eyes away from that drawer." He looked into the hall, closed the door.

"No one there. I'm getting jumpy. Hope I'm not developing nerves. Go on. You said that Fenton turned cheques into cash and you wondered —"

"I wondered if perhaps he put some of the money into his own pocket. He didn't. I kept the house books and his expenditures and receipted bills balanced to a cent. My dislike of him has been tempered since he has been so kind to Andy. Now it has been turned to admiration by his loyalty. I think loyalty is the grandest quality in the world."

"Is that why you're sticking to Johnny Grant?"

The question was on the air before Carson realized that he was asking it. It brought a pink stain to Lissa's face.

"What do you mean by sticking?" she demanded truculently.

"Oh, running round with him, swimming and dining and — well, just sticking."

"I don't like that word. You've cross-examined me before about my — my friendship with Johnny, and as I told you then, I don't consider it your business. I'm not swimming and dining with him any more than I am with Tod Kent or the two electrical engineers — I forgot, they aren't engineers, are they — or —"

"Ralph Packard?"

"How did you know?" She set her teeth hard in her lips as if disciplining them for having allowed the startled question to escape.

"I'm not so submerged by business problems that I don't know and care what happens to you, beautiful."

"That's nice of you. Especially when you have other persons in whom you are so deeply interested."

She took a step toward the door, turned; reminded in a low voice;

"Fenton said that Simonds is 'badly specked.' He may be one of the men you're looking for."

"I was thinking that myself," Carson agreed. "Bring me the leases and references of the three cottages, will you?"

His eyes followed her as she left the room. Would he never learn? Just when she appeared interested and friendly he had gone haywire and lugged Johnny Grant into the picture. His inductive reasoning might pick up clues and link one into another till it solved a crime mystery but it was a total loss when it came to helping him with the girl he loved.

Lissa returned and dropped some papers on the desk.

"What's happened?" he demanded. "You're white."

"The leases of Red Chimneys and the Packard references are gone."

"Gone! Don't you keep the filing cabinet locked?"

"Why should I? There has never been anything in it that anyone would want."

"Except that lease and the references, evidently. You may have mislaid it. It isn't important. I'm interested in the Pirates' Den lease and the references of Major Fane."

"Those are among the papers on your desk."

"Then that's all right. I'll keep the leases in my safe for the present. Better keep the filing cabinet locked after this, Lissa."

"I'll lock it this minute."

He waited until she had left the room before he scooped up the papers she had dropped to the desk. He thought as he placed them in the safe without looking at them;

"Lissa couldn't have suspected from my bluff that the absence of that lease and reference is just one more link in the chain of evidence. This has been what she would call 'Just one of those days.' "

"I'm not so submerged by business problems that I don't know and care what happens to you, beautiful."

During the night the words echoed and re-echoed through Lissa's mind. She couldn't sleep. How had Lex Carson dared say that to her barely ten minutes after she had seen Madge in his arms? After her experience with Johnny Grant, she'd been a weak sister to have taken him seriously for a minute. Why shouldn't he think a girl would believe anything he said, who, after seeing him making love to a married woman, had rushed to him with the news that she had sold a story? When she had seen that envelope on her desk, she had forgotten everything but the fact that her story was sold — which it wasn't — and that Lex must hear the wonderful news.

Suppose he had sounded sincere? Hadn't

Johnny said the same sort of thing to her and didn't he fall in love with Cleo the first time he saw her? She knew now by the way it had hurt when she saw Lex's arms around Madge that she had not been in love with Johnny. He had hurt her pride, not her heart. He had been just someone who eased her loneliness after the loss of her father.

No wonder Lex's words haunted her, she excused herself, the tenderness of his voice and eyes had drawn her like a magnet. She had saved herself by thrusting the memory of Madge between them. There was no excuse for allowing herself to care for Lex Carson, she'd had warnings.

She sat up and hugged her knees. She must thrust Lex and Madge from her mind. She'd much better think of the reason for the arrival of The Sphinx in the harbor. The memory sent little icy chills skittering through her veins. It was incredible that government investigation had narrowed to an area on the coast and that she was in the very middle of the storm belt. If only she could help. What an adventure to have a part in! Who would have suspected Lex Carson, with his clear amused voice, his quizzical eyes, his perfectly cut clothes, his social technic, of being a secret-service man — call it by any name you liked — that was what he was. Was it possible that the papers missing from the filing cabinet had anything to do with his quest? No. He had been interested only in Pirates' Den lease. Was he suspicious of Major Fane?

What a waste to spend time in bed when the very air outside might be tingling with sinister signals, beating with the wings of mystery. It was almost morning, she wouldn't stay in her room another moment.

She slipped a shimmering green satin lounge coat over her pale blue pajamas, thrust her bare feet into silver mules and scuffed her way to the balcony.

The sheer beauty of the world outside tightened her throat. The east was crimsoning. Glow from a hidden flame turned silvery clouds to saffron islands and tinted the edge of those higher up with rose. Stars were silver-gilt. The quiet sea was indigo, the riding lights of the cruiser paled as the mounting glow turned its brass trimmings to swaying flames. The lighthouse loomed like a blood-red tower. A gull soared like a faint white spirit faring forth to greet the rising sun.

Arms on the balcony rail, thoughtful gaze on the glittering eye of the light, accompanied by the chirp, chirp of crickets, Lissa reviewed what Lex Carson had told her of the hunt for the counterfeiters. His startling story strengthened her in her belief that she had seen a signal from the lighthouse the night before he had come to Tarry Farm, that the flash had not been part of a dream.

Who could have given the signal? There wasn't a person in the village whom she would suspect of dishonesty. She had told Lex that Nino had asked to go to the lamproom but he hadn't seemed disturbed by the fact.

"Simonds, the foreman, is badly specked."

The words echoed through her mind as distinctly as if Fenton were beside her saying them.

Simonds! Did he suspect that the law was on his trail? Was he planning this walk-out to switch attention to that? Attention would be switched good and plenty if fifteen employees deserted Tarry Farm. No matter how evil Lem Simonds might be, Marty, his wife, knew nothing of it, she was sure. She would give the foreman and men time to think it over. If they didn't take back their threat to walk out at the end of the week if Lex didn't accept their terms, she'd talk with Marty. Marty was a power with the wives and daughters. She'd better stop thinking about it and get some sleep.

"And so to bed," she said aloud.

The glow had reached lawn and gardens now. Great heads of hydrangeas, just coming into bloom, blushed faintly in the light. Moisture on trees and shrubs sparkled like pink diamonds. Trap nets that blood-thirsty spiders had woven cunningly in the night were scattered on the lawn like filmy handkerchiefs dropped by fairies fleeing as dawn crept up on them.

She stretched up her arms, lifted her face and filled her lungs with the dew-washed air.

"Thanks for this lovely world, God," she whispered. With a backward glance at the lighthouse, which appeared to regard her with a knowing eye, she entered her room.

16

Lissa slowly walked along a road bordered by yellow tansy and white yarrow blooming against the blended grays and browns, the gleaming marble and silver-flecked granite of a stone wall, which dipped and mounted and dipped again as if determined, old as it was, to keep pace with the modern black highway, which ran ahead to cities and villages it would never reach.

At dawn six days ago, talking over the proposed walk-out with Marty Simonds had seemed a brilliant idea, she told herself, but as she neared the foreman's vine-smothered cottage set in a tidy, colorful garden, it didn't seem such a world-beater.

She crossed her arms on top of the white fence. G-Man beside her stuck his nose close to the pickets as he furtively regarded Goldie, a big tortoiseshell cat with back hunched, who stared at him with hypnotic topaz eyes.

"Morning, Marty!"

The wispy woman in a black and white print dress, on her knees attacking weeds in the border of purple petunias and orange-king calendulas against the house, nodded and smiled and kept on with her work. As Lissa watched her, her courage oozed. Opening up the disagreeable subject didn't seem so simple. She deployed:

"It's a lovely day, isn't it? I've never seen the sky bluer nor the water more like a mine of shimmering sapphires. Listen to that thrush!"

Marty Simonds' busy hands stilled, as a firm, flute-like sound was followed by ascending and descending notes of incredible sweetness, rising higher and higher in the scale only to climax in a clear silvery tinkle.

The woman on her knees released her breath in a soft sigh.

"Isn't it wonderful! So rich and mellow and poured out so easy, as if the bird couldn't help its coming. Wish some of the radio singers would take lessons of a thrush. What have you been doing, child?" She tipped her head and looked sidewise at Lissa with bright, dark eyes.

"What I've been doing seems stodgy after listening to that heavenly song. I've just come from the shore. I wanted to be sure that everything needed for the lobster-bake was on hand, that the rocks were the right size and that the men understood that they were to be red hot before they were put into

209

the bottom of the barrels, that they hadn't scrimped on cheese cloth in which to wrap the tinker mackerel, and that there were buckets and buckets of clean salt water, plenty of canvas and heaps of rock weed. Everything was okay and the lobsters, clams and fish are ready to cook."

"Got potatoes ready to go in?"

"Yes, sweet, white, and green corn. The watermelons are packed in tubs of ice."

"I guess you've thought of everything. The weather an' the lobster-bake weren't what you came here to talk about, were they, Lissa? When I saw you coming in that lilac cotton, you know is my favorite color, I knew you had something serious you wanted to talk over with me."

"I've told you before, Marty, that you're psychic, and I've told you also, that talking things over with you has kept me from blowing-up emotionally heaps of times during these last three years."

She opened the gate and barely escaped squeezing the dog's nose as she quickly closed it.

"You can't come into Marty's garden, G-Man, until you've learned to be a perfect gentleman. Have you forgotten that the last time you were here you treed Goldie and ran off with Marty's black cape she was airing on the line?"

She turned her back on the Irish terrier's reproachful eyes, ignored his sharp bark of protest, and sat down on a yellow wheelbarrow. Hands clasped about one knee, she watched the woman's knotty fingers work with expertness and despatch in spite of the tortoiseshell cat who was rubbing its back against them.

"It would be a help if flower plants would grow as fast and luxuriantly as weeds, wouldn't it?"

Marty Simonds sank on her heels and brushed back a wisp of gray hair with earth-stained fingers.

"Isn't that just the way with folks, Lissa? Don't their faults grow faster than their virtues? Leastwise, sometimes I think that's the way it is round here." She vented disapproval of her neighbors on a stubborn root. Lissa plunged.

"That's really what I came to talk to you about, Marty. The walk-out at Tarry Farm."

The sudden capitulation of the weed sent Marty Simonds back on her heels. It dangled from her hand as she demanded;

"What walk-out?"

Lissa told of Carson's decision to cut wages and of the foreman's threat. She concluded;

211

"Your husband accused Lex Carson of pleading poverty, but, it's not true, Marty. I've kept accounts for Aunt Hetty for three years, and I know that expenses are terrific. The men have given him until tomorrow to take back the cut. If he doesn't, they'll walk out. I supposed you knew about it."

"Know about it! They wouldn't let me know. I've scolded too much about their fool ideas. I'll bet their wives don't know." She threw tools into a garden basket and rose with the agility of a girl.

"What will you do?"

"Talk to the women. They're all knitting crazy. Making dresses. Do you think they'll stand for an idle man hanging round the house asking what they're making, an' why they're making it, an' don't they think they'd better be canning or braiding? I know how it is. How long did you say the men are giving Mr. Carson to take back the wage-cut?"

"Until tomorrow noon."

"They picked a good time. The County Fair opens tomorrow an' the wives'll be busy gettin' their exhibits arranged. You should have told me before, Lissa."

"It seemed so like telling tales that I waited, hoping that the men would realize how well they had been paid through the years, be sports and take the cut. Even then,

212

Lex Carson is paying them more than he can afford."

"I like that young man. Nice mannered. Lem and I went to the big house to welcome him when he first came and he called on me one afternoon, couldn't have treated me better if I'd been First Lady. If I had youngsters, I'd starve manners into them if I couldn't make them learn any other way. Surprising what starving will accomplish with those who love their food." Her laugh was brittle. "After honor, good manners is about the best asset a person can have. Your aunt realized that. What a lot she did for our young people. She gave them something better than money — they earned a nice little pile of that too — when she gave them the training they got at Tarry Farm. They're showing the result of it in the choices they're making as they go on in life. Land sakes, how I am running on."

"I love to hear you 'run on,' Marty. I think you're wonderful and — and I'm terribly fond of you."

Marty Simonds blinked a mist from her snapping eyes.

"You're a sweet child, Lissa, perhaps sweet isn't just the word, spicy fits you better, neither is fond the word that expresses my feeling for you. Run along an'

213

get ready for the lobster-bake. I'll be on hand to help dish up as usual. I suppose Ozy'll be there to open the lobsters — he won't miss the chance to hear what's goin' on. Don't tell him about the walk-out or t'will be all over town by night. Everybody'll blame Lem, he isn't very popular, but except for the fact that he's terrible close with money, he's a good husband."

Simonds was close with money. Did he love it enough to pass bad money? The thought sent the blood in a quick tide to Lissa's hair. Marty was looking at her sharply. Could she possibly suspect what she was thinking? She asked hurriedly;

"Do you really think you can stop the walk-out?"

Marty Simonds picked up the tortoise-shell cat brushing against her skirt. Her laugh was like a dry cough.

"My tongue's in good working order. All I need besides that is plenty of gas in the flivver and time. Don't worry, child. Run along and get ready for your party."

Later, as Lissa fastened the green belt of her white frock, she stepped out on the balcony of her room. Time had slipped away since that dawn when, arms folded on this very railing she had wondered what she would do next. Now, the borders of the path

214

to the shore were a riot of gorgeous color. Mammoth zinnias, gold, rose, lemon, nodded in the soft breeze; towering lilies swung in the air like rusty red bells; shafts of purple and lavender monkshood made a soft background for phlox, clumps of it, salmon, white and cherry red and off in a bed by themselves where their jewel tints would not be dimmed by the strong colors in the border, hundreds of gladiolas raised their dainty faces to the sun.

Weeks had passed, she thought again, and still she had no definite plans for the future. How could she plan until she knew how long she would be needed at Tarry Farm? She certainly would be needed if the men walked out. Would they walk out? She chuckled as she visualized Marty Simonds' expression as she had said;

"Surprising what starving will accomplish with those who love their food."

Would she starve Lem into subjection? Apparently she loved him even if he were "close." Love did strange things to people. There was Johnny Grant who had been so desperately in love with Cleo, hanging round the house in which she was living, apparently not caring at all for her, but again devoting himself to the girl to whom he had been first engaged. And Lex in love with his

215

friend's wife. There she was again, thinking of Lex and Madge! If she didn't watch out, she'd begin to be sorry for herself. Love wasn't the only thing in the world, was it? Not when one had an ambition and determination to be an arrived writer, not when a new life lay ahead with fascinating adventures lurking in the offing, not when this perfect afternoon had been made for the swimming party and lobster-bake.

There wasn't a cloud in the clear turquoise sky except for a few piled like a snow-drift on the western horizon, probably for the sole purpose of adding a spectacular effect or two when the sun set. The sea was smooth. The green of distant hills fused into hazy purple as it neared the peaks which were reflected in the still water as in a gigantic blue mirror. The lighthouse on her island shone like a mother-of-pearl shaft with one great eye. It wasn't an island now, the ledge which connected it with the mainland was a sandy road upon which two automobiles were parked. A picnic party, probably. From the shore rose white plumes of steam from cooking shellfish and seaweed. She sniffed. Delicious smell! It made her ravenously hungry.

She ran down the broad stairs singing under her breath;

" 'There is a green hill far away
Without a city wall.' "

She had played the hymn on the organ in
church last Sunday. She broke off with a
laugh as she remembered how the congre-
gation had dragged on the last line as if they
couldn't bear to let it go.

"Lissa! Wait!"

Cleo hailed her from the threshold of the
library. The rich woodwork of the room
behind her accentuated the delicacy of her
pale blue sports suit, the gold of her hair, the
rose-leaf perfection of her skin.

"She looks positively angelic — sweet as
sugar — and her eyes are like glowing sapphires," Lissa thought. No wonder Lex
Carson said she was a knockout. She, herself, felt like a splashy oil-painting beside a
delicate water color.

"What do you want, Cleo? Make it
snappy. I ought to be at the pool. I'll have to
do a marathon now to get there before the
first guests arrive."

"Got any money, Lissa? I'm being
hounded by shops to pay overdue bills. Let
me have five hundred dollars, will you? I can
throw that to the pack and it will stop them
for a while."

"Five hundred dollars! I haven't it, Cleo."

Lucky she had asked Lex Carson not to pay her salary or income until she was ready to leave Tarry Farm.

"I've got to have it! How much have you?"

"Oh, perhaps the magnificent sum of ten dollars."

"I don't believe it. Hasn't Lex paid your income?"

"Aunt Hetty's estate is still being settled."

"Then you'd better get another trustee. If the present one spent more time on your business and less at the Treasure Chest — appropriately named — it holds his treasure, doesn't it — perhaps he'd push your business along."

Evidently Cleo knew of Lex's devotion to Madge. In spite of her certainty that the insinuation had turned her heart to a hunk of hard, cold ice, Lissa said lightly;

"You'd be a find for a newsreel outfit, Cleo. You belong to the ancient and honorable order of sees-all-hears--all-suspects-all."

Cleo's face flushed with anger.

"I see enough to know that you've fallen for Lex Carson and fallen hard. Is Johnny Grant coming to the lobster-bake?"

"I haven't invited him. Johnny isn't what you'd call intuitive but even he may suspect

218

from that fact that he isn't wanted."

"I want him, I'll try him for money. If he won't loan me five hundred, well, there's a last resort — fortunately."

"What do you mean, Cleo? You —"

"Ahem!"

The sound was the first intimation of the butler's presence. Cleo whirled angrily;

"For heaven's sake, Fenton, where did you come from?"

"I'm sorry, Miss Barclay, if I startled you. I clattered a bit before I entered. You are very nervous, aren't you, Miss? You are wanted on the phone, Miss Lissa."

"Who is calling?"

"He wouldn't say, Miss. Quite mysterious, the party was. Shall I tell him you won't answer till you know the name?"

There was a thread of eagerness in his voice. Lissa had suspected that somewhere deep in the butler's impenetrable calm was concealed a well developed bump of curiosity. Now she knew it. She was curious about the message herself. What mysterious "party" would call her? Was it Simonds to ask her help to prevent the wage cut?

"I'll answer on the office phone, Fenton."

As she crossed the hall, Cleo reminded;

"Don't forget about Johnny Grant, Lissa."

"If you want him at the lobster-bake, do your own inviting. There are two phone lines to Tarry Farm."

What scheme was the lovely Cleo about to put across now? Would she ask Johnny for money? Her eyes and voice had been desperate. She must owe a great deal, Lissa thought as she lifted the phone. The voice at the other end of the wire scattered all speculation as to her sister's debts.

"That you, Lissa?"

Ozy! Wasn't he coming to open the lobsters? Whom could she get to take his place this late in the day? She put her mouth close to the transmitter;

"Don't tell me that you can't come to the lobster-bake, Ozy!"

"Sure, I'll be there. I just wanted to know if Lex is home."

"He went away two days ago. He said he would be back in time for the bake, but that he might be late."

"By mighty, that's bad. Will Tod Kent, the fella that owns the cruiser be there?"

"Yes."

Lissa didn't need the aid of television to get a picture of the little man with his forward thrust head and his bright eyes at the other end of the wire.

"He'll have to do, I guess. Don't let

220

anyone know I inquired for Lex. Sure, now. I'll be on hand as usual to open the lobsters."

Lissa was aware that Cleo had entered the room. Was Ozy helping Lex and Tod? She said hurriedly into the transmitter;

"All right, I'll expect you. Good-bye!"

As she cradled the phone Cleo asked;

"Who was the mysterious party? Your voice was shaking with excitement."

"It's a wonder I spoke at all. When I found it was Ozy at the other end of the wire, I thought he was phoning that he couldn't open the lobsters. Then where would I be? He'd have to be mysterious, mystery is that man's first name."

"Is he coming?"

"Yes."

"So is Johnny." Cleo's eyes glinted above the cigarette lighter. "I told him you wanted him."

17

In her flame-color swim suit, Lissa sat on the rim of the pool of sun-warmed water and watched Tod Kent mount the steps to the high diving board. For an instant his figure was outlined against the clear blue sky. He dove.

"That was clean cut," Ralph Packard approved as he established himself in a beach chair behind her. "Kent is so heavy that I always expect he'll land flat and be knocked into a cocked hat."

"But he never does." She turned to look at him. "In that white suit you might have stepped from the Well Dressed Man page. Don't you ever swim?"

"Sometimes with your sister. I'm not keen for it. You're lovelier than ever today; in this light your hair looks as if it were on fire."

Lissa turned her head away. When he spoke in that voice it had the effect of a grade-crossing bell clanging a warning. During the summer she had seen him almost every day, she had typed two stories for him. In all that time she had kept up the bars of formality. He had been "Mr.

222

Packard" to her. Once he had called her "Lissa." She must have shown her annoyance as ever since he had said "Miss Barclay." Why should she object to his familiar use of her name? she asked herself, and could find no answer. Each time they met, he had made her feel that she was becoming of increasing importance to him. Not that she thought him really in love with her — it was merely a where-have-you-been-all-my-life mannerism. Lots of men had it, evidently thought it made them invincible in the love game. It had quite the opposite effect on her. It froze her. Why did she give his manner a moment's thought? He and Cleo had motored, swum, danced and dined together, to Mrs. Barclay's evident satisfaction. She said lightly;

"Miss Packard is marvelous in that swimsuit of sequins. It gleamed in the water like a strange tropical fish all shiny flame-color scales. That costume belongs to Hollywood, not here. Never before has anything so gorgeous swam in this pool."

Her eyes roved on to where Cleo, in a black satin water frock, which was a perfect foil for her delicate coloring, was animatedly talking to Johnny Grant who sat beside her on the rim of the pool. Was she cajoling for five hundred dollars with which to pay those overdue bills? What was the "last resort" she had threatened if she didn't get it?

"I'd give a dollar a word to know what you're thinking. First you smiled and now you're frowning."

Ralph Packard's voice brought Lissa's eyes back to him. Curious about his voice. It hadn't the quality one would expect from a man of his polished appearance and profession. Smooth as it was, it wasn't well, cultured was a snobbish word, but that expressed it. She acknowledged gaily;

"Pity I can't find an editor who is in accord with you who will give a dollar a word for what I write." She remembered the four magazine subscriptions and disciplined a catch in her voice. "At the moment you made your munificent offer, I was deciding that Major Fane, standing behind your sister's chair, is not at all my idea of what a Major in the United States Army should be, even a Major on sick-leave. Instead of being tall and trim with a the-world-is-mine manner, he's short and stocky and slightly furtive. Ever notice his eyes? They're opaque. I wonder what goes on behind them."

"I forgot when I made an offer for your thoughts that you are fiction-minded. Are you keeping notes on all of us?"

"I am. The Major is Case History No. I."

"What number am I?" There was a slight edge to the question.

"Haven't reached you yet, but, I warn you, you're under the microscope, so is your sister. I finished typing your short-story yesterday. I left it on my desk in the lighthouse. We can go to the island and get it after the bake, if you want it tonight."

"I do —"

"What ho, beauteous gal! Where's Himself?"

"Okay for the lighthouse," Packard whispered before Tod Kent followed his hail.

Lissa didn't like the whisper. It made her feel that she was conniving at something clandestine. She answered Kent;

"If you mean by Himself, Lex — he hasn't returned from Boston and points north. He said he would be late getting here, but that he would come."

"Running out on us is getting to be a habit with that lad. He didn't tell me he was going."

"Are you Carson's keeper?" Packard inquired smoothly.

Lissa noted the quickly subdued flash in Tod Kent's eyes before he answered jovially;

"Wish I were. I brought my boat to be here while Lex was on vacation — he hasn't had one for years — and he's hardly been at Tarry Farm two days in succession. He and I had planned to finish up this party on the cruiser. Hope you'll all come. Marty Simonds is making cabalistic signs at you, Lissa."

"That means that the clams are done to a turn. Tell the men to dress, will you, Tod, and I'll round up the girls."

Ralph Packard's confidential whisper recurred to Lissa, as in her knit frock, she left the boathouse. The more she thought of it the less she liked it. It had turned the friendly act of stopping at the island for the manuscript into a secret date.

She looked at the white cloth spread on the pebbly beach. On it piles of green tin trays, paper plates, cups and napkins flanked glass pitchers of melted butter and pans heaped with clams that had been steamed till their shells gaped and their round, plump bodies were succulently tender.

Apparently she was the one member of the family who felt a sense of hostess responsibility. Ralph Packard was sitting close to Cleo, and Mrs. Barclay was cooing at Major Fane, who was devotedly — if

226

clumsily supplying her wants. Curious how out of place some men seemed at a picnic. He was one of them. If she had known that Lex Carson couldn't be present, she wouldn't have planned the party, it was his pool and his shore, he ought to play host. Perhaps he was side-stepping it, perhaps it was out of tune with the problems he was facing! Problems! What a load he was carrying. On top of his love affair with Madge Millard and the financial mess of his uncle's estate, had fallen the trusteeship of her legacy, and the hunt for the counterfeiters. As if those were not enough for any one man, along had come the threatened walk-out.

"Ahem!"

Fenton, with a rattle of shells, stopped beside her, Fenton in a chef's white uniform. He had a flair for theatrical effects. He held out a green tray on which was a paper plate heaped with clams.

"Do sit down, Miss. You've been busy about this bake all day and with Mrs. Simonds here to take charge of unpacking the barrels, you needn't do anything more."

"Has she plenty of help?"

"Yes, Miss. Captain Ozias is cracking the lobsters, there are two maids from the house, two men unpacking the barrels besides that Italian from Red Chimneys who's getting under everybody's feet. I don't know who invited him, Miss."

"That Italian from Red Chimneys" — the words clanged through Lissa's mind. With them came the memory of Nino's face as he had leered at her from the door of the light-house. Was it possible that he had stolen the Red Chimneys' lease and the Packards' references? What possible use could he make of them?

"Ahem — as I was saying, Miss —"

"I'm sorry, Fenton. What were you saying?"

"That's quite all right, Miss. I know you have much on your mind. I was saying that there's a lot of strangers about. Look at those two automobiles parked on the road to the island. It's indecent for them to stay there and watch while you are entertaining, Miss."

"That is public land, Fenton. I doubt if they are paying any attention to us. A short time ago, I saw two persons walking on the island."

"But that's not public land, it's yours, Miss Lissa."

"What harm can they do? The lighthouse is locked." She dropped to a rug. "Give me the tray. Those clams are cooked to perfection. Is there enough of everything?"

"Yes, Miss. There'll be plenty of food after everyone here has eaten all he can."

"I'm glad the provisions are holding out. The leftovers won't be wasted. The men will take them home to their families." She asked in a low voice; "Are they helping willingly, Fenton? You know what they have threatened?"

"I do, Miss Lissa, but they aren't growling. Oh, no, they're just tumbling over each other to help. Act to me like parties who've been shaken up a bit and set down hard. I suppose Mr. Carson will be back before they — they walk out, Miss?"

"He expected to get here in time for the lobster-bake. If he doesn't come, you and I will have to carry on, Fenton."

"We can do it, Miss. It's a pity Master Andy wasn't allowed to come. He would have liked this, but I suppose they have to be very careful of him. He's a wonderful boy, Miss Lissa. He and I are great friends, if it's not presuming of me to say so. I'll serve the mackerel, Miss."

He walked away with his long white apron flapping against his ankles. Lissa dangled a clam in melted butter and dropped it into her mouth.

"Aren't you a course behind, Miss Barclay?" Major Fane inquired and carefully lowered himself to the rug beside her.

"I am. Aren't these clams luscious? I've never tasted plumper ones. Forgive me if I neglect the gentle art of conversation while I catch up, will you, Major Fane?"

"Go on, eat. Wish I could, the smell of the steaming seaweed and cooking shell fish is likely to bring on one of my dizzy spells. I wish I'd stayed home. The doctors have put me on a strict diet. I've been a sick man."

Was he about to repeat the Inside Story of his body, Lissa wondered. He had given it in such detail once that she had felt like nothing so much as an X-Ray on an exploring expedition. She said hurriedly;

"If you can't eat, you can feast on the beauty of the world, though that's not particularly satisfying to a hungry man. The gold rim of sun capping that purple hill makes me think of the tiaras women were wearing a few years ago. There's just enough of a shore breeze to bring the scent of the pines and spruces. The sea is quiet except for an occasional swell. Looks as if it had had a permanent wave. I miss the floats of the lobster-pots that tossed like little white boats. Ozy has moved his traps to the other side of the island."

"Why?" the sharpness of the Major's

voice was in startling contrast to his dull eyes.

"More lobsters, of course. Here come the gulls! Gray. Brown. White. The air beats with the whir and flap of wings. Curious how they know when food is about. They are flocking from all directions like mammoth snow flakes in a blizzard. The white ones are the old fellows. The men must have thrown bread on the water to attract them."

Major Fane watched the soaring, diving, floating birds.

"Lucky devils to be able to eat."

"Cheerio, Major, after a month or two more in this glorious air, you'll be able to eat anything you want. Wasn't that kingfisher that flew by, blue? Do you recognize the tune Johnny Grant is playing? It's the latest smash-hit. There goes the sun in a blaze of color. It's a gorgeous world!"

Major Fane grunted skeptically;

"It may be to those who have digestions." He shook his head at Fenton who was tempting him with a small, plump mackerel, flanked by a potato whose snowy interior, dusted with paprika, was bursting through its thin pink skin.

"New potatoes," the Major groaned. "I love 'em."

He drew a small box from his pocket and

extracted a white tablet. He chewed on it solemnly as he watched Lissa daintily de-bone the fish.

"Good?" he asked and swallowed hard.

"Perfect. Can't you eat anything, Major?"

"I'll have some of the watermelon when it comes along. They're cutting it now! I never saw anything so pink and crisp." He crunched his teeth in anticipation.

"I'm glad there is something you can enjoy. Ozy cracked this lobster to perfection, Fenton," she approved as she accepted the tin plate with its crimson cargo the butler offered.

"Who's Ozy?" the Major demanded testily as Fenton turned away. "I understood when I accepted the invitation that only the family from the big house, Kent and his guests and the tenants would be present. I don't like strangers." He was shaky with resentment.

"Don't be disturbed, Major. Is it possible that you have been here for weeks and haven't heard of Captain Ozias who does any kind of an errand, for anybody? You may need him yourself some time. I hope your digestion has improved since you came to Pirates' Den?"

His answer was good for a five minute monologue at least. The tide swished a soft accompaniment to the drone of his voice and Lissa's thoughts as her eyes traveled from group to group seated on rugs flung on the pebbly shore. Everyone seemed content. Fenton was helping Ozy carve the melons. Lex hadn't come.

"And he was paying just as much attention to what I was saying as you are paying now," Major Fane reminded pointedly.

Startled, Lissa met his eyes. They were strange, sharp eyes, eyes she never had seen before. Even as she stared back at them, they dulled. Had they changed at all, or had she imagined it? She apologized;

"I'm sorry, Major. My attention did wander. You see, I feel the responsibility of this party as the host isn't here. I —"

"What's that dog dragging down the garden path? Where'd he get that?" the Major demanded as the Irish terrier proudly laid a coat at Lissa's feet. It was a man's tweed coat, much the worse for wear.

"G-Man, where did you get this?" she demanded sternly.

The dog looked up at her with beady, brown eyes that twinkled, opened his mouth and ran out a pink tongue.

The Major caught the coat from her hand, scowled at it, turned it insideout, examined the lining. Returned it.

"Thought it might be mine. I like old coats. But it isn't. Shall I take charge of it for you?"

The hint of restrained eagerness in his voice had the effect of a red Stop! signal on Lissa's mind. The Major wanted that coat. All the more reason why only Lex should have it. Apparently none of the other guests had seen G-Man bring it. Fenton, who might know to whom it belonged, was talking with Ozy. She would make no inquiries about it until Lex had seen it. She tucked it securely under her arm.

"Nice of you, Major, to offer, but as my dog stole it, I feel the responsibility of returning it. At last! Here comes Lex Carson!"

18

"Come over and enjoy your melon with Mrs. Barclay, Major," Lissa suggested in an effort to divert his attention from the coat. "She told me she liked you. What's the secret of your devastating fascination for women?"

"You're laughing at me, Miss Melissa. Nobody loves a dyspeptic."

"But apparently most of them marry," Lissa responded dryly.

She left him seated on a rug beside her stepmother and heard him launch into a description of his late operation before she turned away. A hand caught her arm.

"Watch your step, beautiful! You'd have plunged into that pan of clam shells in a minute!"

She looked up and met Lex Carson's eyes. Why, why should they set her heart aflame when she knew that he loved Madge Millard? For an instant she saw the gorgeous western sky through a mist, had to steady her voice before she answered;

"I've had the responsibility of this party on my mind, Lex. Atlas upholding the heavens on his shoulders and hands had nothing on me, and to add the last perfect touch, G-Man stole this coat."

He took it, looked it over, frowned intently at the lining.

"No tailor's name on it. Any idea where it came from?"

"Not the slightest. That bad dog was three quarters of the way down the garden path before we saw him. He might have brought it from a neighbor's, the big house, or the Packards'. Your guess is as good as mine. G-Man moves in a mysterious way, his snitching to perform. Major Fane looked it over just as you did. He offered to take charge of it till the owner was found." She added the last sentence in a lowered voice. Lex Carson's eyes questioned hers.

"He did? Nice of him, but as the coat was deposited on my land, I'm responsible for it." He dropped it behind a boulder. "I'll pick it up later. Realize I haven't seen you for three days, Lissa? What have you been doing?"

"Writing every morning."

"How's the old imagination working?"

"Overtime. Better plots and more of them is its slogan. I've been doing some village visiting and each family suggested a story. I love people. They're my assets. They are interesting to me even when they're shallow and inconsequential. Maupassant and O. Henry would have written masterpieces from some of the things I saw and heard."

"If you get ideas here, you'll get a kick from living in Washington. There's a story to every square inch there."

Lissa's eyes were wide with surprise as she looked at him. A smile lurked in the depths of his.

"But I'm not going to Washington."

"Oh yes, you are. You don't know it, but you are. I'm psychic!" he added in a perfect imitation of her voice and inflection. Before she could reply, he asked confidentially;

"Any news about the proposed walk-out?"

"Nothing definite. I talked with Marty Simonds today. I think she'll stop it."

"More power to her. I don't want things stirred up here now, if I can prevent it. By the way, I'm through my estate business for the present, if nothing breaks, I've put across a deal. I'll take two weeks vacation before I return to Washington. You and I are going places, beautiful. We'll begin to celebrate tonight. Tod wants us to wind up this party on his boat. I'll take you out."

Lissa quickly turned away. She flung over her shoulder;

"Sorry. I have a date!"

237

"Perhaps now Lex will understand that I won't pinch-hit for Madge Millard," she told herself.

"G-Man, why are you such a bad boy?" she demanded of the Irish terrier, who trotted along beside her.

The dog sniffed, put his forepaws on her knees and looked up with adoring eyes. She pulled his ears.

"Old splendid! You know I'm crazy about you. You know while you've been helping Andy get well, I've missed you, don't you? You may stay if you won't beg for anything to eat. Remember the last picnic? I was up with you all night. Come on! Let's speak to Marty." She raced along the shore with the dog at her heels.

"Lands sake how red your cheeks are, child," Marty Simonds exclaimed. "Look as if you'd been bending over these steaming barrels, but I know you haven't." She lowered her voice. "I called on all the wives today and you may tell Mr. Carson that there won't be a walk-out."

"Really? What magic did you use?"

Marty Simonds cocked her head. Her eyes snapped like those of an angry sparrow.

" 'Twasn't magic. It was only my tongue and their common sense. I told them that the men were going to give up their pay rather than take a cut in wages — they didn't know about the planned walk-out — and I guessed they'd better make the most of those dresses they were knitting as it would be a long time before they bought so much as a shoe-lace. They just firmed their jaws and said, 'There won't be a walk-out.' And if I know women, and I do, there won't be one. Ozy is wig-wagging to you, child. Be sure you don't let on to him a word of what I told you."

"I won't, Marty."

Lissa crossed the beach to Captain Ozias. Whispered;

"Did you want me, Ozy?"

He handed her a pie-shaped slice of melon. She bit deep into its pink lusciousness. The dog whined suggestively.

"No. Not even a scrap, G-Man. Thanks ever so much for helping, Ozy."

The Captain pushed back the brim of his hat, sniffed like a hound, flashed his ferret-like eyes around before he warned;

"Don't grin at me like that, folks'll suspect something. Is the light unlocked, Lissa?"

"You mean the lighthouse on my island? No, but I have the key in my pocket. I'm planning to stop on my way to the cruiser to get some papers I left there. Do you want it?"

"Shsh! Keep the key but when you shut the lighthouse door, leave the latch up, so's I can git in later. Tell Lex I got to talk with him. Tell him to stay behind after the others have gone."

"I will, but —"

"Git goin'! Git goin'! Here comes Tod. Don't let him come now. I can't be bothered."

Lissa slipped her hand under Kent's arm.

"You'll take your life in your hands, Tod, if you approach the melon carver. I asked him a simple question and he did everything to discourage me but brandish his knife. Bend your head as if you were looking at my sports bracelet. Lex told me why The Sphinx is here. Ozy wants to speak to him. Tell him to wait after the others have gone to the cruiser. Tell him also that I think there's something queer about Major Fane."

"Why?"

"Haven't time to explain. The Major is looking at us." She raised her voice.

"I'm going to the cruiser in our small motorboat. I have to stop at the island and I'm taking Mr. Packard along."

It took some diplomacy and a certain

amount of dodging of Johnny Grant before, with Ralph Packard in the stern, Lissa swung the wheel of the motorboat for the island. She had a feeling that if Lex had not been talking to Ozy, she wouldn't have gotten away, no matter how much she dodged.

"What's on your mind, Miss Barclay?" Ralph Packard asked. "You haven't smiled since we left the pier."

"Nothing on my mind, now that the lobster-bake is behind me. I did want it to be a success and I think it was. Isn't The Sphinx a beauty? Already it is strung with lights. See the shimmery reflections."

The man in the stern did not answer. Hands on the wheel, she turned to look at him. He was regarding the rocky, white fringed shore ahead. Her eyes followed his.

"Perfect, isn't it? I never approach the island without being thrilled that it is mine. I love every inch of it. Aunt Hetty asked me not to sell it, except under dire necessity, but, if editors remain firm in their refusal to see in me a potential best-seller and to assist in a wider distribution of the fruits of my industry — that last is a quotation, in case you care — I may have to. That topmost ridge looks like the back of a seamonster rising from the water. The shallows and

241

tide-pools have been dyed claret by the afterglow. Here we are."

The boat slid into a sheltered cove and along the side of the float. G-Man jumped out and dashed away. Packard took the painter from the girl's hand.

"I'll fasten it."

"Thanks. When I come ashore here, I can't decide whether I feel more like Robinson Crusoe or the-world-is-mine Monte Cristo."

They mounted the runway, crossed the pier and followed the path to the light. Lissa called;

"What are you digging at, G-Man? Did you cache a bone the last time we were here?"

She dropped to her knees beside the dog who was pawing furiously in a bed of hardy pink and red Shirley poppies beneath a window of the white house. She pulled him away by the collar.

"You're ruining my flowers. My word — there is something."

She pulled at a scrap of black oilcloth sticking up from the damp earth. She dug around it with a sharp flat stone.

"Help, Mr. Packard! Buried treasure!"

He stood behind her with his hands in his pockets.

"Take care! You may pull up something infernally unpleasant, perhaps a skull."

She sank back on her heels and pushed her hair away from her eyes.

"Think I'm afraid of an old skull?" she demanded scornfully. "Where's your spirit of adventure? I intended to go fifty-fifty with you," her words came breathlessly as she dug, "but if you won't help — hooray! I have it!"

She sank back on her heels and raised a heavy pouch of black oilcloth, the size of an able-bodied coconut. G-Man sniffed at it, lost interest and rolled on his back on the pebbly walk that circled the light.

Now that she had the thing in her hand, Lissa's heart beat uncomfortably fast. What was inside? Not a skull. It was too heavy for that. She looked up at the man who was staring at the black oilskin pouch in her hand. She shook it.

"Listen! It sounds like money!"

"Better put it back where you found it, Miss Barclay. Whatever is in it may have belonged to a pirate — pirates were a dirty lot — the man who buried it may have had scarlet-fever or —"

"Scarlet-fever! I believe you are frightened, your voice is shaky. If you're imagining horrors, think of something worse than

243

scarlet-fever. Have you a knife? Cut the cord for me, will you?"

"I will not. I won't help you. I don't believe in touching that dirty thing."

"All right, if you feel that way about it, I'll untie the cord. I won't be stumped."

Lissa tugged at the tarred twine. Stopped to flex her fingers and tugged again.

"Darn! There goes my pet fingernail! It's coming! It's untied! Stand back! This is the dramatic moment for the cameras to start turning. Pandora loosed a wicked genie when she opened a buried box, I may loose a demon germ. I —"

One corner of the pouch slipped from her fingers. A stream of silver poured forth and scattered on the ground. She stared at the coins incredulously.

"That hasn't been buried here since piracy was in flower. It's nothing but a lot of our own money, half dollars, quarters."

She dropped to one knee and picked up a coin. She turned it over.

"It's new money! Brand new money!"

She looked from the scattered coins up into the eyes of the silent man frowning down at them.

"Who could have put it here?"

Even as she asked the question she remembered the automobiles parked on the road which connected mainland and island, and saw as plainly as if pictured on a screen, two figures walking toward the lighthouse. That didn't help. The pouch had been buried more than a few hours.

Packard shrugged and thrust his hands deeper into his blue coat pockets.

"Why ask me who put the money there? You jeered when I told you not to open the pouch. I'd advise you to tie it up and put it back where you found it. We don't need a crystal-gazer to tell us that it is stolen money which has been hidden here till the hue and cry of pursuit dies down. It gives me the creeps to think what may happen to you if the crook who buried it suspects that you've found those coins."

19

Crook! Stolen money! The words exploded in Lissa's mind like depth bombs catapulted from the smooth flow of his voice. Coins!

Her heart stopped and raced on. Lex had said that he was after a man who made bogus bills and coins. Ozy had asked her to leave the lighthouse door unlatched! He had had something to tell Lex. Did he know about the money? If he did, ten to one he would mess things up. These might be counterfeit coins! Lex must know of her find. She had promised she would help him and the chance had come. She must be careful that Ralph Packard did not suspect what she was thinking. She said breathlessly;

"Isn't this the most exciting thing? What a story I could make of it! What a grand story! I'm not crazy, though, about your suggestion as to what crooks might do to me. It loosed a million little nerve wigglers up and down my spine. Now that you're sure that this isn't germ-ridden pirate gold, help me put it back, will you?"

"Why put it back? You own this island. If I know my law — and I think I do — anything buried here is yours legally. Let's take the pouch along. Hide it under the seat of your boat and in the morning I'll see that you get it."

"I could do that — but — no, no, I'll leave it here. It might start trouble were I to take it to Tarry Farm."

She scrambled up the coins. Packard dropped to one knee and helped. She pleaded;

"Hurry, please hurry! I'm getting jittery. I read the papers. I know what horrid things happen. Only a few more. Is anyone coming? I'll finish. Is there a boat in sight?"

As he stood up to look at the harbor, she slipped a coin into the pocket of her white frock. If she couldn't get the pouch to Lex, she could produce a sample.

"All in! Help me tie it up. Please! My fingers are thumbs. Lucky you didn't have a knife with which to cut the cord, isn't it? There! It's back in the hole."

She spread the earth carefully in place and stood up.

"Directly under the kitchen window," she said to herself before she suggested;

"Now we'll pray for rain to cover our tracks. Look at my hands and the dirt on my gown! That will take some explaining when we get to the cruiser."

"Why go to the cruiser? Let's get my manuscript and return to Tarry Farm. We can sit on the terrace and talk writing till the others come. I detest parties."

Something in his voice and eyes sent Lissa's heart to her throat. "Silly," she derided herself. "You like him, don't you?" Aloud she insisted;

"I must go to the cruiser, I promised Tod I would. Hear the woodpecker! He had to start drilling to add to the eeriness of the situation. I wish those gulls we disturbed would stop screaming. I'm on edge. I'll unlock the lighthouse and get your story while you stand guard. The person who buried the coins may have a side-kick who's hiding here."

She put the key in the lock and swung open the door. For an instant the service room was still, uncannily still — then — the wicker chair creaked.

Lissa's heart beat like a drum. Who had been sitting in it? Had Ralph Packard noticed the sound? Apparently not. He was frowning a little as he lighted a cigarette.

She dashed across the room, snatched up the manuscript beside the typewriter and joined him at the door.

"Here's your story. It's good. You have a fine style. Who was it said 'style in writing is like good manners in human intercourse'? It reminds me of one of the big writers. Can't remember which, the resemblance keeps teasing at my mind. Let's go."

"Why hurry? I'd like to see the lamp-room again. Want to use it — for atmosphere. May I?"

"Of course. Meanwhile I'll get some of this grime off my hands in the kitchen."

The sound of his footsteps clanged through the still tower as he ran up the narrow circular iron stairway. Lissa bathed her hands hurriedly and returned to the entrance door. She heard the swish, swish, of the tide against the rocky shore. The music of Johnny's ukulele and Jack Millard's voice singing came from the cruiser;

> " 'You are my lucky star
> I saw you from afar —' "

Green and red lights had blossomed on boats swinging with the tide. A pale egg-shaped moon was tip-tilted above a hill like Humpty Dumpty peering with owlish eyes above his wall. Tiny white ruffles rimmed the ledges. A brilliant star pricked through the darkening sky. The juniper scented air was like wine, it left a salty taste on her lips.

Ralph Packard was coming down the

stairs. Cautiously she adjusted the door-latch. What curious impulse had prompted her to make him believe that she was frightened? There had been something in his expression as he had looked down at the scattered coins, a flash of triumph that went as quickly as a flash of lightning — that had caught at her breath. He had been almost eager when he had suggested that she take the pouch with her. She'd better make sure that the coin was secure. If by mistake, she pulled it from her pocket it would take some explaining.

Quickly she tied the bright quarter in the corner of her handkerchief and thrust it in her blouse.

"Ready to go?" she asked eagerly as Packard crossed the room.

His eyes sharpened.

"All over your attack of jitters, aren't you?"

She wished he wouldn't stand so near. Only yesterday she had read an article on thought transmission, how minute electric waves, constantly being produced by the brain, will respond to suggestion. The writer was all for it. Ralph Packard must not suspect that she was planning somehow, someway, to get that pouch to Lex. She corrected;

"Attack of imagination expresses it better. You, if anyone, ought to realize that my imagination is my fortune, kind sir, she said. I haven't recovered so entirely that I want to hang around this light with dusk coming on. Enter Jupiter, the brightest star to become visible in the twilight. Look at the fireflies in that dark clump of arborvitae darting and flashing for all the world like a lot of fallen stars making whoopee. Scram, G-Man and don't stop to dig up any more buried treasure."

Packard followed as she and the dog ran ahead. She was on the float untying the painter when he came up.

"Why didn't you wait and let me do that?" he demanded. "I'm crew."

"He's too slow to be crew for us, isn't he, G-Man?" she inquired of the Irish terrier, already sprawled on the bow of the motorboat. She frowned at the dog. "What shall I do with you? I forgot when I brought you along, that we were going to the cruiser. You'll have to go home across the bar. Come here!"

The dog jumped to the float. As he sat back stubbornly on his haunches, she caught his collar and dragged him up the incline to the pier and into the road. She pointed.

251

"Go home, G-Man. You know the way, you've walked across the bar with me often enough. Go! I can't take you with me."

She watched him as he trotted forward a few feet, stopped and looked back.

"Go on!" she called.

Lissa followed him with her eyes until he reached the bar road. She returned to the float.

"He'll go home now. Let's go!"

Packard stood beside her as the boat glided through a smooth sea toward the cruiser. He suggested;

"Why mention the coins you found? Let's keep the buried treasure a secret between us. Finding that pouch and working out the mystery of its being there will make a grand story. You and I will collaborate, make a hit with it and sell it to the movies. No danger that you will have to sell your island after that."

"You must believe in fairies. If we are going to do all that, perhaps we should have brought along the coins, instead of leaving them behind us on the island."

She glanced back over the white wake the boat was kicking up.

"Look! See that speck on the pier? It's G-Man, bad boy! I won't go back for him. If he doesn't cross the bar road before the tide turns he'll have to stay there. It will be good discipline. Here we are at The Sphinx. Isn't she a beauty!"

The white-capped sailors with boat-hooks were posted at the head of the boarding ladder to catch the motorboat as it drew alongside the cruiser. Ralph Packard warned quickly;

"Don't mention the coins. Mum's the word or someone may steal our plot stuff. Is it a bargain? Shake on it." He held out his hand.

"Hi, you two!" Tod Kent hailed from the forward cockpit. "Get a hustle on, will you? What's the big idea standing there holding hands? We've been waiting for you. Now that my guests have inspected the refrigerating system, engines, radio, housekeeping and living quarters, they're frothing at the mouth to be off on a cruise down the bay."

Lissa hastened on board. Good old Tod! His hail had come just in time. She hadn't promised Ralph Packard that she wouldn't tell about the coins. He had a reason for wanting to keep secret the finding of them besides using the buried pouch for plot material, she was sure of it. She must tell Lex. She apologized eagerly;

"I'm sorry to have held up the party, terribly sorry, Tod. We were detained by —"

253

"My awkwardness, Kent," Ralph Packard's smooth voice took up the explanation. "I fumbled the painter, my burned fingers are still all thumbs — and the rope got mixed up in the propeller."

There was warning in his eyes as they met Lissa's. How silly for him to tell that rigmarole about the rope and the propeller, she thought.

"Glad to know why you were so late. I was just coming after you," announced Lex Carson, who was standing behind Kent.

"Why should you feel anxious about Miss Barclay when she is with me?" Ralph Packard questioned aggressively as he stood at the girl's shoulder.

"I've told you before, my sense of responsibility. Tod, the launch has been hoisted aboard and your guests are clamoring to start."

Lissa's mind was in a tumult as she passed along the wide side deck to the after cockpit. Was Ralph Packard really a writer? For the first time she doubted it. There had been something familiar about his stories which teased at her memory.

"Sit here, Lissa." Jack Millard rose from one of the gayly cushioned wicker chairs. Cleo detained Packard by a white hand.

"Thanks no, Jack. I'll sit at the stern. I

love the smooth motion of the boat, love to hear and see the water rush by, especially when there's phosphorescence as there is tonight. Johnny, bring your ukulele over here. The night and the boat were made for it. Jack, if you want to add the perfect touch to Tod's party you'll sit here and sing for us. Johnny, don't scowl. It's frightfully unbecoming."

Jack Millard perched beside her. They sat with their feet on the great circular leather seat in the stern. His blue eyes were alight with laughter. He took one gray flannel knee into his embrace.

"Am I unpopular with the gentleman on your left? I'll say I am. But when an old married man like myself is singled out to sit beside a swell girl, like you, does he hesitate? He does not." He added so that Lissa alone could hear; "Has Packard been annoying you? You were a long time on that island."

"How did you know where I was?"

"Lex had to go to the big house and was the last to come aboard. When he found that you and Packard hadn't arrived, Tod and I had all we could do to keep him from going after you. For some reason he doesn't like your glossy friend. I don't either. Know what I suspect, that he's looking for a wife to help him socially. Apparently, he doesn't need money, but he needs social backing, there's a suggestion of toughness under his gloss."

"He may be glossy but he's interesting to me."

"But you tried to shake him a few minutes ago, didn't you? You didn't ask me to sit here because of my irresistible charm, did you now?"

"You're too modest," Lissa retorted gaily. "I do like you immensely. When the world seems topsy-turvy I look at you and your wife and things steady. You seem so honestly in love after fifteen years of marriage. You are so — so courteous to one another."

"Why that word, 'seem'? I don't like it. We are. What did you expect, that I would beat her? Sounds as if you'd been unfortunate in the husbands and wives you've met." The laughter left his voice and eyes; "No one could help adoring Madge, she has such a lovely soul. She is looking a lot better, isn't she? She's coming out of the fog of fear she has lived in since Andy's illness. She has plenty of time for me, now. With the crushing anxiety of the boy off our minds, we're honeymooning a bit. You've helped tremendously, Lissa."

As if she felt that he was speaking of her, his wife turned her head and smiled. Soft color mounted to her forehead as her eyes met her husband's. That didn't look as if she were in love with Lex. Evidently he was doing the loving, Lissa decided.

"Why is your world topsy-turvy tonight?" Jack Millard asked.

"Can't tell you why, it just was. It isn't now. Do you get the scent of flowers from shore? Reminds me of the fragrance that drifted toward us from Flores, an island miles away, when my father and I were sailing past the Azores. Isn't Jupiter brilliant? How red Mars looks. I've never seen them so close together. The Milky Way makes me think of a bride's veil of malines being trailed across the sky, it is made of star dust and thousands of baby stars, isn't it? See the dark patches? Until recently, they were thought to be holes into the atmosphere. Now astronomers have discovered that they are collections of nebulae that do not shine. Those fleecy clouds sailing along look like a fleet of airships with silver-tipped wings. Truly 'The heavens declare the glory of God; and the firmament showeth his handiwork.' "

"You'd get a better effect from the bow cockpit, Miss Barclay."

257

Ralph Packard's suggestion broke into Lissa's rapturous study of the heavens with the devastating effect of an elephant plunging through a rose garden.

"She will not," Johnny Grant declined for her belligerently. "She asked me to park beside her, and she's spent every moment since either monologuing about the perfect husband at her right, discoursing on the heavens, or quoting Shakespeare. I'll bet she's practicing on us in the hope of landing a job as lecturer in a planetarium. Scram, Packard. She now talks to me. Jack may keep his seat if he wants to, but the girl is mine."

"In that case, 'The Captains and the Kings depart,' — that isn't Shakespeare, Johnny, I'll go too." Jack Millard linked his arm in Packard's. "It has been subtly indicated that we are not wanted. Come on. I need a smoke."

20

As the two men walked forward, Lissa's glance lingered on Sidonie Packard who was talking to Lex Carson. It could hardly be called talking, she was looking glamorous and seductive and he appeared as fascinated as a gentleman-spider gazing at a lady-spider's web. Men certainly were easy marks. Johnny Grant twanged a few soft notes.

"Why that impatient sigh, sweet thing? You're right, about Millard, he and his wife do restore one's faith in the honorable estate of matrimony, and they have a great kid. I've never cared much for small boys, but I like that one. Jack and Madge are corking together, not mushy, but somehow you just know that their love is the real stuff, though he did do a bit of hovering about Cleo. I'm willing to bet my roadster that she did the hovering. Packard's her love interest at present and he seems that way about her. Watch Sidonie the Dumb angling for Lex Carson. She isn't the first woman who's tried for him. There was a story going the rounds in Washington that his heart is buried in the grave of his first love, as if that happened in this age and generation."

"Cynicism in tweeds! What a gossip you are, Johnny!"

"Perhaps I am, but I noticed you listened with all your ears. I wouldn't be a cynic with you, and I'm not so dumb as you and Jack Millard think I am, either. I knew you were quoting the nineteenth Psalm, took a course in Bible Lit in college. I called it Shakespeare to get a rise out of you. Marry me, will you?"

Lissa shook her head.

"Why — because of Cleo?"

"No. I've had days and years in which to think since we were engaged, Johnny. I've been growing a lot of principles for living. In my travels I've had a chance to play round with the sort of people you like, the 'restless moderns' someone called them, people who rush from one social date to another, who dally with thoughts of tawdry infidelities and tarnished adventures until they slip into fact. I've also met the normal healthy-minded people — I don't mean that they're perfect — who still believe in the Ten Commandments; the comfort and healing of prayer; in large doses of humor in their daily lives and the working efficacy of the Golden Rule. I like them best and they would bore you to death."

"Straight from the shoulder! Got anything else against me except the set I run around with?"

"Not much. I like you, Johnny, I've grown to like you more than ever this summer, but liking isn't loving, besides, I won't marry a man who gets even a little drunk. It will get him down after a while and I don't want a husband who is down."

"How long since you've been a teetotaler?"

"I've always been a teetotaler for myself, you know that. I hate cheapness, and if you could see and more particularly hear yourself — you've made my face burn like fire — when you are in what you call an 'incandescent glow,' you'd know what I mean by cheap."

"Thanks for them kind words. I suppose you picked up your anti-glow ideas from your trustee, Carson. I've never seen him drink anything stronger than coffee. I've wondered a lot about that lad. He's a lawyer, he has an office and I know some of his clients, but, sometimes I suspect that's not all of it."

"What else could there be?"

"Don't get excited. I don't mean anything shady. I like him even if he is inclined to be high-handed with me and treat me as if I

261

were a kid — he's the straightest-shooter I know — but, when the modern man doesn't drink, it makes one suspect he may be keeping his head clear for a purpose. I know an actor who won't touch sherry even for fear it might crack up his memory while he's in the midst of a speech on the stage. Must be wearing to have a job like that."

Lissa looked at him incredulously. Johnny Grant was the last person she would have supposed would see below the surface of a personality. It would be wise to get off the subject of Lex. She said quickly;

"I wonder why Fenton is here. In his Tarry Farm regalia, too. He must have been a lightning-change artist at some time in his career. I've never yet found out what that lavish sprinkle of silver buttons on the tail of his dark green coat means."

"They're as big as quarters, aren't they, and as bright as new money."

New money! The words flashed a picture of the buried coins. Lissa put her hand to her breast. The coin was there. She could feel its hardness against her flesh. She had been foolish to leave that pouch behind. Hadn't Ralph Packard said that it was hers legally? Of course it wasn't and she wouldn't touch the money, but how stunned Lex and Tod would be if she produced it and told where she had found it. She must get it. How?

"When stuck go into reverse."

The words echoed through her mind as clearly as if broadcast from a radio. Why? She had sent her hero into reverse when she had pulled her novel out of a threatened impasse. Was it an answer to her quandary about the coins? Go into reverse. She had left the island. Did that mean that she was to return to it? If she didn't heed that inner voice it might be discouraged and never help her again. G-Man might not have crossed the bar. She could use him as an excuse for returning to the island.

It wouldn't do to start back alone. She must have someone with her. Not Lex nor Tod, she wanted to stage a surprise. Why not Johnny? Perfect! She whispered;

"My own motorboat, the one Aunt Hetty willed to me, is at The Sphinx mooring. When we get back to it, insist upon taking me home, then we'll slip over to the island, will you, Johnny?"

Johnny Grant stared at her as if doubting his ears.

"Have you gone haywire or have I, sweet thing? Of course I'll take you, but —"

"Shsh! Miss Packard is looking at us —"

"Ahem!"

Fenton, who had appeared with the suddenness of a rabbit prestidigitated from the air, presented a tray.

"I opened some sparkling catawba for you, Miss Lissa." He lowered his voice; "I hope you don't mind my coming on board, but Mr. Kent's steward is indisposed and Mr. Kent asked me if I would help out. I was very glad to be of service. It's a beautiful boat. Quite the last word in cruisers, I'd say, Miss Lissa."

"Why should I mind, Fenton? Mr. Carson is your employer, not I."

"Of course, Miss, but I've taken orders from you for so long, it seems natural to ask you. I hope the punch is quite as you like it, Mr. Grant?"

"Quite, Fenton. What this country needs is more butlers like you. If you mixed that, you may have a job with me any time you're out of one."

"Thank you, sir, but I don't expect to be out of one. I'm hoping that Mr. Carson will need me in Washington, sir." He moved on with the tray.

"Isn't he ripping? Quite the last word in butlers, I'd say, Miss Lissa."

"You've missed your vocation, Johnny. You should be giving impersonations before a mike. That was Fenton's voice to a tone.

Does — does Lex Carson keep house in Washington?"

"I think not. I know that he gives small, select parties at his club. I met him the first time at a dinner. As he and I are both bachelors, we are invited out a lot. Now what's coming? Fenton's setting up a table and Kent is producing a book and a fountain pen. Let's go see."

Lissa caught his sleeve.

"Johnny! Wait! You will take me to the island, won't you? I've left G-Man there. I can't bear the thought of his spending the night alone."

"Sure, I'll take you, but you make a baby of that dog. Do him good to be lonesome."

"I know it would, but I love him. Don't let anyone know we are going. We might be stopped."

The cruiser, trailing a wake like a coiling, fiery serpent all shimmering scales, glided through a smooth sea, past wooded islands, a ghostly beach and an anchored vessel loaded to the gunwales with lumber. Washing on lines strung from cabin to mast hung limp and motionless like bodies with the filling gone out of them. The port light peered into the night like a great red eye. From the ship drifted a bar of dance music.

The wash of the cruiser roused the buoy. It moaned faintly. The moon hung in the heavens like a gleaming one-sided twenty-dollar gold piece. The stars of the Great Dipper shone steadily. Polaris, which tipped the handle of the Little Dipper, glowed like a jewel in a spangled canopy. A flaming meteor hissed through the purple velvet sky and vanished.

Tod Kent picked up a book and opened it to show a page.

"Fingerprints! Now what do you know about that," Johnny Grant exclaimed. "Quite the last word in autograph albums, I'd say, old boy. What?"

Lissa pinched his arm as Fenton, who was holding a tray with the rigidity of a cigar-store wooden Indian, glanced at him from between narrowed lids. Apparently the imperturbable calm of the butler could be pricked, he knew that he was being mimicked. Tod Kent laid the open book on the table.

"It's an original with me, Johnny, and am I proud of it? Got the idea when I heard that the precinct stations alone are registering about three hundred civilian fingerprint volunteers a day. Most of the high-bracket income lads are on file. It's a fool-proof method of identification. I've got the prints of the great, near-great and not great-at-all within those covers. So far everyone who has sailed on this boat, even to the crew and Jap boys, has been willing to come across."

As he talked, he removed a metal ink-pad, a rubber roller, cotton waste and a bottle labeled "alcohol" from the tray Fenton held and laid them on the table.

"I don't want anyone to do it who'd rather not. I've given orders to anchor, the least motion might blur the prints. This way boys and girls! It's quick and painless! Who'll be the first?"

There was an instant of silence broken only by the creak of anchor chains and a splash, before Lissa Barclay held up her hand as if she were a school girl answering, "Present!"

"Good little sport! Come on!"

Kent pulled out a chair at the table.

"I don't know why the thought of pressing inky fingers on that blank page should set little shivers tobogganing down my spine, but it does," Lissa confided as she sat down. "Hope my hand won't be shaky, and blur the prints. The rest of you have the advantage of watching me. You'll know just how to do it."

She looked up at the faces about the table. They had the intent look of persons expecting something, they knew not what, to jump from a box. Ralph Packard's eyes were narrowed, his lips were touched with a cynical smile. His sister's face was expressionless, as arm linked in his, she looked down. Cleo stood beside Johnny Grant, arm in arm the Millards smiled at Lissa.

"Jack and I have done it, it doesn't hurt," Madge encouraged.

"Hurry, Melissa! I'm so anxious to try it," Mrs. Barclay twittered, "aren't you, Major?"

Major Fane, perched on the rail, shook his head.

"Don't believe in it! Wouldn't have come aboard if I'd thought I'd be asked to do such a darnfool thing." He puffed out his lips with little explosive breaths.

Tod Kent grinned at him.

"Calm yourself, Major, as has been said before, nothing obligatory about this. You'd better come off that rail or resentment may pitch you overboard." He held out a pen.

"Put your name and the date at the bottom of the page, Lissa. All set? Here goes."

He ran the roller over the pad and then over her hands.

"There you are! Nicely inked. Lay the fingers of your right hand, one at a time, on the page. Don't press hard! Now all the fingers at once. That-a-girl! Repeat with the left. Perfect! Lex, I'll appoint you hand-cleaner extraordinary."

That, Carson acknowledged, was handsome of him. He picked up some cotton waste and the alcohol bottle.

"Come over here, Lissa, and get your hands cleaned."

"But, I want to see someone else do it. Johnny's sitting down."

He led her to the stern before she could protest.

"Sit up here with your feet on the seat and you can see your adored Johnny. Is he your adored Johnny?"

He looked up from the hand he was swabbing with alcohol-soaked waste. She kept her eyes on her inky fingers.

"Who are you to probe the secrets of a maiden's heart?" she demanded flippantly.

"The man who loves you."

Her lashes flew up.

"Loves me! Who's fiction-minded, now? Hero rescues lovely girl from watery grave — that's me, in case you don't recognize the description — and embraces wife of friend."

"I can explain that, Lissa."

"You're crushing my hand. Now Mother

269

Barclay is being fingerprinted. I want to see it done."

"Forget the fingerprinting. Look at me! Straight! Do you think I'd tell you I loved you if I were even pretending to love another woman? Something happened to me that never had happened before as my eyes met yours when I pulled you from the water. Believe me, darling?"

Lissa's heart soared with the speed and lightness of a runaway balloon. He mustn't know it, though. He had said that he could explain about Madge but he hadn't. "Remember Johnny, my girl, remember Johnny," she prodded herself. She veiled her eyes from the ardor in his.

"I don't believe you or any man. You're not an expert de-inker, are you? If Tod intends to take up fingerprinting as a leisure industry, he'd better get another helper. I wish Major Fane would come off that rail. If he were to have one of his dizzy spells, he'd go overboard. Fenton is standing beside him, but I doubt if he'd be much good pulling him out of the water."

The hard pressure on her hands sent her eyes to Carson's.

"Why are you scowling at me like that?"

His unsteady laugh tightened her throat.

"You'll have to read expressions better

than that before you'll make good as a writer. That wasn't a scowl, that was concentration. I was deciding whether to shake you or kiss you. Tod Kent saved you that night in my study, but now I've decided —"

"Our genial host is calling for the alcohol bottle," Ralph Packard's smooth voice flowed between them. "There are other hands to be cleaned, Carson. Much ink has rolled over fingers since Miss Barclay's were printed. Did he do a good job?"

Lissa held out smooched fingers.

"Not what you'd call perfect, but they'll do. Better hurry on to the next clean-up, Lex."

"Remember, I've come to a decision," he reminded and returned to the table.

"Did you tell him about the coins?" Ralph Packard demanded.

"Coins? What —" Lissa regarded with amazed eyes the man frowning at her. "Would you believe it? This fingerprinting drove that buried loot completely from my mind. Not only I haven't told anyone about the coins, I haven't thought of them."

"Now, Sidonie, it's your turn. After your fingerprints, we'll get Fenton's if he doesn't mind." Kent sent his voice over the heads of the group about the table to the butler who stood beside Major Fane perched on the rail. "You don't mind, do you, Fenton?"

Fenton put his fingers to his lips.

"Ahem! I should be proud to have my hands in such company, sir. I — My God, sir, am I losing my mind? Is that a flash from the lighthouse off the left side, sir?"

Everyone turned to look in the direction of the butler's pointing finger. The Major leaned backward. Ralph Packard rushed to his side and stared at the island. Lissa's heart pounded in her throat. A flash! From her light. Was someone signalling about the buried coins? Fenton wasn't imaginative. He was leaning over the rail straining his eyes — Oh —

"Quick! Quick!" she called. "The Major's overboard!"

21

Lex Carson flung off his coat. Kicked off his shoes. Dove from the rail. The boarding ladder was lowered. In a moment it was all over but the exclamations. White and shaky the Major was boosted to the deck. Between shivers he spluttered;

"Must have been one of my dizzy spells. Get me home, quick."

The order was given to make all speed ahead to The Sphinx's mooring. The Major was bundled in blankets and given something hot to drink. Ten minutes later in the shadow of the wheel house, Kent advised Carson, wrapped in a woolly top-coat;

"Better take the Major home, it will give you a chance to go ahead of the rest and change to dry clothes. Be at Tarry Farm float half an hour after the launch drops you. The wind has shifted. Those dark clouds rolling up mean a thunder storm. I've carried out your orders. The 'electrical engineers' have the coat you brought aboard. Ozy and I couldn't wait for you to get back from Boston so we went ahead and planned. If that infernal Major hadn't gone overboard, I would have had all the finger —"

"Of course Lex is all right, Sidonie," he answered the question of the woman who had appeared suddenly beside them. "He's going ashore with the Major as soon as we get back to our mooring. That officer and gentleman certainly smashed up my little party. It's gone cold. I'll never get the other fingerprints for my book now. Perhaps though, you'll let me have yours at some later date when you're on board?"

"I will, Tod. I wouldn't miss having my hands in such distinguished company. Will you mind if Ralph and I go ashore when the Major goes? I'm tired. I'll call this a day."

"Sure, you may go. They can land you on the way to the Major's. Pick up your things. There go the anchor chains."

As she turned away, he said in a low voice;

"Taking the Packards will delay you a little, Lex, but it's a break for me. I'll go with the second load and pretend to come back to the cruiser. I won't. I'll wait in the lee of the boathouse for Ozy."

As the launch got under way, Lex Carson spoke to the man at the wheel;

"To Red Chimneys first, Prescott."

He was aware of the brother and sister side by side in the stern, the murmur of their voices. They did not speak to him until the launch drew alongside the Red Chimneys float. As she stepped out of the boat, Sidonie Packard extended her hand;

"Thanks for bringing us home, Mr. Carson. I hope you've come to Tarry Farm to stay. It's your duty to devote some time to becoming acquainted with your tenants, isn't it, Major Fane?"

The Major grunted. Carson responded cordially;

"I wouldn't call that a duty, pleasure is the word. I'm through with estate matters now and have two weeks of pure vacation ahead, no work and all play. Good-night. Good-night, Packard. Push off, Prescott. If we don't get the Major home quick, we'll have a sick man on our hands."

He looked over his shoulder as the launch shot ahead through water which rippled darkly. The motorboat which Lissa had said was part of the equipment of Red Chimneys was not at its mooring. Where was it?

The moon was as indistinct as a face behind a veil of cigarette smoke. The same haze dulled mountains and islands. The tower of the lighthouse was faintly luminous as if it had been coated with radium that no amount of darkness could quite dim. The

275

lights on the cruiser were chunks of clouded amber.

"Tune her up, Prescott, looks like rain. Not that a little more water in our clothing would make much difference to you and me, eh Major?"

Major Fane's reply was muttered into the blanket muffled about his chin. As the launch slid up to the Pirates' Den landing, Carson jumped ashore and held out his hand.

"Here we are. I'll go to the house with you, Major. You might be dizzy again. I'm afraid you looked too long upon the lobster when it was red."

Major Fane glared from beneath shaggy brows.

"Didn't touch the lobster," he growled. "Wasn't dizzy. Someone pushed me."

"Who pushed you?" Lex Carson demanded sharply.

"It was either the butler or Packard. I don't like that brother and sister. I don't like their Italian houseman, either. He's always snooping round my place. Next time I hire a cottage, I'll find a landlord who's careful about his tenants. It's the last time you'll ever get me on a boat. Here come my house-boys. Must have been watching for me."

He climbed clumsily to the float and

joined the gesticulating Filipinos. Carson frowned as he watched the three cross the landing.

"He doesn't like the Packards, the oily Nino snoops around his cottage and he thinks Fenton or Packard pushed him overboard," he said to himself. "It wouldn't be Fenton's technic and Packard has too much at stake to risk an investigation. Get under way!" he ordered. "I felt a drop of rain."

Prescott tipped his white cap to a sharper angle;

"The Major certainly gave you an earful. Grateful, ain't he, Mr. Carson. Never said so much as 'Thank you'! for pulling him out of the water. Next time you'd better let him drown, and not risk your life, sir."

"There was no danger for me in that smooth sea. The Major is subject to dizzy spells and I feared he wouldn't be able to help himself."

"Dizzy, is it? Huh! I guess he's an old kill-joy from what I hear. They tell me he's got a radio outfit that's so powerful he could send or receive messages from the moon, if he wanted to. Something to do with the Army, he's a radio expert keeping in practice while on sick leave, folks in the village say. The other launch from the cruiser is at Tarry Farm pier, sir. See the dark figures scurrying to the Treasure Chest and up to the big house?"

"Here we are," he announced five minutes later as the boat slid alongside the lighted float. "Better hustle before you get caught in the rain, sir, there's a thunderstorm on the way."

Carson hustled, not because he cared about the rain — he couldn't be much wetter than he was — but because he wanted to speak to Lissa before she reached her room. When on the beach she had flung over her shoulder, "Sorry, I have a date," he had flamed with fury. At that moment he had been in perfect accord with the primitive man who dragged the woman he wanted off to his cave.

As he entered the hall, Cleo ran half way down the curving staircase. She stopped with one hand on the banister, the other over her heart. The hammered satin of her pale blue pajamas reflected the light in the sconce above her, her hair was a fluff of gold about her head.

"Where's Lissa?" she demanded.

"Lissa! Didn't she come home with you?"

She descended a few stairs, her gold sandals gleaming against the Oriental rug that covered them.

"No, she and Johnny Grant left the

cruiser in her motor boat. They were very secret about it, acted as if afraid someone would notice them."

Carson's heart contracted unbearably.

"Sure she's not in her room?"

"I'm sure. She's been trying to get Johnny back all summer. She has probably persuaded him to elope with her."

Carson's laugh didn't ring with mirth but it served.

"Lissa persuade Grant! That's the funniest thing I ever heard, Cleo. You're fooling yourself if you can't see that he is doing the persuading. They've probably stopped at the Treasure Chest for a bite. Excuse me, if I dash past you. I'm wet to the skin. Goodnight."

He took the stairs two at a time. As he opened his door, G-Man brushed by him into the room, flung himself to the hearth-rug and gazed up with beseeching eyes.

Carson closed the door and looked down at the Irish terrier.

"Where's Lissa?" he demanded.

There was a faint rumble of thunder in the distance. The dog whined.

"Afraid of the storm, are you? All right, stay here. Make yourself at home."

Speedily he changed to dry clothing. As he brushed his wet hair furiously before the

279

mirror, Cleo's intimation that Lissa and Johnny Grant had fared forth on a clandestine adventure pricked unbearably at his mind. Of course it wasn't true. If they wanted to be married, why should they make a secret of it? Lissa marry the man who had jilted her? It was unbelievable. Cleo was a cat. She was trying to make trouble. Of course the two were at the Treasure Chest.

He'd better stop worrying about Lissa — pronto — and concentrate on the job ahead. His pulses thrummed. This promised to be an exciting night. It had started off at high with the Major's plunge overboard. So even the crew aboard the cruiser knew that he had a high-power radio. He, himself, had known it weeks ago. It was his business — as a landlord — to know what went on in the cottages he leased. Something to do with the army, a radio expert keeping in practice while on sick leave, Prescott had said. That explanation would keep the curious from snooping around Pirates' Den for the present. After tomorrow —

Tomorrow! The blood raced through his veins and set his pulses quickstepping. If nothing broke, the last link in his chain would fit into place tomorrow. Meanwhile —

He glanced at his wrist watch. Time for him to start. He went to the window. Pitch dark outside. He shrugged into a Burberry, thrust an electric torch into one pocket. He felt for an automatic in a drawer of the desk. Should he take it? This was only a reconnaissance trip, if they were in luck, they'd get out and back without interference. Suppose they didn't have luck? Suppose there was rough stuff? Even so, he wouldn't take the gun. Guns bred trouble. He looked at the Irish terrier curled up on the hearthrug.

"Where did you get the coat you dragged down the garden path, G-Man?" he demanded. The dog opened one eye and with a beatific sigh rolled over on his side.

"You're the world's No. 1 helper, aren't you, boy?" Carson laughed and closed the door.

He descended the stairs cautiously. Why the dickens did they have to creak? Was that furtive sound behind the wainscotting a mouse? The hall was faintly fragrant of wood fires. The old clock ticked loudly enough to waken the Seven Sleepers. As he reached the hall the overhead light flashed on. His heart stopped for an instant and raced on. Fenton stepped from the living room.

"Oh, is it you, sir? I thought I heard someone coming down secret-like. For three years I was the only man in the house, and I've felt the care of the place, sir."

"I appreciate your interest, Fenton. As I went up to change my wet clothes —" Carson glanced over his shoulder and lowered his voice, "Miss Barclay told me that Miss Lissa had not returned, even suggested that she and Mr. Grant had eloped. I'm going out to find her. Understand, Fenton?"

"I do, sir. It wouldn't be like Miss Lissa to do that, sir. Wouldn't you like me to phone round the neighborhood?"

"No, Fenton. That would start gossip. I'm sure they've stopped at the Millards'. I want to find her myself. Perhaps you understand that, too?"

"Yes, sir, I do, sir. Miss Lissa is a beautiful character, if I'm not presuming to say it, sir."

"She is, Fenton. Leave the terrace door unlocked. Don't wait up. I shall go back to the cruiser after I find Miss Lissa. Mr. Kent wants me to finish up the party."

"I'm afraid I spoiled it, sir. For a minute I thought I saw a flash from the lighthouse. Of course it couldn't have been the light hasn't been used for three years, sir, it must have been the reflection of a meteor. Perhaps you noticed that the sky was full of them? If you're late getting home, you'll meet many boats coming into our harbor. They'll begin arriving at midnight to be here for the Fair tomorrow. It's a pretty sight, sir, when they're all lying at anchor."

"It must be. Good-night, Fenton."

"Good-night, sir."

22

Unfortunate that he had run into Fenton, Carson thought as he crossed the terrace. Perhaps, though, it wasn't such a bad break. He had learned from the butler that from midnight on, boats would be arriving in the harbor for the Fair. That meant that Tod and he could shoot around in Ozy's dory without attracting attention till the business of the night was finished. Where was Lissa? If only he could be sure that she was with the Millards. If Tod wasn't waiting when he reached the pier, he'd sprint to the Treasure Chest and find out.

He felt his way down the path. The stepping-stones were no longer visible. He stopped. Strained his eyes to make out the path ahead. Went on. Thunder rolled, lightning flashed in the distance. Soughing trees, scattering the smell of the sea with every move, added a touch of somber mystery to the night. Shrubs were but darker blurs in the gloom.

Once he lost the path and found himself waist high in the flower border. It wouldn't do to use the electric torch. There might be eyes watching.

Queer, he thought, as he picked his way cautiously down the path, that this hunt for the man whom the Treasury Department considered one of the largest makers of spurious plates and printers of counterfeit notes and coins in the country, should have fitted in with the settlement of his uncle's estate, which had threatened soon to be operating entirely in the red. That danger was past if the plan he was negotiating went through, he was to know in the morning.

His work for the Government had helped him bear the uncertainty of Lissa's feeling for him, too. Not that he thought she wouldn't be his in the end, but it looked like rough going till he had a chance to explain Madge's collapse against his shoulder. He had two weeks ahead of him in which to do that. Madge had no reason now to fear Cleo. Apparently Jack had become wise to her tactics. This evening he had politely but firmly snubbed her. Ralph Packard had been her shadow on the cruiser. Ought he to warn —

"Sst!"

The sound scattered Carson's thoughts like dry leaves caught in a miniature vortex. Was that a white boar or a shadow swaying at the pier?

"Sst!"

285

He followed the sound. A hand gripped his arm. A hoarse voice asked;

"Can you see Ozy's dory?"

He caught the odor of dead fish and oil in the moisture-soaked air.

"No, but I smell it, Tod."

"Take care. Don't make a sound."

"Hold on a minute. Seen Lissa?"

"Saw her boat at the Treasure Chest float as we came along. We're crazy to stand here, come on."

With a mind relieved as to Lissa, Carson stepped cautiously into the dory. He could make out a dark form at the wheel. The far off din of the storm sounded like the finale of a fireworks show. He heard a sniff. Ozy was on the job.

"Okay!" Tod Kent called softly and the boat shot forward. He huddled beside Carson in the stern, whispered;

"Doesn't this boat smell like thunder? Had to use it, because if we're seen everyone knows that Ozy pulls his lobster traps at any old time. Had a noiseless engine installed under cover, the very day I got your orders. Guess the old one couldn't have been heard in this storm, though. The tide is high enough on the bar to allow the dory to shoot straight across to the other side of the island. Hope you'll approve of what

286

I've done, Lex?"

"You bet I approve, Tod. I'll recommend you for a G-Man job. Here comes the rain. Hear it hiss!"

The wind increased in violence. Spray broke over the bow of the boat which creaked and strained in all its joints, shuddered and tossed like a chip. The cabin shed Niagaras of water, now to left, now to right.

Tod Kent crept forward and spoke to the man at the wheel.

"Can we make it, Ozy?"

Captain Ozias sniffed.

"Why don't you talk up? Who do you think's goin' to hear you in this blow? Sure we're goin' to make it. Course my lobster-float may be the only one there, but if I yell 'two' you fellas git ready to haul in."

"You're the skipper!" Tod Kent pulled off a slicker. Rain beat through Carson's polo shirt when he flung Burberry and hat on the seat behind him.

"Here we are, fellas! Look sharp! Two floats! Can you see 'em? Reach for both! We ain't got time to waste."

"I've got it," Carson whispered and hauled in a lanyard. "Thunder! No, I haven't. It's a lobster-trap!"

"Don't let that trap scrape against the gunwale! Don't you fellas know nothin'?"

287

The captain's voice cracked from excitement. "We ain't got a minute to waste! Thought I heard an engine on the harbor side of the island. One of you take the wheel, I'll try myself!"

"Don't move, Ozy! Don't move! I've got one!"

"Haul it in! Quick! Can't hold this boat much longer. I'll rap if anything's comin', though I guess I couldn't hear a fleet of planes in this racket."

"Got it, Lex?" Tod Kent's voice rasped.

"Yes."

"Can you lift it?"

"Yes. It's about a foot square."

"All right. Beat it to the cabin. The window is covered and we'll close the door."

"Keep the dory steady, Ozy," Carson cautioned. "We've got to drop the float in the same place."

Kent closed the sliding door of the box-like cabin. Shut in, almost smothered by the smell of oil and dead fish, the two men knelt in water sloshing from side to side on the bottom of the rolling boat. Carson snapped on an electric torch and played the light over a watertight case at the end of the lanyard. He worked at the cord which bound it. Once he stopped to put his hand to his head.

"Go on, Lex, go on! I'm sick as a horse too and I've spent my life in boats. We've got to open it boy, we've got to."

"Sure we have! What else are we here for? For the love of Pete, give us a little air!"

"Can't! While we have the light. Keep on!"

"Okay, but if this boat doesn't stop rolling —" he swallowed hard. "It's untied. Unclamp the cover! Don't bend it! We've got to put it back, remember."

The rolling boat, the sickening odor, were forgotten as the two men stared down at the contents of the watertight case. Greenbacks. Tied and labeled. Carson looked at Kent whose face was ghastly in the faint light.

"They've gone into big money, Tod." His voice broke from excitement. "One hundred dollar notes on a Federal Bank in —"

Rap! Rap! Rap!

"Ozy's signal! Something's coming!" He drew on a pair of cotton gloves. Slipped off the top note of a package of greenbacks.

"Take it, Tod! We'll get the fingerprints on it tonight. Quick!"

Kent drew an oiled silk folder from his trousers' pocket. Carson laid the bill in it.

"Pull the roll from my pocket, Tod. Tuck one of the bills from it among these. It will

289

keep the count correct. They won't miss the one we've taken till they check up."

Rap! Rap! Rap! Rap! Rap! Rap!

"Hurry! Okay! Looks just as we found it, doesn't it?"

Carson drew off his gloves, clamped on the lid of the case.

"We've got to get this thing tied up!" he muttered. Black spots danced before his eyes, his fingers slipped as he tried to tie the wet cord in the exact pattern in which he had found it.

"Don't fumble! Don't fumble, Lex!" Tod Kent wailed.

Rap! Rapl Rap! Rap! Rap! Rap!

"Hustle, Lex! We've got to get that thing back!"

"You're telling me, fella! Try it your-self!"

"Don't get sore, boy. You're the boss, but since you asked me to help I haven't slept nights I've been so excited! Hurry! It will give the show away if they find they're one case short. Got it? Got it?"

Carson nodded. Speech was beyond him. He soundlessly slid back the cabin door, took a long breath, staggered to the side of the boat. The dory dipped to the gunwale as he and Kent paid out the lanyard.

"Careful, Tod! Don't let it splash. Someone may be watching! Pay out the line. It's down!"

He flung the float over and dropped to the stern seat. The rainy air was as cooling as a drink of spring water. There had been an instant when his one burning desire had been to follow that watertight case into the sea. A spear of red flame slashed the sky. Thunder reverberated among the hills. Tod Kent crept back from a whispered conference with Captain Ozias.

"He didn't rap because of a boat. It was to hurry us. He was afraid we might be seen when lightning flashed. Wants to know if he'll take us to the other floats?"

"No. One's enough. Tell him to shoot for the island."

"Jiminy, what a flash! It crackled like a forest fire. The lighthouse looked like a pink ghost. Hear the thunder bump away among the hills! This isn't rain. It's a flood. Something burst overhead. I'll —"

His sentence was drowned in a crash which shook the heavens.

"I wonder where that hit? Gosh, when I was in that cabin —"

"If you mention cabin, I'll strangle you, Tod."

"My mistake. One hundred dollar notes! Those boys are flying high. Ozy'll land us

291

near the light and if we have luck, we'll see the airtight cases picked up."

"If someone doesn't beat us to it and reach the lamp-room first. Did you arrange to have the lighthouse unlocked?"

"I did. Ozy asked Lissa to leave the latch up. When I got your message that his yarn about the extra floats had set you thinking that two mugs of beer were not a reasonable explanation of his double vision, I got hold of him and told him what you suspected. Did you pick that hunch out of the air, Lex? If you did, I'll believe in the theory of vibrations. Ozy's gone sleuth-minded, too. He remembered then that there had been a strange vessel which looked like one of the kind that buy pulpwood anchored beyond the ledge that night. He was all excitement. Said he'd be on the lookout."

"He was. This afternoon at the lobster-bake he told me that a strange vessel had anchored in the same place and offered to hang round Tarry Farm pier tonight and take us out to check up on the floats. When your skipper reported that two red lights, one above the other, had glowed for an instant on the lumber vessel, I was certain that some funny business was on foot."

"Who put that bogus money there? Someone near at hand must have done it."

"If they come in from the vessel for that case, or cases, I presume there are others, we stand nine chances out of ten of running into their boat," Carson evaded.

"Ozy's bound for a cove in which he claims the dory will be as invisible as a gray cat in a fog. There might be a dozen boats lurking in these coves and we couldn't see them tonight. He'll wait for us there while we're in the lighthouse. He says we'll have to do the chamois act climbing the rocks."

The chamois act was a perfect description of their climb up the rocky side of the island. Breathless, dripping, with hands scratched and numb from pelting hail, they stole and stumbled toward the lighthouse. It seemed miles. At each flash they crouched and ran forward. Then waited for another glare to show them the location of the ghostly tower.

"Let's make a break for it in the dark," Kent whispered, ran and came down with a crash.

Carson helped him up. He controlled a frantic desire to shout with laughter as lightning showed Kent's grieved expression. This night of adventure was doing things to his nerves.

"Here we are, Tod. Blind luck. We've landed at the door."

He put his hand on the knob. Jerked it

293

back. Caught Kent's arm. Whispered;

"Someone ahead of us! Listen!"

They put their ears close to the door. A flash revealed Tod Kent's bulging eyes as he choked;

"Boy! It's Fenton talking!"

23

It had been a simple matter to slip away from The Sphinx in the motorboat, to linger in the shadow of the float at the Treasure Chest until the launch from the cruiser had landed its second load of passengers and gone back, then to steal away. Lucky the engine was almost noiseless, Lissa exulted as she steered for her island. Common sense tugged at her complacence to remind that the get-away would not have been so simple had not Lex Carson gone ahead with Major Fane and the Packards. She had been throbbingly conscious of him while on the cruiser, had felt his eyes on her, had —

"Hi, sweet thing!"

Coat collar turned up, Johnny Grant stood beside her.

"Is this little excursion the reason you invited me to the lobster-bake?"

"I didn't invite you, Johnny."

"Aha! Methinks I detect the fine Italian hand of my former fiancee. I had a hunch to that effect when she asked for a loan."

"Did she get it?"

"She did not. She had the nerve to tell me

when she broke our engagement that she never had cared for me, had thought it amusing to try to get me away from you. She did it. A girl like that couldn't chisel a cent from me if she were starving. Why spend a minute talking about Cleo? Did you hear that roll of thunder? Thought I felt a drop of rain. The sky's gone black. We're in for a storm. We'd better come about and run ahead of it to Tarry Farm."

Lissa looked up at the spongey mass of sky. Not a star to be seen. How the gloom dramatized this ordinarily sleepy harbor. The lighthouse loomed like the tower of the Empire State Building and the cruiser took on the proportions of the Queen Mary. The air was saturated with moisture. A perfect night for someone to retrieve those coins. She'd get them first.

"I must go, Johnny. I wouldn't sleep a wink if I knew that G-Man was alone on the island tonight. Storms frighten him. He'll probably be curled up in a sheltered corner of the porch at the lighthouse. Besides, there's another reason. I'm after buried treasure."

She swore him to secrecy, told him of the pouch of coins she had found. Instead of sympathizing with her, he was furious.

"You're crazy! We may get mixed up with

the guy who put them there."

"We'll scout around first, Johnny. They are directly beneath the kitchen window. I have a reason, a very serious reason for wanting them. Listen! Thought I heard a boat the other side of the island. Hear it?"

"No. You heard the echo of the launch returning to the cruiser probably. You don't think people are sailing round this bay tonight for pleasure, or treasure, do you? They're not so crazy."

"Cheerio, Johnny, it won't take us ten minutes from the time we leave the island pier for the lighthouse till we get back to it."

"All right. You may bet your last dollar I wouldn't have come had I known what you were after. It's a fool stunt but you're the captain. Better let me take the wheel. Felt another drop of rain."

"What's a drop of rain to a couple of adventurers en route to Treasure Island?" She sang a snatch of the song. "A thunder storm always sets me a-tingle. I'll stick to the wheel. I know the location of every ledge in this bay. I've run into them in the outboard times enough, and the outboard finished its career by smashing into one all by its lonesome. See that sudden glow of light behind the hills! Looks as if someone had hung up an arras of copper-gold lame. That storm is

297

coming up fast. Here we are!"

She stepped to the float. With the painter in his hand, Grant scrambled after her.

"How hushed the world seems. It's weird —"

With a snarl and a shriek the wind swept down on them and wrenched Lissa's soft hat from her head. She clutched the air.

"Johnny! My hat! Catch it!"

Grant lunged, tripped, dropped the painter. He grabbed for it, but with a demoniac howl the wind whirled the boat out of his reach. A crackling blaze split the sky. A tree-crested ledge stood out in sharp relief. The great eye of the light shimmered in the unearthly glow. The tower shrank to half its size. Brasses on the runaway boat, tossing like a cockleshell, were tiny flames. The world went black. With a noise like the turning on of a Gargantuan hose, the torrent burst. The rain Lissa had wished for to cover the roughened earth above the buried pouch had come, buckets of it. She clutched Grant's sleeve.

"Where do we go from here, Johnny?"

He patted her wet hand.

"Good little sport. You take life on the chin, don't you? I'm terribly sorry, Lissa. Honest I didn't mean to let that boat get away."

"Of course you didn't. You have your faults, Johnny, but they're not in that class. Hear the rain hiss-s-s!"

For the first time, the consequences of the loss of the boat flooded Lissa's mind with dismay. She swallowed hard. It wouldn't help to get panicky.

"Let's make one try for the pouch, Johnny, I didn't bury it deep. We can't be any wetter than we are." She put her mouth close to his ear to make herself heard above the rain and wind. "Ooch! What a flash! Smell the sulphur! The lighthouse stood out like a close-up. Now it has disappeared. The thunder's deafening. Here comes another crack! Quick! While the sky's like a sheet of brass. Run for the light!"

Hand in hand they ran while the storm turned its light on and off as if it were manipulating giant push buttons. The tops of tall pines and cedars beyond the lighthouse twisted and bent and writhed in the fury of the wind.

Lissa stopped under a window. Whispered;

"Dig among those poppies, Johnny. Dig! Where is it? Oh, where is it? Someone's taken it! There's the hole!"

"I'm glad of it! Beat it for the house, you crazy nut."

At the door of the lighthouse, Lissa panted;

"Where do you suppose G-Man is? I tried to whistle as I ran but my throat was too dry. Find — the knob. I left — the latch up — this afternoon. That last flash — stung my eyes. I can see only two great gold discs."

They stumbled into the chintz-hung service room and with difficulty closed the door against the wind. Rain beat upon the roof, streamed down the windows, made little pink rivers when lightning slashed the sky. It poured from a broken spout outside with the roar of a miniature Niagara.

"At the next flash, pull down the shades, Johnny. I've found the lamp. I'll light it as soon as we've shut out the storm. I feel as if I were in a nightmare, as if in a minute I'd wake and find myself in my own room at home."

"I'd give a fortune to have you in your own room at home, Lissa." Grant's voice choked.

"Someone came for that pouch after Ralph Packard and I left for the cruiser," she whispered. "Who could it have been?"

She touched a match to the wick of the brass lamp which shone like gold. She looked furtively over her shoulder as the room leaped into life and color. The huge hollyhocks on the chintz never had looked so richly crimson and rosily pink, the old map over the fireplace, the brass candlesticks on the mantel, the rhythmic tick-tock of the clock, the book-laden shelves, her typewriter on a table, her knitting bag on a hook, gave her a sense of reality, of safety. She drew a ragged breath of relief.

"There! Now let the storm do its worst. We're safe, but I wish we had what we came for. When I start a thing I like to put it through."

She smiled at Grant, who, white faced, hair drenched, looked back at her gravely.

"You're telling me! As if I didn't know by now that you're the she-died-but-she-did-it type. We're in a jam, Lissa. We both can't stay here all night. Think of your stepmother's tongue and Cleo's. I'm going."

"You're not going out in this storm, Johnny Grant! Listen! Isn't that hail tick-tacking against the windows? It's only a shower. It will be over in a few minutes and the moon and stars will be out. Then we'll go home."

"The boat's gone. Thinking of walking the waves?"

"Goodness, aren't things screwy enough without going sarcastic on me?" She glanced at the brass-framed clock on the

301

wall solemnly ticking off the seconds. "I am thinking of walking, but not on the water. In two more hours we can cross the bar on foot."

Color came back to his face, his eyes sparkled.

"Bar! That word sounds good to me. Got any —"

"Sorry, that shiver and sneeze were well done, Johnny, but the only beverages I have here are tea and coffee. I'll find something dry for us to put on, then we'll remove a large portion of my real estate from our hands."

She lighted one of the candles on the mantel, shaded the flame with her hand and entered the bedroom. A chain of fire crackled through the heavens. Everything in the small room burned red. A crash shook the building and put out the candle. She groped for the closet, pulled two woolly house coats from their hangars. Dashed into the service room.

"That last flash — was ter-rific, J-Johnny. I've always boasted that I loved — thunderstorms. Never again! I don't — if only I could — find G-Man."

"Don't worry about that terrier. When he decided you weren't coming back for him, he probably beat it across the bar for home.

That dog thinks."

"He does, Johnny. If he hadn't gone home, he would have known that I was here, wouldn't he? Put on this blue coat, blue's your color — while I'm in the kitchen slipping into the green one and making coffee, nice strong coffee that will curl our eyelashes. Lucky I had these coats here last fall to bundle up in while I was writing. Even with a big fire on the hearth, my hands would get so numb I could hardly type."

"Let's light the fire now."

"No, no. I think we'd better not, Johnny. The man who took the pouch might smell wood smoke and come bursting in." That wasn't the only reason, she added to herself. Ozy had asked to have the latch left up that he might get in. Wood smoke from the chimney might upset his plan. She smiled at Grant ingratiatingly even while she disciplined a shiver of nerves.

"You wouldn't like to go into the kitchen first and pull down the shades, would you, Johnny?"

He preceded her into the small kitchen, drew the shades at the two windows, waited until she had lighted the lamp and a burner on the oil stove, before he pumped water in a basin and bathed his hands.

"That's better. I felt like a ditch-digger.

Golly, that was a crash! The buoy sounds as if it were moaning mad. Hear the waves lash against the ledge. No one will come near this island tonight. Want me to stay here until you've made the coffee?"

"No, I'm all right now. You're sneezing again, Johnny. Go into the other room and get off that wet suit. I'll never forgive myself if you get pneumonia."

"Pneumo-chu! I'll go. You'd better change your clothes, sweet thing."

"I will, Johnny, as soon as I start the coffee."

"What this country needs is more girls like you," he attested gruffly and closed the door.

Lissa scrubbed her hands, pumped water into the glass globe of the percolator, lighted the lamp under it, and measured coffee for the container. She pulled off her one-time white frock, now a pale gray with a cubistic design of green which had run from the leather belt, and draped it over a small clothes horse. A soggy wad dropped to the floor.

"My word, lucky I didn't lose that, now that the pouch has disappeared," she thought and picked it up. "Just as bright as you were when I found you," she added under her breath as she looked at the silver quarter in the wet handkerchief. She wadded it up again and dropped it into the pocket of the green house-coat as she slipped into it.

She had acquired plot material for a story tonight, for a dozen stories. Noble of Ralph Packard to offer to work with her, but she preferred to depend on herself. If only she were an expert in handling it like Kipling or Stevenson or O. Henry. O. Henry! A close-up of Sidonie Packard shrinking against a background of books flashed on the screen of her mind. The stiffening went out of her knees. She shivered. Now she knew why Ralph Packard's stories had seemed familiar. Those she had copied were O. Henry's with names and locales changed! There was a complete set of O. Henry on a shelf at Red Chimneys.

Dazed, incredulous she stood in the middle of the room while the storm crackled and thundered and howled outside. Why had he done it? What could have been his object in deceiving her? She would tell Lex. Terribly disappointing that she could not help him by producing that pouch.

"If you don't believe him when he tells you he loves you, why believe his story about the counterfeiters?" she asked herself. The shell of disbelief in a man's faithfulness in which she had encased her heart helped mighty little against Lex's demanding eyes, his husky voice.

"Deep down in your soul you do believe him, you know you do. You don't dare meet his eyes because they make you ache to creep into the warmth of his arms," she accused herself passionately.

The vision she had conjured caught at her breath, set her pulses racing. Close on its heels came the memory of Madge sobbing against his shoulder.

She closed her eyes tight to shut out the picture and shut it in. It hurt, hurt unbearably. Only a surgical operation could cut that out. Was getting engaged to Johnny the answer? In an effort to thrust back the thought, she looked about the spotless kitchen. Shining rows of copper pans and pots hung from hooks. Watteau figures on china simpered behind the glass doors of a cupboard. Tin goods by the appetizing half-dozens stood shoulder to shoulder on a shelf.

She prepared a tray with cups and saucers, thin wafers, and the percolator, now sending forth a delicious aroma. She answered an impatient knock on the door.

"Ready, Johnny. Come and take out the tray, will you? My, but you're devastating in blue," she mocked gaily, as she followed him into the chintz-hung room.

"You're not so bad in green, sweet thing, if your head didn't look like a wet-chu!"

"Don't sneeze when you're carrying that coffee percolator, Johnny Grant!"

"Think I'm sneezing because I like it? I didn't ask to come on this adven-chu! did I?"

"Give me the tray, Johnny. Quick before you drop it. Pull out that table. There!" She did things to the percolator and poured him a cup of steaming coffee.

"Doesn't the smell of that grow wings on your spirit? That's condensed cream, but what's condensed cream between friends? Drink it quickly, before you sneeze again."

Lissa watched him anxiously as he put the cup to his lips. She would never forgive herself for dragging him to the island on a night like this if he took a serious cold. He grinned at her.

"It's beautiful. Quite the last word in coffee, I'd say, Miss Lissa."

"Johnny, that was Fenton to the life," she gripped his arm, whispered;

"Don't speak! Someone's at the door!"

24

Johnny Grant flung his arm about Lissa as the entrance door banged open and two men burst into the room.

"Lex! Tod!" she whispered.

Her heart, which had stopped, picked up and poured blood through her veins till her face, her finger tips burned. Why was Lex here? His eyes, enormous and black, were burning pools of fury in his livid face, the muscles of his jaw tightened and relaxed, tightened again. If Tod's balloon cheeks got much redder, they'd burst. What were they thinking to look at her like that? Condemning her without a hearing because she and Johnny were here together? Well, let them. She freed herself from Grant's arm and said flippantly;

"I suppose, gentlemen, that this is what might be called adult drama. Is it time to warn me that anything I say may be used against me?"

"Lissa —" Carson's voice broke with anger — "Lissa —"

A blinding glare filled the room. Something outside creaked and tore. A shower of splinters struck roof and window. The building rocked from the crash that followed. Something bumped down the curving iron stairs, something clinked and rolled from step to step. Lissa raised her face which had been crushed against Lex Carson's shoulder. She freed herself from his arms, how had she come in them, she wondered dazedly, as she stared at the heap on the floor, at the river of silver coins pouring down the stairs.

"Nino!" she breathed incredulously.

Carson and Kent bent over the Italian.

"He's only stunned," Carson whispered. "Now that we've found what we came for let's get away. Quick! Where's Fenton, Grant? Don't quibble. We heard his voice."

"You heard me imitating him to amuse Lissa."

"To amuse Lissa! How did you get to the island?"

"In a boat, do you think we swam?"

"Cut the comedy, Johnny," Lex Carson's voice was like a blast of liquefied air against Lissa's heart, it froze it. "Where's the boat?"

"It got away from me when we landed."

"Oh, it got away from you?"

Lissa shook back her wet hair and prepared for battle.

"Don't speak to Johnny like that, Lex.

He's not to blame because we are here. He didn't want to come. I persuaded him."

"Oh, you persuaded him."

"Stop echoing my words! When Ralph Packard and I started from the island for the cruiser this afternoon, I told G-Man to go home, waited until he reached the bar. Half way across the harbor, I looked toward the island and saw that bad dog on the pier. I couldn't go back for him then and when I saw the storm coming I knew he'd be frightened and persuaded Johnny to come here with me to get him. I — came for something else, too, but the moment we landed, the storm burst and my hat blew off — Johnny, don't interrupt — and when Johnny tried to catch it, he dropped the painter and the boat got away and — and here we are."

Kent gripped Carson's arm. "Let's go. Quick! We don't want that —" he nodded in the direction of the unconscious Italian — "to know we saw him."

"You're right, Tod! Got a coat, Lissa? Get it."

His tone infuriated her. He didn't believe what she had told him about her reason for coming to the island. She defied;

"Just because you have the right to dole out my money, Lex, doesn't mean that you have the right to order me about, does it?"

"Get that coat."

"I won't —" Lissa met Grant's eyes. What was he trying to tell her? Why were the two men here? They hadn't come for her or they wouldn't have been dumb with surprise when they saw her. They had been on the trail of someone, of course. Nino? Had she messed things up hopelessly? As if answering her question, Carson snapped;

"Lissa, get that coat."

She dashed into the bedroom. Pulled a sports coat from its hanger. Changed to old dry shoes. How quiet the world seemed after that world-shaking crash.

When she returned to the service room, Nino had been lifted to a chair. The tray with the coffee percolator was on the table beside him. Johnny had changed to his wet suit. Lex Carson seized her arm.

"Come along!" he ordered in a voice which suggested pent-up explosives.

"Will he — he be all right?" She nodded toward the lax figure in the chair.

"He's coming out of it." Carson flung open the door. "We must get away before he sees us. Where's the key to this door?"

Lissa took a key from a nail on the wall.

"I keep an extra one here in case the one I carry is lost."

"Don't stop to explain. Lock the door,

311

Johnny — on the outside! Put the key on that right-hand window-ledge. Step on it, all of you!"

The storm had passed, all that remained of it were pale flashes and the distant sound as of giants bowling. The mouth of the moon tipped up at the corners as it gazed down upon a gigantic pine which had been stripped open from tip to root; its light laid a quivering trail of quicksilver across the water, turned boulders to platinum; arborvitae, spruce and clumps of juniper to dusky purple, and dropped a bridal veil of silver over the lighthouse tower. A chorus of crickets serenaded the stars which spangled the sky. The buoy moaned. Somewhere a cowbell tinkled. The air was crystalline and fragrant with the pungent scent of wet juniper.

"Gorgeous night isn't it?" Lissa whispered. She laughed softly. "I've seen a prisoner on the screen, gripped on each side by an officer being rushed along as you and Lex are rushing me, Tod. What's the idea? 'Fraid Johnny and I will escape the strong arm of the law? Have you forgotten we haven't a boat?"

"We've forgotten nothing," Lex Carson reminded icily.

"Do you know, Lex, the more I see you, the more convinced I am that you are

312

wasted in this country, you should get into the Dictator business," Lissa asserted flippantly. "Can't you stop sneezing, Johnny? You've advertised every step we've taken."

"Why not advert-chu! it? Is this a secret expedition?"

"It was, until you joined it," Lex Carson answered drily.

"I knew you were something besides a law-chu! Carson. Didn't I tell you so, Lissa?"

"Whatever you think I am, keep it to yourself till after tomorrow, Grant. Beat it, Tod. Locate Ozy and the dory. I'll look after Lissa." As Kent disappeared beyond a clump of scrub pines, Lissa confided;

"Believe it or not, Lex, Johnny and I came to the island to help you."

"What do you mean, help me?"

His thoughts ran on a double track as she gave him the coin from her pocket, told of her discovery of the pouch; of her determination to return to the island for it. A ton of depression slid from his heart. She had not come to be with Johnny Grant.

One part of his mind was engaged with speculation as to who had buried the coins, the other concerned with a plan to get Lissa home. If it had been a tough climb for Tod and him coming up, what would it be for her

313

going down? She would have to make it. There was no other way. The road across the bar wouldn't be clear again for an hour. It would be like her stepmother and Cleo to find out that she had gone to the island with Johnny Grant. His heart had been so numbed by the sight of them together at the light, that he had forgotten for a moment why he was there. The crash had sent her straight into his arms. In danger she had turned from Grant to him. The memory of the confiding unrestraint of her body set his pulses quickstepping. If she —

He'd better keep Lissa out of his mind until the business of the night was finished. The question as to who would signal the waiting vessel had been answered when Nino pitched down the iron stairs in that flood of silver coins. Undoubtedly they had been given him in payment for buoying the watertight cases of bogus bills and signalling from the light to the dark vessel anchored off shore. He must be spirited away from the island before the man whose tool he was could learn what had happened. A radio message from the cruiser would take care of that.

"It may be your idea of a fitting finale for the evening to pitch off this bank —" Lissa's voice cut into his planning — "but I've had water enough, if you ask me."

Carson ignored her jibe.

"Ozy's below in a boat. Grant, the trail down is a tough one. I'll go ahead. Grab Lissa's left hand, I'll take her right. If she slips, hold her with all your strength, understand? Ready, Lissa?"

She nodded. Good little sport not to make a fuss about it, he thought, and felt for a footing in the jagged rock. Step by careful step they descended. Once Lissa slipped and fell heavily against him, pine needles above them rained a shower of crystal drops. He felt the rock crumble under his foot, grabbed at a stout trunk of creeping cedar, bent flat by winter winds, and prayed that it would hold.

"I'm sorry," she breathed.

"Don't move! Hold her, Johnny!"

"I've got her, but I'm hanging on by a twig myself."

"I'll get a foothold in a minute. Don't be frightened, Lissa."

"I'm not frightened, I'm thrilled," the catch in her voice belied its lightness.

Johnny Grant sniffed. "You may be, but if ever I get back to the mainland, me an' the island is done."

Grant wasn't such a bad sport himself, Carson thought, as Lissa chuckled at his imitation of Ozy. For a youth who spent his days and most of his nights speeding in a fire-engine-red roadster, he was doing this chamois act without a protest.

"Wait! Don't move!" Carson warned. "Crouch behind those junipers! Quick!"

"Look, Lex! That's Ozy's boat! He's going to his lobster-traps," Lissa whispered. "Why don't you call?"

"Ssh!" Carson gripped her arm. He watched a white dory with a shoebox cabin steal cautiously along a ledge and stop. A search light from it played along the shore.

"Lie flat! Both of you! If you sneeze, Grant, I'll choke you!" Carson threatened.

From behind a clump of junipers he watched the light. It was coming nearer. It lingered on the bushes above them! Had they been seen? Whoever was handling that search light would not have dared use it on the Tarry Farm side of the island. Nothing but ledges and ocean between them and Europe this side.

After what seemed ages the light went out. The dory was a blur of white. From it came the sound of wood scraping. Lissa shook Carson's sleeve;

"Someone's stealing Ozy's lobsters!" she whispered. "Shout and stop them, Lex!"

"No! No! They're not stealing lobsters.

They are after something else. Don't move!"

From behind the shelter of the junipers, he watched the white dory move from ledge to ledge. Must have come from the lumber vessel. Clever idea to make it a dead ringer for Ozy's. Anyone seeing it would think that the Captain was pulling his traps after the storm. Were there five of those watertight cases? He must get to the cruiser's radio. He couldn't move until that dory finished its collections, though. It was going! Going fast! Running straight for that dark hulk with the red eye on the horizon.

"We can go now. Come on," he called softly into the shadows behind him and stood up.

"Come on! Just like that! I'm so stiff I can hear my joints crack when I move." Lissa rose slowly and stretched her arms above her head. "Are you dead or only sleeping, Johnny?"

"I'm-chu!"

"Stop sneezing, Grant. Grab Lissa's hand," Carson commanded. "I'm stepping down."

He caught at the creeping cedar to steady himself. Went on. Step by cautious step the two above followed. This wasn't the way he had come. The cliff was almost perpendicular. He'd taken the wrong trail. They'd have to go on now.

"Look out for the wet moss," he warned. "The rain has soaked it."

He slipped and slid holding Lissa tightly with one hand and grabbing at wet rocks with the other.

"Not much farther to go. I can see a narrow beach below. Don't let Lissa slip, Grant. I'll drop. When I hold out my arms, let her go and I'll catch her. Ready!"

Carson had to twist his hand from the girl's clutch before he dropped. It seemed as if he slid miles down the cliff — though it couldn't have been more than twelve feet — before he landed on a pebbly beach. He called;

"Come!"

Lissa jumped. He caught her before her feet could touch the beach. Held her close.

"All right?"

She nodded and freed herself.

"Can't we help Johnny?" she asked breathless from her plunge.

"Always and forever 'Johnny' with you, isn't it? He seems to be doing extremely well without help," Carson observed drily as Grant contacted the beach with a crashing impact. He looked up at Lissa and blinked;

"Are my lower teeth protruding through

the top of my head, sweet thing? I felt them sky-rocket when I landed."

Lissa leaned weakly against the cliff and shook with laughter.

"I don't see anything so hilariously funny," Grant growled and pulled himself stiffly to his feet.

"I'm not laughing at you, Johnny, it's — it's just everything. What a night! What a night!"

"Pull yourself together, Lissa," Carson commanded unfeelingly — she mustn't suspect that he was anxious about her — "or we'll have an hysterical girl on our hands and that would be the last straw."

"I'm not hysterical. I'm —"

"All right, you're not hysterical. Prove it. Stop laughing. We'll have to follow the shore till we find Tod and Ozy."

Curious what had become of the Captain's dory, he thought, as the three splashed into water in coves, ploughed through wet pebbles, slipped and slid over boulders. They must realize that he had mistaken the trail. This side of the island wasn't so long that the white boat couldn't be seen. Perhaps they were in some dark cove and had seen the cases picked up. The man, Nino, must have been leaning over the stairs listening, when that world-rocking crash came. Had he heard their voices? And if he had, before morning he would be where what he suspected or said would do no harm.

It was almost as light as day. The stars looked as if the rain had polished them and hung them up to dry. The sea rolled in noisily, dashed against boulders, receded with a swish, dragging pebbles and foam with it, like a dainty woman trailing fluffy white ruffles behind her. The moon was slanting now and lighting every crack and cranny among the ledges. There must be a million or two crickets chirping.

Carson's thoughts kept pace as he hurried on. His work on the estate was finished for the present. If the agreement he had signed yesterday went through, he could handle the rest of the business from Washington. If his program for tomorrow — it was today, now — went through — if — the word beat in his mind like a muted drum. There shouldn't be an "if" — it must go through.

25

"Are you sure we haven't hiked along the whole Maine coast, Lex?" Lissa asked breathlessly. "All these coves and boulders I've slipped and slid over can't belong to my island."

"Your treasure island," Grant puffed. "You'll never get me on one of your excursions again, sweet-chu!"

"There's Ozy's dory!" Carson exclaimed. "If you two are as glad as I am to see that white boat, it makes it unanimous!"

In a dark cove Kent and the Captain stood in water to their waists holding the gunwale of the dory at the stern of which a motorboat took the wash sidelong.

"For Pete's sake where've you been?" Tod Kent demanded.

"Keep your voice down. Took the wrong path over the ledge. Where'd you get that motorboat?"

"It was beached in one of the coves so we towed it along. Decided it belonged to the man we left behind us. See the name, Red Chimneys, on the side? What shall we do with it, Lex? He isn't going to need it for the

321

present." Kent chuckled.

"But you and I are."

Captain Ozias sniffed, jerked Carson's sleeve, and pointed at the wet line on the shore that showed the drop of the tide.

"Say, Lex, if you folks don't get started we won't git this boat over the bar, the tide's ebbin' fast. I guess you don't want to give yerselves away by going round the light, do ye? Thet's the only other way to git back to Tarry Farm landin'."

"Tod and I are not going back with you, Ozy, Take Lissa home. Grant, go with her, will you, and see that she gets to the house safely?"

"Sure, I'll take her home. Left my roadster there when I came to the lobster-bake. Golly, that seems years ago. Aren't you coming, Carson?"

"No. Kent and I are going to the cruiser to finish a job. After that —" he looked at Lissa standing in the shadow of a huge boulder. "I shall devote all my time to settling another matter."

"Say, if you folks expect me to git this boat over the bar —" rasped Captain Ozias.

Carson caught Lissa by the elbows and swung her into the dory. "Hop aboard, Grant. All set, Ozy!"

"Good-night, Lissa," he called softly as

the dory nosed its way out of the cove.

"Good-night!" her voice came faintly across the fast-widening strip of water, came also a loud, "Chu!"

"When you can take time off from watching that boat out of sight, perhaps you'd tell me what we do next," Kent suggested crisply.

Carson turned his back on the dory.

"Next, we'll push this motorboat out where we can start it. We're both wet to the skin now, a little dampness won't hurt us. There she goes! Jump in, Tod!"

He swung himself aboard, seized the wheel, and switched on the engine. Kent caught his arm. Pointed to a dark hulk, with one red eye, which was moving slowly toward the open sea.

"Suppose she's got those bogus bills aboard?" he whispered.

"Sure of it." As he swung the wheel to avoid a whirl of white water, Carson told of the dory he had watched hover about the ledges. He concluded;

"From the cruiser we'll radio the revenue cutter that's standing by to help us, to board that lumber vessel, seize the crew and those bogus bills before they flood the country."

"I didn't know there was a revenue cutter

in the offing. Think of everything, don't you, Lex?"

"I haven't had a chance to tell you before, Tod. I've worked at white heat since I had the hunch where to locate the Ace. I'll bet I've been over every square foot of the area pegged off on the map. No, I haven't thought of everything. We'll radio the revenue officers to send a gig to the island to pick up the Italian and the coins, but what's to prevent the man whose tool he is, from suspecting when Nino doesn't report in the morning, that there's something in the air and making his get-away? I can see all our summer's work cracking-up."

"Course it won't crack-up. You're having an attack of the jitters, Lex. The moan of that confounded buoy is enough to send one's spirit into low. Taking it by and large, you've had a tough night. Seeing Lissa in that room with Grant's arms about her gave me an awful jolt for a minute. Only for a minute, though, you can't look at that girl without knowing she's about as fine as they come."

"You're not apologizing for Lissa to me, are you?" Carson demanded savagely.

Kent chuckled;

"That-a-boy, bite the hand that feeds you. I was merely trying to pull your spirits out of a nose-dive. To return to the slick

Nino. I have an idea. This is his boat, the Red Chimneys' boat, isn't it?"

"Yes."

"We'll have Prescott tow it to the bar, beach it and turn it upside down. Conclusion: that Nino was swept overboard in the storm. Get it?"

"Sure, I get it. You're a wonder, Tod."

"I'm good when I put my mind to it. Grand night after the storm. We'll take it as an omen that we'll pull off our coup without a hitch."

Carson nodded and looked up at the silvery mackerel clouds. Patches of indigo sky were dotted with stars which twinkled like gold sequins on a lacy dance frock. In the east where sea and sky met spread a rosy glow. A pale moon was riding westward. A drift of mist lay on a hillside like a film of chiffon against a rich fur. The cool smell of pines drifted from the shore.

As the boat shouldered her way heavily through the rough sea, he looked toward Tarry Farm. No lights in the cottages. Had the Major put himself and his radio to bed or was he reaching out into the night to contact with a ship? Had the Packards discovered that their houseman was missing?

The house at the crest of the slope was dark except for one lighted window in the

325

ell. Fenton's room? Lissa had said that he kept late hours reading. Would she get into the house without being heard by him? Did she love Grant? He felt again the pressure of her head against his shoulder, the pulsing warmth of her. If she loved Johnny, would she have flung herself into another man's arms when frightened? That question, along with one or two others, would be answered within twenty-four hours. Meanwhile, he had the message to the revenue cutter to code. The cruiser at last.

With heavy top coats over their damp clothing, he and Kent paced the forward cockpit smoking, waiting for an answer to his call. The radio operator lowered his window and held out a slip of paper.

"Here it is, Mr. Carson. Had some difficulty getting it through. The static witches are riding the air on their broomsticks tonight good and plenty. It's the storm in the distance I suppose, but I've never before heard such weird wails and shrieks."

"Thank you, Connor."

Carson read the slip of paper. Kent looking over his shoulder, nodded.

"Okay? Well, that's that. Now for the boys."

Carson had believed that the last weeks had taught him all he ever could know of

326

suspense; he knew now, that he had but touched the surface of it. As he followed Kent along the companionway, it played wild tricks with his imagination, chilled his blood, turned his fingertips to ice. Only a few hours more, but, empires and governments had crumbled in a few hours.

The tense muscle in his cheek was the only surface sign of his turmoil of spirit as he entered the pine-paneled cabin and questioned the two men tilted back in their chairs.

"Well?" The word cracked like a ringmaster's whip.

The black haired man with light gray eyes and the light haired man with dark eyes, nodded. Before they could speak Carson held up his hand.

"I understand. Don't say a word. Words get into the air."

He stood at the window for an instant looking at a bright star, hearing the wash of waves against the side of the cruiser and the incessant moan of the buoy. The last link in his chain of evidence had been forged. Now, if there were no weak links —

"If you were in the army you'd get a D. S. C. for this job, Lex," the dark haired man said.

Carson turned.

"The job isn't finished yet. If you can honestly say that to me tonight, I shall be inclined to agree with you."

26

Lissa crossed the sunny breakfast room to the open French windows. Above the terrace, the sky was pure turquoise patched with a few clouds delicate as new-spun cobwebs. Hills, stretching ridge by dusky ridge, towered into infinite space. Some of them were green at the base, marked off like checkerboards by stone walls. The sapphire water of the harbor was dotted with anchored crafts of many sizes and varieties and blotched with ultramarine and malachite where cloud shadows darkened it. A fragrant breeze stirred the mauve hangings. A bird poked a red-topped head from a vine, regarded the girl with bead-like eyes and chirped a greeting.

Gorgeous day after last night's shower. Life is like that after showers, she thought. Storm and stress and the rain of tears followed by clearing skies and the sunshine of hope and joy and courage. It all made for living. The days of this summer had been vivid days, so different from those she had spent as companion and comfort — she hoped — to an ill woman.

"Hello, Lissa!"

Lex Carson greeted her from the threshold as she sat down at the table. He dropped
on a chair the coat G-Man had stolen.

"I like you in that green linen. Makes me
think of a cool cucumber. Grand day for the
Fair."

His voice was buoyant. Some quality in it
set her pulses quickstepping. Was it suppressed excitement? She was imagining.
There was no excitement in the eyes that
met hers, they were quizzically friendly. No
hint in his manner that he remembered the
unceremonious way in which he had swung
her aboard Ozy's dory last night, or his
anger when he had seen her with Johnny at
the light, or that she had flung herself in his
arms when the crash came that had seemed
like the end of the world. She hadn't been
aware that she had run to him, she'd just
found herself there. She agreed;

"It's a gorgeous day and the World and
his Wife will be at the Fair. We always give
the house-staff the day off, and have our
luncheon at the Country Club. Will that be
all right with you, Lex?"

"Okay. I shan't get round for lunch. The
top of the morning to you, Mrs. Barclay.
Morning, Cleo," he greeted the mother and
daughter who appeared in the doorway.
They looked like sisters in their linen frocks,

330

one amethyst, one orchid.

"Good morning, Lex. Well, Lissa, you didn't elope with Johnny?" Cleo asked as she peered under the cover of a silver chafing-dish. There was a glint of blue steel in her eyes as she glanced over her shoulder. "Perhaps you did elope, after all. Perhaps the happy bridegroom is concealed somewhere about the place?"

"An imagination like yours ought to get you a Hollywood job as scenario writer, Cleo," Lex Carson cut in before Lissa had recovered sufficiently from her surprise at the suggestion to answer. "When I ran her down there was no bridegroom among those present nor in the offing, so far as I could see."

"Then you went for her after I left you in the hall?" Cleo asked as he drew out a chair for her at the table.

"Sure, I went for her. You gave me a jolt when you suggested that she had run off with Johnny Grant. Isn't she my ward? No wonder you didn't hear us come in, the thunder made such a racket. Good morning, Fenton," he turned to the butler who entered from the pantry. "That was some storm last night. Do you have many like it here?"

"Not often, sir. We got back from the

cruiser just in time, didn't we, sir, though you went out again. It was a busy harbor after that, sir, with boats arriving from everywhere for the Fair. I sent down to inquire for the Major this morning, sir. His Filipino boy reported that he was none the worse for his ducking. There's been a sad accident, sir." Fenton's tone was lachrymose.

"Accident!"

Carson joined in the chorus of exclamations. He stood close behind Lissa's chair as he asked;

"What happened?"

"It's the Italian houseman at Red Chimneys, sir. This morning the Red Chimneys' motorboat was found turned over on the bar road. Mr. and Miss Packard haven't seen him since he asked them at the lobster-bake if he might take the boat to the village. I believe he's quite a movie-fan. They think he was caught in the storm and was washed overboard. Very sad. Shall I pour your coffee, sir?"

Lissa knew now why Lex stood behind her chair. It was a warning to her not to exclaim. Nino had been left at the light. Ozy and Tod had picked up his boat. Did Lex want the story to get about that he had been lost in the storm? She asked breathlessly;

"Have they — have they looked for the —

332

for him, Fenton?"

"Not yet, Miss. The boat has just been found. I'm sorry I spoke of it, Miss Lissa. I'm afraid I've spoiled your breakfast."

"You've spoiled all our breakfasts, Fenton," Cleo flared. "And because of a sneaky houseman. Nino gave me the shivers. Let's talk about something else, Lex."

"I'll see Mr. Packard after breakfast, Fenton. Miss Lissa tells me that the house-staff usually has Fair Day off."

"Yes, sir. It's usual, sir, but if you want me —"

"No. No. Enjoy the holiday. I'm on vacation myself." He backed up before the mantel. "By the way, Fenton, I rescued that coat on the chair from G-Man — you'll have to do something about that dog, Lissa, if he doesn't stop robbing clotheslines. Perhaps you can find the owner, Fenton."

The butler picked up the coat.

"Why that's mine, sir. It's old and comfortable and I wear it in my room. I hung it on the line yesterday to freshen it. Sorry you've been troubled with it, sir."

What was there about that old coat to send a faint wave of color to Lex's hair, Lissa wondered.

"Nothing like an old coat for comfort, Fenton. Glad you have it back. What's the

333

rest of the program for Fair Day? I'm new to it, remember. Do we dine here?"

"Mother and I don't, Lex." Cleo flung her napkin on the table. "The Packards are giving a small dinner at the Club before the ball. We are invited." Her voice was not so cool and indifferent as usual. Was she also caught in the undercurrent of excitement sweeping through the house? Lissa asked herself.

"What ball?"

"The County ball. Everyone goes. Mixed party, but something to kill time," Cleo shrugged.

"Are you dining with the Packards, Lissa?"

"No, Lex. I was not invited to the dinner, but I've accepted an invitation to lead the opening march at the ball with the chairman of the Board of Selectmen. Doesn't that sound exciting?"

"It does. The ball sounds festive to me, as has been said before, I'm on vacation, now. I may be late, but I'll get there. Save me some dances, Lissa."

"The phone is ringing in the sports-room, sir."

Lissa's eyes followed Lex Carson as he left the room. A certain timbre in his voice had confirmed her in her belief that he was

334

rigidly controlling inner excitement.

"Where were you last evening, Lissa?" Cleo's voice was as sweetly acid as a lemon drop. "I saw you leave the cruiser in your own boat with Johnny Grant."

"Why not cross-examine Johnny?" Lissa flung over her shoulder from the threshold. "He knows where I was."

Would Cleo question Johnny about last night, she asked herself as with Andy Millard squirming with excitement beside her, she drove the yellow roadster along roads bordered with feathery purple and white asters, goldenrod and a tangle of ferns and shrubs. Above them an occasional flame of scarlet and crimson maple press-agented the approach of autumn. Sunlight on the chromium trim of the car dazzled her eyes as she followed closely in the wake of crowds of people, vehicles, automobiles, farmtrucks, motoring tourists stopping over, a yoke of oxen, all converging on the County Fair.

It was the first moment she had had in which to review the hours which had passed since the conversation in the breakfast room. There had been flowers to arrange for exhibition at the Fair; telephone calls for the employees to answer; water had stopped running at Pirates' Den. The Major had gone for the day, the excited Filipinos had reported, and because neither plumbers nor electricians would work on Fair Day, she had labored side by side with them until the temperamental engine had coughed a speck of dust from its larynx and started.

She had been quite alone in the house when Lex had arrived with two genial, interesting looking men.

"They've come to look over the property," he had said to her in an aside. His voice had been strained as he added, "I think I've sold it, Lissa. It will be like dropping the Empire State Building off my shoulders, if I have. Wish me luck."

For lunch she had made herself a sandwich in the pantry at Tarry Farm. No time for the Club. She had heard the voices of Lex and the men in the conservatory balcony as she slipped into an exotic print frock. Then the Millards' maid had arrived with the boy — and here she was.

Andy bounced in his seat. His white suit accentuated his faint coat of tan.

"Hear the music, Lissa! Isn't it 'citing? I smell popcorn and molasses boiling. Do you think Fenton will be here to take me on the merry-go-round? He said he would."

"Then he will," Lissa answered and devoutly hoped that she was right. Merry-go-rounding as a sport, left her cold. "You like Fenton, don't you?"

"Rath-er — Johnny Grant taught me that — rath-er. When I'm big I'm going to be a butler and stand straight and wear a coat with silver buttons on the tail. Look! The plane! Flies like a gull, doesn't it? See its wings shine. Can't you drive faster, Lissa? Mother is coming for me in an hour. She said I mustn't stay longer. I have two half dollars to spend. Lex gave them to me. See?"

Lissa pressed the accelerator with a slim green shoe as he clinked the silver in a hand grown slightly plump and in a palm more than slightly grimy. She remembered the white, emaciated fingers he had laid on G-Man's head, not so many weeks ago. Living down by the sea and tender care had worked a miracle of healing. She hugged him.

"Andy, you're sweet, I love you."

"All right, but gee, can't you hurry?"

Quickly she folded the wings of sentiment.

"Sorry, I bubbled over. Suppose we leave the roadster in this parking place and walk the rest of the way. We'll get along faster."

"Okay with me — Johnny taught me that,

too. What's the man shouting?"

"Mr. Alexander Carson is wanted at the judges' stand! Mr. Carson wanted at the judges' stand," a megaphoned voice proclaimed.

"Does he mean Lex?" Andy asked. "Is he coming to the Fair?"

"He'll be here later. Are you still clutching those half dollars? Better put them deep into a pocket of your shorts or you may lose them. Let's go."

Hand in hers the boy hopped and skipped beside her as they were swept to the gate by the crowd. He wriggled with impatience while she bought tickets at something which looked like a sentry box.

They passed through the turn-stile and stepped at once into a haze of dust, into the midway broiling under a hot early afternoon sun. A potpourri of smells greeted them, frying hot dogs, popping corn, boiling coffee, crisping fat from roasting beef turning slowly on a spit. From the big barn drifted the scent of hay tinted by the strong smell from the bodies of cattle, the lowing of cows, punctuated by an occasional bellow; the grunt of pigs, the ba-a-a of sheep, the crow of cocks, the cackle of hens.

Behind tents and booths the old sedans of the concessionaires sagged as if inexpressibly weary of the welter of shabby household goods spread on the ground about them. The sounds would have put to shame those of the Tower of Babel. Shrill cries of innumerable vendors, "Lemonade! Five cents!" clashed with the barking of showmen, "Step in and see the Wild man! He eats raw meat!" "The Wonder of the World! Molly, the calf with two heads and three tails!" "Hit the chink's head and you get a cane!"; the distant pounding of horses' hoofs on tan bark, mingled with the tin-panny music, the shrill whistle of the merry-go-round, and a radioed voice singing the latest popular song.

Swinging slim black canes she had bought at Andy's insistence, Lissa and the boy made their way through the milling crowd which mopped its brow with one hand and risked its money on chances with the other. She nodded to summer residents who hailed her; stopped to speak to villagers who smiled at her; edged by rough looking men who ogled her, shook her head at vendors who importuned her. The boy tugged like a dog on leash.

"We'll never get to the merry-go-round if you stop to talk to everybody in the world, Lissa," he protested. "Here's Fenton! Here's Fenton!" he shouted.

He hopped up and down with excitement as the butler approached. He was a stranger to Lissa in his tweed suit and straw hat which last could be described best as "natty." The combination of hat and side-burns tickled Lissa's funnybone. She bit her lips to keep back a laugh. Fenton held the hat in his hand as he greeted her.

"Good afternoon, Miss. Sorry if I've kept Master Andy waiting, but, the house-staff and I have been having our lunch in the grove outside the Fair grounds and it took me sometime to get back. A mixed crowd, Miss, a very mixed crowd. All sorts of riff-raff comes to a place like this, if you get what I mean, Miss." He cast a scathing glance at a man with burning eyes and an out-at-elbows coat, who lingered near.

Lissa's hand tightened on the boy's, until the man slouched away.

"I understand, Fenton. We —"

Andy tugged.

"Lissa! Lissa! Why do you and Fenton talk so much? If we don't go to the merry-go-round, we'll never get there and I only have an hour."

"He's right, Miss. I'll take him along now, Miss, if you'll trust him with me."

A distant trumpet sounded a fan-fare. "The races are on, Miss. You'll want to see the horses run, I know, and you really should take a look at our cattle. They've won the blue ribbon, Miss. The late Madam would have been proud."

"Lissa! Please let me go!"

"All right, Andy. Don't let him ride too long, Fenton. They've been broadcasting for Mr. Carson, doubtless to inform him about the ribbons. I'll look at the Tarry Farm cattle then I'll come to the merry-go-round tent. Mrs. Millard may get there first, she's driving over for Andy."

Lissa watched the tall man in the jaunty straw hat with the small boy hopping and skipping beside him until they were lost in the crowd. She had a curious feeling, a sort of why-did-I-let-him-go sinking of the heart. The old imagination working overtime again she jeered at herself, hadn't Madge told her that Andy might ride with Fenton?

She stopped at the rail of the track. Between races a red-headed woman in a spangled green velvet dress was walking a tightrope. The rope snapped. The woman fell. "Oh!" moaned the crowd. The sound swept the air like the soughing of the wind.

The tight-rope walker, ghastly under the rouged spots on her cheeks, picked herself up, gallantly threw kisses and limped to a tent. Her audience cheered and one by one and in groups drifted on to fresh fields of entertainment.

As Lissa approached the cattle barn she saw Ralph Packard with Cleo in a blue frock and floppy matching hat. She dodged into a food booth to avoid them. A man with a double gap in his upper teeth set in a moonshaped face grinned at her in friendly inquiry;

"What'll you have, Miss?"

Lissa looked up but she wasn't seeing him, she was seeing Lex Carson's white face as he had stared incredulously at her as she had stood with Johnny Grant's arm about her in the service room at the light. What had he thought? He had asked Johnny to take her home. He had been too disgusted to think she would run around with the man who had jilted her to care who took her home, probably. She had fought back the memory for hours and now here it was without any warning, to submerge her.

"What'll you have, Miss?"

The concessionaire's question, tinged with impatience, snapped Lissa out of her abstraction. She looked about the tent with its small tables set close to the canvas wall, before she smiled and asked;

"What can I have?"

342

The moon-face melted into mushy admiration.

"Ice-cream cone? Root-beer?" He winked. "Real beer, if you like."

"Coffee ice-cream, please."

Cone in hand, she retreated to a small table as a group of customers entered the tent. She would remain here until Ralph Packard and Cleo had passed. Since she had discovered his deception about the short stories, she couldn't bear to look at him, much less speak to him. What had been his object in deceiving her? When the coast was clear, she would pick up Andy and meet Madge Millard.

"Say, listen! Did you see the Ace?"

The low, sinister question broke into Lissa's troubled thoughts. It came from one or two shadows on the canvas wall beside her. The man outside who had asked the question must be sitting almost shoulder to shoulder with her. The Ace! The words slashed her mind wide open. The Ace was the man Lex was looking for! The counterfeiter! He was here? At this Fair? Never again would she believe that a mind couldn't rock from shock. Hers was swaying. She mustn't lose a word.

She nibbled at the cone. Leaned closer to the canvas wall. Not too close; she might

343

touch the shoulder of the man outside.

"Say, are you seeing things?" another low voice jeered. "The Ace made his get away out of this country four years ago. Do you think if he'd come back, we wouldn't have knowed it? Slick as he is, he wouldn't got by us, not with what we have on him."

Slick. The word flashed a close-up of Ralph Packard on Lissa's mind. Ralph Packard and his man Nino. Absurd, hadn't the Packards had A 1 references? Those references had been stolen! Was she about to find out why?

"I tell you he's here," the sinister voice insisted. "I had a tip he's been living in this hick town lately. That's why I came. I saw him talkin' to a dame. He got away before I got close. Me not know the Ace! You make me sick! Come on. We'll find him! We'll stick him for a grand."

The Ace! at the Fair! The words whirled round and round in Lissa's mind. She tried to stop them. He had been talking with a dame! That was a help. There were at least a thousand men among those present talking with women. What should she do? Find Lex, of course. Wherever he was, she must find him. Perhaps he was still at Tarry Farm with the men who were looking over the property but if she left the Fair grounds, she might miss him.

If, as the man outside the canvas wall had said, the "Ace" had been living in this town lately, the counterfeiting plates also were here. No time to waste. The men she had overheard might warn the hunted man. She must find Lex. What should she do about Andy? She'd think up a reason to cut his merry-go-rounding short and find someone with whom to leave him until his mother came. Too bad to burden Fenton with him, the butler doubtless had plans of his own. She mustn't sit here, the two men who had been outside might enter and see her.

She pulled her soft green hat rakishly over one eye and approached the counter. She smiled at the moon-faced man.

"Your ice-cream is wonderful."

He leaned on his elbows and invited;

"Say, girlie, have one on me, now."

"Thanks, I couldn't eat another mouthful," Lissa responded and forced herself to make a leisurely exit.

She wanted to run, go somewhere, anywhere to find Lex. How could she walk? "Walk you will, my girl," she disciplined herself and serpentined her way through the crowds. Once she met burning eyes. Were they the eyes of the man whose whispered words she had overheard? Ice feathered through her veins. Did he know that she had been on the other side of that canvas wall when he had hissed his discovery? Was he following her? If only she hadn't worn such a gayly printed frock. Why worry? The Fair grounds were a riot of color from gayly printed frocks.

The raucous music was thinning to a finale when she reached the opening of the merry-go-round tent, chariots, prancing horses, lions and tigers, revolved more and more slowly. In spite of her burning impatience to get away, Lissa bit back a laugh. Fenton in straw hat and sideburns sat stiff-spined as a riding-master on a wooden white charger and on a high-stepping bay beside him rode Andy Millard.

The machinery creaked to a stand-still. The music faded away. Fenton swung the boy to the ground. Andy ran ahead to Lissa. His eyes sparkled with excitement, his cheeks were red as if rouged.

"Lissa, it was grand! May I go round again? Fenton said he would take me if you said I could. Please, Lissa! Please!"

They were outside the tent now, a tent deserted by the crowd which had flocked to the aviation field. She looked at the boy hopping up and down, then at the butler who had joined them.

346

"I'll be glad to take him again, Miss. I —"

He snapped up his head to look at the genial, ruddy man who tapped his shoulder. His skin turned the color of yellowed ivory, lines cut deep in his face, his eyes chilled, his lips thinned and hardened, his hand shot to his left breast.

Another man caught his arm and held it. A voice behind him warned;

"Take it easy, Mr. Fenton. No shooting allowed in the Fair grounds. Say good-afternoon to the boy. You're late for an engagement, several years late if you ask me."

"You've made a mistake —" the butler's protest was strident, disjointed.

"Oh, no. Your stooge, Nino, is waiting to tell you we haven't."

Fenton looked behind him. His eyes turned, his voice snarled; "Major Fane! I thought there was something phoney about you. It's a pity I didn't drown you when I pushed you overboard last night."

Major Fane! Lissa stared at the short, stocky man incredulously. His eyes were not opaque now. They were keen, cold steel. He poked Fenton in the back.

"Get going!"

Andy, who had been listening and looking up with puzzled eyes, twitched a corner of the butler's coat.

347

"Aren't we going on the merry-go-round again, Fenton?"

The man looked down at him. "Not again today, Master Andy — but sometime." He cleared his throat. Nodded to the man beside him. "You win. Let's go."

Lissa watched the four walk toward the gate in close formation. Two of them were the men who had come to the big house with Lex to look over the "property." What did it mean?

"Quite the last word in arrests, I'd say, Miss," observed a perfect imitation of Fenton's voice.

Lissa wheeled. Johnny Grant stood behind her.

"Arrest! Was Fenton arrested, Johnny?"

"Sure, 'twas an arrest. Modern methods. No melodrama. No shooting. No yelling. Just a hand on the shoulder — 'You're late for an engagement, Mr. Fenton!' — and there you are. Remember I told you that butler was too English to be genuine? Hi! Hold everything! You're chalky! For the love of Mike, don't pass out here, sweet thing!"

Lissa clutched the sleeve of his blue coat to steady herself. She smiled with stiff lips.

"I'm not faint, Johnny. Just thought of something. I'll be all right in a min—"

"Lissa! Lissa!" Andy tugged at her hand. There was a hint of tears in his voice and in his startled eyes;

"What does arrest mean? Why couldn't Fenton take me on the merry-go-round again?"

Johnny Grant caught his shoulder.

"Fenton had to keep a date but I'll take you, stout fella. Am I good on horseback? You ain't seen nothin' yet! You ought to see me at a rodeo if you want to know how good I am. What the country needs is more riders like us fellas, you and me. Come on!"

Andy's face was radiant. His laugh was like a peal of silver bells. "You're awful funny, Johnny. Funnier than Fenton. Okay, I'm ready." He turned to Lissa. "Don't let mother stop me if she comes before we've been around a lot of times, will you?"

Lissa nodded. She couldn't speak. Her mind was awhirl. No need now to rush to Tarry Farm to find Lex, Fenton was the Ace!

27

The orchestra in the red, white and blue draped Town Hall was playing a request number, "Beautiful Lady In Blue," a hit of several seasons past, when Lex Carson appeared in the doorway. Lissa's heart stopped and raced on. He was evidently looking for someone. His white dinner-jacket was conspicuous against the tweed and blue coats of the men standing behind him.

Madge Millard and Tod Kent stopped beside her and immediately Lex started forward. He was coming for Madge, of course. Lissa reminded;

"You haven't asked me to dance tonight, Tod."

"And why? You've had 'em in swarms about you. Perhaps it's that silver tissue thing you're wearing. It floats. Of course it may be —"

"Oh, I got charm!" Lissa laughed. "Come on, Tod. Must I beg you to dance with me?"

"Wait a minute, Lissa," Madge pleaded. "Lex is coming. Before he gets here, I want to thank you for being so wonderful to Andy this afternoon. He'll never forget it. His hero-worship is divided now. He had almost as much to say about Johnny Grant as about Fenton when he came home."

"What's that about Fenton?" Lex Carson inquired sharply as he joined them. Lissa's smile in return for his was faint and fleet. Did he know about Fenton? Of course.

Madge Millard's eyes were brimful of tenderness, her mouth unsteady as she smiled at him;

"I was telling Lissa about Andy's afternoon. He didn't seem a bit tired when he got home. I'm a happy woman, Lex, not much like the woe-begone creature who flung herself in your arms that day in the sports-room, and cried her heart out. I burn with shame when I think of it."

"Don't think of it, Madge, mine's a sort of community shoulder. They're playing the Beautiful Blue Danube. Come on, Lissa, this is our dance, isn't it?"

Lissa turned away from the demanding question in his smiling eyes.

"I had promised Tod —"

"Tod can wait, I won't."

He put his arm about her and swung her among the dancers. A goodly number of summer-residents in gala attire danced elbow to elbow with native sons and daughters also dressed for an occasion, their faces dim in the amber light.

"Realize that this is the first time we've danced together, beautiful?" His arm tightened about her until she looked up. "You got wings, chile."

Lissa couldn't tell him that when Madge had smilingly explained that episode in the sports-room, that wings had lifted her heart until they beat in her throat. She glanced up;

"Good, aren't we? There's always the movies for talent like ours." A voice which came from her lips but didn't seem to be hers, asked wistfully;

"Is your heart buried in a grave, Lex?"

He looked at her as if he couldn't believe his ears.

"Is my heart — what?" His arm tightened. "I'll show you where my heart is. Here comes Grant. He can't have you. You're mine. The other girls will have more chance if I take you off the floor. Get your wrap."

He waited for her to get her flame-colored Mandarin coat. In the corridor Simonds stopped them, Simonds glowering and beet-red with suppressed anger, twirling the pencil at the end of his chain, till it cast off golden sparks like a fiery pin-wheel.

"Just a minute, Mr. Carson. I don't believe in it but the men asked me to tell you they'd take that cut."

Carson's eyes narrowed. "They took till the last minute to make up their minds, didn't they, Simonds? Come to the house tomorrow morning. I have something for you to tell them."

In the metallic brilliance of the light from half a moon, Lissa, nestled in the deep leather cushions of Carson's roadster, could see the firm line of his mouth. A man of power, someone to hold to in time of trouble, she thought, as she had thought once before. Why, why had she asked that silly question about his heart?

"Where are we going?" she inquired, to break the silence broken only by the purr of the engine and a crooning surf. A salty breeze blew her hair in a red-gold aureole.

"Want to know what happened this afternoon?"

"Oh, yes. Yes."

"Then we'll go home. I have something to show you. Warm enough? There's a touch of autumn in this crisp air."

"Yes."

He didn't speak again until they were in the library at Tarry Farm. The room was fragrant with the warm scent of smoldering birch logs and the breath of red Radiance roses in a tall silver vase. He poked up the dozing fire. She established herself in a deep chair and faced him as he stood before the mantel. The firelight touched her tender eyes, tinted the smooth curves of her throat, rouged her gallant mouth.

"Now for the story of this summer," he said and plunged his hands into the pockets of his coat. "Do you realize how tempting you are, beautiful?" he asked huskily.

Lissa hurriedly avoided his disturbing eyes and suggested;

"Let me tell my story first."

She told of the conversation she had overheard in the tent; of her determination to reach him before he left Tarry Farm; of meeting Fenton and Andy, of the men who had personally conducted the butler from the Fair. Long before she had finished, she was standing looking up at him. She concluded breathlessly;

"Not until Johnny spoke did I realize that it was Fenton — Fenton whom you wanted. When did you know?"

"Sit in the big chair again, Lissa, I can't think when you're so near. That's better."

She looked away from the dark intensity of his eyes, watched for an instant the tropical fish flash and flame in the crystal cylinder in the wrought iron sconce against the wall. Her eager eyes came back to him as he went on;

"Tod, the criminologists — known hereafter in my story as 'the boys' — and I, had come to this harbor with no expectation that our man was here. My inheritance seemed an excellent excuse for us to use it as a base from which to forward our investigations. When, the day of our arrival, you said that you imagined you had seen a flash from that abandoned light, even the roots of my hair tingled. The next days, perhaps you remember, I stopped to buckle my shoe in the lamp-room, at the same time I picked up a cigarette stub. You may remember also that I relaid the fire in the service room. Sticking from between the logs was a newspaper with a portion torn out. You said you hadn't torn it, that you cut items from a paper. Anyone might have torn out that scrap, but, when one is on a hunt, one doesn't let a straw of a clue escape, and there was the flash and cigarette stub to be explained. I sent for a copy of the newspaper of the same February date, finally fitted this into the torn place. Read it aloud."

Lissa read from the diamond shaped piece of paper he dropped into her lap;

"FRENCH FISHERMAN'S FEAR CLUE TO A SMUGGLING PLOT. SEEING TWO LOBSTER-TRAP FLOATS WHERE HE PUT ONE CAUSES HIM TO REFUSE DRINK AND THE CUSTOM OFFICERS TO INVESTIGATE. MERCHANDISE OF A HIGHLY DUTIABLE CHARACTER WAS FOUND IN WATERTIGHT CASES AT THE END OF LANYARDS ATTACHED TO FLOATS."

"Was that what you and Tod were doing in the storm, pulling up lobster traps?" Lissa asked in a thrilled whisper.

"Not lobster traps. We pulled up a water-tight case full of bogus bills." He returned the clipping to his breast pocket. "A few minutes before the newspaper for which I had sent came, Ozy had told Tod and me that one night he had found two lobster-trap floats where he had buoyed one."

"Did you suspect then that Fenton was the Ace?"

"No, I liked Fenton. But when, that very day, you told me that he had done all the buying for the place, that your Aunt Hetty gave him cheques and he would pay cash — something clicked in my mind. It works that way, sometimes. I made you think I had heard a suspicious sound outside the door.

356

My hunch seemed too improbable to believe, but I followed it. I didn't dare search Fenton's rooms for fear he would find out and disappear. The Ace had slipped away so many times when the authorities thought they had him. That fingerprint party on the cruiser was to get his but he was too smart for us, he pushed the Major overboard.

"For weeks I have followed signposts pointing to his trail, oftentimes such a faint trail, that I was tempted to think that my hunch was nothing but a brainsquall, but I kept on and on, as it twisted and turned until it ended under this roof. Even then I wasn't sure I had the Ace. Last night we found his fingerprints on one of the bills. The boys on the cruiser vacuumed the coat G-Man stole and found in the bag, tin, antimony and lead dusts, the metals counterfeiters use. You heard Fenton claim the coat. Today while he was at the Fair a photo-engraving and printing plant, with any number of bogus bills, was uncovered behind the bookshelves your aunt had had built into his room."

"Fenton has been making counterfeit money in this house! I can't believe it. No wonder he was content to stay here three years. How did he dispose of it?"

"Cautiously. An occasional bill tucked in

with a payment made around here, but, recently, most of it on his week-end trips to different places. He has sizable sums of real money cozily tucked away in real banks under different names."

"Do you remember that Fenton called Simonds a specked-apple — I thought for a minute that the dour foreman was your man — Remember when he said, 'There's something in the world besides money'? What a hypocrite!"

"What an actor, I'd say. I thought he was about to burst into tears when he proclaimed his passion for cows. He has been so secure that he got careless and ambitious. When back in February he read in the paper of the way in which dutiable merchandise had been smuggled, he must have thought up the plan of having watertight cases filled with his bogus money picked up by an alleged lumber vessel and dared make the bills bigger. The fact that I worked on the case must not be known. It would destroy my usefulness to the Treasury Department. You understand that, Lissa?"

"Yes. Instead of a G-Man, you're a T-Man, aren't you? Do you like unearthing criminals?"

"No! No! But, it is like spy service in war — it has to be done. It is part of the battle against crime which cannot be won unless every citizen does his part."

Lissa's silver frock shimmered with little pink rivers of reflected firelight as she clasped her hands about one knee. She said thoughtfully;

"Each year I have wished that one of the tenants would provide a plot for a story and all the time a mammoth plot was being hatched under this roof. I'll confess now, that deep down in my mind, I've suspected Ralph Packard. I can't understand why he posed as a writer."

"You suggested the idea to him by assuming that he came here to write, didn't you? He jumped at the chance to hold your interest by posing as an author. I eliminated him as a suspect, when you told me that he was beating at those blazing curtains. No counterfeiter would risk his fingers. Even after I found that the stub in the lamp-room, the cigarette his houseman dropped on your doorstep, had his monogram I knew that he was not our man, that Nino had been helping himself to his employer's cigarettes."

"And Major Fane? Is he really a dyspeptic? I suspected him, too."

"He's another good actor. He eats anything and everything. It must have been torture for him to pass up that lobster-bake. He was here to help me, though we communicated only through headquarters. I'll answer the phone.

"Carson speaking — Mrs. Barclay! Where are you? — She has! Oh, No! No! — of course I'm not jealous. I was surprised, that's all. I hope she'll be happy — That was generous of him — Okay. Be as late as you like getting home. I'll sit up to let you in." He cradled the phone.

"What's happened? What did Mother Barclay tell you, Lex?" Lissa's voice broke from excitement.

"Cleo married Packard tonight! Your stepmother's voice shook with triumph."

"Married! Cleo married! To Ralph Packard? He must be the 'last resort.' Why did you say, 'No! No!'?"

"Because Packard is a millionaire bootlegger-baron gone respectable and — cultured — even Cleo ought to do better than that. I had his record before I had been at Tarry Farm a week. Sidonie is his sister, but she has had no education — grew up with no advantages. She was afraid to talk for fear her deficiencies would betray them both. When she felt she was out of her depths socially, she'd have a headache and go home. The electric shock at the light evidently loosened the screws that held Nino's nerve together for when the revenue men picked him up he babbled that he had been a body-guard for Ralph Packard in his bootlegger days; that Packard had deliberately burned off his fingerprints that he might wipe out the past and marry a girl who was 'a swell' — that's the Italian's word, not mine — that his boss liked the red-headed sister better, but that the blonde had more friends."

"Did he confess about Fenton?"

"Yes, information rattled from his rocking mind like pennies from a bank shaken by a small boy. He whined that last night after he had lowered the watertight cases, he had dug up a pouch of coins he had buried for safekeeping, had flashed a signal to the lumber vessel by inserting an electric torch in the great lens, — as he had done twice before — and was about to make his getaway forever with the pouch and a pocketful of bills Fenton had paid him, when you and Grant burst into the lighthouse and he was trapped in the lamp-room."

"Then I did help you! I so wanted to! My writing has accomplished something. I wouldn't have gone back to the island if memory hadn't flashed 'When stuck go into reverse,' on the screen of my mind."

"I'll say you helped, you and G-Man. The

Treasury Department ought to award that Irish terrier a medal. He was prophetically named. He stepped into a G-Man's role when he produced that coat. It clinched the evidence against Fenton. In some underground way he had heard that the Packards were looking for a summer place, and after he conceived the dazzling plan of buoying the watertight cases beside Ozy's lobster floats, he suggested to Nino that it would be to his advantage to steer them to Red Chimneys. Nino confessed that the references were forged, and that as they were a menace to Fenton's safety, Fenton stole them and destroyed them. Packard must have suspected that his houseman had buried those coins, that he was mixed up in shady doings. He wanted to get hold of the pouch that he might hold it as a threat over his one-time bodyguard."

"Do you think Ralph Packard believes that Nino was drowned?"

"Not for a minute. He probably figures that the man made his get-away for reasons connected with the coins. He may have thought them real money and that Nino stole them. Whatever he suspected he was taking no chance of having his plan to marry Cleo upset by a story the Italian might tell, so persuaded her to marry him before his

362

preprohibition record leaked. I doubt if it ever does. So much has happened since then, that that era is almost forgotten. He made correct tax-returns and had no criminal record. He was a product of his times. He gave his bride a cheque for a hundred thousand dollars."

"Now she can pay her bills. I'm dazed. What a plot for a story. Perhaps Cleo will establish Ralph Packard socially, she has a lot of friends and you say he has heaps of money. That's an unbeatable combination these days. Cleo is proud. It will hurt her terribly if ever she finds out what he has been. I'm sorry, terribly sorry for her. I'll send her Aunt Hetty's aquamarines and diamonds for a wedding present."

"Lissa, as has been said before, you're adorable. Prepare for more shock. I've sold this house."

"How grand! To those men who were here yesterday?"

"No, they were here to check-up on Fenton. I've sold it to a summer resident. He has had his eye on Tarry Farm for years. I sacrificed it, but, I won't have it to carry and the money will pay off some of the mortgages on the other property. This summer has done so much for Andy that Jack Millard has bought the Treasure Chest."

"Ready, Lex? I'm so glad for you. Have you sold the other cottages?"

"No. You said Red Chimneys was your favorite. I'm keeping that for — us. I asked you to give me one summer — now — I want all your summers. Don't back away. Come here!" He caught her hands. "You can write, just the same. 'Melissa Carson' will be a lot better looking on the cover of a book than Melissa Barclay."

"Not above bribery are you?" she teased with breathless gaiety.

His look set her heart pounding.

"I'm not bribing, I'm just telling you that you're going to Washington with me as my wife, beautiful."

He drew her into his arms, tipped her head back against his shoulder, kissed her tenderly. Then as if the touch set him ablaze, his mouth crushed down on her throat, her eyes. Her lips burned under his, her blood raced through her veins. He said huskily;

"Any doubt now where my heart is?"

His arms stripped away her defense, his voice banished the faint phantom of Johnny Grant's faithlessness.

"No. I know. I know also that I've never been kissed before, — really kissed, I mean."

"You don't mind, do you?" Laughter pricked through his unsteady voice.

She rumpled her red-gold hair against his shoulder. Lifted eager tempting lips to his, reminded softly;

"You do ask foolish questions, don't you?"